UNIVERSITY OF STRATHCLYDE
30125 00440363 9

D1609784

ANDERSONIAN LIBRARY
WITHDRAWN
FROM
LIBRARY
STOCK
UNIVERSITY OF STRATHCLYDE

# Instrumentation and Test Gear Circuits Manual

*Newnes Circuits Manual Series*

**Audio IC Circuits Manual** R.M. Marston
**CMOS Circuits Manual** R.M. Marston
**Diode, Transistor & FET Circuits Manual** R.M. Marston
**Electronic Alarm Circuits Manual** R.M. Marston
**Instrumentation & Test Gear Circuits Manual** R.M. Marston
**Op-amp Circuits Manual** R.M. Marston
**Optoelectronics Circuits Manual** R.M. Marston
**Power Control Circuits Manual** R.M. Marston
**Timer/Generator Circuits Manual** R.M. Marston

# Instrumentation and Test Gear Circuits Manual

R.M. MARSTON

*To Esther, with love.*

Newnes
An imprint of Butterworth-Heinemann Ltd
Linacre House, Jordan Hill, Oxford OX2 8DP

PART OF REED INTERNATIONAL BOOKS

OXFORD LONDON BOSTON
MUNICH NEW DELHI SINGAPORE SYDNEY
TOKYO TORONTO WELLINGTON

First published 1993



**British Library Cataloguing in Publication Data**
Marston, R.M.
Instrumentation and Test Gear Circuits
Manual. – (Newnes Circuits Manual Series)
I. Title II. Series
621.3815

ISBN 0 7506 0758 0

**Library of Congress Cataloguing in Publication Data**
Marston, R.M.
Instrumentation and test gear circuits manual/R.M. Marston.
p. cm. – (Newnes circuits manual series)
Includes index.
ISBN 0 7506 0758 0
1. Electronic circuits. 2. Testing – Equipment and supplies.
I. Title. II. Series.
TK7867.M355 92–24955
621.3815'48–dc20 CIP

Printed and bound in Great Britain by
Biddles Ltd, Guildford and King's Lynn

# Contents

# Preface

This unique book is primarily a manual of modern instrumentation and test gear circuits of value to the industrial, commercial, or amateur electronics engineer or designer. It presents the reader with almost 500 outstandingly useful and carefully selected practical circuits, diagrams, graphs and tables, backed up by over 60 000 words of highly informative 'how it works' and 'how to design it' text. The practical circuits range from simple attenuators and bridges to complex 'scope trace doublers, timebases, and digital frequency meters.

The manual is split into twelve chapters. The first explains basic instrumentation and test gear principles, and the remainder are devoted to practical circuitry. Chapter 2 deals with the design of passive attenuators, and Chapter 3 with passive and active filter circuits, including those used in oscillators and DFMs. Chapter 4 takes an in-depth look at modern 'bridge' circuits, and presents a unique range of high-precision 'laboratory grade' practical designs. The next seven chapters progress through analogue and digital metering techniques and circuitry, signal and waveform generation, and power-supply generation, etc., presenting hundreds of practical circuits on the way. The final chapter deals with a variety of specialized items of test gear, including bar-graph meters, probes, go/no-go testers, capacitance and frequency meters, transistor testers, Q-meters, and oscilloscope accessories, etc.

The book, though aimed specifically at the practical design engineer, technician, and experimenter, will doubtless be of great interest to all amateurs and students of electronics. It deals with its subject in an easy-to-read, down-to-earth, mainly non-mathematical but very comprehensive manner. Each chapter starts off by explaining the basic principles of its subject and then goes on to present the reader with a wide range of practical circuit designs. All of the practical circuits have been designed, built, evaluated and fully copyright protected by the author.

Throughout the volume, great emphasis is placed on practical 'user' information and circuitry, and this book, like all others in the *Circuits Manual* series, abounds with useful circuits and data. Most of the semiconductor devices used in the practical circuits are modestly priced and readily available types, with universally recognized type numbers.

*R.M. Marston 1992*

# 1 Basic principles

This first chapter starts off by looking at the basic terminology of modern electronic measurement and signal generating systems, then surveys the many different types of practical instrumentation and test gear system that are available. It ends by looking at the vexed question of whether it is better to buy or build certain types of test gear.

## Basic terminology

The terms **instrumentation** and **test gear** mean different things to different people. In the context of this volume, an *instrumentation circuit* is one that translates an intangible quantity such as voltage, resistance, inductance, speed or temperature, etc., into a tangible form (such as an analogue or digital meter reading or an alarm signal, etc.) that is meaningful to a human operator. Such circuits consist of a *converter* that changes the intangible quantity into an easily processed form (such as a d.c. voltage), and a *translator* that changes that into a tangible form.

If the instrumentation circuit gives an output that is read close to the point of conversion (see *Figure 1.1*), it may be called a *metering system*, but if it is one that enables the reading to be

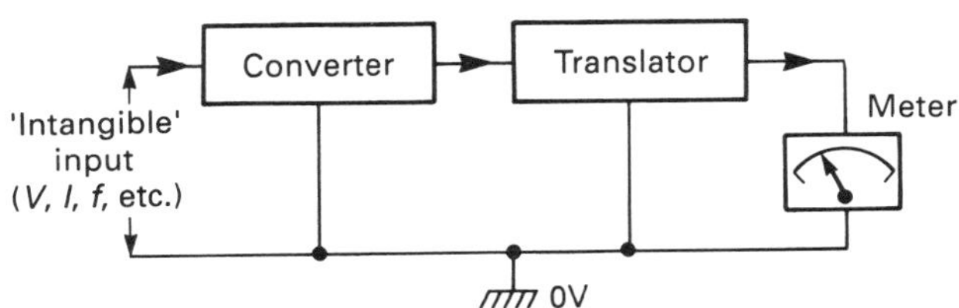


Figure 1.1. *Basic metering system.*

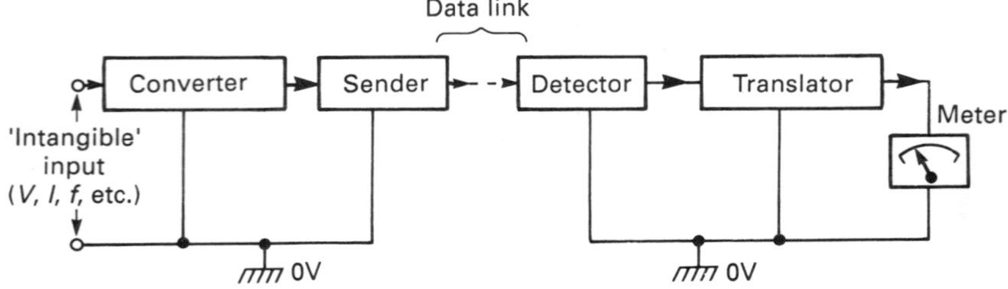


Figure 1.2. *Basic telemetering system.*

made at a point very distant from that of conversion (see *Figure 1.2*) it is known as a *telemetering* system. In the latter case a *sender* and a *detector* are interposed between the converter and the translator and are interconnected via a *data link* such as a ground line or an infra-red or radio link, etc.

A piece of **test gear** (or test **equipment**) is a unit specifically designed to generate, simulate, or analyse electrical/electronic signals or parameters. It may be designed for either *laboratory* or *industrial* use. Laboratory test gear is usually very versatile and meant for use in a wide range of general applications. Industrial test gear is specialized and designed to perform a dedicated function or production-testing task. Thus, a laboratory RF signal generator (see *Figure 1.3*) may be able to generate good CW, AM or FM sine-wave signals over the full 100kHz to 220MHz frequency range and to give an output fully variable from zero to hundred of millivolts, but an industrial RF generator (see *Figure*

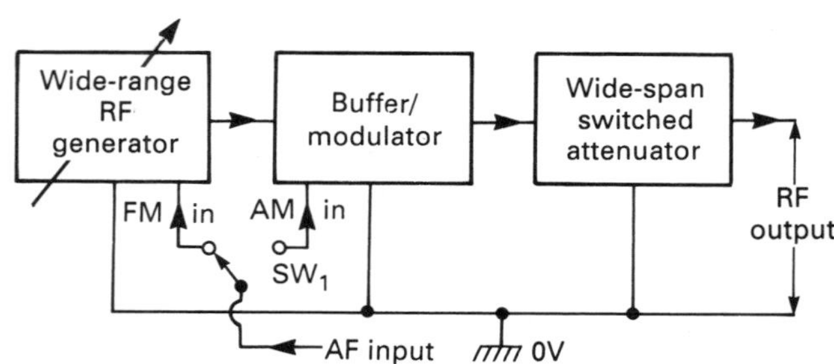


Figure 1.3. *A laboratory RF signal generator is a versatile wide-range instrument.*

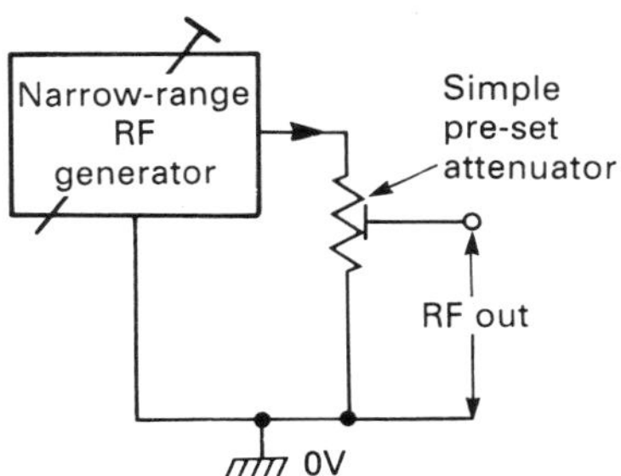


Figure 1.4. *An 'industrial' RF signal generator is usually a simple non-flexible circuit.*

*1.4*) may simply be designed to pump out a 465kHz CW signal at 100μV.

Most practical electronic testing operations call for the use of two or more items of interconnected test gear. For example, the items needed to carry out a simple performance check on an audio amplifier are a variable sine-wave generator (to generate a test signal), a wide-range a.c. millivoltmeter (to read input/output signal levels and thus facilitate frequency response checks), and a 'total harmonic distortion' or THD meter (to check the amplifier's reproduction quality or fidelity). If such a performance-testing facility is made by **temporarily** interconnecting or 'hooking up' a number of individual items of test gear (see *Figure 1.5*), the resulting assembly is known as a *test rig*, but if it is made by

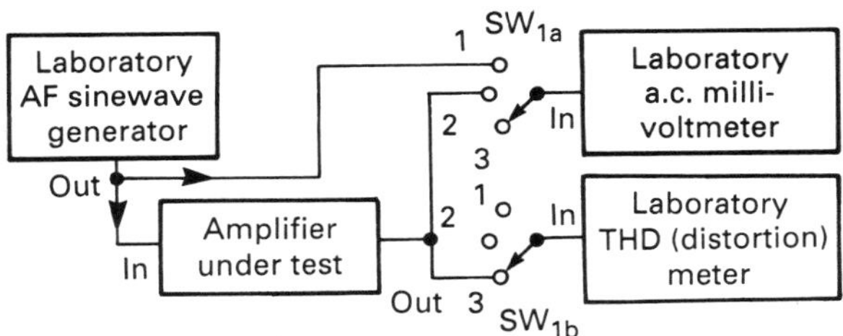


Figure 1.5. *This amplifier-testing* **test rig** *is made by temporarily interconnecting a number of items of laboratory test gear.*

**permanently** interconnecting a number of test-gear items (see *Figure 1.6*) the resulting unit is known as a *test set*. Many industrial test-gear engineers spend their working lives eternally designing new test sets for use on their company's production testing and quality control lines.

Note that some of the above technical terms can be interchanged. Thus, a simple multimeter is an item of *test gear*, but when in use it becomes a *metering system*. Again, a THD meter is correctly called an item of *test gear* if it requires the use of an external low-distortion sine-wave generator, but should be called a *test set* if it has such a generator built in.

Test sets are usually far easier to use than temporary test rigs. Thus, to measure the dB voltage gain of an amplifier via the *Figure 1.5* test rig, the sine-wave generator should be set to give (say) 1V output from the amplifier (read with $SW_1$ in position 2), and the amplifier input voltage must then be read (with $SW_1$ in position 1) and the 'gain' value calculated from the difference between the two readings. This same measurement can be made via the *Figure 1.6* test set by merely setting the attenuator input to 1V (read in $SW_1$ position 1) and then adjusting the attenuator setting to give the same reading (in $SW_1$ position 2) from the amplifier output, at which point the dB gain value can be read directly from the attenuator setting.

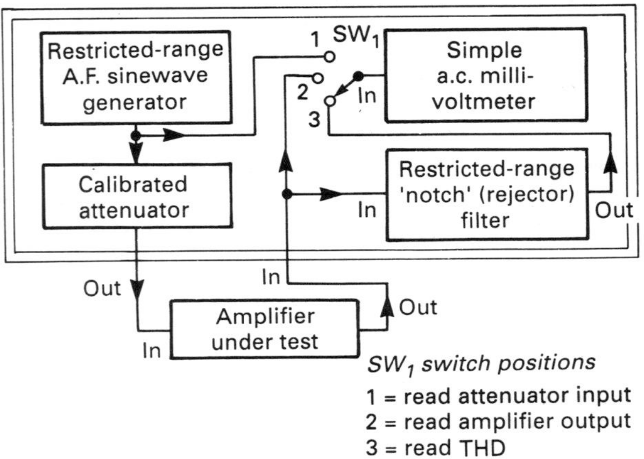


Figure 1.6. *This amplifier-testing* **test set** *is made by permanently interconnecting a number of items of dedicated (industrial) test gear.*

## Types of test gear

There are four broad categories of test gear, and these can be named as **generators**, **indicators**, **composites**, and **standards**. A **generator** is simply any item of test gear that acts as a source of signals or power (e.g. AF and RF signal or pulse generators, power supplies, etc.), and an **indicator** is simply any item of test gear that gives a visual or audible indication of the absolute or relative value of a monitored parameter (analogue and digital meters, audio/visual **go/no-go** testers, and oscilloscopes, etc., are examples of these).

A **composite** is any item of test gear that can directly carry out a complete test action and contains the equivalent of two or more individual items of test gear ($L-C-R$ bridges and 'distortion' meters are classic examples of 'composite' test gear). A **standard** is any item of test gear that has such high precision that it can be used to calibrate or corroborate the accuracy of other items of test gear; precision voltage references, crystal frequency standards, and precision $R$ and $C$ substitution boxes and attenuation boxes are typical examples of these.

## 'Generator' types

The following 'generator' types of test gear are in common use:

(1) *AF sine-wave generators*. These are designed to generate low-distortion (typically 0.1 per cent at 1kHz) low frequency (usually 20Hz to 30kHz) sine waves, and are normally based on a Wien-bridge or Twin-T oscillator. *Figure 1.7* shows an example of a thermistor-stabilized Wien-based design that can be used in fixed-frequency 'industrial' application, and *Figure 1.8* shows, in block diagram form, how a wide-range version of the oscillator can be used, in conjunction with a sine–square converter and a variable attenuator, to make a laboratory sine–square waveform generator.

(2) *LF function generators*. These generate a basic 'triangle' waveform from which simultaneous sine and square waveforms are synthesized; typically, they can span the 1Hz to 100kHz range and their sine waves produce about 2 per

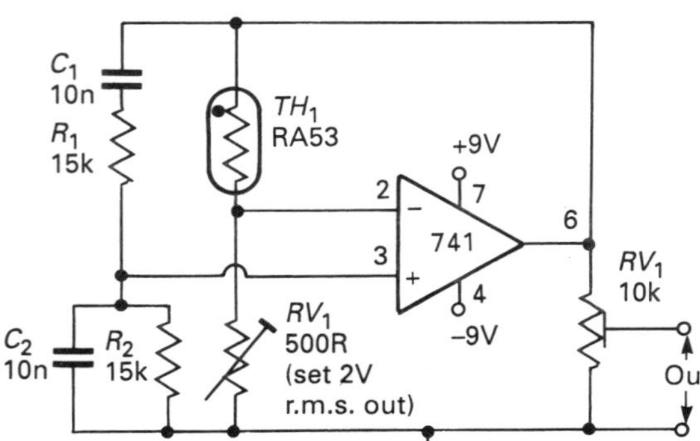


Figure 1.7. *Simple 'industrial' 1kHz Wien-bridge sine-wave generator.*

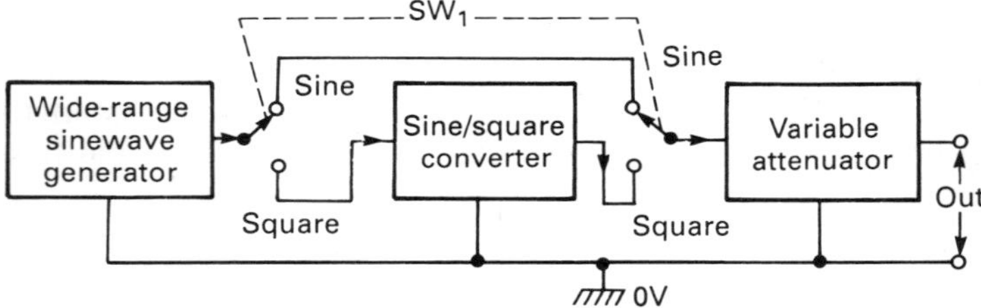


Figure 1.8. *Block diagram of a wide-range laboratory-standard sine/ square generator.*

cent distortion at 1kHz. Usually, the operating frequency can be controlled either resistively or via an external voltage, enabling the frequency to be voltage-swept if required. Several companies produce dedicated 'function generator' ICs that enable a complete generator to be built from a single chip.

(3) *Pulse generators*. These produce an output pulse on the arrival of a suitable input trigger signal, which may be generated either internally or externally. *Figure 1.9* shows the block diagram of a simple pulse generator that produces a single variable-width output pulse on the arrival of each rising edge of a rectangular input signal. *Figure 1.10* shows a modified version of the above generator, in which the initiation of the output pulse can (when $SW_2$ is

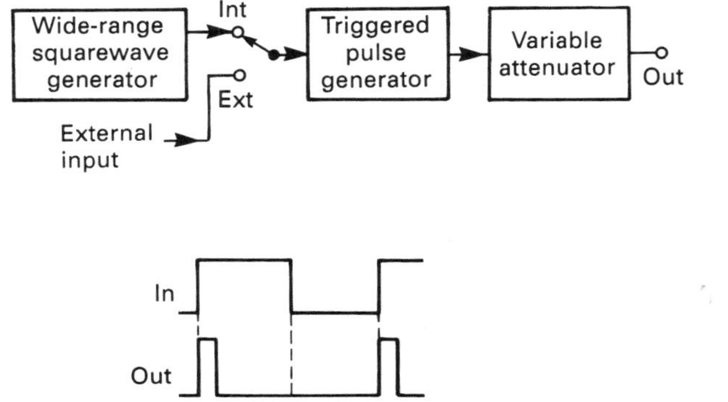


Figure 1.9. *Typical pulse generator block diagram.*

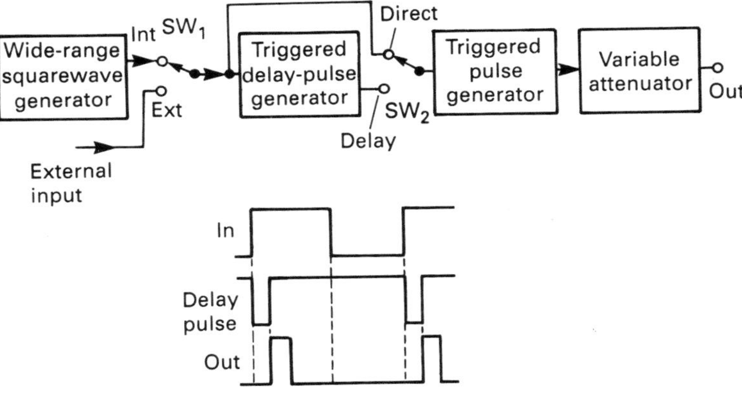


Figure 1.10. *Typical delayed-pulse generator block diagram.*

set to the 'delay' position) be delayed by a period equal to the width of the delay-pulse generator. Typically, both pulse widths can be varied from a fraction of a microsecond to hundreds of milliseconds.

(4) *RF generators*. These produce high-frequency sine-wave outputs (of 100kHz upwards), and usually have some type of modulation facility (AM and/or FM) and some means of varying the output signal amplitude; *Figures 1.3* and *1.4* show (in block diagram form) examples of laboratory and industrial (dedicated) RF generators.

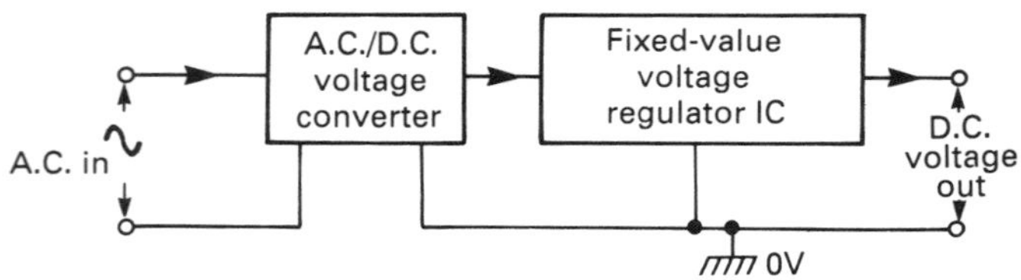


Figure 1.11. *Typical 'industrial-type' stabilized P.S.U.*

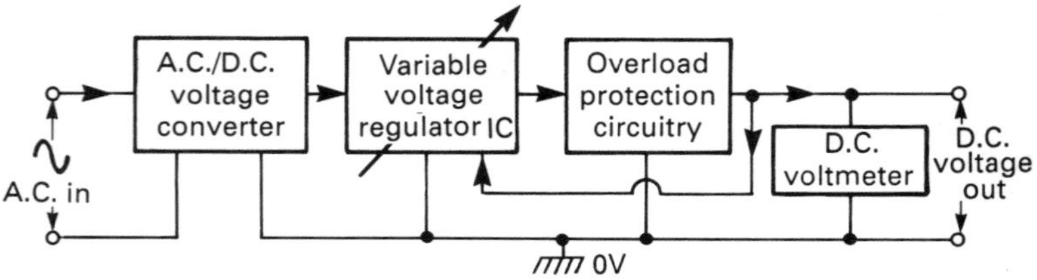


Figure 1.12. *Typical 'laboratory standard' P.S.U.*

(5) *Stabilized power supplies.* These generate a mains (A.C. power line) derived D.C. supply in which the output voltage remains constant in spite of wide variations in load current, etc. Modern versions of these are usually based on one or more dedicated 'voltage regulator' ICs. Industrial versions of such a PSU (power supply unit) usually consist of little more that a transformer–rectifier–capacitor A.C./D.C. converter and a fixed-value voltage regulator IC, as shown in *Figure 1.11*. Laboratory-type PSUs are more complex, and include a variable-voltage regulator IC, overload protection circuitry, and an output voltage monitor (see *Figure 1.12*).

## 'Indicator' accuracy

The next major category of test gear is the 'indicator', which usually consists of some type of analogue or digital meter. Before looking at the various types of indicator, mention must be made of the system of specifying the accuracy of meters.

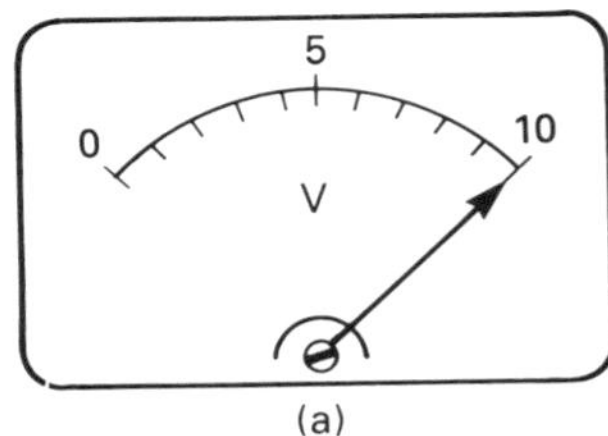


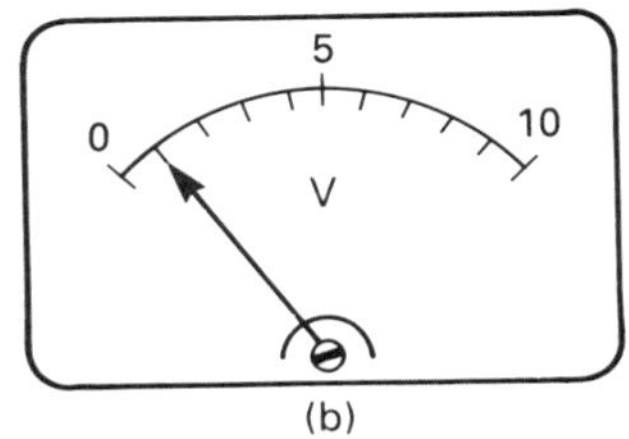


Figure 1.13. *This 10V meter has a basic 'accuracy' (see text) within 3 per cent of F.S.D.; its readings are accurate to within (a) 3 per cent at 10V, and (b) 30 per cent at 1V.*

The accuracy of analogue meters (i.e. moving coil types, etc.) is specified by the statement that the actual meter reading is 'accurate to within $\pm x$ per cent of the F.S.D. value of the meter'. By convention, this statement is usually abbreviated to the simple but rather ambiguous statement that the meter has an 'accuracy of $x$ per cent', the remaining qualifying parts of the full statement being accepted (by practical engineers) as implicit and self-explanatory. Thus, if a meter has a specified 'accuracy' of 3 per cent (a typical value) and has an F.S.D. (full scale deflection) value of 10V, as shown in *Figure 1.13*, it is implied that the meter has a true input in the range 9.7 to 10.3V when it reads 10V, and in the range 0.7 to 1.3V when it reads 1V. Note in the latter example that meter errors may be as high as 30 per cent.

Digital meters usually give three or more digits of readout, as shown in *Figure 1.14*. A simple 3-digit type can give a maximum reading of 999. Most general-purpose digital voltmeters (DVMs) can give a maximum reading of 1999, and are known as $3\frac{1}{2}$-digit DVMs; high-precision types can give a maximum reading of 19999 and are known as $4\frac{1}{2}$-digit DVMs. Their precision is fully specified by the statement that their reading is 'accurate to within $\pm x$ per cent of the actual reading, $\pm y$ digits'. By convention, this

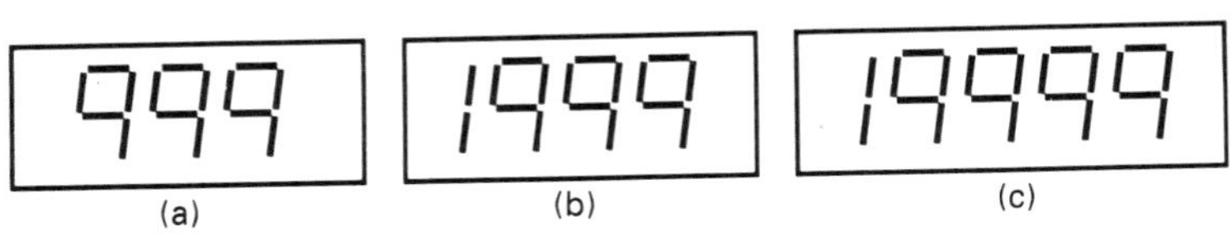


Figure 1.14. *Full-scale readings on digital meters with (a) 3 digits, (b) $3\frac{1}{2}$ digits, and (c) $4\frac{1}{2}$ digits.*

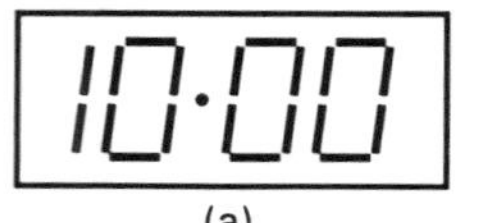


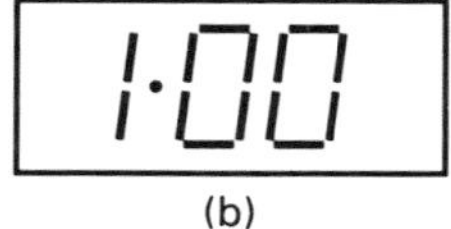


Figure 1.15. *This $3\frac{1}{2}$ digit meter has a full-scale sensitivity of 19.99V and a basic 'accuracy' (see text) within 0.5 per cent ±2 'digits': its readings are accurate to within (a) 0.7 per cent at 10V, and (b) 2.5 per cent at 1V0.*

statement can be abbreviated to a simple statement that the meter has an 'accuracy of *x* per cent, ±*y* digits'. Thus, if a $3\frac{1}{2}$-digit 19.99 voltmeter has an 'accuracy' of 0.5 per cent ±2 digits (a typical value), as shown in *Figure 1.15*, it is implied that its reading are accurate to within 0.7 per cent at 10V, and to 2.5 per cent at 1V0.

## 'Indicator' types

The following 'indicator' types of test gear are in common use:

(1) *Analogue meters*. These are designed to give a visual representation of a monitored parameter value by moving a pointer or a dot or bar of light a proportionate distance across a graduated scale. *Figure 1.16* shows examples of a 7V reading given on 10V meters using (a) moving pointer and (b and c) ten-LED bar-graph and dot-graph 'moving light' displays.

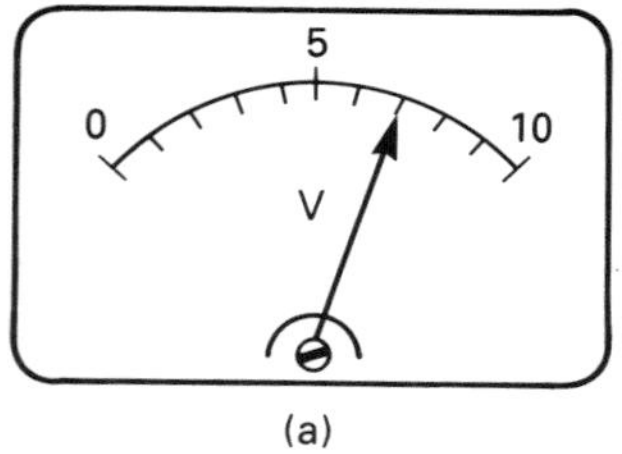


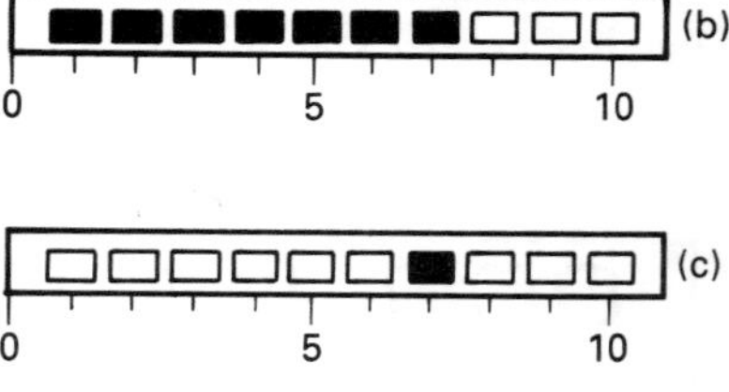


Figure 1.16. *Representations of 7V readings on 10V meters of the following types: (a) moving pointer; (b) 10-LED bar graph, (c) 10-LED dot graph.*

The reader should note that analogue meters have two major advantages over digital types. The first is that they give clear indications of measurement variations (digital displays present a confused jumble of numbers under this condition), making them uniquely well suited to applications such as 'peak point' and 'null point' indicating. The second great advantage is that they can be inscribed with both linear and non-linear scales, enabling, for example, a single meter to read both linear and dB voltage values.

In instrumentation and test gear applications, the most widely used type of analogue meter is the 'moving coil' type. These are actually current-indicating meters in which the test current flows through a coil and causes the meter's pointer to deflect by a proportional amount. The coil has a finite resistance, and the performance of the meter can thus be depicted by presenting it as shown in *Figure 1.17*; in this instance the meter has an F.S.D. sensitivity of 100μA and an internal resistance of 1000Ω, and thus has 100mV generated across its terminals at F.S.D.

The sensitivity of the *Figure 1.17* meter can be effectively reduced (so that it needs a greater current to give a F.S.D. reading) by shunting the meter's terminals with a suitable resistor ($R_x$), as shown in *Figure 1.18*. Alternatively, the meter can be made to act as a D.C. voltage indicator by wiring it in series with 'multiplier' resistor $R_x$ as shown in the '10V F.S.D. meter circuit of *Figure 1.19*; here, the 100μA meter has, by definition, a basic sensitivity of 10KΩ/V, so $R_m$ (which equals the sum of $R_x$ and the meter's internal resistance) needs a value of 100kΩ. The meter can be made to indicate A.C. current values by

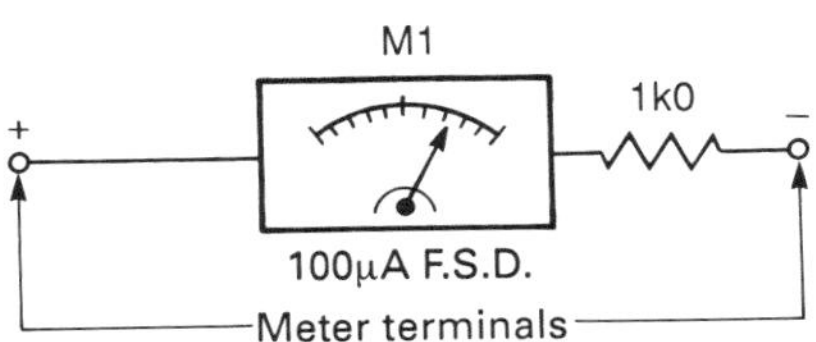


Figure 1.17. *Representation of a moving-coil meter with an F.S.D. sensitivity of 100μA and 1000Ω internal resistance.*

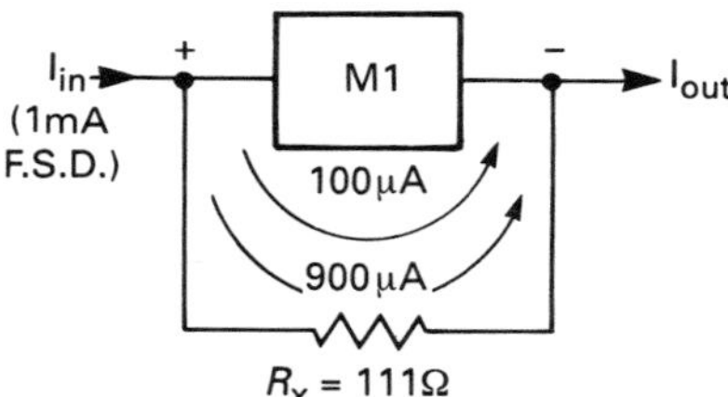


Figure 1.18. *External shunt* ($R_x$) *used to convert the above meter to read 1mA F.S.D.*

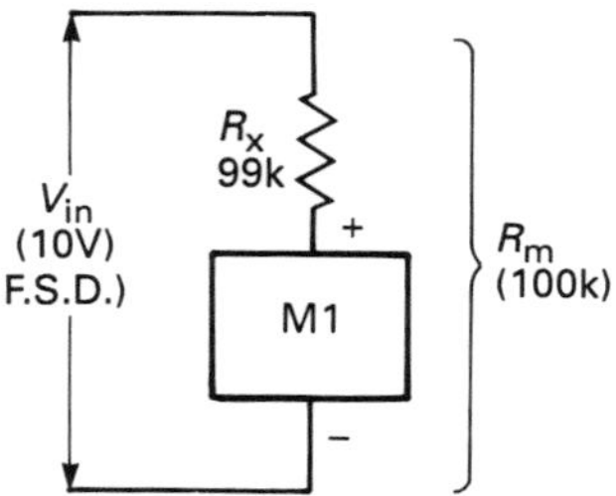


Figure 1.19. *Series multiplier resistor* $R_x$ *used to convert the 100μA meter to read 10V F.S.D.*

feeding them to the meter via a bridge rectifier; *Figure 1.20* shows how the meter can be made to indicate A.C. voltage values by feeding them to the meter via a multiplier resistor ($R_x$) and a bridge rectifier.

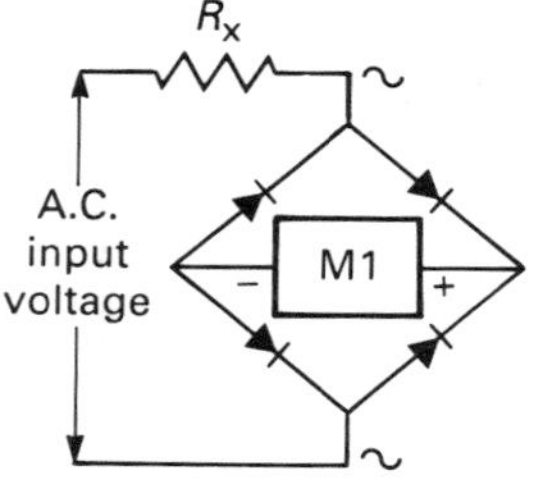


Figure 1.20. *Multiplier resistor and bridge rectifier used to convert the 100μA meter to an A.C. voltmeter.*

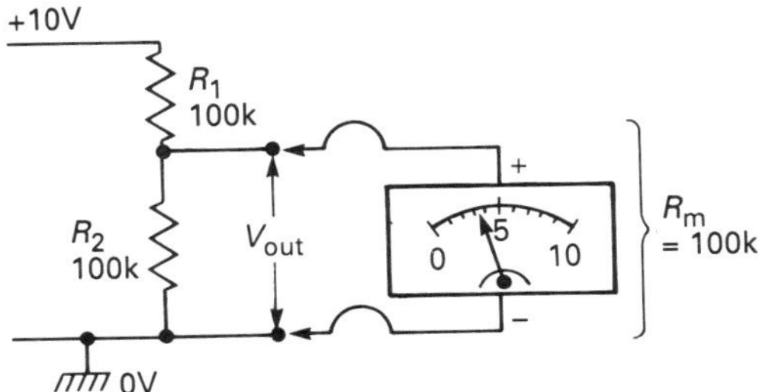


Figure 1.21. *This voltage divider gives an unloaded output of 5V, but this simple test meter gives an output reading of 3.3V, due to its loading effect.*

(2) *Analogue multimeters.* These consist of a good-quality moving coil meter with a wide span of switch-selected A.C. and D.C. voltage and current ranges, plus a battery-powered addition that enables the meter to indicate a wide range of resistance values. When using a simple multimeter, always consider its effect on the circuit under test; *Figure 1.21* illustrates this point. Here, the $R_1$–$R_2$ divider gives an unloaded output of 5V, but when the meter is connected across the output its 100k $R_m$ value shunts $R_2$ and reduces its effective value to 50k, thus reducing the output voltage to the 3.3V value indicated by the meter.

(3) *Electronic analogue multimeters.* These unite a normal moving coil meter with an electronic buffer/amplifier and a high-impedance input attenuator, as shown in *Figure 1.22*, to greatly increase the meter's effective sensitivity

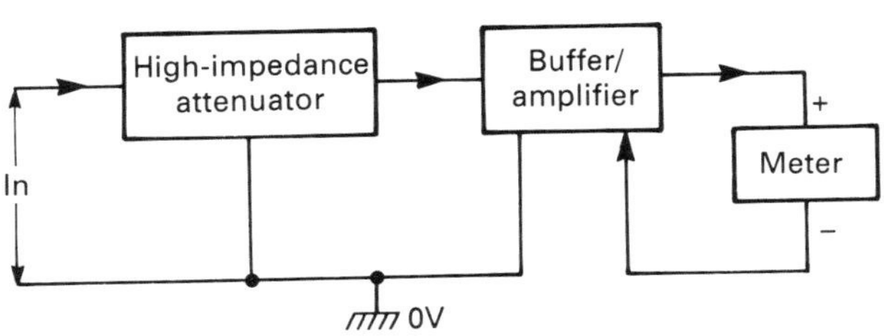


Figure 1.22. *Block diagram of an electronic analogue multimeter.*

and input impedance, etc. Such meters may typically have an input impedance of 10mΩ and a maximum a.c. or d.c. F.S.D. sensitivity of 1mV.

(4) *Digital voltmeters (DVMs) and digital panel meters (DPMs)*. These are usually $3\frac{1}{2}$- or $4\frac{1}{2}$-digit instruments with an LED or LCD readout and an F.S.D. sensitivity of 199.9mV (or 199.99mV) and an input impedance of 100MΩ; they are readily available in 'module' form, in which they are usually known as 'digital panel meters' or DPMs, and can easily be made to read various F.S.D. values of a.c. or d.c. voltage or current, or resistance or capacitance, etc., by connecting the inputs to the meter via simple 'conversion' circuitry.

(5) *Digital multimeters*. These combine a DVM or DPM module and various switch-selected 'conversion' circuits to make a versatile and very accurate battery-powered general-purpose test meter that can outperform the ordinary analogue multimeter in many respects.

(6) *Digital frequency meters*. These are six- to eight-digit instruments that give a direct readout of input frequency or period with crystal precision.

(7) *Oscilloscopes*. These are complex instruments that enable waveforms, etc., to be displayed in real-time form on a cathode ray tube's (CRT's) flat TV-like screen, which is fitted with a calibrated graph-like graticule. The CRT is fitted with an electron gun that enables a sharp spot of light to be generated on the screen; this spot can be moved up and down the screen (on the *Y* axis) by signals applied to a pair of *Y* plates, or left and right across the screen (on the *X* axis) by signals applied to a pair of *X* plates. The spot intensity can be varied via signals applied to a *Z* grid, thus giving *Z* axis control.

*Figure 1.23* shows, in simplified block diagram form, the basic elements of an oscilloscope (or 'scope, as it is usually called). The external test signal that is to be displayed is fed to the 'scope's high-impedance (typically 10MΩ) input attenuator and passed on to the CRT's *Y* plates via a wide-band amplifier and a push–pull driver. Part of the amplified signal is tapped off to activate a 'trigger' generator, which synchronously fires a 'time-base' generator that feeds a linear sawtooth waveform to the CRT's *X* plates via a push–pull driver; the time-base generator also activates a

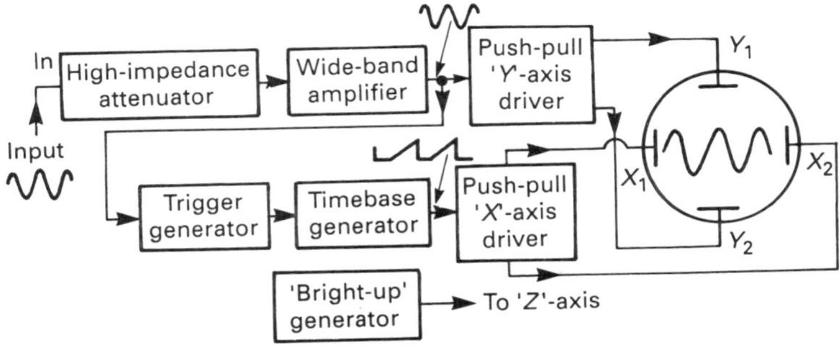


Figure 1.23. *Basic elements of a simple oscilloscope, or 'scope.*

'bright-up' generator that gives $Z$ axis control of spot intensity. These elements act together to draw or 'trace' a graphic display of the input waveform, with the $Y$ axis tracing the vertical movements on a volts-per-centimetre basis, and the $X$ axis tracing the horizontal left-to-right movements on a microseconds-per-centimetre basis.

In practice, the sensitivity of most simple modern 'scopes can be varied, in calibrated steps, from about 5mV/cm to 5V/cm in the $Y$ axis, with a bandwidth extending from d.c. to 20MHz, and from 0.5μs/cm to 0.5s/cm on the $X$ axis. Some 'scopes have bandwidths that extend to 100MHz or more, and others have multi-trace facilities that enable waveforms from two or three different parts of a circuit to be displayed simultaneously.

## 'Composite' test gear types

The following 'composite' types of test gear are in common use:

(1) *L–C–R bridges*. These combine a passive 'bridge' network and an energizing generator and a balance indicator, to form a stand-alone test set that can be used to measure values of inductance ($L$), capacitance ($C$), and resistance ($R$). *Figure 1.24* shows the basic elements of a resistance-measuring 'Wheatstone' bridge unit; the actual bridge ($R_1 - R_2 - R_3 - R_x$) is energized by a low-frequency (typically 50 to 1000Hz) oscillator, and the bridge's

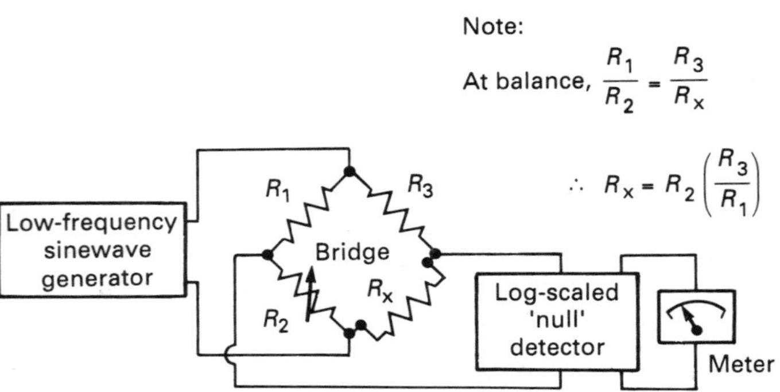


Figure 1.24. *Basic elements of a resistance-measuring Wheatstone bridge unit.*

output signal is monitored via a null-indicating logarithmically scaled meter.

The bridge's action is such that its output is zero when the ratio of $R_1/R_2$ equals that of $R_3/R_x$, and under this condition the bridge is said to be 'nulled' or 'balanced'. Thus, at balance, the $R_x$ value equals that of $R_2$ multiplied by the ratio $R_3/R_1$. In practice, variable resistor $R_2$ is fitted with a calibrated scale, and the value of $R_3$ can be varied in switch-selected decades, to give a 'decade value multiplier' action; the $R_x$ value is found by simply adjusting $R_2$ and $R_3$ until the bridge is balanced, and then reading off the $R_2$ value and multiplying it by the $R_3$ factor. The bridge can be adapted to measure values of inductance or capacitance by replacing parts of the Wheatstone bridge with reactive, rather than resistive, elements.

(2) *Distortion-factor meters*. These instruments enable the inherent distortion of a sine-wave signal to be accurately measured in terms of total harmonic distortion (THD), and are used in checking the linearity performance of audio amplifiers, etc. They consist of an ultra-low-distortion sine-wave generator, a high-performance twin-T (or similar) adjustable notch or 'rejector' filter, and an electronic millivoltmeter that gives a reading of true r.m.s. values, all interconnected as shown in *Figure 1.25*. Here, the sine-wave generator is first set to the desired test frequency (usually 1kHz) and its output is fed to the input of the test amplifier; the output of the amplifier is connected to the input of the notch filter. The output level of the amplifier is then set to

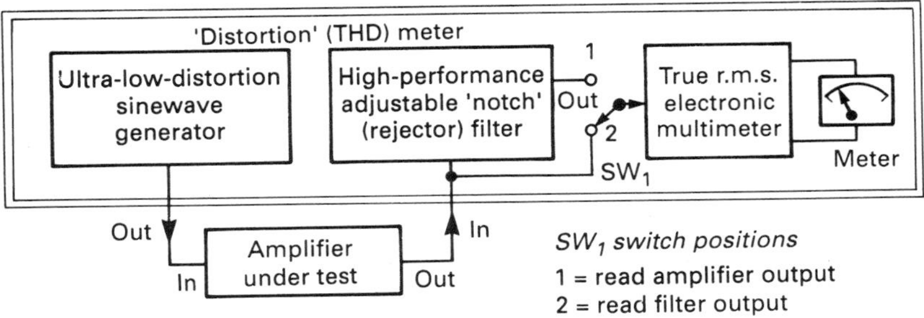


Figure 1.25. *Basic elements of a 'total harmonic distortion' (THD) meter.*

some convenient reference value (e.g., 1V), which is read on the built-in meter with $SW_1$ set to position '1'; $SW_1$ is next set to position '2', to monitor the output of the notch filter, which is then tuned about the 1kHz test frequency to give the minimum possible meter reading. Under this condition the notch filter totally rejects the fundamental 1kHz test signal, and only its harmonics reach the r.m.s.-reading meter, which thus gives an accurate reading of THD (e.g., a reading of 1mV corresponds to 0.1 per cent of the filter input signal, and thus represents a THD value of 0.1 per cent).

## Electrical 'standards' types

Every professional electronics laboratory should hold a selection of electrical 'standards', which can be used to check the fundamental accuracy of other types of test and measuring gear. These are high-quality, high-accuracy units that (ideally) carry a certificate of calibration, which is periodically checked against national or international standards. All 'standards' should be held in a thermally regulated environment. Standards are in common use for the checking and measurement of the following parameters: *ATTENUATION*, *CAPACITANCE*, *FREQUENCY*, *INDUCTANCE*, *RESISTANCE* and *VOLTAGE*. The attenuation standard usually takes the form of a switched, precision, attenuator box. Capacitance, inductance, and resistance standards can take the form of individual components, or switch-selected components in 'boxes'. Frequency standads may take the form of a thermally stabilized crystal oscillator, or a special radio receiver that is tuned to a dedicated 'reference standard' broadcast station. Voltage reference may take the form of a 'standard' cell, or a modern precision voltage-reference IC circuit.

## Test gear: to buy or build?

The electronics amateur or the professional working on a low budget is, when wanting to acquiring new instrumentation or test gear units, faced with the question of whether to buy or build them. As a general rule, the following items are relatively easy and cost-effective to build and calibrate:

(1) simple analogue and digital meters and multi-range meters;
(2) low-frequency (up to 150kHz) waveform generators of all types, including function generators and pulse generators;
(3) simple RF generators;
(4) all types of power supply;
(5) most 'dedicated' or 'industrial' types of test gear;
(6) *L*, *C*, and *R* bridges;
(7) distortion-factor meters;
(8) all 'simple' to 'medium complexity' circuits.

As a general rule, the following items are either very difficult to build or to calibrate to an adequate standard, or are too expensive in terms of time or money (or both) to be worth the effort of building, unless you are an exceptionally ardent enthusiast:

(1) wide-range analogue and digital multimeters (they are rarely cost-effective to build);
(2) wide-range 'laboratory standard' RF generators (the problem here is one of providing adequate RF screening and adequate calibration);
(3) *modern* laboratory oscilloscopes (another problem of cost effectiveness); note in this case, however, that a good performance can be obtained from an old or second-hand model by updating it with home-build 'add-ons' such as trace doublers, calibrators, triggered timebases, and probes, etc.

Before leaving this 'to build, or not to build' theme, note that it was quite normal in the 1950s, 1960s and 1970s for ordinary electronics enthusiasts to build all three of the above-mentioned types of test gear, often making extensive use of war-surplus components or equipment, of which there was a great glut in those days. There was, in any case, little alternative then, since good commercial test gear was in short supply and was very expensive. Fortunately, things have (in the electronics world) changed for the better since then, and it is now possible to buy excellent ready-built multimeters, RF generators, and 'scopes at a lower price than the modern do-it-yourselfer would have to pay for the component parts of those instruments.

## Basic test gear circuit elements

Virtually all practical instrumentation and test gear circuits are made up of one or more of the following basic types of circuit element, which are described in detail in following chapters of this volume.

(1) *Attenuators and filters*. These passive networks are used to correctly condition or adjust the amplitude or quality of signals reaching the inputs of indicating instruments, or coming from the outputs of generators. Some types of frequency-selective (notch) filter can form the basis of precision sine-wave generators or THD meters, etc.

(2) *Bridges*. These passive networks come into balance only under sharply defined conditions of impedance matching, and can be used in a variety of test gear applications for measuring parameters such as resistance, capacitance, inductance, or impedance, or for matching resistance values with ultra-high precision.

(3) *Analogue and digital meters*. These can be used as the basis of a whole range of single- and multi-range 'indicator' instruments, to give accurate readings of all types of voltages and currents, as well as frequency, resistance, and other parameters.

(4) *Waveform generators*. These form the basis of many types of test gear; a vast range of waveform types can be directly generated or synthesized.

(5) Finally, *power supply* circuits have almost universal application; they can be used to provide simple 'rough' voltages, or

ones that are precision regulated to provide a specific voltage almost irrespective of output loading conditions.

Circuits of all the above types are described in detail in the next eleven chapters of this volume.

# 2 Attenuator circuits

Attenuators are widely used in modern instrumentation and test gear circuits to correctly condition or adjust the amplitudes of signals reaching the inputs of indicating instruments or coming from the outputs of generators. This chapter looks at a wide range of practical versions of these basic circuit elements.

## Attenuator basics

Attenuators are used to reduce an awkward value of input signal to a lower and more convenient output level. The simplest attenuator is the 'L'-type (so named because of its diagram's resemblance to that letter), which (as shown in *Figure 2.1*) is

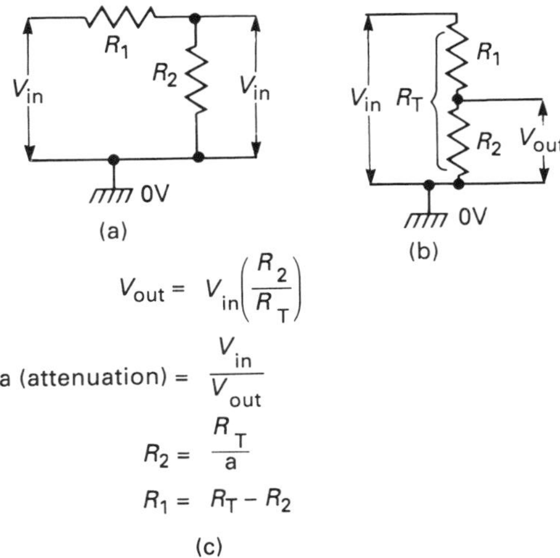


Figure 2.1. *The basic 'L'-type attenuator (a) is really a simple potential divider (b); its design is controlled by the formulae in (c).*

really a simple potential divider that consists of two resistors ($R_1$ and $R_2$) wired in series. The degree of attenuation (a) is set by the ratio of $R_2/(R_1 + R_2)$, as shown. Note that the output of this type of attenuator must be fed to an impedance that is very large relative to the $R_2$ value, so that the load does not significantly shunt $R_2$ and thereby increase the overall attenuation of the circuit. The attenuator's input impedance equals $R_1 + R_2$ ($= R_T$).

The method of designing an 'L'-type attenuator with desired values of attenuation *a* and total resistance $R_T$ is to first work out the value of $R_2$, and then the value of $R_1$, on the basis of

$$\text{(i) } R_2 = R_T/a \qquad \text{and} \qquad \text{(ii) } R_1 = R_T - R_2.$$

Thus, to design a basic 'L' attenuator that has an $R_T$ value of 10kΩ and an '*a*' value of 10 (= 20dB), $R_2$ needs a value of 10kΩ/10 = 1k0, and $R_1$ needs a value of 10kΩ − 1k0 = 9k0.

The simplest type of variable attenuator is the variable 'pot' type shown in *Figure 2.2*, which may be used as a volume control in an audio system or as an output level control in a simple audio generator, etc. Note that this pot has upper and lower arms, and is merely a variation of the 'L'-type attenuator.

Another variation of the 'L' attenuator is the switched variable type shown in *Figure 2.3*, which can provide a selection of values of attenuation. The procedure for designing this type of circuit is similar to that already described (using obvious variations of the (i) and (ii) formulae), except that a separate calculation is made for each attenuation position, starting with the greatest. Thus, the *Figure 2.3* attenuator has an $R_T$ value of 10k, so the first step in the design is to work out the $R_3$ value needed to give '÷100' attenuation, which works out at 10k/100 = 100Ω. Similarly, the

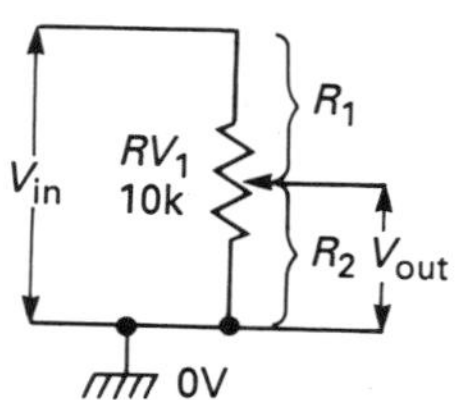


Figure 2.2. *This 'pot' attenuator is a fully variable version of the 'L'-type attenuator.*

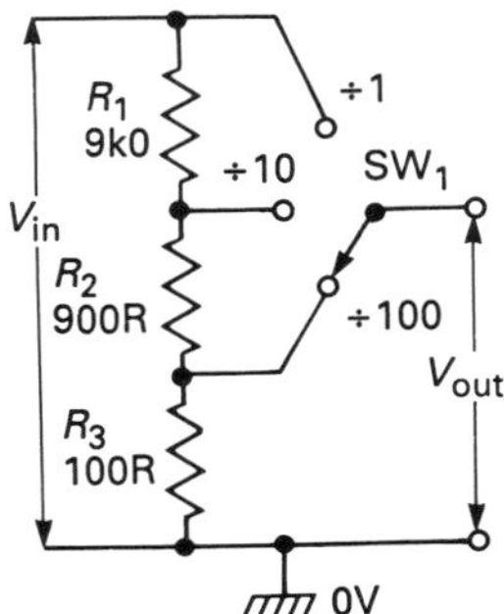


Figure 2.3. *The design of this switched attenuator is fully described in the text.*

'lower arm' (i.e., $R_2 + R_3$) value needed in the '÷10' attenuation position equals 1k0, but 100Ω of this is already provided by $R_3$, so $R_2$ needs a value of 1k0 − 100Ω = 900Ω. $R_1$ needs a value of 10k − 1k0 = 9k0, as shown. This basic design procedure can be expanded to give as many attenuator steps as are needed in any particular application.

*Figure 2.4* shows how modified versions of the *Figures 2.2* and *2.3* circuits (with greatly reduced resistance values) can be combined to make a fully variable wide-range attenuator that can serve as the output of an audio sinewave generator, etc; $RV_1$ should be provided with a hand-calibrated scale.

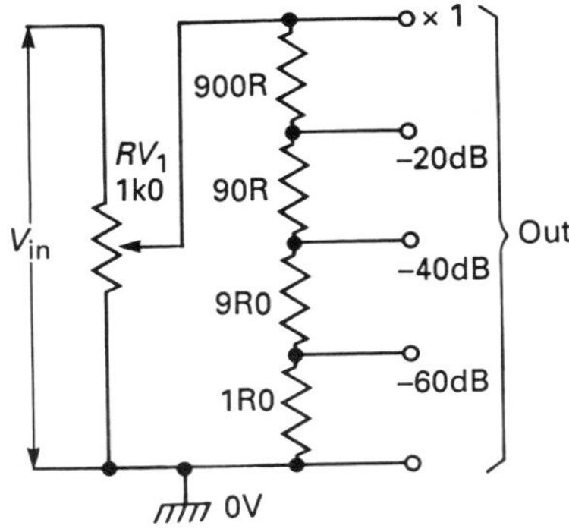


Figure 2.4. *This fully variable wide-range attenuator can be used in the output of a simple sine-wave generator, etc.*

## Voltage ranging

One popular application of the multi-step 'L' attenuator is as a 'voltage ranger' at the input of an electronic voltmeter, as shown in *Figure 2.5*. Here, the actual voltmeter has a fixed F.S.D. value of 1V, but the instrument is 'ranged' to indicate other F.S.D. voltage values by feeding them to the voltmeter via a suitably scaled switched 'L' attenuator. The attenuation ratios ($V_{IN}/V_{OUT}$) are chosen on the basis of

'*a*' = desired F.S.D./actual F.S.D.

Thus, the *Figure 2.5* attenuator is designed to give output ranging of 1–10–100V, which in this case correspond to attenuation values of 1, 10 and 100. Note in the diagram that the meter's range is extended to 1000V F.S.D. by connecting the high voltage via a separate input terminal (marked '1kV' and '÷10') and a 9M0 resistance chain made up of six series-wired 1M5 resistors, thus ensuring that (at F.S.D.) a maximum of only 150V appears across any resistor or pair of switch contact; when inputs are connected to this terminal, the meter's sensitivity is effectively reduced by a factor of ten on all ranges.

*Figures 2.6* to *2.8* show some useful variations of 'L'-type voltage-ranging attenuators. *Figure 2.6* shows two versions of an attenuator designed to feed a 1V F.S.D. meter with 1–3–10–30–100–300V ranging. The version shown in (a) has a total

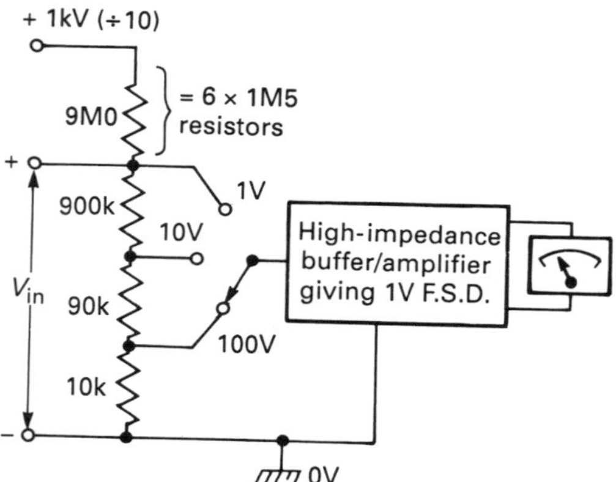


Figure 2.5. *This attenuator is used for 'ranging' an electronic voltmeter.*

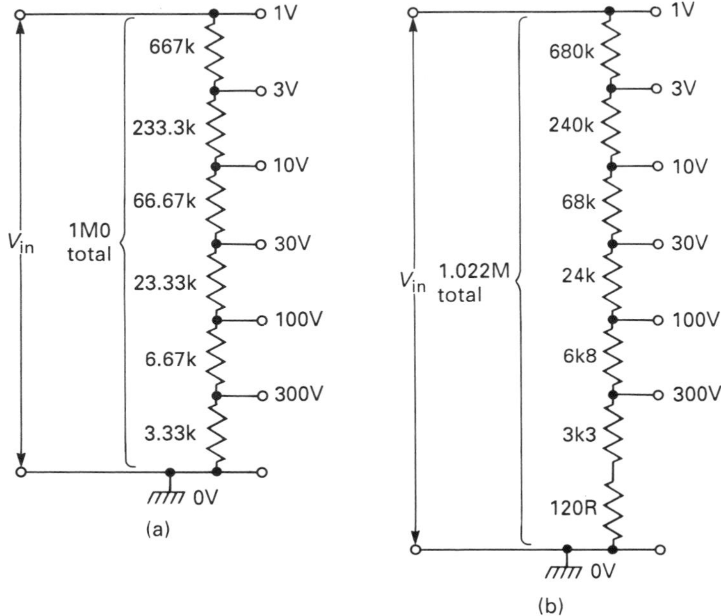


Figure 2.6. *These attenuators give 1–3–10, etc. voltage ranging; the one in (a) uses 'odd-ball' resistor values, which total 1M0; the one in (b) uses standard values, which total 1.022MΩ.*

resistance of 1M0 and calls for odd-ball values of resistance; the version shown in (b) uses standard resistors and generates maximum ranging errors of less than 0.4 per cent, but has a total resistance of 1.022MΩ.

*Figure 2.7* shows two more 1M0 attenuators designed to give 1V F.S.D. outputs; that in (a) gives 1–2.5–10–25–100–250V ranging, and that in (b) gives 1–2–5–10–20–50V ranging. Finally, *Figure 2.8* shows a 1M0 attenuator that gives an output that is variable from 0dB to −20dB in 2dB steps.

Note that all the attenuators shown in *Figure 2.3* to *Figure 2.8* can be made with alternative total resistance ($R_T$) values by simply multiplying or dividing all resistor values by a proportionate amount. Thus, any of the '1M0' designs can be adapted to give an $R_T$ value of 10K by dividing all resistor values by 100, etc. Odd-ball values of resistance can be created by wiring two or more standard resistors in series or parallel.

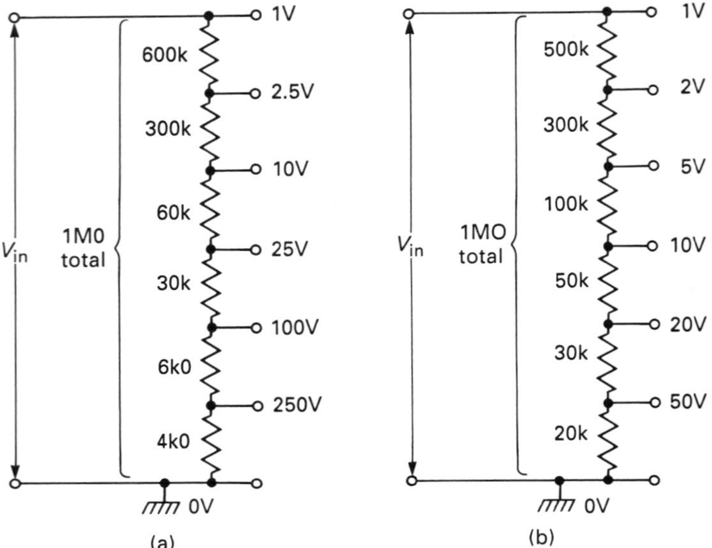


Figure 2.7. *These 1M0 attenuators give (a) 1–2.5–10, etc., and (b) 1–2–5–10, etc., voltage ranging. For alternative total resistance values, simply multiply or divide all resistors by a proportionate amount (e.g., divide by 100 for 10k total).*

## Frequency compensation

'L'-type attenuators of the types shown in *Figures 2.1* to *2.8* are accurate only at d.c. or low frequencies or when made up of low-value resistors. Stray capacitances invariably shunt all resistors and make their impedance decrease as frequency increases, and in the case of the 'L' attenuator this may affect its attenuation ratios. This effect is particularly acute when high-value resistors are used; a mere 2pF of stray capacitance represents a reactance of about 800k at 100kHz and can thus have a significant affect on any resistor value greater than 10k or so. This problem can be overcome by deliberately shunting all resistors with correctly chosen values of capacitance, as shown in *Figure 2.9*.

Here, each resistor of the chain is shunted by a capacitor, and these have reactance values that are in the same ratios as the attenuator's resistive arms. The smallest capacitor (largest reactance) is wired across the largest resistor and typically has a

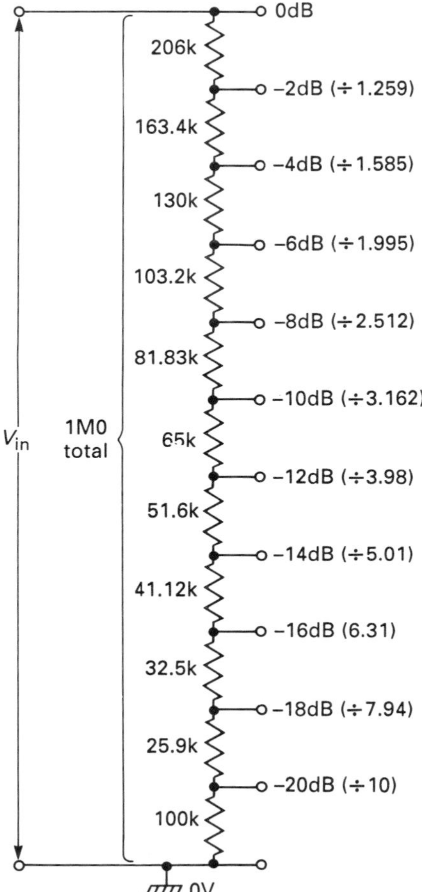


Figure 2.8. *The output of this 1M0 attenuator is variable in 2dB steps.*

value in the range 15 to 50pF, which is large enough to swamp strays but small enough to present an acceptably high impedance to input signals. The attenuator's frequency compensation is set up by feeding a good square wave to its input, taking its ÷100 or ÷1000 output to the input of a 'scope, and then trimming $C_1$ to obtain a good square-wave picture, as shown in (b) in the diagram.

Oscilloscopes invariably use compensated 'L'-type attenuators at the input of their 'Y' amplifiers. *Figure 2.10* shows part of a

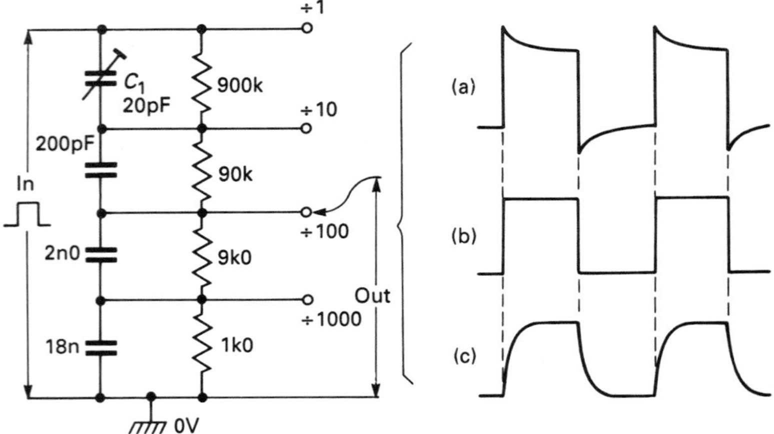


Figure 2.9. *A basic 'compensated' wide-range 'L'-type attenuator, showing square wave output waveforms when the $C_1$ trimmer setting is (a) over-compensated, (b) correctly compensated, and (c) under-compensated.*

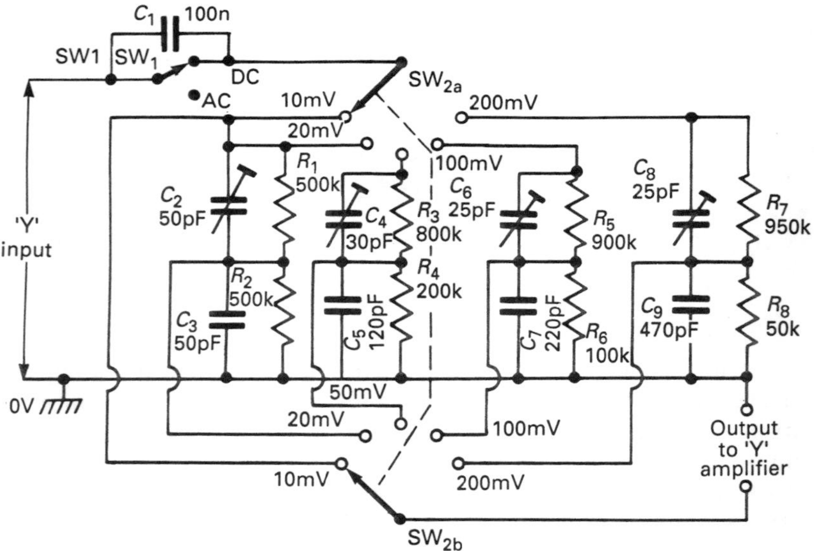


Figure 2.10. *Part of a typical 'scope Y amplifier attenuator.*

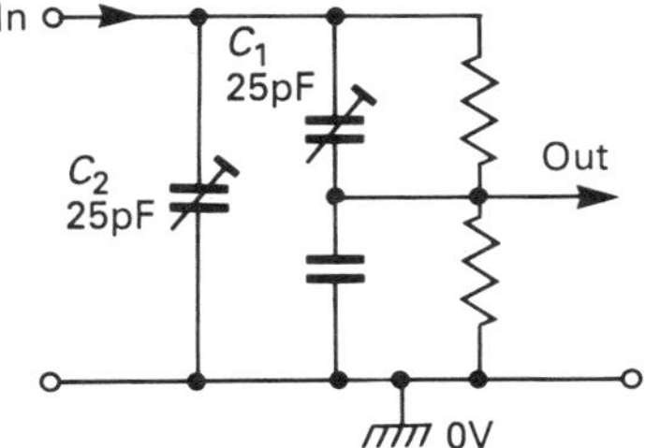


Figure 2.11. *Alternative type of* Y *amplifier attenuator section;* $C_1$ *sets frequency compensation;* $C_2$ *sets input capacitance.*

typical example, in which an individually trimmed 1M0 attenuator section is used on each range. *Figure 2.11* shows a variation of one of these sections; in this case $C_1$ is used to set the section's frequency compensation, and $C_2$ is used to adjust the section's input capacitance so that the '*Y*'-channel attenuator presents a constant input impedance on all ranges.

*Figure 2.12* shows how a two-range compensated 'primary' attenuator and a low-impedance uncompensated six-range 'secondary' attenuator can be used together to help make an a.c. millivoltmeter that spans 1mV to 300V F.S.D. in 12 ranges. The primary attenuator gives zero attenuation in the 'mV' position and ÷1000 attenuation in the 'V' position. The secondary attenuator is a modified version of that shown in *Figure 2.6b*, with all resistor values reduced by a factor of 1000. Note that if readily available metal film resistors with values greater than 10Ω are to be used throughout the construction, the 6.8Ω and 3.42Ω resistors can be made by wiring three or four resistors in parallel, as indicated in the diagram.

## An 'L'-type ladder attenuator

One snag with the basic 'L'-type attenuator of *Figure 2.1* is that it must use two greatly different resistance values if used to give a large amount of attenuation, e.g., for 60dB attenuation $R_1$ must by 900 times greater than $R_2$. In this example, if $R_2$ has a value of 10Ω minimum, $R_1$ needs a value of 9k0 or greater, and must be frequency compensated if used above 20kHz or so. An easy way round this snag is to build the attenuator by cascading several

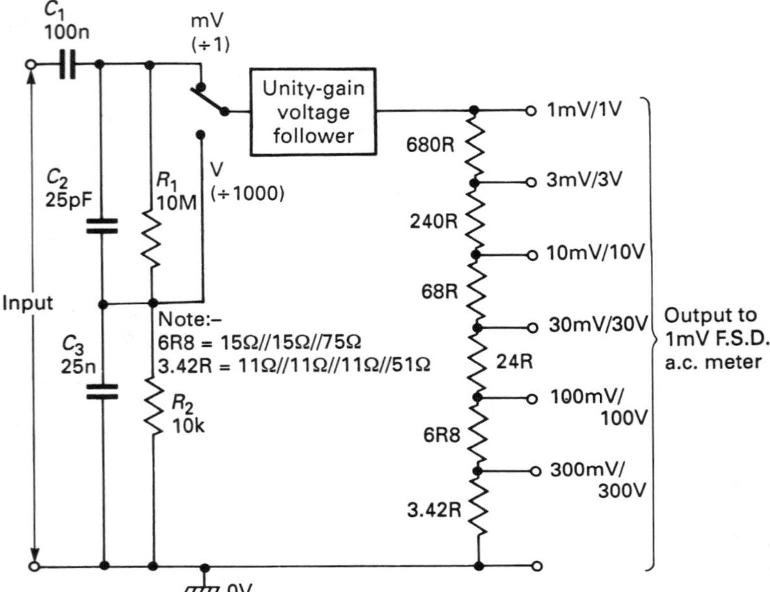


Figure 2.12. *Use of primary and secondary attenuators in an a.c. millivoltmeter.*

lower-value attenuator stages, with sensibly restricted resistor values, as shown in the practical circuit of *Figure 2.13*. Such a circuit is known as a *ladder* attenuator.

The *Figure 2.13* ladder attenuator consists of three cascaded 20dB attenuator stages, each with a maximum resistance value of 820R and with a useful uncompensated bandwidth extending to hundreds of kHz. Note that the right-hand (1mV) stage has '$R_1$–$R_2$' (see *Figure 2.1*) values of 820R and 91R, and that these shunt the lower '$R_2$' 101R leg of the middle (10mV) attenuator and reduce its effective value to 91Ω. Similarly, the middle attenuator shunts the lower leg of the first (100mV) attenuator and reduces its effective value to 91R. Thus, each stage effectively consists of an 820R/91R 20dB attenuator that is accurate within +0.2 per cent. The odd-ball 101Ω resistors are made by series-wiring 33R and 68R resistors.

The *Figure 2.13* attenuator is an excellent design that can be used as the output section of a variety of audio and pulse generator

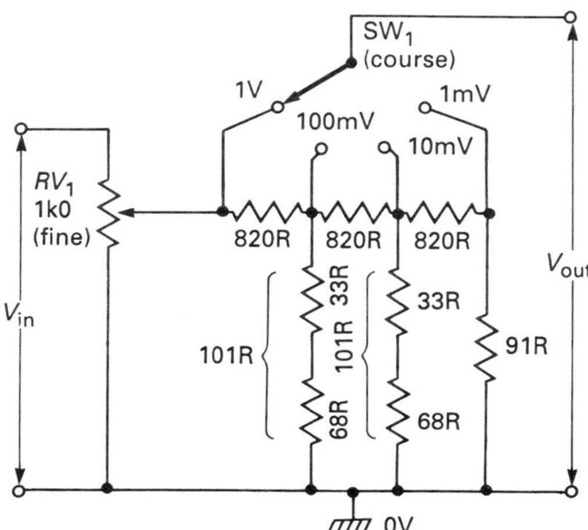


Figure 2.13. *This fully variable attenuator uses an 'L'-type ladder network and makes an excellent wide-band output section for audio and pulse generators, etc.*

circuits. Its output is fully variable via $RV_1$. The attenuator's output impedance, on all but the '1V' range, is less than 90Ω, so its output voltage is virtually uninfluenced by load impedances greater than a few kilohms.

## Matched-resistance attenuators

A serious weakness of the 'L'-type attenuator is that its output impedance varies with the attenuator setting, and that its input impedance varies in a similar way if the output is externally loaded. The significance of this latter effect is illustrated in *Figure 2.14*, where the attenuator is represented by the load on the output of the waveform generator, which has an output impedance of 100Ω. If the generator is set to give 1V output into a 1k0 load, the output varies between 1.048V and 0.917V if the load is then varied between 2k0 and 500Ω, thus invalidating the attenuator's calibration.

It follows from the above that, as illustrated in *Figure 2.15*, the 'ideal' variable attenuator should have input and output impedances that remain constant irrespective of the attenuation

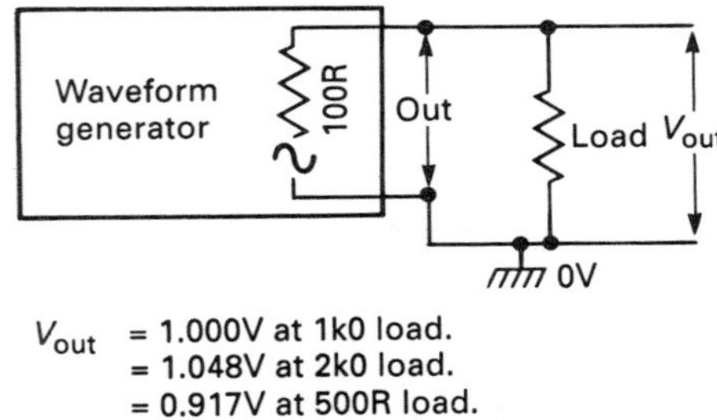


Figure 2.14. *The output voltage of a generator varies with changes in its load impedance.*

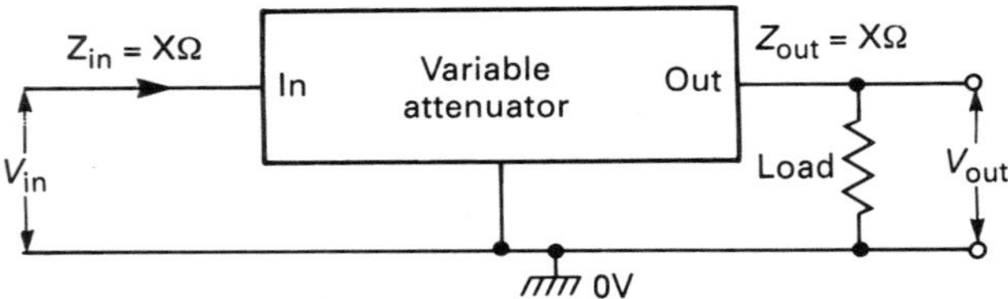


Figure 2.15. *The 'ideal' variable attenuator presents constant input and output impedances.*

setting. Such attenuators do in fact exist, and are usually based on a number of switch-selected fixed-value attenuator pads. These pads come in a variety of types, and the five most popular of these are shown in *Figures 2.16* and *2.17*, together with their design formulae. Note that these attenuators are perfectly symmetrical, enabling their input and output terminals to be transposed, and that they are each designed to feed into a fixed load impedance, *Z*, which actually becomes part of the attenuator network. Note that the pad's input and output impedances are designed to equal that of the designated load, thus enabling impedance-matched pads of any desired attenuation values to be cascaded in any desired combination, as shown in *Figure 2.18*.

The two most popular types of pad attenuator are the 'T' and 'π' types; the 'H' and 'O' types are simply 'balanced input' versions of these, and the 'bridged-T' type is a derivative of the basic 'T' type.

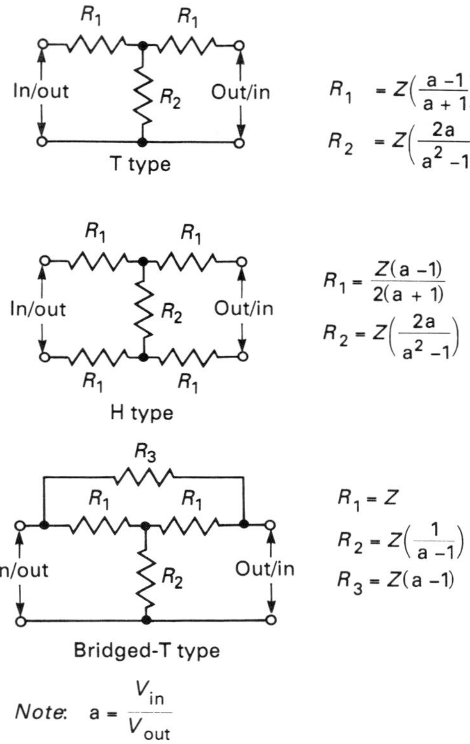


Figure 2.16. *Circuits and design formulae of the basic 'T' type attenuator and its 'H' and 'Bridged-T' derivatives.*

*Figure 2.19* shows a practical version of a π-type attenuator, designed to give a matched impedance of 1k0 and to give 20dB (= ÷10) of attenuation. Working through the design of this example from the back, note that the 1k0 load shunts $R_2$ and brings its effective impedance down to 550Ω, which then acts with $R_1$ as an 'L'-type attenuator that give the 20dB of attenuation and has an input impedance (into $R_1$) of 5501Ω, which is shunted by $R_3$ to give an actual input impedance of 1000Ω. Note that the output load forms a vital part of the attenuator, and that if it is removed the pad's attenuation falls to only ÷5.052, or −14.07dB.

*Figure 2.20* shows a practical version of a T-type attenuator, which is also designed to give a matched impedance of 1k0 and

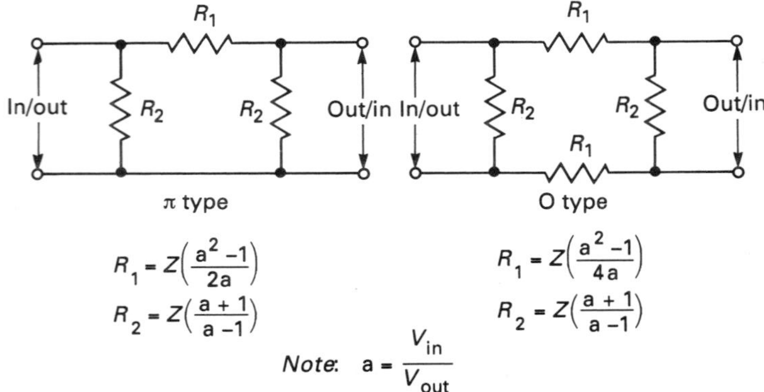


Figure 2.17. *Circuits and design formulae for the basic 'π' type attenuator and its 'O' type derivative.*

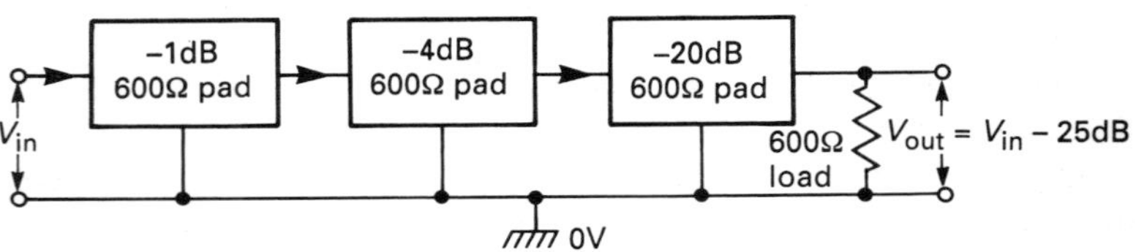


Figure 2.18. *Matched attenuator pads can be cascaded in any combination.*

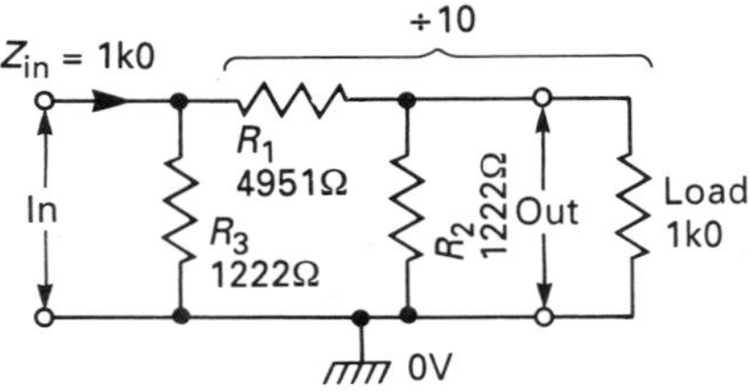


Figure 2.19. *Worked example of a 1k0, −20dB 'π'-type attenuator; its unloaded attenuation is ÷5.052, = −14.07dB.*

20dB of attenuation. Working through this design from the back, note that $R_3$ and the 1k0 load form an 'L'-type '÷1.8182' attenuator that has an input impedance (into $R_3$) of 1818.2Ω. $R_1$ and $R_2$ also form an 'L'-type attenuator, but in this case $R_2$ is shunted by the

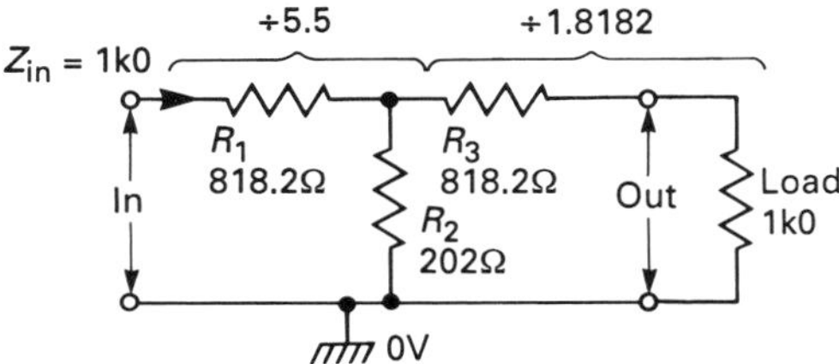


Figure 2.20. *Worked example of a 1k0, −20dB 'T'-type attenuator; its unloaded attenuation is ÷5.50, = −14.81dB.*

above 1818.2Ω impedance and has its effective value reduced to 181.8Ω, so this stage gives an attenuation of ÷5.5 and has an input impedance of 1000Ω. Thus, the T-type attenuator actually consists of a pair of cascaded L-types, which in this example give individual attenuation ratios of 1.8182 and 5.5, or ÷10 000 overall. Note that if the output load is removed from this attenuator its attenuation falls to only ÷5.50, or −14.81dB.

*Figure 2.21* shows a chart that makes the design of 'T' and 'π' attenuators very easy. To find the correct values of $R_1$ and $R_2$, simply read off the chart's $r_1$ and $r_2$ values indicated at the desired attenuation level and multiply these by the desired attenuator impedance, in ohms. Thus, to make a 100Ω, −20dB pad, $R_1$ and $R_2$ need values of 81.8Ω and 20.2Ω respectively. Note that this chart can also be used to design 'H' and 'O' attenuators by simply halving the derived $R_1$ value.

## Switched attenuators

Matched-impedance attenuator pads can be cascaded in any desired sequence of values and types, and this fact makes it easy to design switched-value attenuator networks and 'boxes', as shown in *Figures 2.22* and *2.23*, *Figure 2.22* shows how four binary-sequenced '1−2−4−8' attenuator pads can be cascaded, using two-pole two-way selector switches, to make an attenuator that can be varied from 0dB to −15dB in 1dB steps, and *Figure 2.23* shows an alternative arrangement that enables attenuation to be varied from 0dB to −70dB in 10dB steps. These two circuits can be cascaded, if desired, to make an attenuator that is variable from 0dB to −85dB in 1dB steps.

| dB Loss | a ($V_{in}/V_{out}$) | 'T'-type | | 'π'-type | |
|---|---|---|---|---|---|
| | | r1 | r2 | r1 | r2 |
| 0 | 1.000 | 0 | ∞ | 0 | ∞ |
| 0.1 | 1.012 | 0.00576 | 86.9 | 0.0115 | 174 |
| 0.2 | 1.023 | 0.0115 | 43.4 | 0.0230 | 86.9 |
| 0.3 | 1.035 | 0.0173 | 28.9 | 0.0345 | 57.9 |
| 0.4 | 1.047 | 0.0230 | 21.7 | 0.0461 | 43.4 |
| 0.5 | 1.059 | 0.0288 | 17.4 | 0.0576 | 34.8 |
| 0.6 | 1.072 | 0.0345 | 14.5 | 0.0691 | 29.0 |
| 0.8 | 1.096 | 0.0460 | 10.8 | 0.0922 | 21.7 |
| 1.0 | 1.122 | 0.0575 | 8.67 | 0.115 | 17.4 |
| 1.5 | 1.188 | 0.0861 | 5.76 | 0.174 | 11.6 |
| 2 | 1.259 | 0.115 | 4.30 | 0.232 | 8.72 |
| 3 | 1.413 | 0.171 | 2.84 | 0.352 | 5.85 |
| 4 | 1.585 | 0.226 | 2.10 | 0.477 | 4.42 |
| 5 | 1.778 | 0.280 | 1.64 | 0.608 | 3.57 |
| 6 | 1.995 | 0.332 | 1.34 | 0.747 | 3.01 |
| 7 | 2.239 | 0.382 | 1.12 | 0.896 | 2.61 |
| 8 | 2.512 | 0.431 | 0.946 | 1.057 | 2.32 |
| 9 | 2.818 | 0.476 | 0.812 | 1.23 | 2.10 |
| 10 | 3.162 | 0.520 | 0.703 | 1.43 | 1.92 |
| 12 | 3.981 | 0.598 | 0.536 | 1.86 | 1.67 |
| 14 | 5.01 | 0.667 | 0.416 | 2.41 | 1.50 |
| 15 | 5.62 | 0.698 | 0.367 | 2.72 | 1.43 |
| 16 | 6.31 | 0.726 | 0.325 | 3.08 | 1.38 |
| 18 | 7.94 | 0.776 | 0.256 | 3.91 | 1.29 |
| 20 | 10.00 | 0.818 | 0.202 | 4.95 | 1.22 |
| 25 | 17.78 | 0.894 | 0.113 | 8.86 | 1.12 |
| 30 | 31.62 | 0.939 | 0.0633 | 15.8 | 1.07 |
| 32 | 39.81 | 0.951 | 0.0503 | 19.89 | 1.052 |
| 35 | 56.23 | 0.965 | 0.0356 | 28.1 | 1.04 |
| 40 | 100.0 | 0.980 | 0.0200 | 50.1 | 1.02 |
| 45 | 177.8 | 0.989 | 0.0112 | 88.9 | 1.011 |
| 50 | 316.2 | 0.994 | 0.00632 | 158 | 1.006 |
| 55 | 562.3 | 0.996 | 0.00356 | 281 | 1.0036 |
| 60 | 1000 | 0.998 | 0.00200 | 500 | 1.0020 |
| 64 | 1585 | 0.9987 | 0.001262 | 800 | 1.00126 |

Figure 2.21. *'T' and 'π' attenuator design chart. To find the correct $R_1$–$R_2$ values, read the $r_1$ and $r_2$ values indicated at the desired attenuation value and multiply by the desired attenuator impedance.*

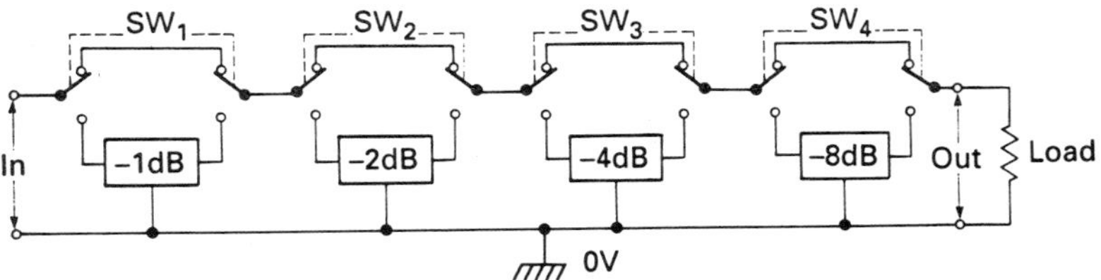


Figure 2.22. *This switched attenuator is variable from 0 to −15dB in 1dB steps.*

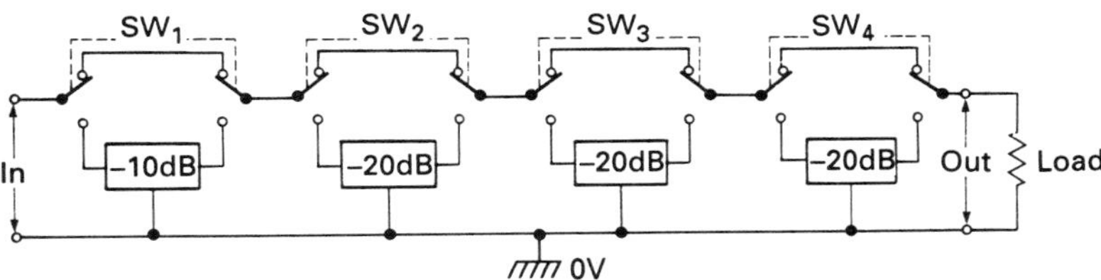


Figure 2.23. *This switched attenuator is variable from 0 to −70dB in 10dB steps.*

The three most widely used values of 'matching' impedance are 50Ω and 75Ω for 'wireless' work and 600Ω for 'audio' work, and *Figures 2.24* and *2.25* show the appropriate $R_1$ and $R_2$ values needed to make 'T' and 'π' pads of these impedances and with attenuation values of 1, 2, 4, 8, 10, 16, 20, or 32dB. Note when designing attenuator pads that the $R_1$ or $R_2$ values may be adversely affected by stray capacitance if the values are excessively large, or by the resistances of switch contacts and wiring if excessively small. Thus, it can be seen from *Figures 2.24* and *2.25* that a −1dB pad would best be made from a 'π' section if designed for 50Ω matching, but from a 'T' section if intended for 600Ω matching.

If large (greater than −32dB) values of pad attenuation are needed, it is best to make the pad from two or more cascaded attenuator networks. If the multi-stage pad is to be made from *identical* 'π'-type stages, as shown in *Figure 2.26a*, an economy can be made by replacing adjoining pairs of $R_2$ resistors with a single resistor with a value of $R_2/2$, as shown in *Figure 2.26b*. A similar technique can be used if the cascaded sections do *not* have

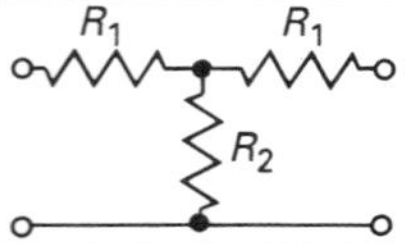

'T'-type attenuator pads

| dB Loss | 50Ω impedance | | 75Ω impedance | | 600Ω impedance | |
|---|---|---|---|---|---|---|
| | $R_1$ (Ω) | $R_2$ (Ω) | $R_1$ (Ω) | $R_2$ (Ω) | $R_1$ (Ω) | $R_2$ (Ω) |
| 1 | 2.875 | 433.5 | 4.312 | 650.2 | 34.50 | 5202 |
| 2 | 5.750 | 215.0 | 8.625 | 322.5 | 69.00 | 2580 |
| 4 | 11.30 | 105.0 | 16.95 | 150.0 | 135.6 | 1260 |
| 8 | 21.55 | 47.30 | 32.33 | 70.95 | 258.6 | 567.6 |
| 10 | 26.00 | 35.15 | 39.00 | 52.73 | 312.0 | 421.8 |
| 16 | 36.30 | 16.25 | 54.45 | 24.37 | 435.6 | 195.0 |
| 20 | 40.90 | 10.10 | 61.35 | 15.15 | 490.8 | 121.2 |
| 32 | 47.55 | 2.515 | 71.32 | 3.772 | 570.6 | 30.18 |

Figure 2.24. *Design chart for 50Ω, 75Ω, and 600Ω 'T'-type attenuator pads.*

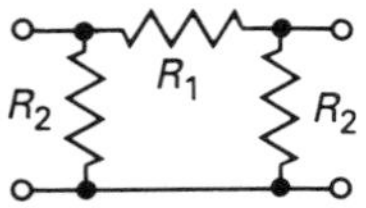

'π'-type attenuator pads

| dB Loss | 50Ω impedance | | 75Ω impedance | | 600Ω impedance | |
|---|---|---|---|---|---|---|
| | $R_1$ (Ω) | $R_2$ (Ω) | $R_1$ (Ω) | $R_2$ (Ω) | $R_1$ (Ω) | $R_2$ (Ω) |
| 1 | 5.750 | 870.0 | 8.625 | 1305 | 69.00 | 10,440 |
| 2 | 11.60 | 436.0 | 17.40 | 654.0 | 139.2 | 5,232 |
| 4 | 23.85 | 221.0 | 35.78 | 331.5 | 286.2 | 2,652 |
| 8 | 52.85 | 116.0 | 79.27 | 174.0 | 634.2 | 1,392 |
| 10 | 71.50 | 96.0 | 107.2 | 144.0 | 858.0 | 1,152 |
| 16 | 154.0 | 69.0 | 231.0 | 103.5 | 1848 | 828 |
| 20 | 247.5 | 61.0 | 371.2 | 91.5 | 2970 | 732 |
| 32 | 994.5 | 52.6 | 1492 | 78.9 | 11,934 | 631.2 |

Figure 2.25. *Design chart for 50Ω, 75Ω, and 600Ω 'π'-type attenuator pads.*

identical attenuation values, but in this case the single replacement resistor needs a value equal to the parallel value of the adjoining pair of resistors that it is replacing.

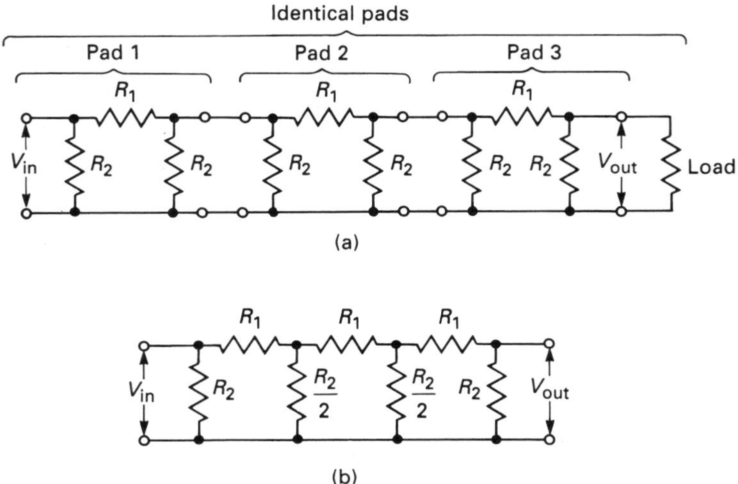


Figure 2.26. *The three-stage 'π'-type ladder attenuator of (b) is a simple development of the three-pad circuit shown in (a).*

Note that although the *Figure 2.26b* ladder attenuator is described as a 'π'-type design, it can in fact also be described as a set of cascaded 'L'-type attenuators with a shunt across its main input terminals. A most ingenious development of the circuit is the switched ladder attenuator, a five-step version of which is shown in *Figure 2.27*, together with its design formulae and with worked values for giving ÷10 (= 20dB) steps and a 1k0 matching impedance. It is important to note that the input signal's effective source impedance forms a vital part of this attenuator network, and needs a value of 2*Z*.

To understand the operation of the attenuator shown in *Figure 2.27* it is best to first imagine it without the external load connected, and to work through the design from right to left. In this case it can be seen that the fifth (output) section ($R_2$–$R_4$) acts as a ÷10 'L' attenuator with an 11k input impedance. This impedance shunts $R_3$ of the preceding section and reduces its effective value to 1100Ω, so that section (the fourth) also gives ÷10 attenuation and an 11k input impedance. Similarly, sections 2 and 3 act in precisely the same way. The '1' input 'L'-type section consists of the generator's source impedance (2k0) and $R_1$, which (since it is

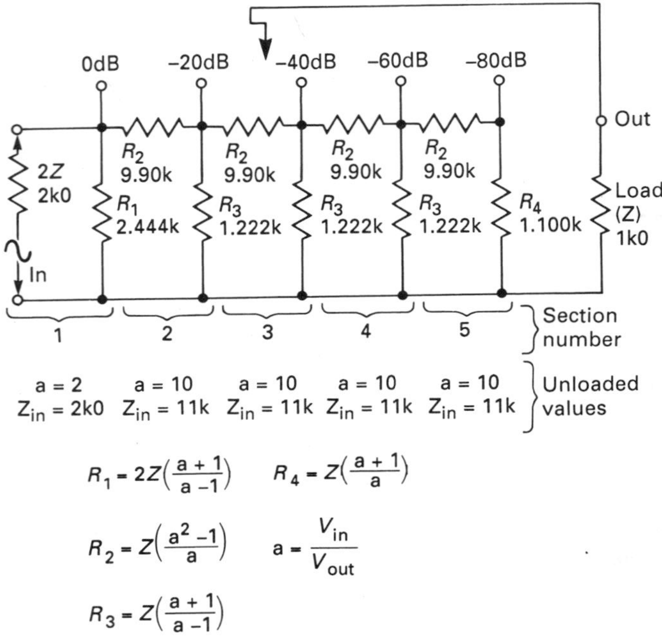


Figure 2.27. *A worked example of a five-step switched ladder attenuator, giving −20dB steps into 1k0, with design formulae.*

shunted by the 11k input impedance of the '2' section) has an effective impedance of 2k0; this section thus has an *effective* attenuation of ÷2.

With the above picture in mind, now imagine the effect of connecting the external 1k0 load to any one of the attenuator's output terminals. If it is connected to the output of the fifth section it shunts $R_4$ and increases that section's attenuation to ÷19.9 and reduces its input impedance to 10424Ω, thereby also increasing the attenuation of the preceding section by 0.5 per cent. The net result is that the attenuation at that particular output terminal increases by a factor of 1.995, or precisely 6dB. Similarly, if the load is connected to the output of any of the '2' to '4' sections, the attenuation at that point increases by precisely 6dB. Finally, if the load is connected to the output of section '1', that section's attenuation increases by a factor of 2.000 (to ÷4), or precisely 6.021dB.

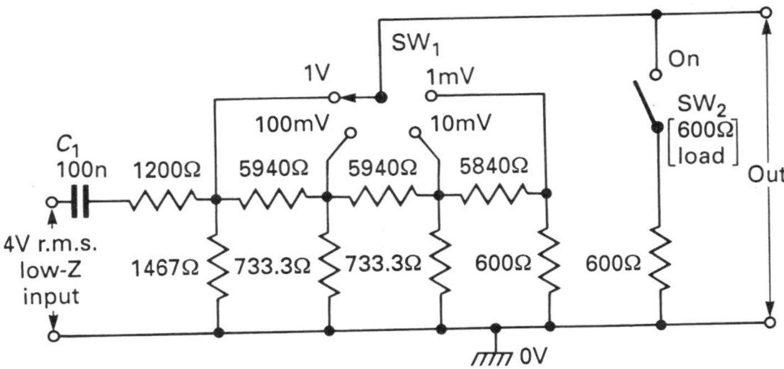


Figure 2.28. *Practical 600Ω four-step switched ladder attenuator for use in an audio generator.*

The important thing to note about this loading effect is that, since the load is connected to *some* part of the circuit at all times, it does not affect the *step* attenuation of the network in any way. Thus, if the load is shifted a 20dB step down the line, from the output of section '2' to that of section '3', the output of section '2' (and the input of section '3') rises by 6dB but the attenuation of section '3' increases by 6dB (to −26dB), to give an overall step change of precisely −20dB. This step-change accuracy is maintained with great precision on all except the first step position, where a trivial error of +0.25 per cent, or 0.021dB, occurs. Consequently, this type of switched attenuator is widely used in the output of audio and RF generators.

*Figure 2.28* shows a practical version of a four-step 600Ω ladder attenuator suitable for audio generator use. It is meant to by driven from a low-impedance source; with a 4V r.m.s. input, it gives outputs of 1V, 100mV, 10mV, and 1mV. Switch $SW_2$ enables the output to be loaded with an internal 600Ω resistor when driving high-impedance external loads.

# 3 Filter circuits

Filters are widely used in modern instrumentation and test gear circuits to correctly condition the signals passing through their input or output terminals or being internally processed. This chapter looks at the design of a variety of passive and active filter circuits.

## Passive *C–R* filters

Filter circuits are used to reject unwanted frequencies and pass only those wanted by the designer. In low-frequency applications (up to 100kHz) the filters are usually made of *C–R* networks, and in high-frequency (above 100kHz) ones they are usually made of *L–C* components.

A simple *C–R* low-pass filter (*Figure 3.1*) passes low-frequency signals but rejects high-frequency ones. Its output falls by 3dB (to 70.7 per cent of the input value) at a 'break', 'crossover', or 'cutoff' frequency ($f_c$) of $1/(2\pi RC)$, and then falls at a rate of

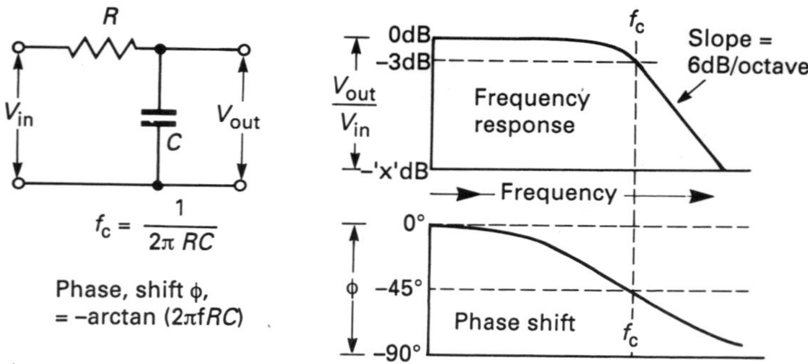


Figure 3.1. *Passive* C–R *low-pass filter.*

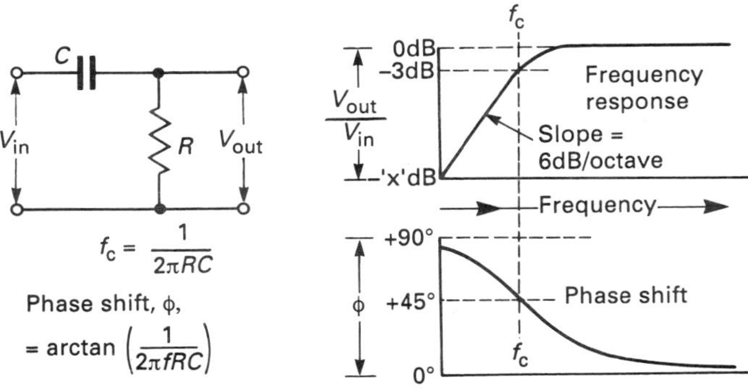


Figure 3.2. *Passive* C–R *high-pass filter.*

6dB/octave (= 20dB/decade) as the frequency is increased. Thus, a 1kHz filter gives about 12dB of rejection to a 4kHz signal, and 20dB to a 10kHz one. The phase angle (ϕ) of the output signal lags behind that of the input and equals $-\arctan(2\pi fCR)$, or $-45°$ at $f_c$.

A simple *C–R* high-pass filter (*Figure 3.2*) passes high-frequency signals but rejects low-frequency ones. Its output is 3dB down at a break frequency of $1/(2\pi RC)$, and falls at a 6dB/octave rate as the frequency is decreased below this value. Thus, a 1kHz filter gives 12dB of rejection to a 250Hz signal, and 20dB to a 100Hz one. The phase angle of the output signal leads that of the input and equals $\arctan 1/(2\pi fCR)$, or $+45°$ at $f_c$.

Each of the above two filter circuits uses a single *C–R* stage and is known as a 'first-order' filter. If a number ($n$) of such filters are cascaded the resulting circuit is known as an '*n*th-order' filter and has a slope, beyond $f_c$, of ($n \times$ 6dB)/octave. Thus, a fourth-order 1kHz low-pass filter has a 24dB/octave slope and gives 48dB of rejection to a 4kHz signal and 80dB to a 10kHz one.

In practice, cascaded passive filters are rather difficult to design accurately, due to the disruptive interaction of neighbouring sections, and are rarely used in this simple form; instead, they are *effectively* cascaded by incorporating them in the feedback networks of suitable op-amps, to make what are known as 'active' filters. One instance where they are used, however, is as the basis of a so-called 'phase-shift' oscillator, as shown in basic form in *Figure 3.3*. Here, the filter is inserted between the output and input of the inverting (180° phase shift) amplifier; the filter gives

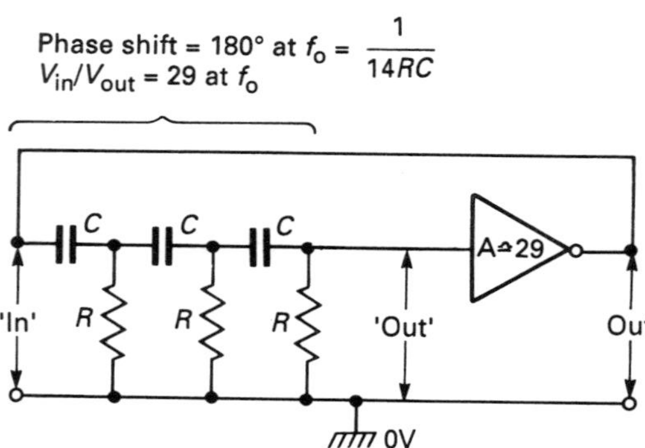


Figure 3.3. *Third-order high-pass filter used as the basis of a phase-shift oscillator.*

a total phase shift of 180° at a frequency, $f_0$, of about $1/(14RC)$, so the complete circuit has a loop shift of 360° under this condition and will thus oscillate at this frequency if the amplifier has sufficient gain (about ×29) to compensate for the losses of the filter and thus give a loop gain greater than unity.

*Figure 3.4* shows a practical example of a 800Hz version of the phase-shift oscillator. $RV_1$ must be adjusted to give reasonable sine-wave purity; the output level is variable via $RV_2$.

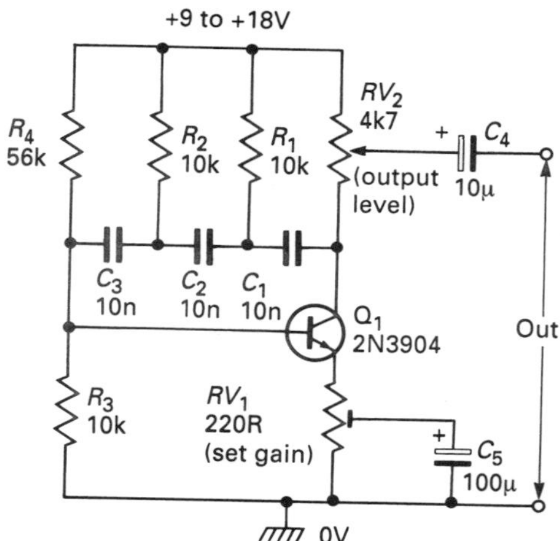


Figure 3.4. *800Hz phase-shift oscillator.*

## Band-pass and notch filters

A 'band-pass' filter is one that accepts a specific band or spread of frequencies but rejects or attenuates all others. A simple version of such a circuit can be made by cascading a pair of $C-R$ high-pass and low-pass filters, as shown in *Figure 3.5*. The high-pass component values determine the lower break frequency, and the low-pass values set the upper break frequency.

Note that if the two filters in the above circuit are given the same break frequency value the circuit becomes a tone-select filter, which gives minimum attenuation to a single frequency. *Figure 3.6* shows a popular variation of this type of circuit, the Wien tone filter. $R_1-R_2$ and $C_1-C_2$ normally have equal values in this circuit, in which case the circuit is said to be a 'balanced' type. The balanced Wien filter gives an attenuation factor of 3 (= −9.5dB) at $f_c$; the circuit's major feature is that its output phase shift varies between +90° and −90°, and is precisely 0° at $f_c$. Consequently, the circuit can be used as the basis of a sine-wave generator by simply connecting its output back to its input via a non-inverting amplifier with a gain of ×3 (to give a loop gain of unity), as shown in basic form in *Figure 3.7*.

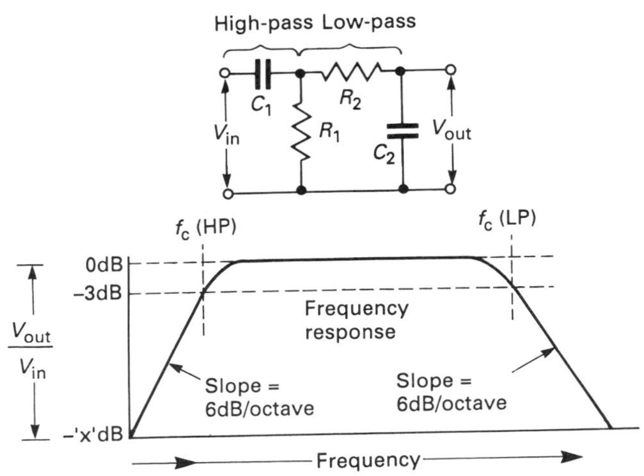


Figure 3.5. *High-pass and low-pass filters cascaded to make a band-pass filter.*

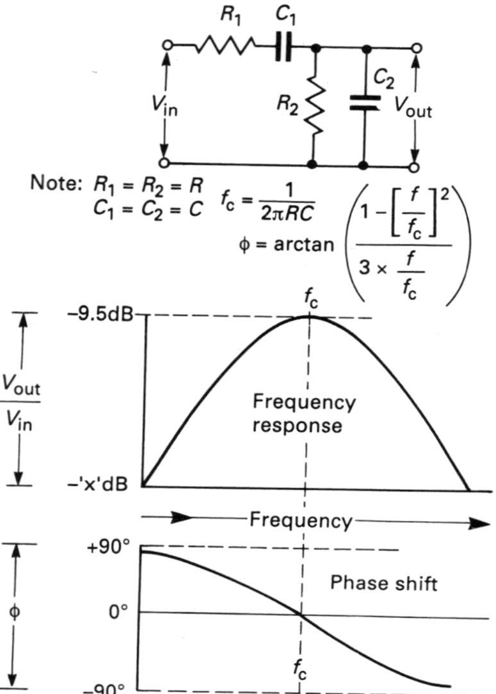


Figure 3.6. *Balanced Wien tone filter.*

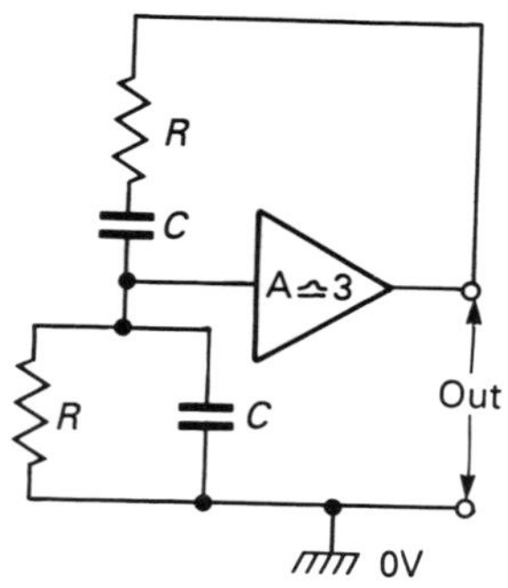


Figure 3.7. *Basic Wien-based oscillator.*

A 'notch' filter is one that gives total rejection of one specific frequency, but accepts all others. Such a filter can be made by wiring the Wien network into the bridge configuration shown in *Figure 3.8*. Here, $R_1 - R_2$ act as a voltage divider with a nominal attenuation factor of 3; consequently, the voltage divider and the Wien filter outputs are identical at $f_c$, and the output (which equals the difference between the two signals) is thus zero under this condition. In practice, the value of $R_1$ or $R_2$ must be carefully trimmed to give precise nulling at $f_c$.

The Wien-bridge network can be used as the basis of an oscillator by connecting it as shown in *Figure 3.9a*. At first glance it might seem here that the Wien's output is fed to the input of a

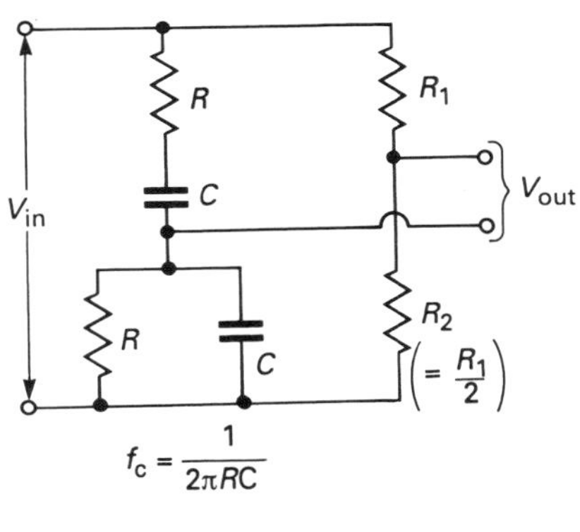


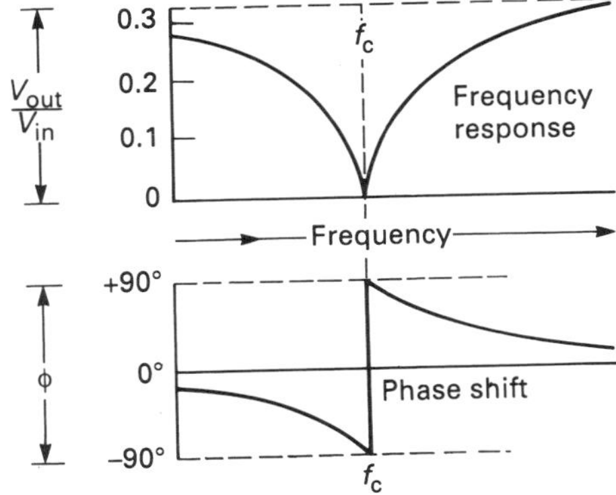


Figure 3.8. *Wien-bridge 'notch' filter.*

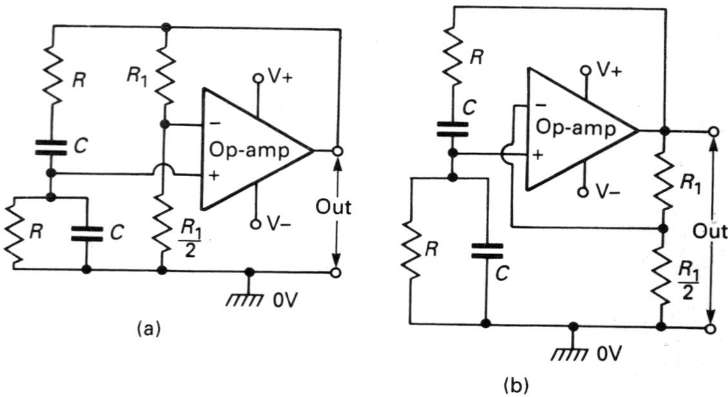


Figure 3.9. *The Wien-bridge oscillator in (a) is the same as that of (b).*

high-gain differential amplifier that has its output fed back to the Wien's input, to complete a positive feedback loop. When the circuit is redrawn as in *Figure 3.9b*, however, it becomes clear that the op-amp is actually used as a ×3 non-inverting amplifier, and that this circuit is similar to that of *Figure 3.7*. In practice these circuits must be fitted with some form of automatic gain control if they are used to generate good-quality sine waves.

A major feature of the Wien-bridge network is that its tuned frequency can easily be changed by simultaneously altering its two *R* or *C* values. *Figure 3.10* shows this facility used to make a wide-range (15Hz to 15kHz) variable notch filter in which fine tuning and decade switching are available via $RV_1$ and $SW_1$, and null trimming is available via $RV_2$.

## The 'twin-T' filter

*Figure 3.11* shows another version of the notch circuit, the 'twin-T' filter. Major advantages of this filter are that (unlike the Wien-bridge type) its input and output signals share a common 'ground' connection, and its off-frequency attenuation is less than that of the Wien. Its major disadvantage is that, if its tuning is to be made fully variable, the values of all three resistors (or capacitors) must be varied simultaneously. This filter is said to be a 'balanced' type when its components have the precise ratios shown; to

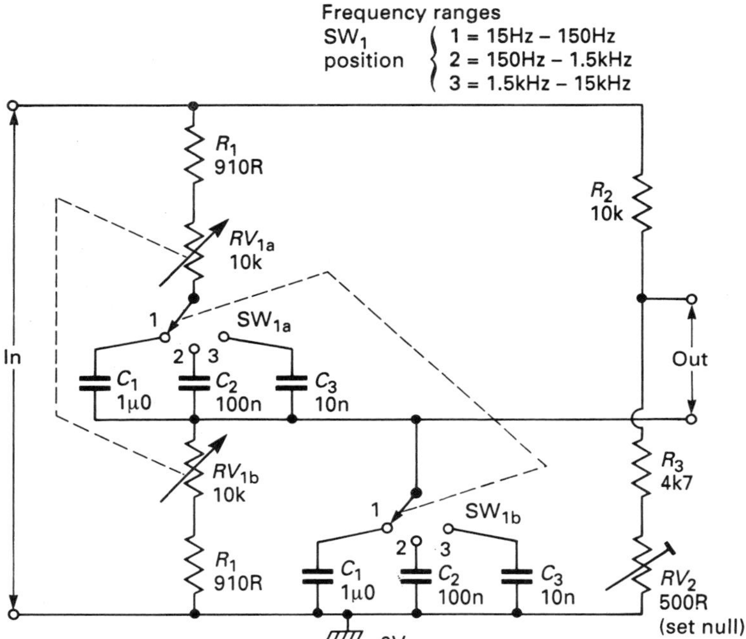


Figure 3.10. *Variable frequency (15Hz to 15kHz) Wien-bridge notch filter.*

obtain perfect nulling, the $R/2$ resistor value needs careful adjustment. Note in particular that the circuit gives zero phase shift at $f_c$.

One weakness of the twin-T filter is that (like the Wien type) it has a very low effective 'Q'. Q is defined as being the $f_c$ value divided by the bandwidth between the two −3dB points on the filter's transmission curve, and in this case equals 0.24. What this means in practice is that the filter subjects the second harmonic of $f_c$ to 9dB of attenuation, whereas an ideal notch filter would give it zero attenuation. This weakness can easily be overcome by 'bootstrapping' the common terminal of the filter, as shown in basic form in *Figure 3.12*. This technique enables high effective $Q$ values to be obtained, with negligible attenuation of the second harmonic of $f_c$.

The action of the balanced twin-T filter is fairly complex, as indicated by the operational representation of it shown in

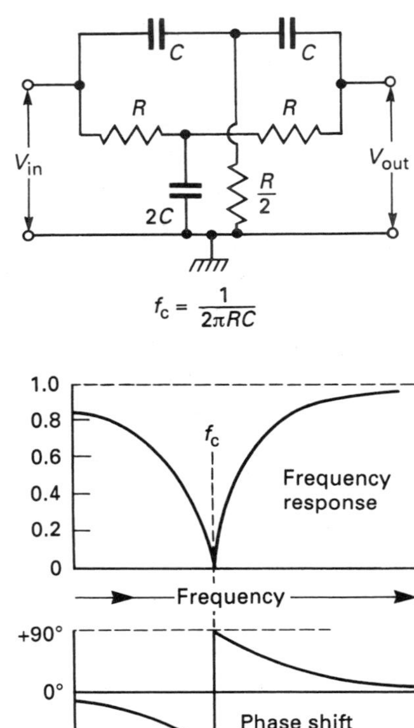


Figure 3.11. *Balanced twin-T 'notch' filter.*

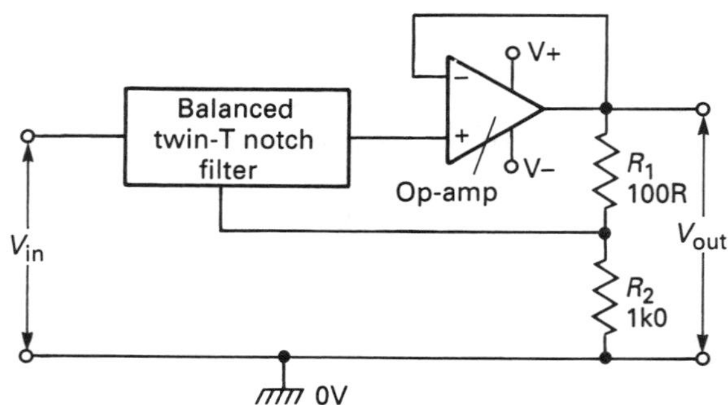


Figure 3.12. *Bootstrapped high-Q notch filter.*

*Figure 3.13*. It consists of a parallel-driven low-pass $f_c/2$ and a high-pass $2f_c$ filter, with their outputs joined by an $R-C$ '$f_c$' voltage divider. This output divider loads the two filters and affects their phase shifts, the consequence being that the signals at points $A$ and $B$ have identical amplitudes but have phase shifts of $-45°$ and $+45°$ respectively at $f_c$; simultaneously, the impedances of the $R$ and $C$ sections of the output divider are identical and give a 45° phase shift at $f_c$. Consequently, the divider effectively cancels the two phase differences under this condition and gives an output of precisely zero, this being the phase-cancelled difference in amplitudes of the two signals.

Thus, a perfectly balanced twin-T filter gives zero output and zero phase shift at $f_c$. At frequencies fractionally below $f_c$ the output is dominated by the actions of its low-pass filter, and is phase-shifted by $-90°$; at frequencies fractionally above $f_c$ the output is dominated by the actions of its high-pass filter, and is phase shifted by $+90°$ (see *Figure 3.11*).

An 'unbalanced' version of the twin-T filter can be made by giving the '$R/2$' resistor a value other than the ideal. If this resistor has a value greater than $R/2$ the circuit can be said to be

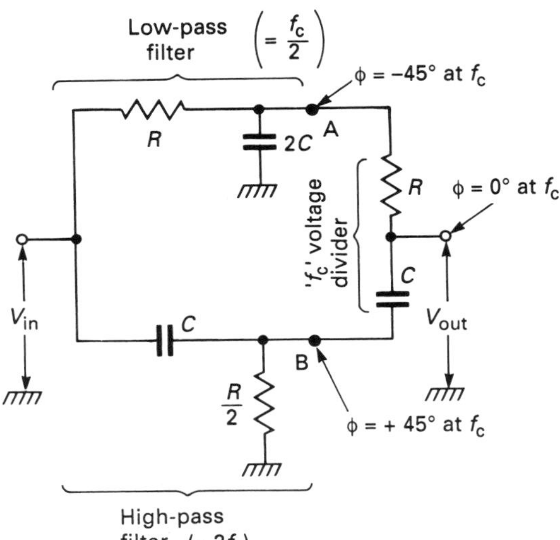


Figure 3.13. *Operational representation of the balanced twin-T filter.*

positively unbalanced; such a circuit acts in a manner similar to that described, except that its notch has limited depth; it gives zero phase shift at $f_c$. If, on the other hand, the resistor has a value less than $R/2$ the circuit can be said to be negatively unbalanced; such a circuit also produces a notch of limited depth, but has the very useful characteristic of generating a phase-inverted output, thus giving a 180° phase shift at $f_c$, as shown in *Figure 3.14*.

*Figure 3.15* shows how a negatively unbalanced twin-T notch filter can be used to make a 1kHz oscillator or a tuned acceptance filter. The twin-T network is simply wired between the input and output of the high-gain inverting amplifier, so that a loop shift of

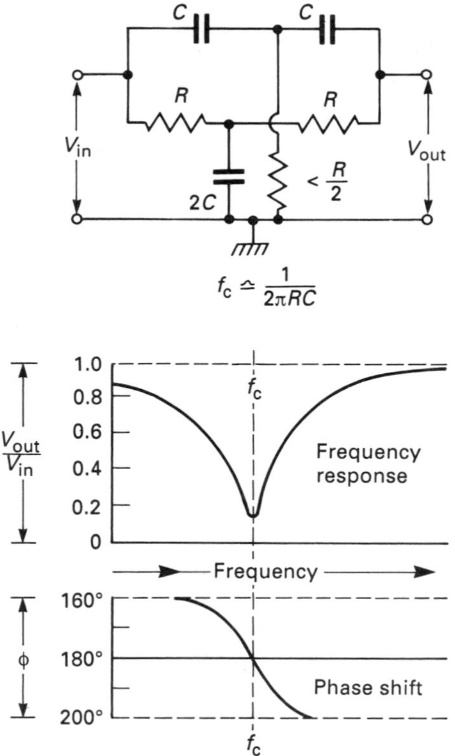


Figure 3.14. *Negatively unbalanced twin-T filter gives 180° phase shift at* $f_c$.

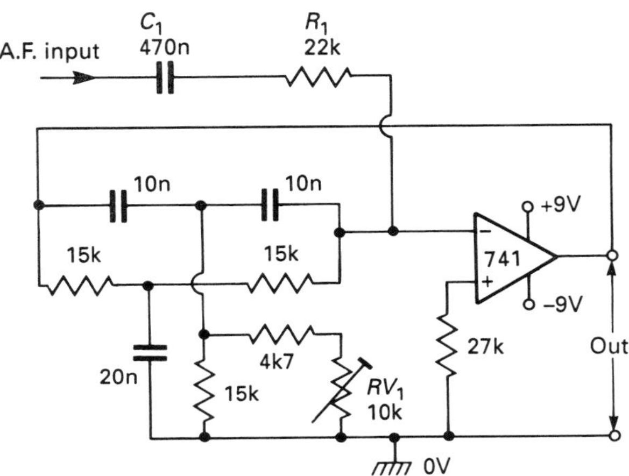


Figure 3.15. *1kHz oscillator/acceptance-filter using negatively unbalanced twin-T network.*

360° occurs at $f_c$. To make the circuit oscillate, $RV_1$ is adjusted so that the twin-T notch gives just enough output to give the system a loop gain greater than unity; the circuit generates an excellent sinewave under this condition. To make the circuit act as a tone filter, $RV_1$ is adjusted to give a loop gain less than unity, and the audio input signal is fed in via $C_1$ and $R_1$; under this condition $R_1$ and the twin-T filter interact to form a frequency-sensitive circuit that gives heavy negative feedback and low gain to all frequencies except $f_c$, to which it gives little negative feedback and high gain; the tuning sharpness is variable via $RV_1$.

## *C–R* component selection

Single-stage *C–R* low-pass and high-pass filters and balanced Wien and twin-T networks all use the same formula to relate the $f_c$ value to that of *R* and *C*, i.e. $f_c = 1/(2\pi RC)$. *Figure 3.16* shows, for quick reference purposes, this formula transformed to enable the values of *R* or *C* to be determined when $f_c$ and one component value is known. When using these formulae it is often easiest to work in terms of kilohertz, kilohms and microfarads, as indicated. Two nomographs or design charts (*Figures A.2* and

$$f_c = \frac{1}{2\pi RC} \qquad f_c = \text{kHz}$$

$$R = \frac{1}{2\pi f_c C} \qquad R = \text{k}\Omega$$

$$C = \frac{1}{2\pi f_c R} \qquad C = \mu\text{F}$$

Figure 3.16. *Formulae for finding the component values of single-stage high-pass or low-pass* C–R *filters and balanced Wien or twin-T networks.*

*A.3*) are included in the Appendix of this volume to make the design work even easier; in this case the unknown component value is found by placing a straight edge against the chart's two 'known value' points, and reading off the 'unknown' value where the straight edge cuts the appropriate component column.

## Resonant *L–C* filters

*L–C* filters are used primarily, but not exclusively, in high-frequency applications. Like *C–R* types, they can easily be designed to give low-pass, high-pass, band-pass, or 'notch' filtering action, but have the great advantage of offering at least 12dB per octave of roll-off, compared to the 6dB/octave of *C–R* types.

The two most important types of *L–C* filter, from which all others are ultimately derived, are the series and the parallel resonant types. *Figure 3.17a* shows the actual circuit of a series resonant filter, and *3.17b* shows its simplified equivalent circuit; resistor *R* represents the coil's resistance. The basic circuit action is such that the reactance of *C* decreases, and that of *L* increases, with increases in frequency, and vice versa, and the circuit's input impedance is equal to the difference between these two reactances, plus *R*. Thus, if at some low frequency *C* and *L* have reactances of 10k and 1k0 respectively, the circuit's input impedance (ignoring *R*) will be 9k0 at that frequency. Similarly, if at some high frequency *C* and *L* have reactances of 1k0 and 10k, the circuit's input impedance will be 9k0 at that frequency also, and so on.

The really important thing about all this is that at some particular frequency, $f_c$, the reactances of *C* and *L* will inevitably be equal,

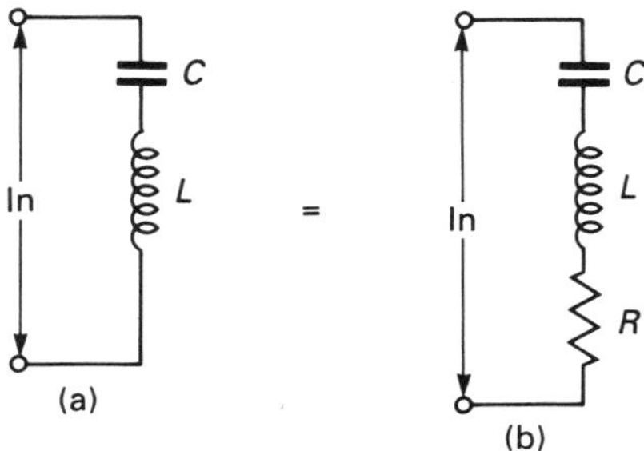


Figure 3.17. *Actual (a) and simplified equivalent (b) circuit of* L–C *series resonant filter.*

and the circuit's input impedance will then equal $R$, as shown in *Figure 3.18a*. Suppose this occurs when the reactances of $C$ and $L$ are each 1000Ω, and that $R$ equals 10Ω. In this case the input impedance falls to 10Ω, and the entire signal voltage is generated across $R$. The signal currents of $R$, however, flow via $C$ and $L$, which each have a reactance 100 times greater than $R$; consequently the signal voltage generated across $C$ and across $L$ is 100 times greater than the actual input signal voltage, as shown in *Figure 3.18b*; this voltage magnification is known as the circuit's $Q$. Note that the $L$ and $C$ voltages are in antiphase, so the voltage generated across the series $L-C$ combination is zero. The $f_c$ impedance of $L$ (or $C$) is known as the circuits 'characteristic impedance, $Z_0$', and equals $\sqrt{(L/C)}$.

*Figure 3.19* shows two basic ways of using a series-resonant $L-C$ filter. In (a) the 2k2 resistor ($R_x$) and the filter act together as a frequency-selective attenuator that gives very high attenuation

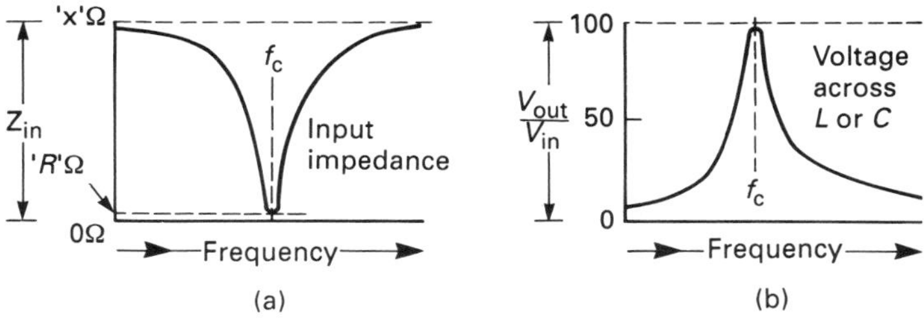


Figure 3.18. *Graphs showing how (a) the input impedance and (b) the* L *or* C *signal voltage of the series-resonant filter varies with frequency.*

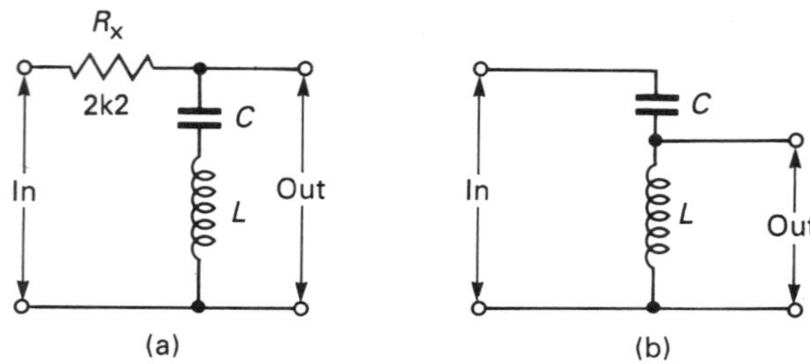


Figure 3.19. *Ways of using a series resonant filter as (a) a notch rejector and (b) a notch acceptor.*

at $f_c$, and low attenuation at all other frequencies, i.e. the circuit acts as a notch rejector. In (b) the input signal is applied directly to the filter, and the output is taken from across $L$; this circuit thus acts as a notch acceptor that gives high gain at $f_c$ and low gain at all other frequencies.

*Figure 3.20* lists the major formulae that apply to the *Figure 3.17* series resonant circuit, and also to all other types of $L-C$ filter described in this chapter. Two nomographs (*Figures A.4* and *A.5*) are included in the Appendix of this volume to make $L-C$ filter design work very easy.

*Figures 3.21a* and *3.21b* show the actual and the simplified equivalent circuits of a parallel resonant filter; $R$ represents the coil's resistance. The basic circuit action is such that $C$'s reactance decreases, and that of $L$ increases, with increases in frequency, and vice versa, each of these components draws a signal current proportionate to its reactance, but the two currents are in anti-

$$f_c = \frac{1}{2\pi\sqrt{LC}} \qquad Z_o = \sqrt{\frac{L}{C}}$$

$$L = \frac{Z_o}{2\pi f_c} \qquad C = \frac{1}{2\pi f_c Zo}$$

$$Q = \frac{X_L}{R} = \frac{Z_o}{R}$$

Figure 3.20. *Basic design formulae for all the* L–C *filters shown in this chapter.*

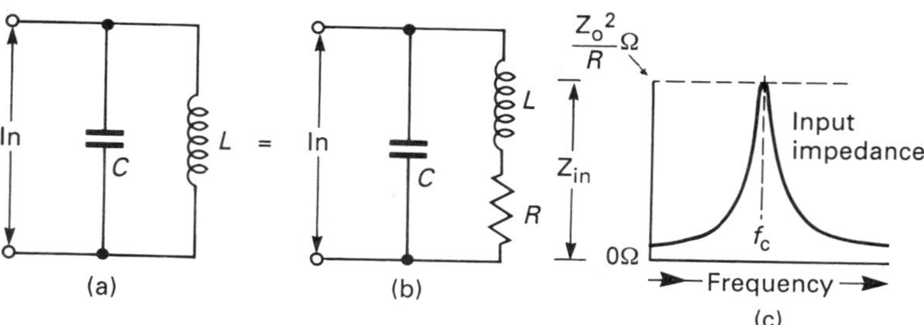


Figure 3.21. *Actual (a) and equivalent (b) circuits of the parallel resonant filter, together with a graph (c) showing how its input impedance varies with frequency.*

phase, so the total signal current equals the difference between the two currents. At $f_c$ the $L$ and $C$ reactance are equal, and the total signal current falls to near-zero, and the filter thus acts as a near-infinite impedance under this condition. In reality the presence of $R$ modifies the action slightly, and reduces the $f_c$ impedance to $Z_0^2/R$. Thus, if $Z_0$ equals 1000Ω and $R$ equals 10Ω, the actual $f_c$ impedance is 100k. *Figure 3.21c* shows how the input impedance varies with frequency. All the formulae of *Figure 3.20* apply to the parallel resonant filter.

## Low-pass and high-pass *L–C* filters

*Figure 3.22a* shows the basic circuit of a 'false' *L*-type low-pass filter. *L* and *C* act together as a frequency-dependent attenuator.

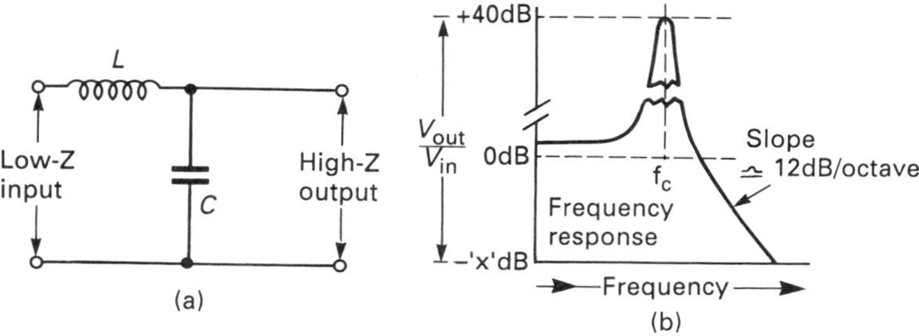


Figure 3.22. *Circuit (a) and performance graph (b) of a 'false' L-type low-pass filter.*

At low frequencies the reactance of $L$ is low and that of $C$ is high, so the circuit gives little attenuation; at high frequencies the reactance of $L$ is high and that of $C$ is low, so the circuit gives high attenuation. The circuit thus acts as a low-pass filter. I have called it a 'false' filter because the circuit will only work correctly if it is driven from a source impedance equal to $Z_0$, but there is no indication of this fact in the diagram. The circuit is actually a series resonant filter (like *Figure 3.17*) with its output taken from across $C$. If the circuit is driven from a low-impedance source the output will consequently produce a huge signal peak at $f_c$, as shown in *Figure 3.22b*. The magnitude of this peak is proportional to the circuit's $Q$ value.

*Figure 3.23a* shows how the above circuit can be modified to act as a genuine $L$-type low-pass filter, by wiring $R_x$ in series with the circuit's input, so that the sum of $R_x$ and $R_S$ (the input signal's source impedance) and $R$ (the resistance of $L$) equals the circuit's characteristic impedance, $Z_0$. The addition of this resistance reduces the circuit's $Q$ to precisely unity, and the low-pass filter consequently generates the clean output shape shown in *Figure 3.23b*.

*Figure 3.24* shows how the above principle can be used to make a good L-type high-pass filter; the output is simply taken from across inductor $L$, rather than from $C$. Note in both these circuits that resistor $R_x$ can be reduced to zero if the filter's $Z_0$ value is designed to match $R_S$, as shown in the design formulae of *Figure 3.20*. Also note that the outputs of these filters, like those of the series and parallel resonant types, must feed into high-impedance loads only.

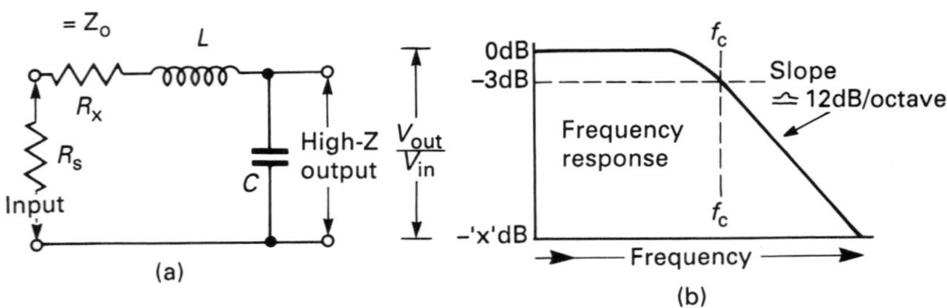


Figure 3.23. *Circuit (a) and performance graph (b) of a genuine L-type low-pass filter.*

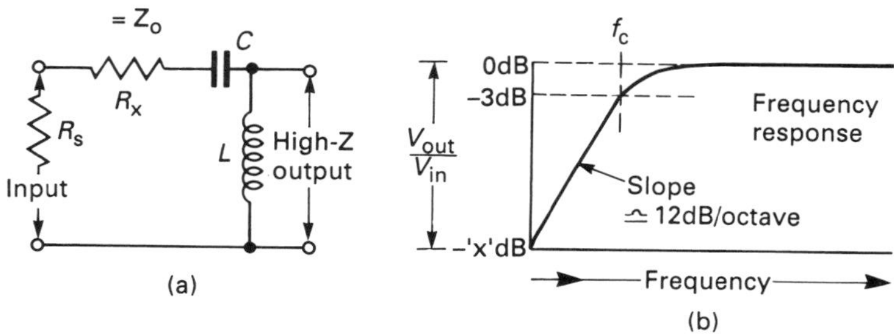


Figure 3.24. *Circuit (a) and performance graph (b) of an L-type high-pass filter.*

The most widely used types of low-pass and high-pass $L-C$ filters are balanced, matched impedance types that are designed to be driven from, and have their output loaded by, a specific impedance value. Such filters can readily be cascaded, to give very high levels of signal rejection. Amongst the most popular of these filters are the T-section and π-section low-pass types shown in *Figure 3.25*, and the T-section and π-section high-pass types shown in *Figure 3.26*. Note that all of these types give an output roll-off of about 12db/octave (= 40dB/decade), and must have their outputs correctly loaded by a matching filter section or terminating load. Their design formula is given in *Figure 3.20*.

A useful 'test gear' application of the T-section low-pass filter is as a power-line filter, as shown in *Figure 3.27*. It will stop mains-borne interference from reaching the test gear, or test gear generated hash from reaching the mains. It is useful up to about 25MHz.

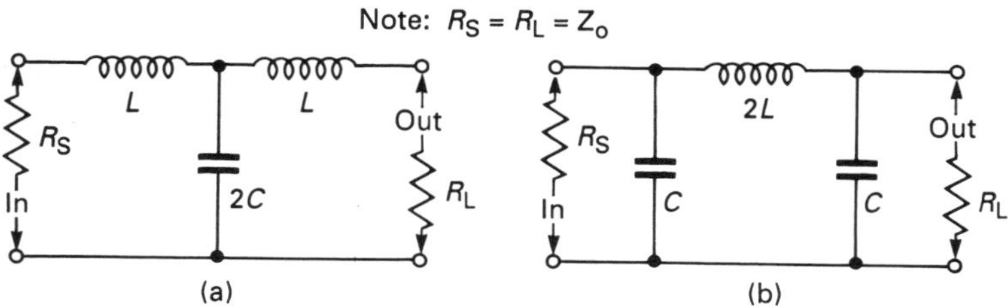


Figure 3.25. *(a) T-section and (b) π-section low-pass filters (see* Figure 3.20 *for design formulae).*

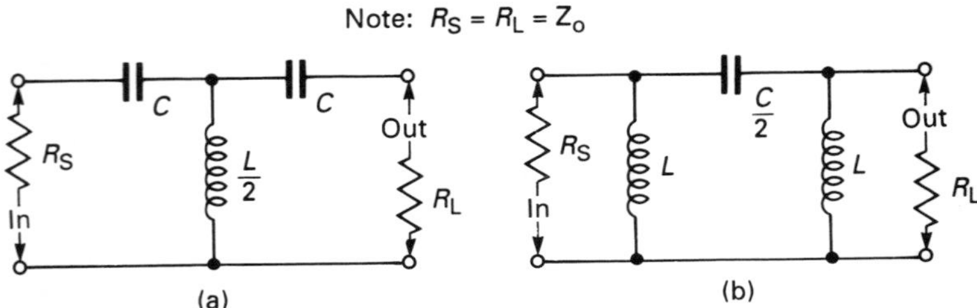


Figure 3.26. *(a) T-section and (b) π-section high-pass filters (see* Figure 3.20 *for design formulae).*

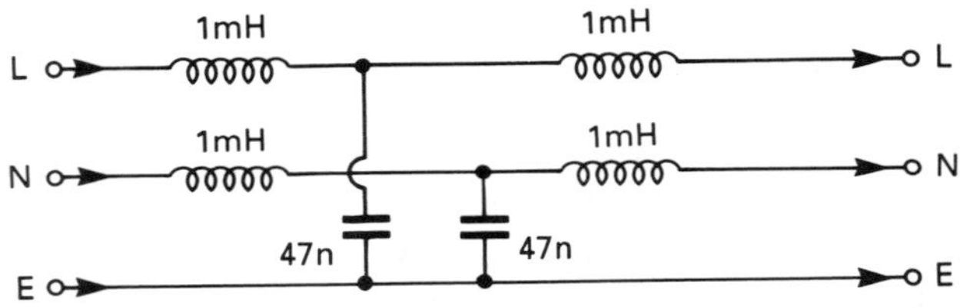


Figure 3.27. *T-section mains (power line) input filter rejects line-borne interference up to about 25MHz.*

## *C–R* active filters

An active filter is a circuit that combines passive *C–R* networks and one or more amplifier or op-amp stages, to form a filter that can either outperform normal *C–R* filters or can give a performance that is unobtainable from purely passive networks. A good selection of practical test-gear-orientated active filters are described in the next few pages. All these circuits are shown designed around standard 741 op-amps and operated from dual 9V supplies, but they will in fact work with virtually any normal op-amp, and from any supply voltages within the op-amp's operating range. If the circuits are to be used above a few tens of kilohertz, wide-band op-amps should be used.

The two most basic types of active filter are the first-order low-pass and high-pass types shown in *Figures 3.28* and *3.29*. These are simple adaptations of the passive types shown in *Figures 3.1* and *3.2*, but each have their output buffered by a unity-gain non-inverting amplifier, to give a low-impedance output with a −3dB

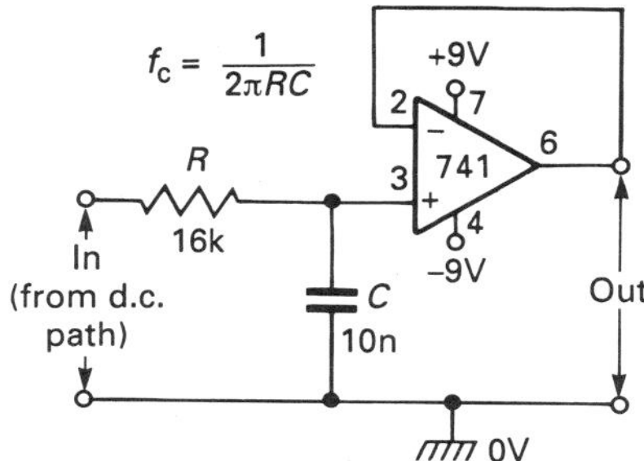


Figure 3.28. *First-order 1kHz low-pass active filter.*

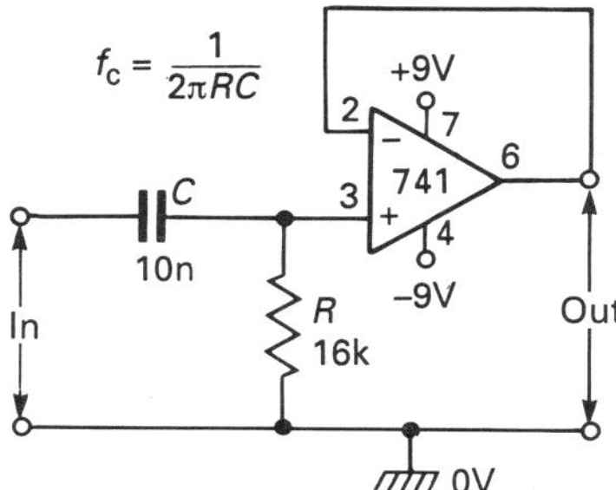


Figure 3.29. *First-order 1kHz high-pass active filter.*

cross-over frequency ($f_c$) of $1/(2\pi RC)$, and an output slope of 6dB/octave (= 20dB/decade). With the component values shown each circuit has an $f_c$ value of 1kHz. Note that the input signal to the low-pass circuit must provide an effective d.c. path to ground.

Each of the above two filter circuits uses a single $C-R$ stage, and is known as a 'first-order' filter. *Figure 3.30* shows the practical circuit and formula of a maximally flat (Butterworth) unity-gain second-order low-pass filter with a 10kHz break frequency. Note that the $2C$ capacitor is subjected to unity-gain bootstrapping from the op-amp's output. This circuit's output falls off at a rate of 12dB/octave beyond 10kHz, and is thus about 40dB down at 100kHz, and so on. To alter the break frequency, change either the $R$ or the $C$ value in proportion to the frequency ratio relative to *Figure 3.30*; reduce the values by this ratio to increase the frequency, or increase them to reduce the frequency. Thus, for 4kHz

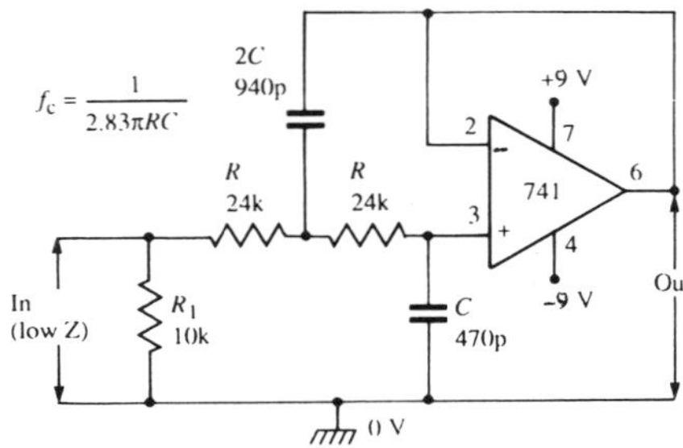


Figure 3.30. *Unity-gain 10kHz second-order low-pass active filter.*

operation, increase the *R* values by a ratio of 10kHz/4kHz, or 2.5 times.

A minor snag with the *Figure 3.30* circuit is that one of its *C* values should ideally be precisely twice the value of the other, and this can result in some rather odd component values. *Figure 3.31* shows an alternative second-order 10kHz low-pass filter circuit that overcomes this snag and uses equal component values. Note here that the op-amp is designed to give a voltage gain of 4.1dB via $R_1$ and $R_2$, and thus gives greater than unity bootstrapping to one of the filter's capacitors.

*Figure 3.32* shows two of these 'equal component' filters cascaded to make a fourth-order low-pass filter with a slope of 24dB/octave.

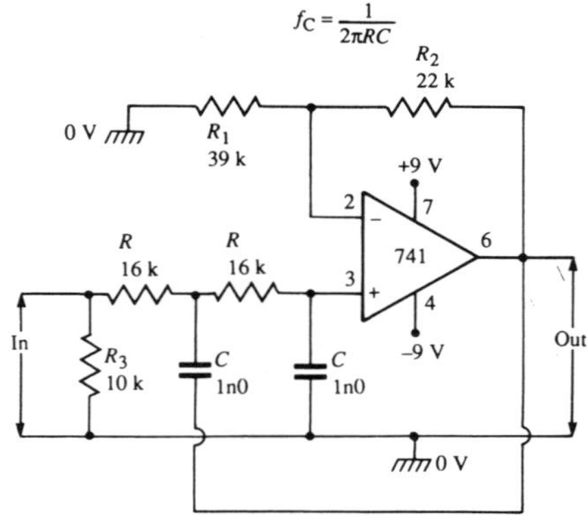


Figure 3.31. *'Equal components' version of the 10kHz second-order low-pass filter.*

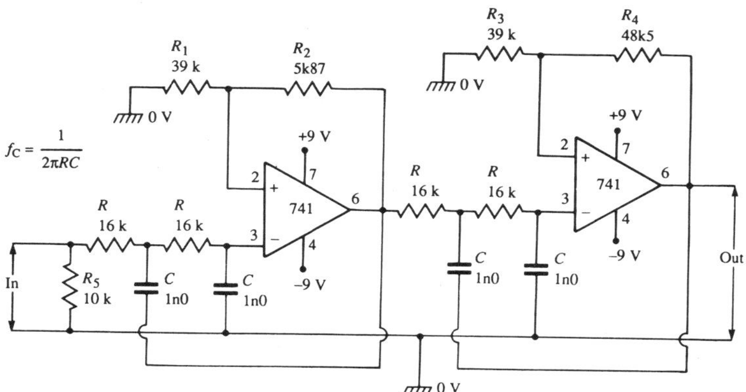


Figure 3.32. *Fourth-order 10kHz low-pass filter.*

In this case gain-determining resistors $R_1/R_2$ have a ratio of 6.644, and $R_3/R_4$ have a ratio of 0.805, giving an overall voltage gain of 8.3dB. The odd values of $R_2$ and $R_4$ can be made by series-connecting standard 5 per cent resistors.

*Figures 3.33* and *3.34* show unity-gain and 'equal component' versions respectively of second-order 100Hz high-pass filters, and *Figure 3.35* shows a fourth-order high-pass filter. The operating frequencies of these circuits, and those of *Figures 3.31* and *3.32*, can be altered in exactly the same way as in the *Figure 3.30* circuit, i.e. by increasing the *R* or *C* values to reduce the break frequency, or vice versa.

Finally, *Figure 3.36* shows how the *Figure 3.34* high-pass and *Figure 3.31* low-pass filters can be wired in series to make (with

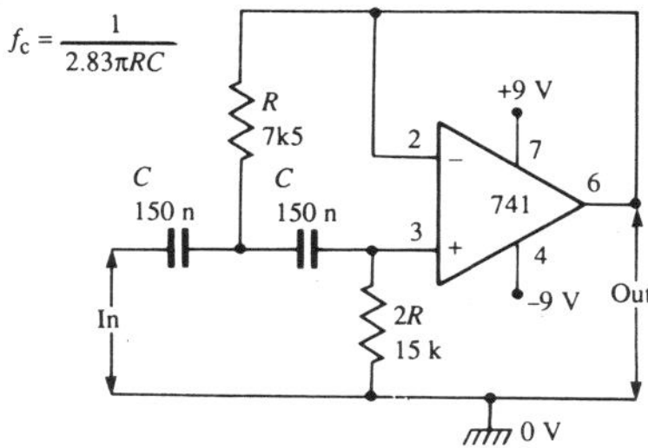


Figure 3.33. *Unity-gain second-order 100Hz high-pass filter.*

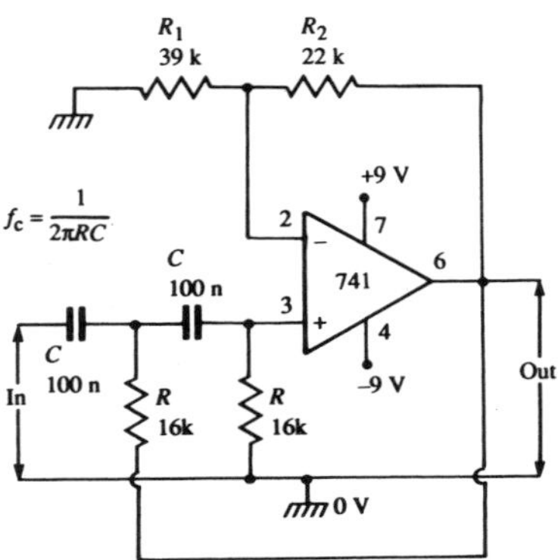


Figure 3.34. *'Equal components' version of the 100Hz second-order high-pass filter.*

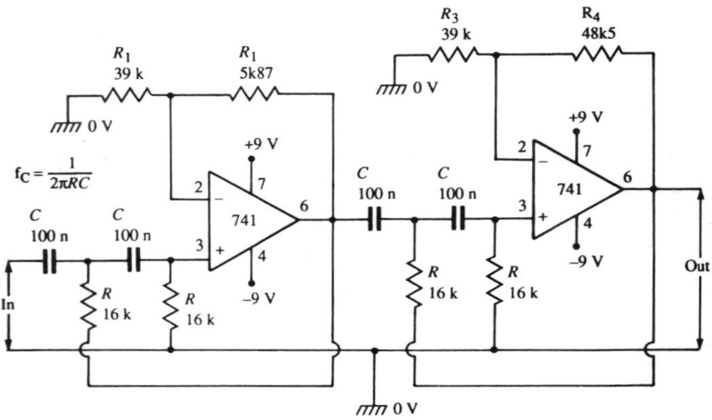


Figure 3.35. *100Hz fourth-order high-pass filter.*

suitable component value changes) a 300Hz to 3.4kHz 'speech' range bandpass filter that gives 12dB/octave of rejection to all signals outside of this range. In the case of the high-pass filter, the *C* values of *Figure 3.34* are reduced by a factor of three, to raise the break frequency from 100Hz to 300Hz, and in the case of the low-pass filter the *R* values of *Figure 3.31* are increased by a factor of 2.94, to reduce the break frequency from 10kHz to 3.4kHz.

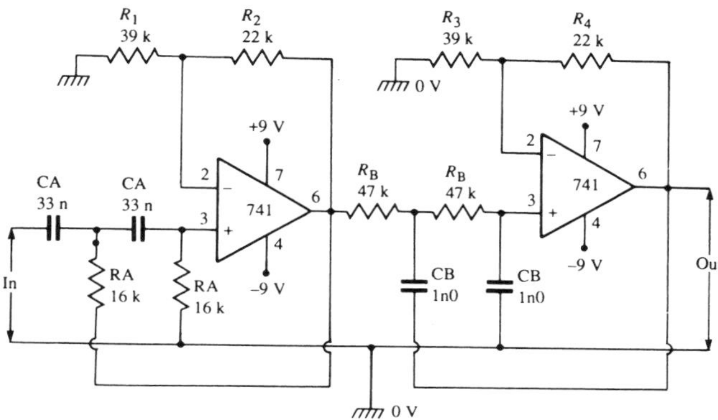


Figure 3.36. *300Hz to 3.4kHz band-pass filter with second-order response.*

## Variable active filters

The most useful type of active filter is that in which the cross-over frequency is fully and easily variable over a fairly wide range, and *Figures 3.37* to *3.39* show three practical examples of second-order versions of such circuits.

The *Figure 3.37* circuit is a simple development of the high-pass filter of *Figure 3.33*, but has its cross-over frequency fully variable from 23.5Hz to 700Hz via $RV_1$. Note in this circuit that the resistive arms of the $C-R$ networks have identical values

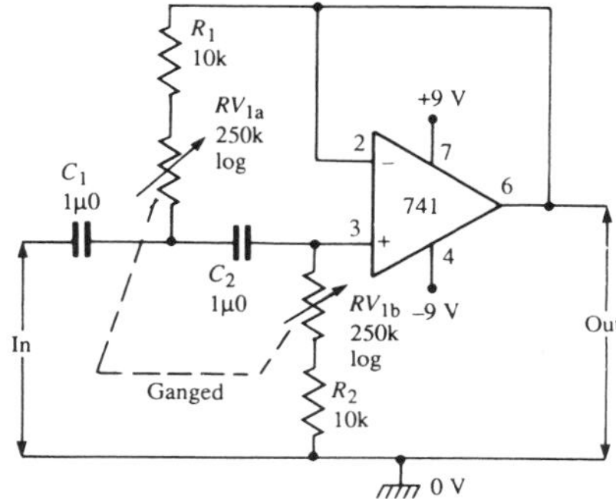


Figure 3.37. *Variable high-pass filter, spanning 23.5Hz to 700Hz.*

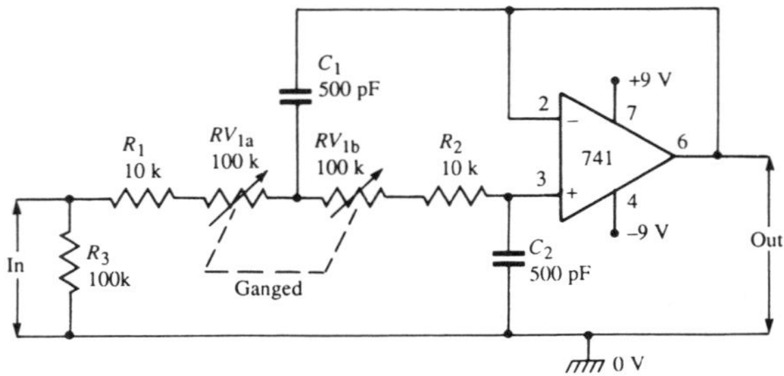


Figure 3.38. *Variable low-pass filter, spanning 2.2kHz to 24kHz.*

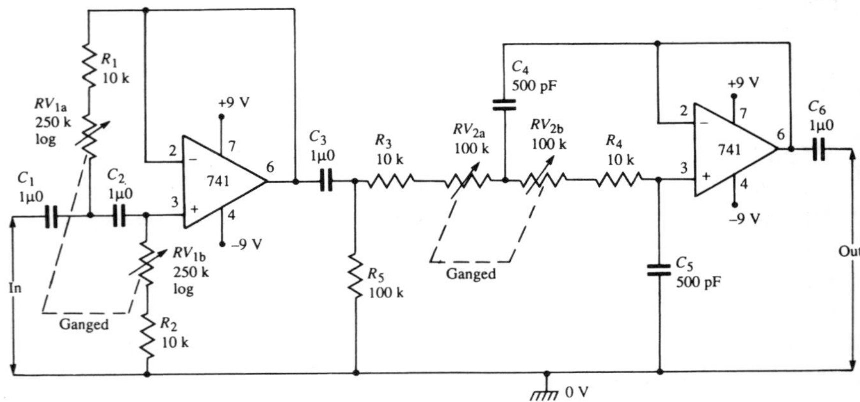


Figure 3.39. *Variable high-pass/low-pass or rumble/scratch/speech filter.*

(unlike *Figure 3.33*), so this design does not give maximally flat 'Butterworth' operation, but nevertheless gives a very good performance. This circuit can in fact be used as a high-quality turntable disc (record) 'rumble' filter; 'fixed' versions of such filters usually have a 50Hz cross-over frequency.

The *Figure 3.38* circuit is a development of the high-pass filter of *Figure 3.30*, but has its cross-over frequency fully variable from 2.2kHz to 24kHz via $RV_1$, and does not give a maximally flat 'Butterworth' performance. This circuit can in fact be used as a high-quality 'scratch' filter; 'fixed' versions of such filters usually have a 10kHz cross-over frequency.

*Figure 3.39* shows how the above two filter circuits can be combined to make a really versatile variable high-pass/low-pass or rumble/scratch/speech filter. The high-pass cross-over frequency is fully variable from 23.5Hz to 700Hz via $RV_1$, and the low-pass frequency is fully variable from 2.2kHz to 24kHz via $RV_2$.

## Tone and notch filters

Excellent active $C-R$ tone filters, with very high effective $Q$ values, can be made by using twin-T or Wien networks in the feedback loops of suitable op-amp circuits. A 1kHz twin-T design has already been described in *Figure 3.15*. *Figure 3.40* shows the practical circuit of a 1kHz Wien-bridge based tone or 'acceptor' filter; the circuit's $Q$ is adjustable via the 10k $R_2$ variable resistor. Note that (like the *Figure 3.15* design) this circuit becomes an oscillator if $R_2$ is reduced too far (to less than twice the $R_1$ value).

The basic twin-T notch filter has a very low $Q$. The filter's $Q$, and thus the notch 'sharpness', can be greatly increased by incorporating the twin-T in the feedback network of an active filter.

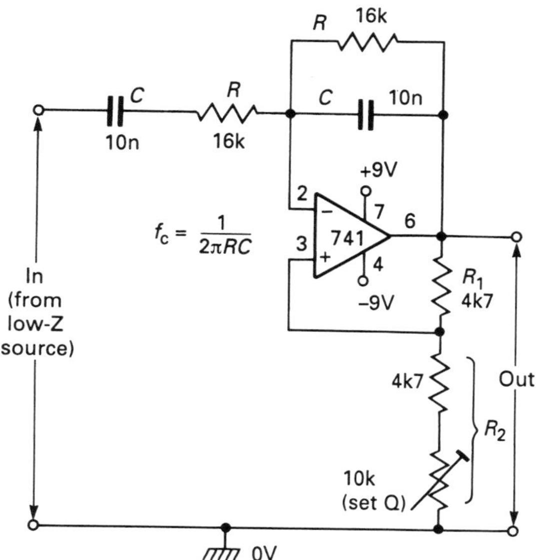


Figure 3.40. *Wien-bridge based 1kHz high-Q tone filter.*

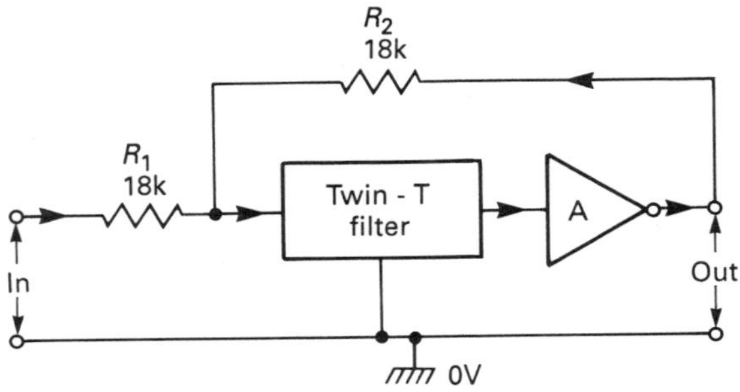


Figure 3.41. *Basic twin-T notch filter using shunt feedback.*

There are two standard ways of doing this. The first way is to use the shunt feedback technique shown in *Figure 3.41*, in which the input signal is fed to the twin-T via $R_1$, and an amplified and inverted version of the filter's output is fed back to the filter's input via $R_2$, which has the same value as $R_1$. *Figure 3.42* shows the practical circuit of a 1kHz version of this type of active filter. The network's null point can be adjusted via the 1k0 variable resistor.

The second (and more modern) $Q$-boosting method is the bootstrapping technique, which has already been described and

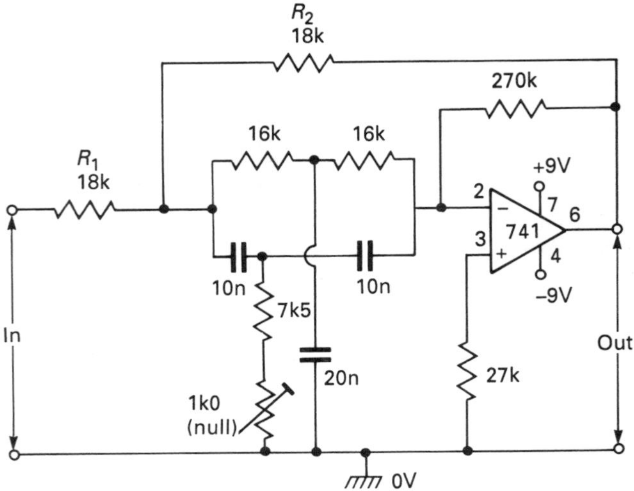


Figure 3.42. *Practical 1kHz twin-T notch filter with shunt feedback.*

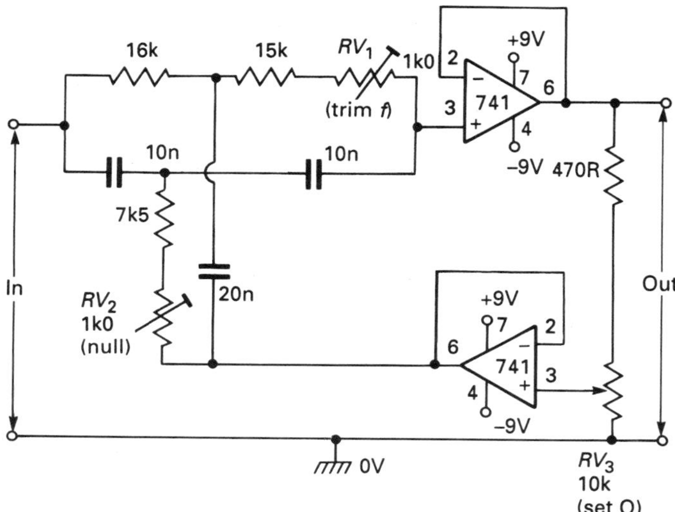


Figure 3.43. *1kHz variable-Q bootstrapped twin-T notch filter.*

shown in basic form in *Figure 3.12*. *Figure 3.43* shows a practical example of a 1kHz variable-$Q$ version of such a circuit. The twin-T's output is buffered by the upper op-amp (a unity-gain voltage follower), and part of the buffered output is tapped off via $RV_3$ and fed to the bottom of the twin-T (as a bootstrap signal) via the lower op-amp (another unity-gain voltage follower). When $RV_3$'s slider is set to the lowest (ground) point the network has zero bootstrapping, and the circuit acts like a standard twin-T filter with a $Q$ of 0.24. When $RV_3$'s slider is set to the highest point the network has heavy bootstrapping, and the filter has an effective $Q$ of about 8 and provides a very sharp notch. The filter's centre-frequency can be trimmed slightly via $RV_1$, and the null point can be adjusted via $RV_2$, which should be a multi-turn type.

## A THD (distortion) meter

The bootstrapped twin-T notch filter can be used as the basis of an excellent THD or 'distortion' meter. Here, the filter's notch is tuned to the basic frequency of the input test signal, and totally rejects the fundamental frequency of the signal but gives zero attenuation to the signal's unwanted harmonics and mush, etc., which appear at the filter's output; the output signals must be read on a true r.m.s. volt or millivolt meter. Thus, if the original input signal has an r.m.s. amplitude of 1000mV, and the nulled output has an amplitude of 15mV, the THD (total harmonic distortion) value works out at 1.5 per cent.

*Figure 3.44* shows the practical circuit of a high-performance 1kHz THD meter. This filter's $Q$ is set at a value of 5 via the 820R–10k divider, to give the benefits of easy tuning combined and near-zero second harmonic (2kHz) signal attenuation. The input signal to the filter is variable via $RV_3$, and the filter's tuning and nulling are variable via $RV_1$ and $RV_2$ respectively. $SW_1$ enables either the filter's *input* or its *dist*orted output to be fed to an external true r.m.s. meter; note that the meter feed line incorporates a 10kHz low-pass filter, to help reject unwanted 'noise' signals.

To use the *Figure 3.44* THD meter, first set $SW_1$ to the *input* position, connect the 1kHz input test signal, and adjust $RV_3$ to set a convenient (say 1V) reference level on the true r.m.s. meter. Next, set $SW_1$ to the *dist* position, adjust the input fre-

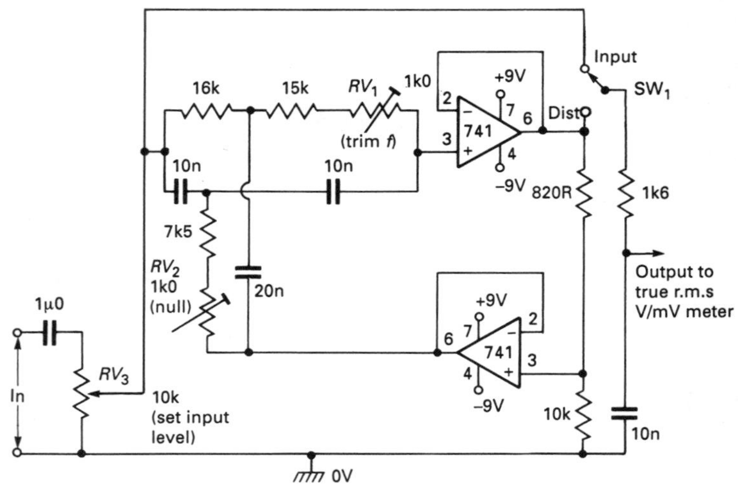


Figure 3.44. *1kHz THD (distortion) meter circuit.*

quency for an approximate null, then trim $RV_1$ and $RV_2$ alternately until the best possible null is obtained. Finally, read the nulled voltage value on the meter and calculate the distortion factor on the basis of

$$\text{THD (in per cent)} = (V_{dist} \times 100)/V_{in}$$

## Active filter component selection

Most of the active filter circuits described in this chapter, including all those based on balanced Wien and twin-T networks, use the standard '$f_c = 1/(2\pi RC)$' design formula. In such cases the filter component values appropriate to a particular operating frequency can be found from either the formulae of *Figure 3.16*, or from the *Figures A.2* and *A.3* design nomograms included in the Appendix of this volume.

# 4 Bridges and $C-R$ boxes

A bridge is a passive network that, when used in conjunction with a suitable energizing generator and a balance detector, enables values of inductance ($L$), capacitance ($C$), or resistance ($R$) to be accurately and inexpensively measured or matched. Bridges were *the* instruments for measuring $R$, $C$ and $L$ values up until the late 1970s, when they were replaced in many applications by the digital multimeter and its derivatives. Nowadays they are used mainly as either cheap-and-simple 'service' type instruments that give an approximate (within a couple of per cent) reading of a component value, or, at the opposite end of the scale, as 'laboratory' type instruments that make measurements with very high precision. Both types of instrument are described in this chapter.

Closely associated with the conventional bridge are the resistance-matching bridge, which enables resistors to be matched to within 0.003 per cent or better, and the $C$ or $R$ 'substitution box', which enables component values to be determined with good precision, using either comparison or substitution techniques. This chapter looks at the theory, practical circuitry, and usage techniques of all of these types of instrument.

## Bridge basics

Modern component-measuring bridges come in two popular general classes, these being the d.c.-energized type which can accurately measure resistance values from a few ohms to a few megohms, and the low-frequency (usually 1kHz) a.c.-energized type which, as well as measuring resistance, can measure capacitance from about 10pF to 100μF, and inductance from about

10μH to 100H. Both of these types of instrument are derived from the ancient (1843) Wheatstone bridge circuit, and it is well worth studying this in order to learn the finer points of bridge design.

The 1843 pattern Wheatstone resistance-measuring bridge uses the basic *Figure 4.1* circuit and consists of a pair of d.c.-energized potential dividers ($R_2/R_1$ and $R_y/R_x$) with a sensitive meter wired between them. $R_2$ and $R_1$ have a 1:1 division ratio, and are known as the 'ratio arms' of the bridge; $R_x$ is the 'unknown' resistor, and $R_y$ is a calibrated variable resistor. In use, $R_x$ is fixed in place and $R_y$ is then adjusted until a zero or 'null' reading is shown on the meter, at which point the two dividers are generating equal output voltages and the bridge is said to be 'balanced' or 'nulled'; under this condition the ratio $R_y/R_x$ equals $R_2/R_1$ equals unity, and the $R_x$ value thus equals that of $R_y$; the bridge's balance is not influenced by variations in energizing voltage.

A major feature of this original version of the Wheatstone bridge is its very high *null sensitivity*. Thus, if the bridge is energized from 10V d.c., 5V is developed across all resistors at balance, and the meter reads zero volts; a shift of a mere 0.1 per cent will then give a 5mV reading on the meter. In practice, this circuit can, when using a fairly simple null-detecting d.c. amplifiers, be expected to have a 'null sensitivity' factor (i.e. percentage out-of-balance detection value) of about 0.003 per cent.

A major *dis*advantage of this 1843 pattern bridge is that $R_y$ needs a vast range of values if it is to balance all possible values

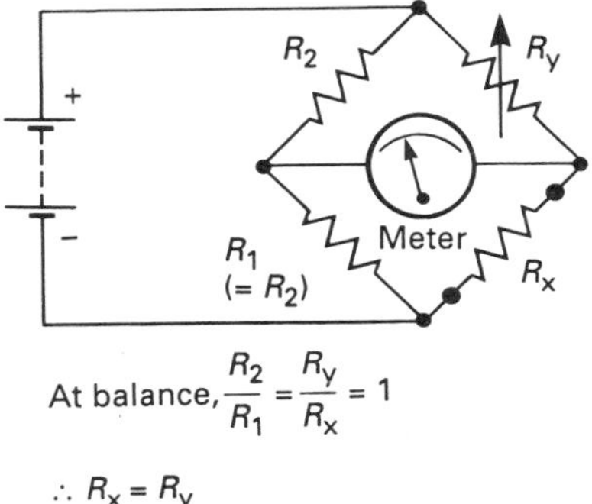


Figure 4.1. *Original (1843) version of the basic Wheatstone bridge.*

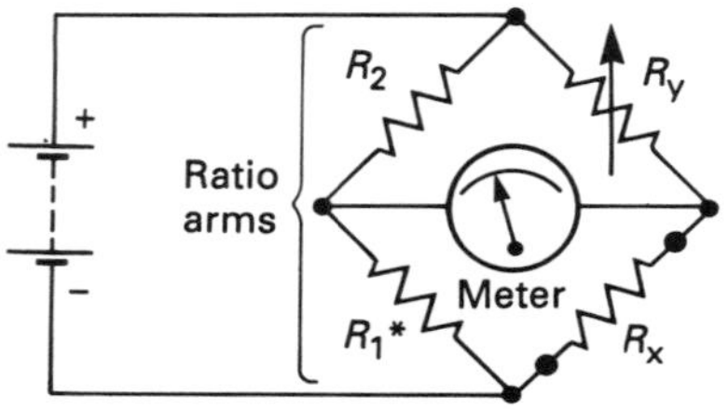

At balance, $\frac{R_2}{R_1} = \frac{R_y}{R_x}$, and $R_1 \times R_y = R_2 \times R_x$

$\therefore R_x = R_y\left(\frac{R_1}{R_2}\right)$

*Note: $R_1$ is a decade multiple or sub-multiple of $R_2$

Figure 4.2. *Conventional version of the Wheatstone bridge.*

of $R_x$. In 1848 Siemens overcame this snag by introducing the *Figure 4.2* modification, in which the $R_2/R_1$ ratio can be any desired decade multiple or submultiple of unity. The following basic truths apply to this circuit:

(1) At balance, $R_2/R_1 = R_y/R_x$
(2) At balance, $R_1 \times R_y = R_2 \times R_x$
(3) At balance, $R_x = R_y(R_1/R_2)$.

From (3) it is obvious that, at balance, the value of $R_x$ equals that of $R_y$ multiplied by the $R_1/R_2$ ratio, and that one easy way to vary this ratio is to give $R_2$ a fixed value and make the $R_1$ value switch-selectable, as shown in the multi-range d.c. Wheatstone bridge circuit of *Figure 4.3*, which is based on one used in a well-known '1970 style' high-quality laboratory instrument.

The *Figure 4.3* circuit can measure d.c. resistances from near-zero to 1MΩ, in six switch-selected decade ranges. $R_y$ is a calibrated 10k variable, $R_M$ controls the sensitivity of the balance-detecting centre-zero meter, and $R_L$ limits the bridge current to a few milliamperes. The *Figure 4.3* table points out the major weakness of this 1970s version of the Wheatstone bridge, and that is that its null sensitivity (which is proportional to the $R_x$ test voltage) degenerates in proportion to the $R_1/R_2$ ratio's divergence from unity. Thus, the sensitivity is nominally 0.003 per cent on the 10k range, where the $R_1/R_2$ ratio is 1/1, but degenerates to

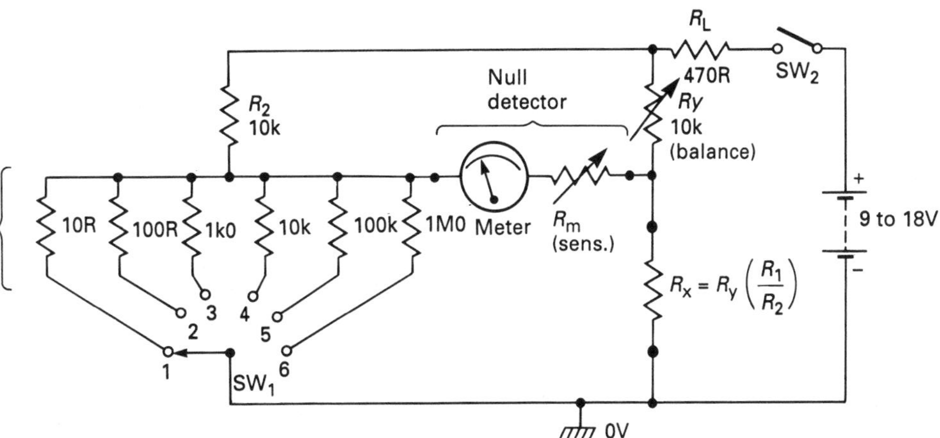


| $SW_1$ range | Bridge range | $R_1$ value | $R_1/R_2$ ratio | Bridge null sensitivity (nom.) |
|---|---|---|---|---|
| 1 | 0 – 10R | 10R | 1/1000 | 3.0% |
| 2 | 0 – 100R | 100R | 1/100 | 0.3% |
| 3 | 0 – 1k0 | 1k0 | 1/10 | 0.03% |
| 4 | 0 – 10k | 10k | 1/1 | 0.003% |
| 5 | 0 – 100k | 100k | 10/1 | 0.03% |
| 6 | 0 – 1M0 | 1M0 | 100/1 | 0.3% |

Figure 4.3. *Circuit and tabulated details of a conventional Wheatstone version of a six-range d.c. resistance-measuring bridge.*

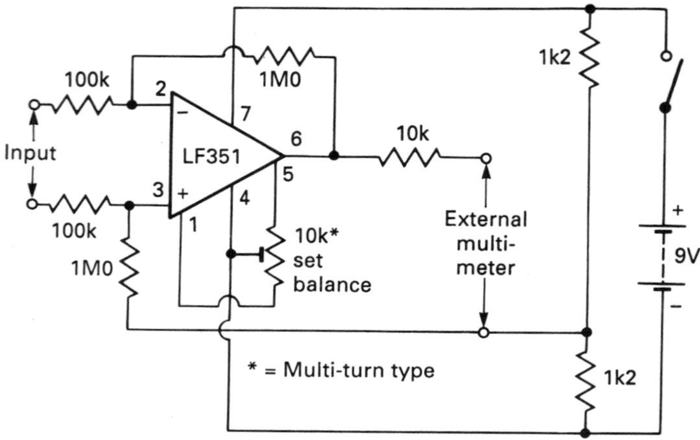


Figure 4.4. *D.C. null-point amplifier, for use with an external multimeter.*

0.3 per cent on the 100R and 1M0 ranges, where the $R_1/R_2$ ratios are 1/100 and 100/0 respectively.

To be of any great practical value the *Figure 4.3* circuit must be used with a sensitive null-balance detector. *Figure 4.4* shows a ×10 d.c. differential amplifier that can be used in conjunction with an external analogue multimeter to make such a detector; this circuit *must* use its own independent 9V battery supply. The external multimeter can be set to its 2.5V d.c. range for low-sensitivity measurements, or to its 50μA or 100μA range for high-sensitivity ones; in the latter case the circuit must, before use, first be balanced by shorting its input terminals together and trimming the multi-turn 10k **set balance** control for a zero reading on the meter.

## Wheatstone bridge variations

The Wheatstone bridge circuit of *Figure 4.2* can be arranged in three other ways, without invalidating the three basic 'balance' truths, as shown in *Figure 4.5*; in each case, $R_1$ and $R_2$ are known as the bridge's 'ratio arms'. Note that the bridge's signal-source and detector terminals can be transposed without upsetting the

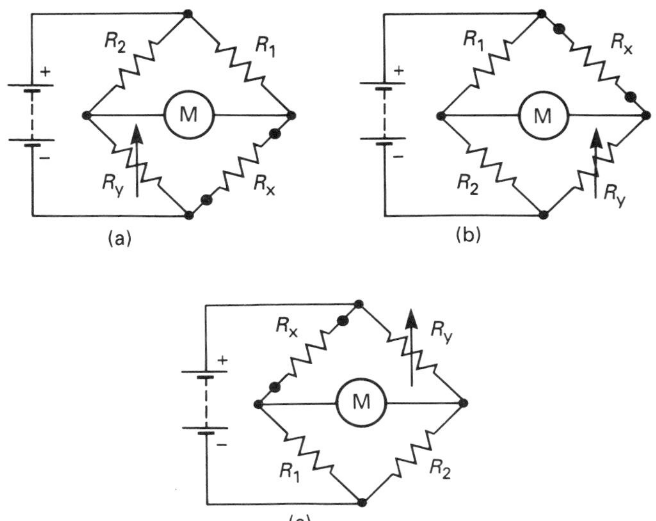


Figure 4.5. *Each of these three alternative versions of the Wheatstone bridge has the same 'balance' formulae as the* Figure 4.2 *circuit.*

circuit's balance equations; this is also true of various types of $C$ and $L$ bridge that will be described shortly.

The most useful Wheatstone bridge variation is that of *Figure 4.5a*; *Figure 4.6* shows a modern six-range version of this, and the table points out its great advantage over the *Figure 4.3* design, which is that its sensitivity (which is proportional to the $R_y/R_2$ ratio at balance) is very high on all ranges, and varies from 0.003 per cent at $R_y$'s full-scale balance value, to 0.03 per cent at one-tenth of full scale, etc. Thus, this particular circuit can, by confining all measurements to the top nine-tenths of the $R_y$ range, measure all resistance values in the 1Ω to 1MΩ range with 0.003 per cent to 0.03 per cent sensitivity.

A Wheatstone bridge can be energized from either an a.c. or d.c. source, without upsetting its balance truths. *Figure 4.7* shows an a.c.-energized version in which the balance condition is obtained via an infinitely variable pair of 'ratio' arms made up by $RV_1$, and balance sensitivity is so high that balance-detection can be made via a pair of 'phones.

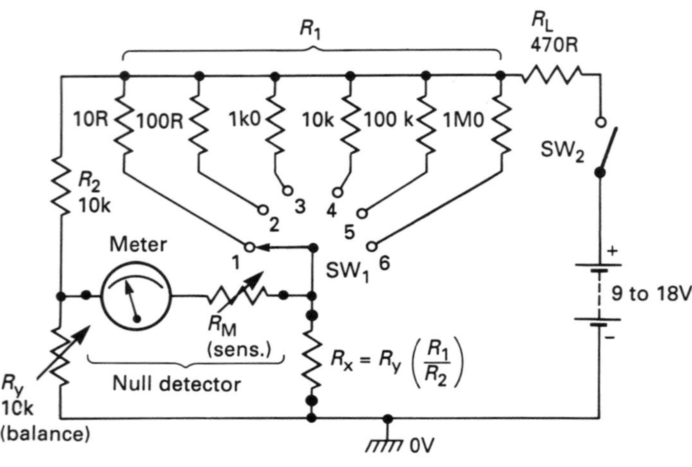


| SW$_1$ range | Bridge range | $R_1$ value | $R_1/R_2$ ratio | Bridge null sensitivity (nom.) |
|---|---|---|---|---|
| 1 | 0 – 10R | 10R | 1/1000 | Proportional to Ry's value, to 0.003% at full scale, on all ranges. |
| 2 | 0 – 100R | 100R | 1/100 | |
| 3 | 0 – 1k0 | 1k0 | 1/10 | |
| 4 | 0 – 10k | 10k | 1/1 | |
| 5 | 0 – 100k | 100k | 10/1 | |
| 6 | 0 – 1M0 | 1M0 | 100/1 | |

Figure 4.6. *Circuit and tabulated details of a high-sensitivity Wheatstone version of a six-range d.c. resistance-measuring bridge.*

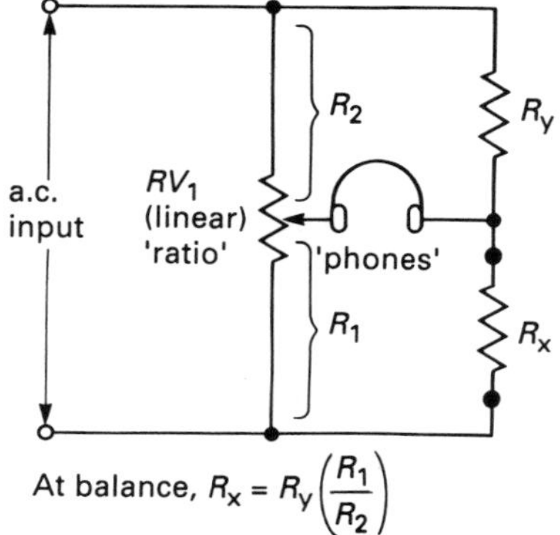


Figure 4.7. *Basic a.c.-energized Wheatstone bridge with variable-ratio-arm balancing and 'phone-type detection.*

*Figure 4.8* shows a five-range version of this circuit; it spans near-zero ohms to near-infinity, with good precision between 10Ω and 10MΩ. The $RV_1$ 'ratio' equals unity when $RV_1$'s slider is at mid-range; the diagram shows the typical scale markings of this control, which must be hand-calibrated on test. To use the bridge, connect it to a 1kHz sinewave source, fix $R_x$ in place, and adjust $SW_1$ and $RV_1$ until a null is detected on the 'phones, at which point $R_x$ equals the $SW_1$ resistor value multiplied by the $RV_1$ scale value. In practice, a balance is available on any range, but to get the best precision the balance should occur with a $RV_1$ scale reading between roughly 0.27 and 3.0.

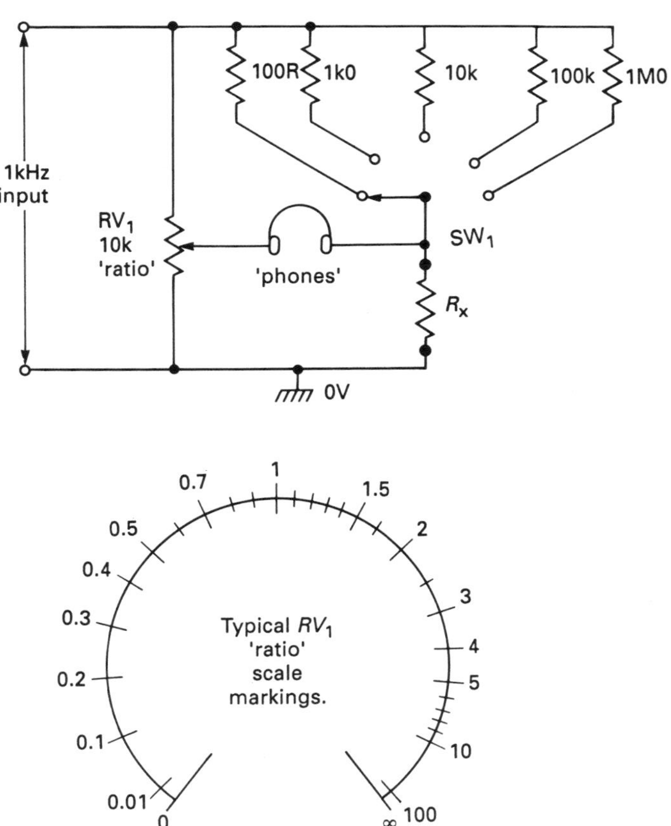


Figure 4.8. *Five-range resistance bridge, with typical* $RV_1$ *scale markings.*

To calibrate the $RV_1$ scale, fit a 10k, 1 per cent resistor in the $R_x$ position, then move $SW_1$ progressively through its 100R, 1k0, 10k, 100k, and 1M0 positions and mark the scale at each sequential balance point as 0.01, 0.1, 1 (mid-scale), 10, and 100. Repeat this process using $R_x$ values that are decade multiples or submultiples of 1.5, 2, 3, 4, 5, etc., until the scale is adequately calibrated, as in the diagram.

## 'Resolution' and 'precision'

The three most important features of a bridge are (apart from its measurement range) its *balance sensitivity* (which has already been described), its *resolution*, and its *precision*. The term *resolution* relates to the sharpness with which the $R_x$ value can be read off on the bridge's controls. Thus, in *Figures 4.3* and *4.6*, $R_y$ gives a resolution of about ±1 per cent of full scale if it is a hand-calibrated linearly variable resistor, or of ±0.005 per cent of full scale if it takes the form of a four-decade $R$ box. The *Figure 4.8* circuit's resolution varies from ±1 per cent at a '1' ratio, to ±2 per cent at a 0.3 or 3.0 ratio, to ±5 per cent at a 0.1 or 1.0 ratio, etc.

The term *precision* relates to the intrinsic accuracy of the bridge, assuming that it has perfect balance sensitivity and resolution, and equals the sum of the $R_1/R_2$ ratio tolerance and the tolerance of the resistance standard ($R_y$). If the $R_1/R_2$ ratio is set by simply using precision resistors, the ratio's precision equals the sum of the $R_1$ and $R_2$ tolerances; note, however, that it is quite easy, using techniques described later, to match resistors so that ratio errors are reduced to only ±0.005 per cent.

Thus, if the *Figure 4.6* circuit is built using 1 per cent resistors for $R_1$ and $R_2$, and $R_y$ is a hand-calibrated variable, the circuit will have an intrinsic precision of only ±3 per cent, but if the $R_1$ and $R_2$ values are correctly matched the bridge's precision rises to ±1.005 per cent. Precision can be further increased, to ±0.105 per cent, by using a ±0.1 per cent multi-decade $R$ box in the $R_y$ position. In reality, additional errors may creep in when measuring very low or high values of resistance, due to the resistances of switches and leads when measuring low values, and leakages when measuring high ones.

The overall quality of a bridge depends on its balance sensitivity, its resolution, and its precision. Thus, the *Figure 4.6* circuit has excellent sensitivity and potentially good resolution and precision, so can be used as the basis of either a cheap-and-simple 'service' instrument, or as a precision laboratory instrument, depending on the details of its construction, but the *Figure 4.8* design has intrinsically poor resolution and precision, and can thus only be used as the basis of a cheap-and-simple 'service' instrument.

## Service-type *C* and *L* bridges

An a.c.-energized Wheatstone bridge can measure both reactance and resistance, and can thus also measure capacitance ($C$) and inductance ($L$). *Figure 4.9* shows how the *Figure 4.7* circuit can be used to measure $C$ or $L$ values by replacing $R_x$ and $R_y$ with reactances of like types, provided that $C_x$ or $L_x$ are reasonably pure and have impedances (at 1kHz) greater than about 1Ω and less than 10MΩ. The problems with trying to measure inductance using this circuit are that accurate inductors (for use in the $Z_y$ position) are hard to get, and that inductive impedances are only 6.28Ω/mH at 1kHz. The only problem in measuring capacitance is that the $C_x$ value is proportional to the reciprocal of the $RV_1$ '$R$' scale markings; if the basic bridge is used to measure both $R$ and $C$, this means that two calibrated sets of $RV_1$ scales are needed.

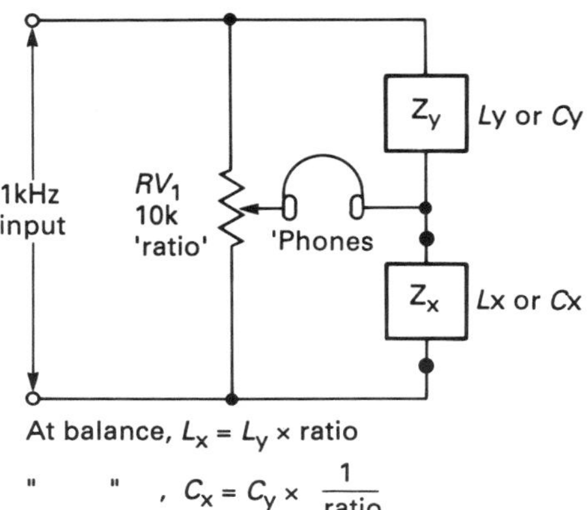


Figure 4.9. *A Wheatstone bridge can be used to balance both capacitive and inductive reactances.*

This snag can be overcome by fitting $RV_1$ with a reversing switch, as shown in the multi-range $L-C-R$ 'service'-type bridge of *Figure 4.10*, so that only a single *Figure 4.8*-type scale is needed.

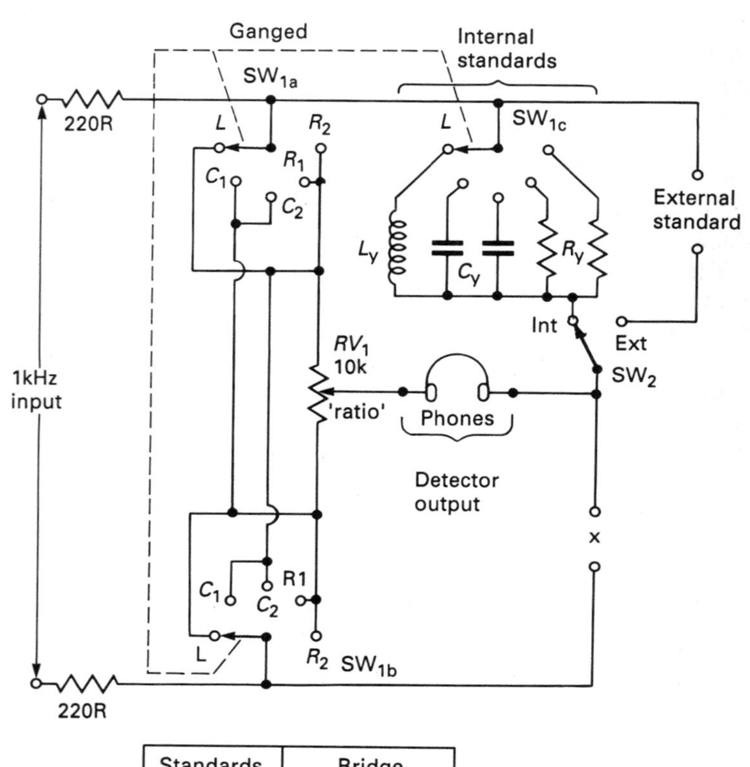


| | Standards value | Bridge range |
|---|---|---|
| Ry | 100R | 10R – 1k0 |
| | 10k | 1k0 – 100k |
| | 1M0 | 100k – 10M |
| Cy | 100pF | 10p – 1n0 |
| | 10n | 1n0 – 100n |
| | 1μF | 100n – 10μF |
| Ly | 1mH | 100μH – 10mH |
| | 100mH | 10mH – 1H |
| | 10H | 1H – 100H |

Figure 4.10. *'Service' type* L–C–R *bridge with 'phone-type detector.*

The *Figure 4.10* circuit is quite versatile; $SW_2$ enables it to be used with either internal or external $L$, $C$, or $R$ standards, and the mid-scale value of each range is equal to the value of standard used on that range, as implied by the table of *Figure 4.10*. Once this instrument is calibrated, it can be used to help create its own alternative measurement standards; thus, if an accurate 10nF standard is fitted in place, a 100nF standard can be created by moving $RV_1$ to the '10' position and then wiring capacitors in parallel across the $x$ terminal until a null balance is obtained, at which point the $C_x$ value equals 100nF. This 100nF standard can then be wired into the bridge and used to help create a 1μF standard, and so on.

The *Figure 4.10* circuit can be built exactly as shown, or can be built as a self-contained instrument with integral oscillator and detector circuits. In the latter case note that, since a bridge cannot share common input and output terminals, the oscillator must be effectively 'floating' relative to the balance detector circuitry. The designer has two basic options in this respect, as shown in *Figure 4.11*. The first option is to power both circuits

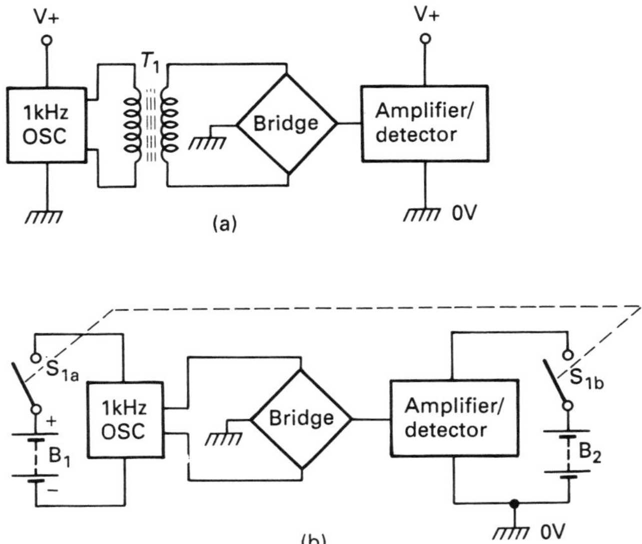


Figure 4.11. *Alternative ways of providing a bridge with independent energization and detection.*

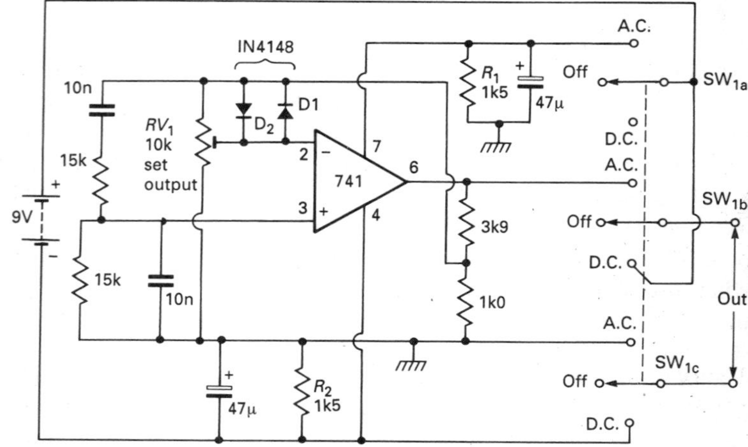


Figure 4.12. *Bridge energizer, giving 9V d.c. and 5V peak-to-peak 1kHz outputs.*

from the same supply but to effectively isolate the oscillator by transformer-coupling its output to the bridge, as in (a). The other option is to power the oscillator from its own floating supply, as shown in (b); this option is highly efficient, and is generally to be preferred.

*Figure 4.12* shows a practical battery-powered 'bridge energizer' that can give either a 9V d.c. output or an excellent 1kHz sine-wave output with a peak-to-peak amplitude of 5V. The oscillator is a diode-stabilized Wien type, effectively operated from a split supply derived from the battery via $R_1$ and $R_2$; it has a low-impedance output, and consumes a quiescent current of less than 4mA. To set up the oscillator, connect its output to a 'scope and trim $RV_1$ to give a reasonably pure sine-wave output of about 5V peak-to-peak.

## 'Precision' *C* and *L* bridges

All 'precision' *C* and *L* bridges incorporate facilities for balancing both the resistive and the reactive elements of test components. The basic principles of the subject are detailed in *Figures 4.13* to *4.15*.

Any practical capacitor has the equivalent circuit of *Figure 4.13a*, in which *C* represents a pure capacitance, $R_S$ represents dialectric

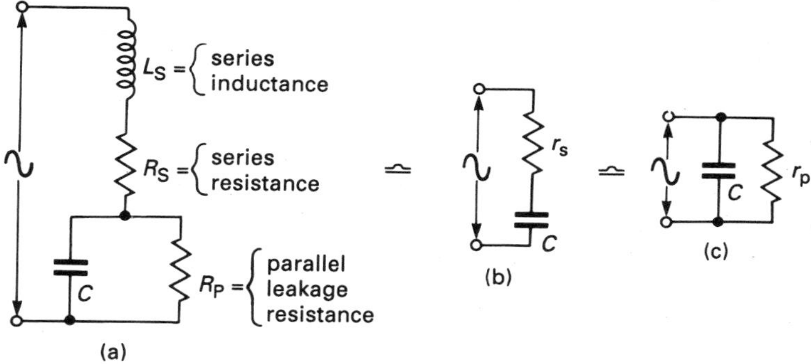


Figure 4.13. *Absolute (a) and simplified series (b) and parallel (c) equivalent circuits of a capacitor.*

losses, $R_P$ the leakage losses, and $L_S$ the inductance of electrode foils, etc. At frequencies below a few kilohertz $L_S$ has (except in high-value electrolytics) negligible practical effect, but $R_S$ and $R_P$ cause a finite shift in the capacitor's voltage–current phase relationship. This same phase shift can be emulated by wiring a single 'lumped' resistor in series or in parallel with a pure capacitor, as in *Figures 4.13b* and *4.13c*.

A similar story is true of inductors, which can, in terms of phase shifts, be regarded as 'negative' capacitors. Either device can, at any given frequency, be treated as a pure reactance, $X$, that is either in series or in parallel with a single 'loss' resistor ($r_S$ or $r_P$), as shown in *Figures 4.14a* or *4.14b*. The ratio between $r$ and $X$ is normally called $Q$ in an inductor, or $D$ or the 'loss factor' in a capacitor; one of its major effects is to shift the device's voltage-to-current phase relationship, $\phi$ (pronounced phi), from the ideal value of 90° to some value between zero and 90°; the difference between this and the ideal value is known as the loss angle, $\delta$ (pronounced delta) of the phasor diagram. Another major effect of $Q$ or $D$ is to shift the component's impedance ($Z$) away from its pure reactance ($X$) value. All the formulae relevant to the subject are shown in *Figure 4.14*.

*Figure 4.15* lists the relationships between phase and loss angles and the $Z/X$-ratios of both series and parallel equivalent circuits at various decade-related $Q$ and $D$ values. Note that components with $Q$ values of 10 or more, or $D$ values of 0.1 or less, have similar $Z$ and $X$ values. Thus, a coil with a $Q$ of 10 and an $X$ of

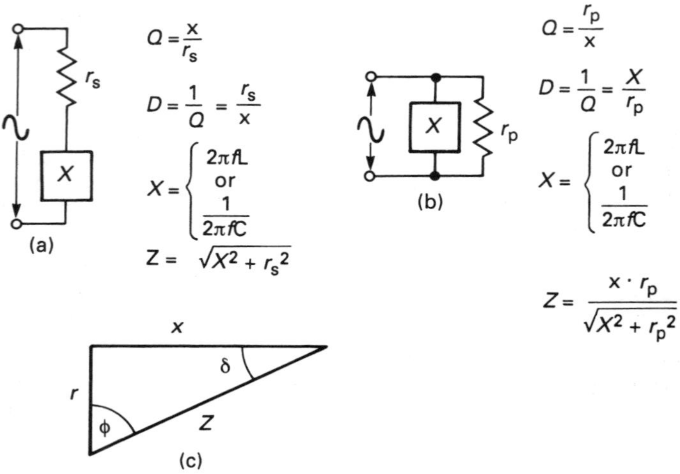


(a) $$Q = \frac{X}{r_s} \qquad D = \frac{1}{Q} = \frac{r_s}{X} \qquad X = \begin{cases} 2\pi fL \\ \text{or} \\ \dfrac{1}{2\pi fC} \end{cases} \qquad Z = \sqrt{X^2 + r_s^2}$$

(b) $$Q = \frac{r_p}{X} \qquad D = \frac{1}{Q} = \frac{X}{r_p} \qquad X = \begin{cases} 2\pi fL \\ \text{or} \\ \dfrac{1}{2\pi fC} \end{cases} \qquad Z = \frac{X \cdot r_p}{\sqrt{X^2 + r_p^2}}$$

$$\delta = \text{loss angle} = \arctan \frac{r_s}{X} = \arctan \frac{X}{r_p}$$

$$\text{"} \quad \text{"} \quad \text{"} = \arctan D = \arctan \frac{1}{Q}$$

$$\phi = \text{phase angle} = \arctan \frac{X}{r} = \arctan \frac{r_p}{X}$$

$$\text{"} \quad \text{"} \quad \text{"} = \arctan Q = \arctan \frac{1}{D}$$

Figure 4.14. *Any capacitor or inductor can be represented by a series (a) or parallel (b) equivalent circuit, which determines its phasor diagram (c).*

| Q | D | Phase angle $\phi$ | Loss angle $\delta$ | Z/X – ratio | |
|---|---|---|---|---|---|
| | | | | Series circuit | Parallel circuit |
| ∞ | 0 | 90° | 0° | 1.000 | 1.000 |
| 1000 | 0.001 | 89.94° | 0.06° | 1.000 | 1.000 |
| 100 | 0.01 | 89.43° | 0.57° | 1.000 | 1.000 |
| 10 | 0.1 | 84.29° | 5.71° | 1.005 | 0.995 |
| 1.0 | 1.0 | 45° | 45° | 1.414 | 0.7071 |
| 0.1 | 10 | 5.71° | 84.29° | 10.05 | 0.0995 |
| 0.01 | 100 | 0.57° | 89.43° | 100.0 | 0.0100 |

Figure 4.15. *Relationship between $\phi$, $\delta$, and Z/X-ratio in series and parallel equivalent circuits at various values of Q and D.*

1000Ω at a given frequency can be said to have either a 100Ω series ($r_S$) or a 10 000Ω parallel ($r_P$) resistance; in either case, it gives a loss angle of 5.71° and an impedance that is within 0.5 per cent of 1000Ω at that frequency. Also note that series and parallel 'equivalent' circuits produce significantly different $Z/X$-ratios at low values of $Q$.

The relevance of all this is that, at any given frequency, the true $X$, $Q$ and $D$ values of a capacitor or inductor can be deduced by measuring the device's impedance and loss angle, and it is this principle that forms the basis of most precision $C$ or $L$ measurement bridges. The best-known precision $C$ measurement bridge is the de Sauty, which is shown in basic form in *Figure 4.16*; it is at balance when $R_y/Z_S = R_1/Z_x$, and under this condition the values of $C_x$, $r_x$, and $D_x$ are as shown in the diagram. The bridge is

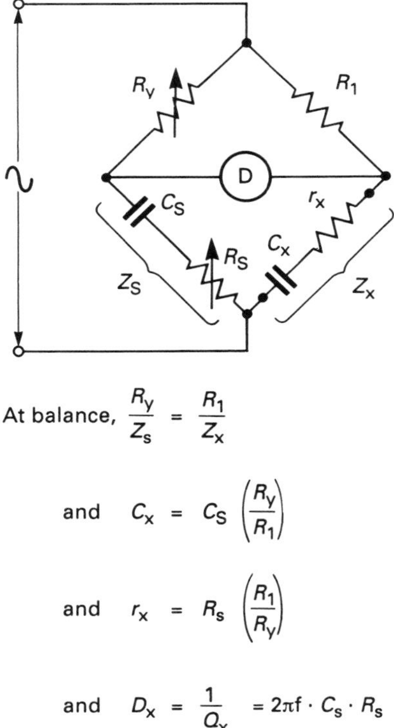


Figure 4.16. *Basic de Sauty capacitance bridge.*

balanced by using $R_y$ and $R_S$ to balance the a.c. voltages and phase shifts on the detector's left side with those on its right.

*Figure 4.17* shows a practical de Sauty bridge that spans 1pF to 10μF in 6 decade ranges. This is a very sensitive design in which roughly half of the a.c. energizing voltage appears at each end of the detector at balance; the detector can thus take a very simple form (such as 'phones, etc). $R_S$ enables nulling to be obtained with $C_x$ capacitors with $D$ values as high as 0.138 (equal to a $Q$ of 7.2); any capacitor with this high a value should be scrapped. If desired, $R_S$ can be calibrated directly in $D$ values, since (in this design, at 1kHz) $D = 0.001$ per 15.9Ω of $R_S$ value.

The two best-known $L$ measurement bridges are the Hay and the Maxwell types of *Figure 4.18* and *Figure 4.19*. These work by balancing the inductive phase shift of $L_x$ against a capacitive shift of the same magnitude in the diametrically opposite arm of the

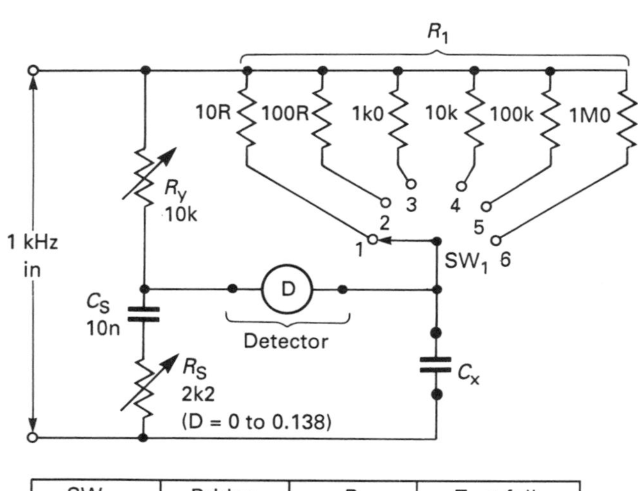


| SW1 range | Bridge range | $R_1$ range | $Z_x$ at full-scale at $R_S$= 0 |
|---|---|---|---|
| 1 | 0 – 10μF | 10R | 15.9R |
| 2 | 0 – 1μF | 100R | 159R |
| 3 | 0 – 0.1μF | 1k0 | 1590R |
| 4 | 0 – 10nF | 10k | 15.9k |
| 5 | 0 – 1nF | 100k | 159k |
| 6 | 0 – 100pF | 1M0 | 1.59M |

Figure 4.17. *Sensitive six-range de Sauty capacitance bridge.*

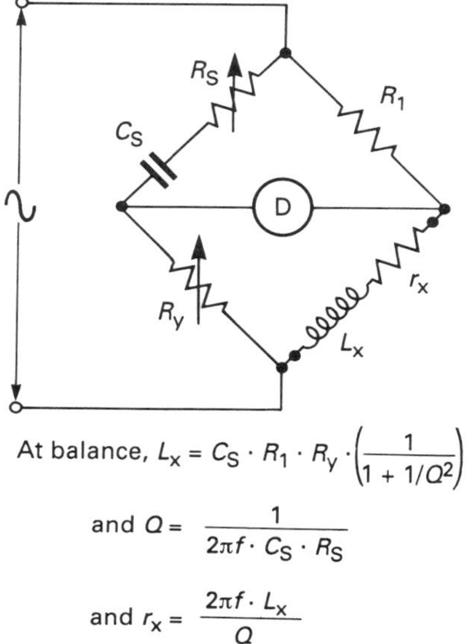


Figure 4.18. *The Hay inductance bridge is useful for measuring high-Q coils.*

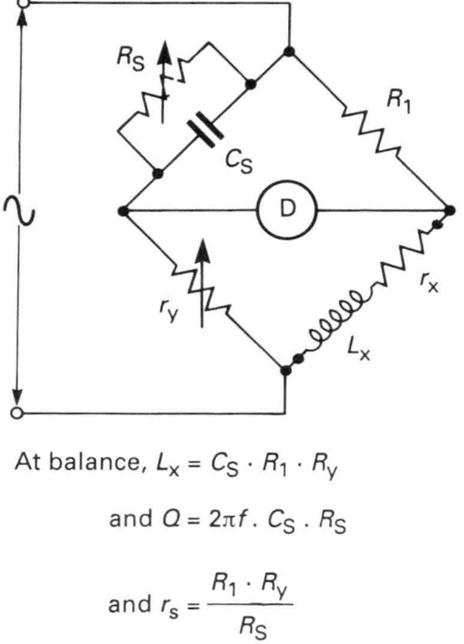


Figure 4.19. *The Maxwell bridge is useful for measuring low-Q coils.*

bridge. The Hay bridge uses a series equivalent ($C_S-R_S$) balancing network, and is useful for measuring high-$Q$ coils (it can be very inaccurate at $Q$ values below 10, as implied by the formulae of *Figure 4.18*). The Maxwell bridge uses a parallel equivalent ($C_S-R_S$) balancing network, and is useful for measuring coils with $Q$ values below 10. Note that the $Q$ values referred to here are those occurring at the test frequency of (usually) 1kHz; a coil that has a high frequency $Q$ of 100 may have a $Q$ of 1 or less at 1kHz.

*Figure 4.20* shows a practical inductance bridge that spans 10μH to 100H in six ranges; it uses a Hay configuration for high-$Q$

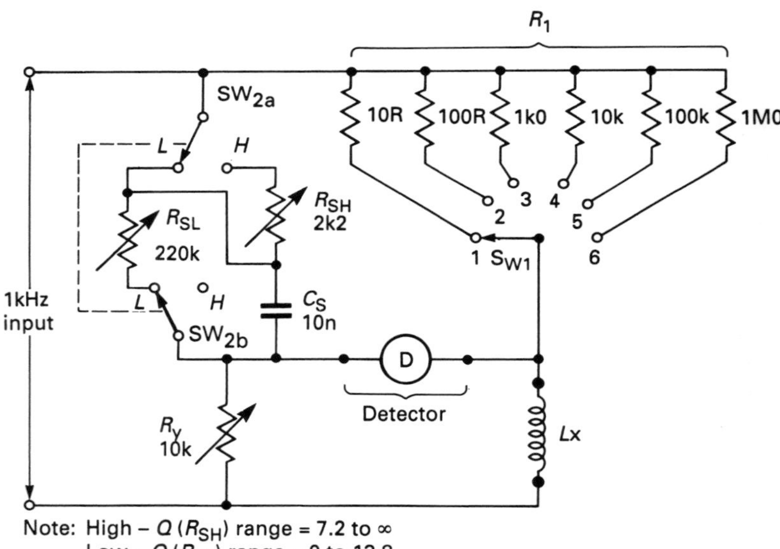


| $SW_1$ range | Bridge range | $R_1$ value | $Z_x$ at 1kHz at full scale |
|---|---|---|---|
| 1 | 0 – 1mH | 10R | 6.2R |
| 2 | 0 – 10mH | 100R | 62R |
| 3 | 0 – 100mH | 1k0 | 620R |
| 4 | 0 – 1H | 10k | 6.2k |
| 5 | 0 – 10H | 100k | 62k |
| 6 | 0 – 100H | 1M0 | 620k |

Figure 4.20. *Six-range Hay–Maxwell inductance bridge.*

measurements (with $SW_2$ in the 'H' position) and a Maxwell layout for low-$Q$ ones (with $SW_2$ set to 'L'). This is another sensitive design, in which the a.c. voltages at either end of the detector are close to the half-supply value at balance, and can use a very simple type of detector.

## A precision $L-C-R$ bridge

*Figure 4.21* shows a precision 18-range $L-C-R$ bridge that combines the circuits of *Figures 4.20*, *4.17*, and *4.6*, to make a highly sensitive design that can use very simple types of balance detector

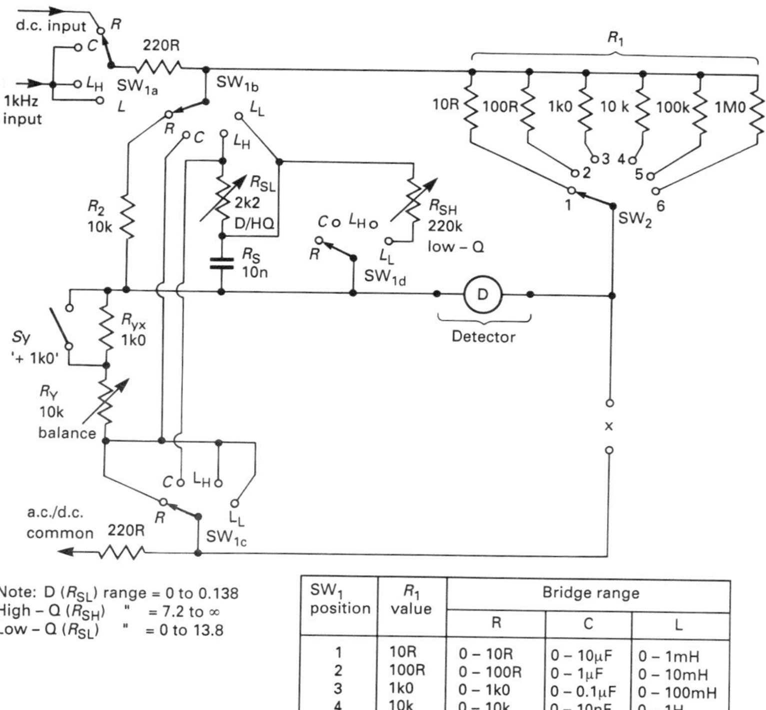


Note: D ($R_{SL}$) range = 0 to 0.138
High - Q ($R_{SH}$) " = 7.2 to ∞
Low - Q ($R_{SL}$) " = 0 to 13.8

| $SW_1$ position | $R_1$ value | Bridge range | | |
|---|---|---|---|---|
| | | R | C | L |
| 1 | 10R | 0 – 10R | 0 – 10μF | 0 – 1mH |
| 2 | 100R | 0 – 100R | 0 – 1μF | 0 – 10mH |
| 3 | 1k0 | 0 – 1k0 | 0 – 0.1μF | 0 – 100mH |
| 4 | 10k | 0 – 10k | 0 – 10nF | 0 – 1H |
| 5 | 100k | 0 – 100k | 0 – 1nF | 0 – 10H |
| 6 | 1M0 | 0 – 1M0 | 0 – 100pF | 0 – 100H |

Figure 4.21. *Sensitive eighteen-range laboratory-standard* L–C–R *bridge.*

(such as a multimeter on the d.c.-driven *R* ranges, or 'phones on the a.c.-energized *C* and *L* ranges. This circuit's '*y*' null-balance network is modified by the addition of resistor $R_{yx}$ and switch $S_y$, which enable the coverage of each range to be extended by 10 per cent.

When this bridge is used on its 0–100pF range, considerable errors occur due to the effects of stray capacitance, and measurements should thus be made by using the 'incremental' method, as follows: first, with no component in place across the *x* terminals, null the bridge via $R_y$ and note the resultant 'residual' null reading (typically about 15pF); now fit the test component in place, obtain a balance reading (say 83pF), and then subtract the residual value (15pF) to obtain the true test capacitor value (68pF).

The *Figure 4.21* circuit can either be built exactly as shown and used with external energizing and null-detection circuitry, or can be modified in various ways to suit individual tastes. *Figure 4.22*, for example, shows how an extra wafer (e) can be added to $SW_1$ to facilitate the use of a built-in d.c./a.c. energizer (which can be based on the *Figure 4.12* design. Similarly, d.c. and a.c. null-balance detectors can easily be built in; the d.c. detector can take the form of a 50μA–0–50μA meter, with overload protection given via a couple of silicon diodes and sensitivity adjustable via a series resistor, as shown in *Figure 4.23*. The a.c. detector can take the form of any single-ended a.c. analogue millivoltmeter circuit; in this case the 'low' input of the detector and the left-hand 'detector' junction of the bridge can both be grounded to chassis, as shown in *Figure 4.24*, which also shows how the a.c.

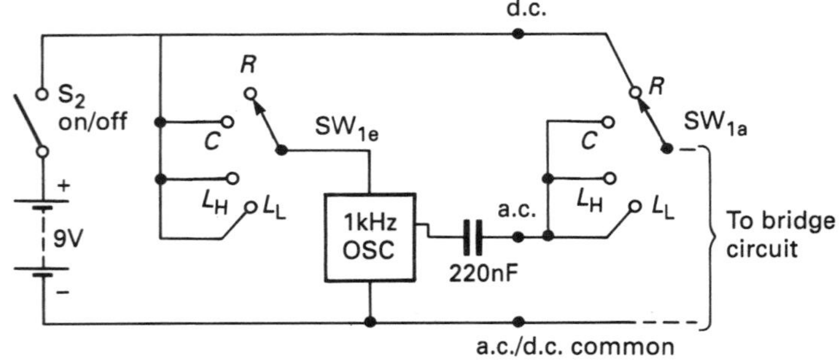


Figure 4.22. *Built-in energiser for the* L–C–R *bridge.*

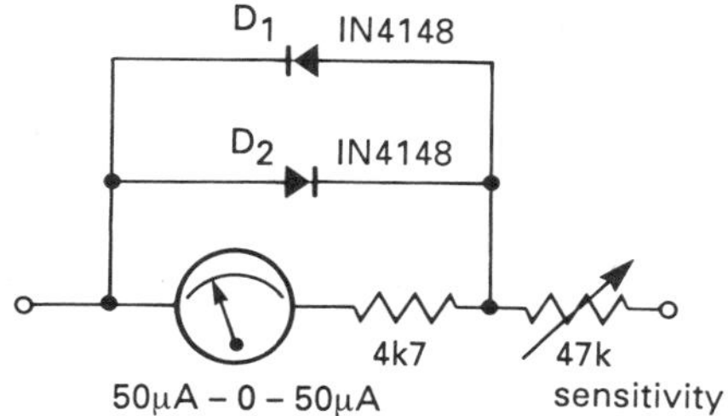


Figure 4.23. *D.C. null detector.*

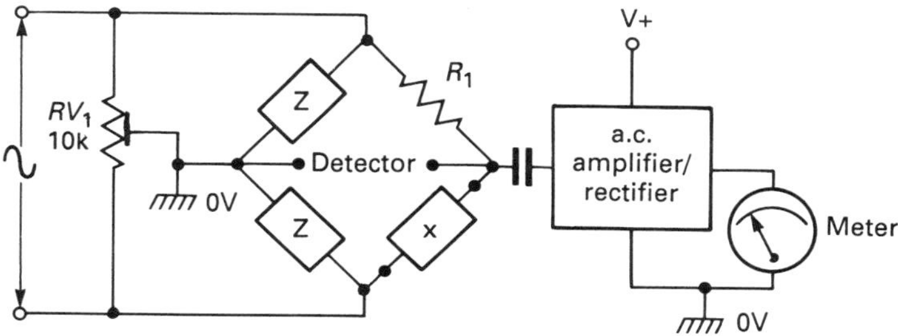


Figure 4.24. *Provision of a Wagner earth and single-ended a.c. null detector.*

energizing signal can be fitted with a Wagner earth, which enables the signal to be balanced to ground (via $RV_1$), to eliminate unwanted signal breakthrough at null.

One of the most important modifications that can be made concerns the bridge's resolution, which is only about ±1 per cent of full scale in the basic design, this being the readability limit of the $R_y$ balance control's scale. *Figure 4.25* shows how resolution can be improved by a factor of ten, to ±0.1 per cent of full scale, by replacing the $S_y$–$R_{yx}$–$R_y$ network of *Figure 4.21* with the switched-and-variable $R_y$ network of *Figure 4.25*; switch $S_y$ enables the $RV_y$ variable control to be overranged by 50 per cent. This high-resolution circuit is best used by first switching $S_y$ and $SW_y$ to 0 and adjusting the bridge's range controls to give a balance on $RV_y$ only; this gives a good guide to the test component's value; a final balance can then be read on a more sensitive range via the full range of $R_y$ balance controls.

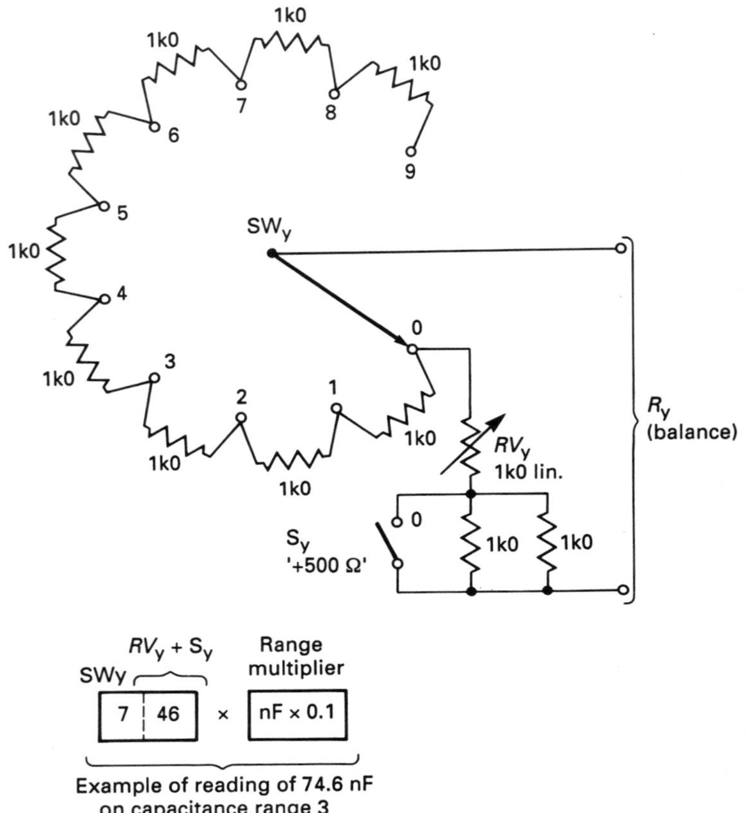


Figure 4.25. *This circuit can be used to raise the null resolution (readability) of the* L–C–R *bridge to ±0.1 per cent of full scale.*

## Special bridge circuits

In addition to the types of d.c. and low-frequency a.c. bridges already described, there are three others that are of special value. The first of these is the transformer ratio-arm bridge, which is shown in basic form in *Figure 4.26*. The value of this bridge's ratio arms (shown as switch-selectable at 0.1/1, 1/1, or 10/1 in this example) depends entirely on the transformer's turns ratios, and can easily be wound with a precision better than 0.01 per cent. The value of an unknown ($x$) impedance can be balanced

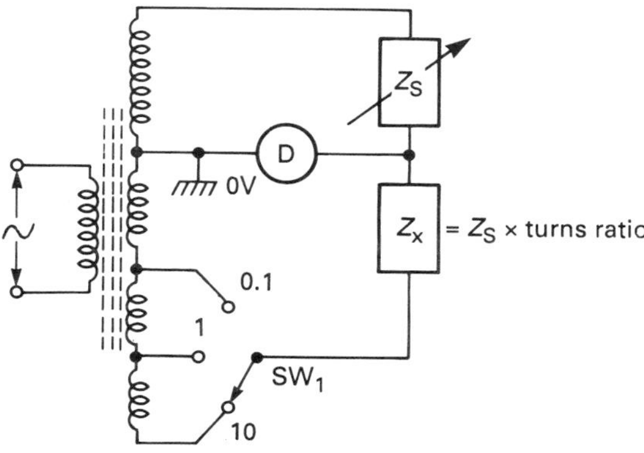


Figure 4.26. *Simple transformer ratio-arm bridge.*

against that of a standard either by varying the value of the standard or the value of the ratio arms. Resistors or capacitors can be balanced against each other by placing them on opposite sides of the bridge as shown, or a capacitor can be balanced against an inductance by placing both components on the same side of the bridge.

Another important bridge is the d.c. resistance-matching type; *Figure 4.27* shows a simple version that enables resistors to be matched to within ±0.1 per cent or better. Two basic principles are involved here; the first is that if $R_A$ and $R_B$ are exactly equal, the value of $R_{MATCH}$ will precisely equal that of $R_S$ at balance; the second is that if $R_A$ and $R_B$ are equal they will generate exactly the same output voltage whichever way they are connected across the supply. With this second principle in mind, $R_A$ and $R_B$ are joined by 500R multi-turn pot $RV_1$ and are connected to the d.c. supply via biased polarity-reversal switch $SW_1$.

To use this resistance-matching bridge, first fit $R_S$ and $R_{MATCH}$ in place, noting that $R_{MATCH}$ is, for simplicity, shown as being made up of a fixed ($R_{M1}$) and a variable ($R_{M2}$) element. With the d.c. supply connected, a meter reading should now be available; if necessary, trim $R_{M2}$ and $RV_1$ to bring this to a sensible level; now repeatedly toggle $SW_1$ and trim $RV_1$ until identical meter readings are given in either toggle position. That completes the $R_A$–$R_B$ adjustment. The value of $R_{MATCH}$ should now be trimmed (via $R_{M2}$) to bring the meter reading to zero, at which point $R_S$ and $R_{MATCH}$ are matched. Note that, after $RV_1$ has been initially

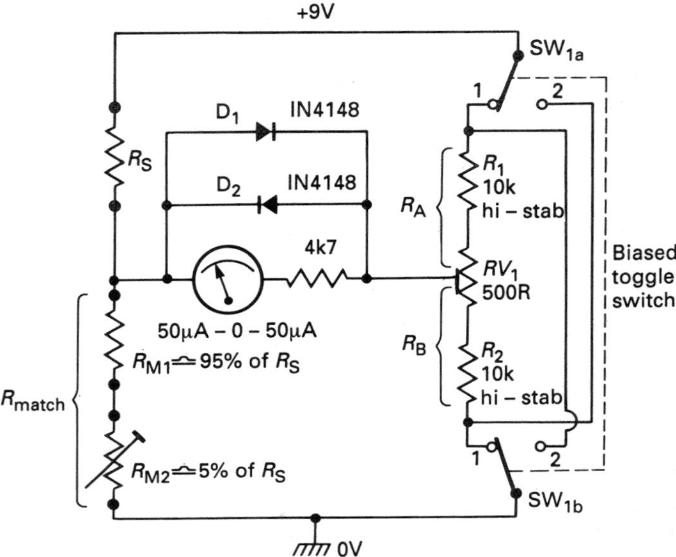


Figure 4.27. *Simple resistance-matching bridge, gives matching within ±0.1 per cent.*

set, it should only rarely need readjustment, and that the circuit's 'matching' fidelity is limited to ±0.1 per cent only by the balance-detection meter's sensitivity.

When building a resistance-matching bridge, or when matching resistors, only low-temperature-coefficient resistors should be used, and these should never by physically touched during balancing/matching operations. *Figure 4.28* helps make this point

| Resistor type | Typical temperature coefficient | |
|---|---|---|
| | ± ppm/°C | ± %/°C |
| Carbon film | 300 – 1000 | 0.03% – 0.1% |
| Thick film metal | 100 – 300 | 0.01% – 0.03% |
| Metal film | 50 – 100 | 0.005% – 0.01% |
| Precision metal film | 15 – 50 | 0.0015% – 0.005% |
| Vitreous wire wound | 75 | 0.0075% |
| Precision wire wound | 5 – 15 | 0.0005% – 0.0015% |

Figure 4.28. *Typical temperature coefficients of modern resistors.*

clear by listing the typical temperature coefficients of various types of modern resistor. Note when using the bridge that the $R_{MATCH}$ value can be trimmed (to make it equal $R_S$) by using series resistance to increase its value or shunt resistance to reduce it.

## A precision resistance-matching bridge

*Figure 4.29* shows a precision resistance-matching bridge that incorporates a meter-driving d.c. differential amplifier that gives such high balance-detection sensitivity that resistors can be matched to within ±0.003 per cent. This bridge also has a facility for indicating, on $RV_1$'s calibrated scale, the percentage out-of-match error of $R_{MATCH}$; this scale spans ±0.05, ±0.05 and ±0.005 per cent in three switch-selected ranges.

To initially set up this bridge, fit $R_S$ and $R_{MATCH}$ in place, connect the op-amp's output to an external multimeter, and connect the supply via $SW_4$. Now close $SW_3$ and trim the op-amp's 10k **set balance** control for zero reading on the meter's most sensitive d.c. current range; release $SW_3$. Now set $RV_1$ to mid-scale and, with $SW_2$ initially set to its ×1 scale, start toggling $SW_1$ and trim $RV_2$ (and if necessary, $R_{M2}$) to find a setting where identical meter readings are obtained in both toggle positions; as $RV_2$ nears the balance point, increase balance sensitivity via $SW_2$, until eventually a perfect balance is obtained on the '×0.01' range. That completes the initial setting-up procedure, and $R_{MATCH}$ can then be matched to $R_S$ by trimming $R_{M2}$ for a zero reading on the meter. Once the circuit has been initially set up as described, $RV_2$ and the op-amp's **set balance** control should only rarely need readjustment, and in all further 'matching' operations the following procedure can (after making a brief initial check that the meter and toggle balances are correct) be used.

Fit $R_S$, $R_{MATCH}$, and the external multimeter in place. Turn $SW_2$ to the '×1' position, and switch the bridge on via $SW_4$. If $R_{MATCH}$ is within ±0.5 per cent of the $R_S$ value it should now be possible to set the bridge to a null via $RV_1$; if necessary, trim the $R_{MATCH}$ value until a null can be obtained. At null, read off the $R_{MATCH}$ error on the $RV_1$ scale (see *Figure 4.29*), and then make the appropriate error correction; to increase the $R_{MATCH}$ value by a fixed percentage, add a series resistor with a value of

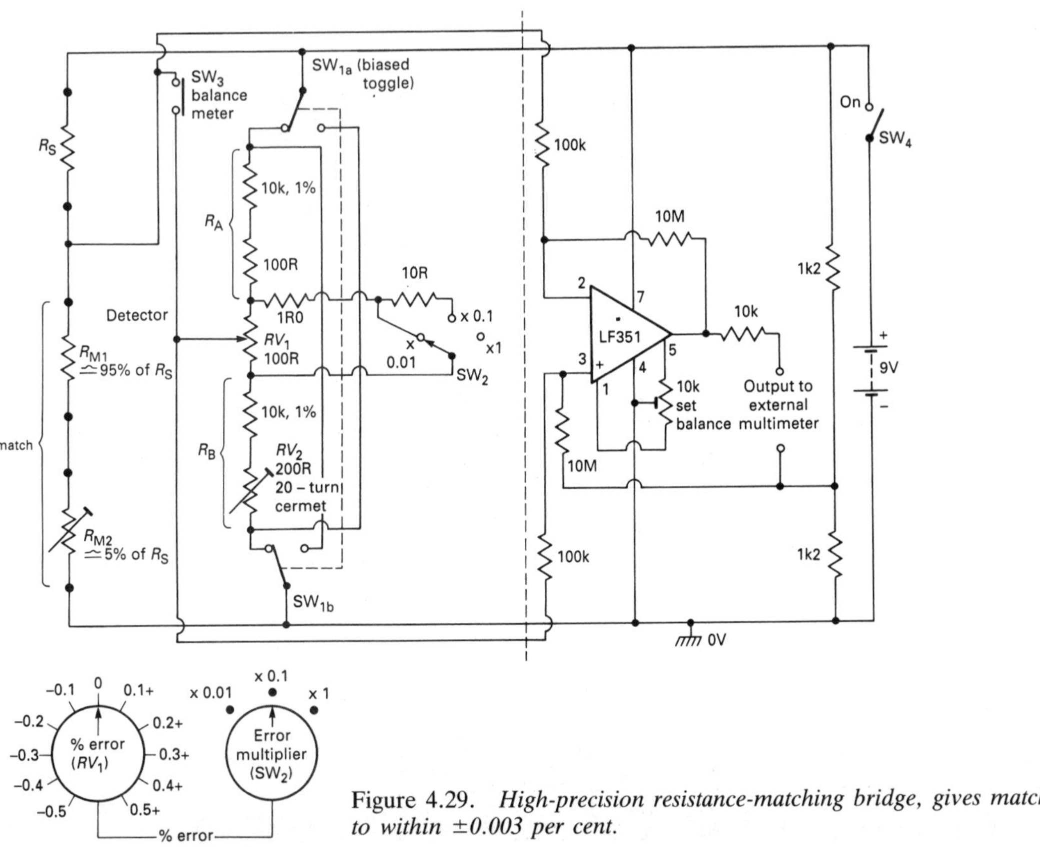


Figure 4.29. *High-precision resistance-matching bridge, gives matching to within ±0.003 per cent.*

$$R_{SERIES} = (R_{MATCH}/100) \times \text{percentage error}.$$

To reduce the $R_{MATCH}$ value by a fixed percentage, add a shunt resistor with a value of

$$R_{SHUNT} = (R_{MATCH} \times 100)/\text{percentage error}.$$

Thus, a 1000Ω (nominal) resistor can be increased by 0.3 per cent by adding a 3R0 series resistor, or reduced by 0.3 per cent by adding a 330k shunt resistor. Once a good match has been obtained on $SW_2$'s '×1' range, repeat the process on ranges '×0.1' and '×0.01', until the match is adequate. An alternative to this technique is to simply leave $RV_1$ in its 'mid-scale' position and trim $R_{MATCH}$ via $R_{M2}$ to obtain a null on all ranges of $SW_2$.

## Resistor-matching bridge applications

A precision resistor-matching bridge has several useful applications in the electronics laboratory. One of these is the duplication of precision resistor values, and *Figure 4.30* shows an example of how this facility can be put to good use. Here, ten duplicates of a precision 1k0 resistor are so wired that they can easily be used in series, to act as a resistance that increases in 1k0 steps up to a maximum of 10k, or in parallel, to act as a resistance that decreases in steps down to 100Ω. Note that as more and more resistors are wired in parallel or series, their ±0.003 per cent duplication errors average out and diminish, so that the precision of the final 10k series or 100R parallel resistance is equal, for all practical purposes, to that of the original 'master' resistor. The actual value of 'summed' duplication error is equal to the original

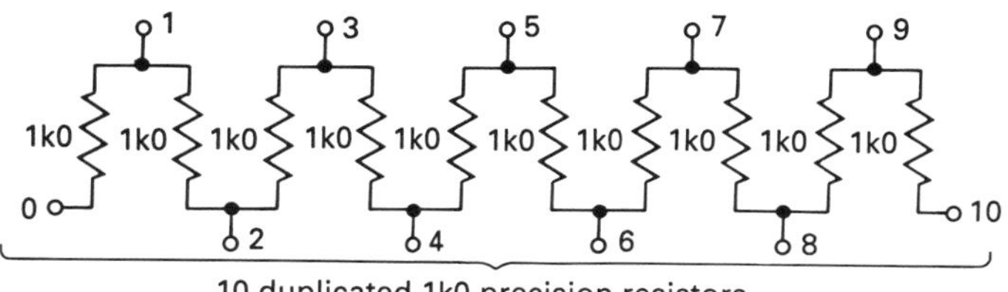


Figure 4.30. *This matrix of 1k0 resistors totals 10k when series connected, or 100R when parallel connected.*

error divided by the square root of the number of summed resistors (10), and equals 0.001 per cent in this case.

Another important resistor-matching bridge application is in the creation of a precision ratio-matching bridge of the type shown in *Figure 4.31*. Here, 14 resistors are duplicated from a 1k0 (nominal) master and wired together to create a three-ratio (10/1, 1/1, and 1/10) divider. The fact that these resistors are all precision-matched to within ±0.003 per cent ensures that the ratios are intrinsically defined with great precision, the actual precision being ±0.002 per cent on the 1/1 range and ±0.005 per cent on the 10/1 and 1/10 ranges. This bridge can itself be used to produce direct or decade multiple or submultiple duplicates of a master resistor. If the bridge is used with a sensitive null detector that gives a duplication precision of 0.003 per cent, the overall precision of duplication is ±0.005 per cent on the 1/1 range, and ±0.008 per cent on the 10/1 and 1/10 ranges.

## *R* and *C* boxes

An obvious application of the *Figure 4.31* circuit is in matching

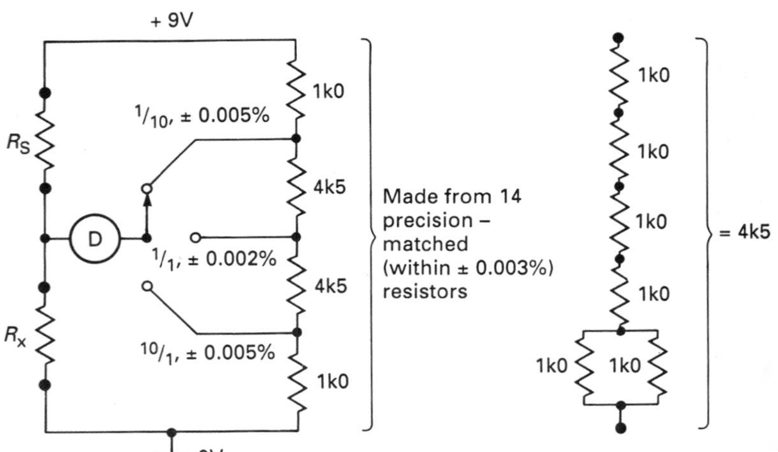


Figure 4.31. *Precision ratio-matching bridge.*

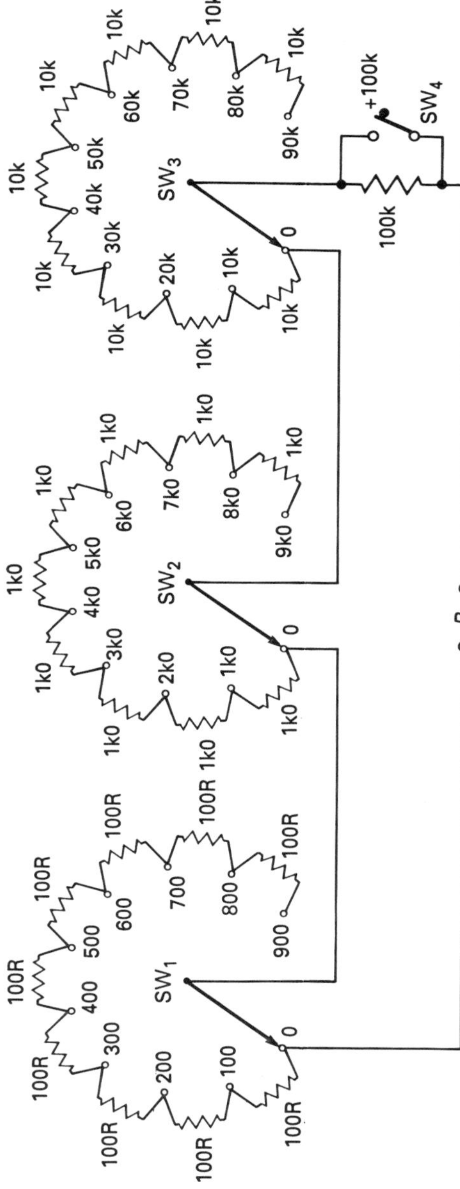


Figure 4.32. *Three-decade* R *box spans 0 to 99.9k in 100R steps.*

the range and ratio arms of conventional bridges, to enhance bridge precision. Another is in generating high-precision resistors for use in decade *R* boxes. *Figure 4.32* shows a three-decade *R* box that spans 0 to 99.9k in 100Ω steps, with 100k over-ranging available via $SW_4$. This type of circuit can be generated from a single precision reference (1k0 in this case), and has a multitude of applications in the laboratory, including those of calibrating bridge scales and finding resistor values by substitution.

A useful companion to the *R* box is the multi-decade 'C' box. In these, capacitors are either selected individually or are connected in parallel to make up specific values. *Figure 4.33* shows, in tabular form, one possible way of making a single-decade (0 to 9n0) unit, using only four basic capacitors (the 5n0 value can be made by padding up a 4n7 type). Note that three capacitors must be connected in parallel to make up the box's 9n0 value, so this design calls for the use of a three-pole ten-way switch.

*Figure 4.34* shows the table and practical circuit of an alternative design of 0 to 9n0 *C* box which uses five capacitors but only a two-pole ten-way switch. Since switch wafers are considerably more expensive than nanofarad capacitors, this is an economic design. Two extra boxes of this type, designed to give 10nF and 100nF steps, can easily be built and wired in parallel with it, to form a three-decade unit that spans 0 to 999nF in 1nF steps.

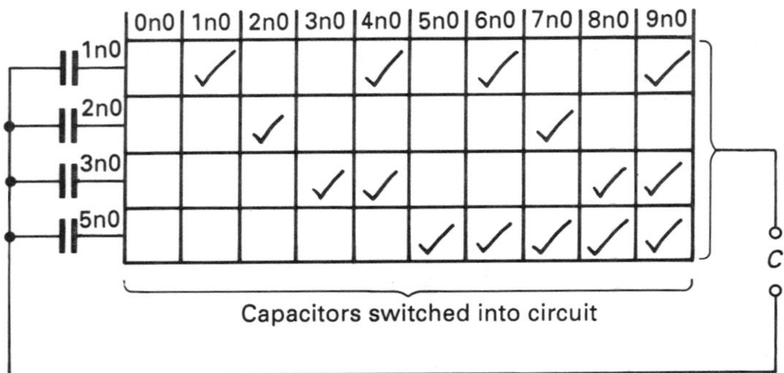

| | 0n0 | 1n0 | 2n0 | 3n0 | 4n0 | 5n0 | 6n0 | 7n0 | 8n0 | 9n0 |
|---|---|---|---|---|---|---|---|---|---|---|
| 1n0 | | ✓ | | | ✓ | | ✓ | | | ✓ |
| 2n0 | | | ✓ | | | | | ✓ | | |
| 3n0 | | | | ✓ | ✓ | | | | ✓ | ✓ |
| 5n0 | | | | | | ✓ | ✓ | ✓ | ✓ | ✓ |



Figure 4.33. *This basic 0–9n0 decade 'C' box uses four capacitors and a three-pole–ten way switch.*

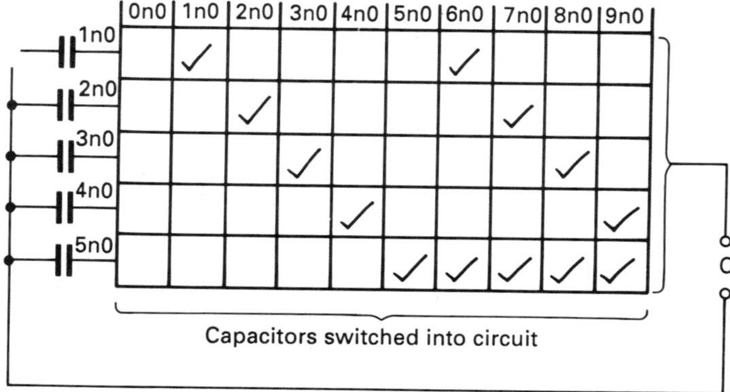


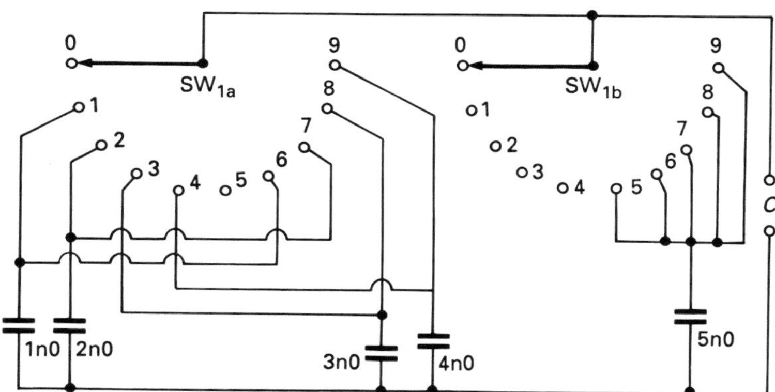


Figure 4.34. *This 0–9n0 decade 'C' box uses five capacitors but only a two-pole–ten way switch.*

## A potentiometric voltmeter

Another important application of the precision resistor-matching bridge is in aiding the creation of a potentiometric voltmeter. This instrument enables D.C. voltages to be measured with such good precision that it can be used to calibrate $3\frac{1}{2}$- and $4\frac{1}{2}$-digit digital voltmeters. *Figure 4.35* shows the basic circuit of such a voltmeter, which operates as follows.

The *Figure 4.35* circuit consists, in essence, of a precision calibrated 110k variable potentiometer ($RV_2$) that is energized with 11.000V D.C., derived via a stabilizer power supply unit and the $RV_1$ 'fine trim' control; 0.1mV is thus generated across each ohm of the potentiometer, which is accurately calibrated in terms of its output voltage. The unit is used in conjunction with a precision voltage reference, which in the diagram takes the form of a Weston 1.0181V 'standard' cell. In use, the potentiometer is first set to read '1.0181V', and $SW_1$ is then moved to the **cal** position and $RV_1$ is trimmed to give a zero or null reading on the meter; under this condition the potentiometer output and standard cell voltages are equal, and precisely 11.000V are applied across the pot. The external D.C. test voltage (which must be no greater than 11V) is then connected in place, $SW_1$ is set to the **use** position, and the pot is adjusted to give a null on the meter, at which point the voltage value can be read off directly on the potentiometer scale. Note that zero current is drawn from the test voltage at null. Voltages greater than 11 can be measured by feeding them to the instrument via a precision attenuator.

*Figure 4.36* shows the practical circuit of the 'potentiometer' section of the above instrument. In this, there are 110k of resistance connected into circuit at all times, and 1V is generated across each active 10k resistance block when the pot is energized with 11V. Thus, with $SW_1$ in position '4' as shown, +4V appears

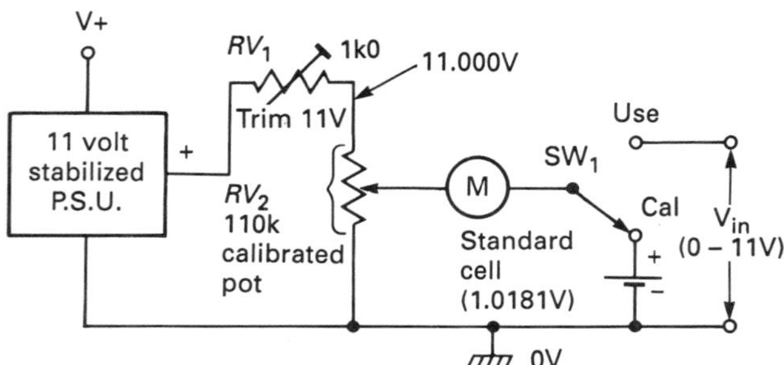


Figure 4.35. *Basic potentiometric voltmeter circuit.*

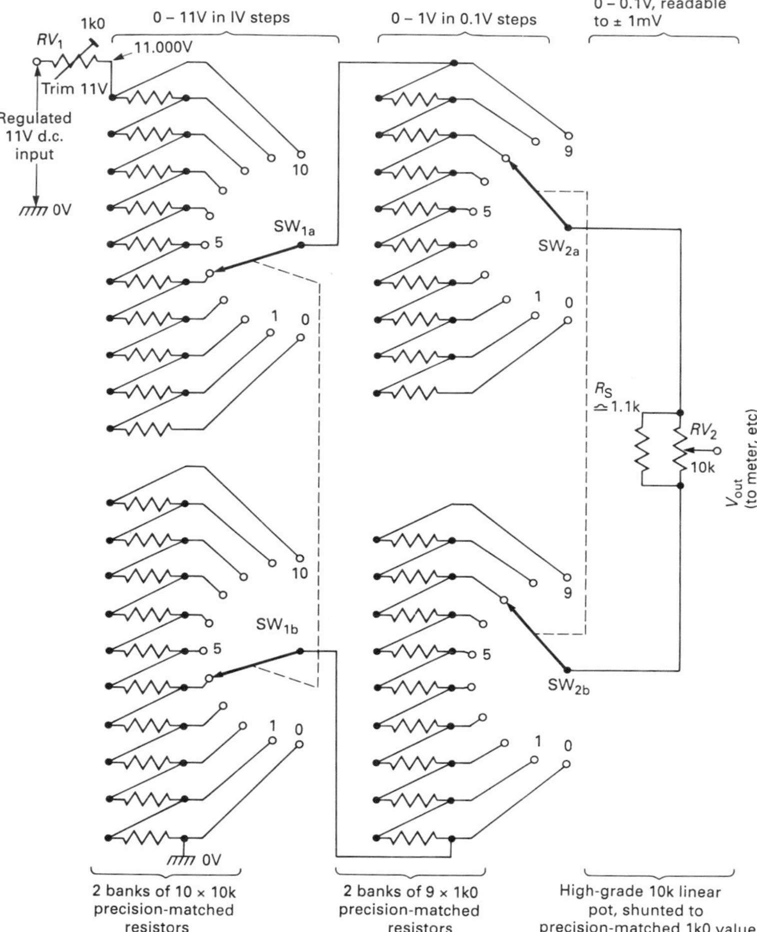


Figure 4.36. *Precision potentiometric voltmeter, set to read 4.750V, has basic accuracy of ±0.005 per cent, ±1mV.*

on the common terminal of $SW_{1b}$ and +5V on that of $SW_{1a}$; these voltages are applied to the $SW_2$ resistor network which, with $SW_2$ in position '7', gives an output of 4.7V to the bottom of $RV_2$ and 4.8V to its top. With $RV_2$ set to mid scale, the unit thus gives an output of 4.750V when the controls are set as described.

The *Figure 4.36* circuit can only read voltages to within the nearest millivolt, so the initial calibration reading must be set to 1.018V when using the standard cell. Note, however, that a further decade of readings can be added to the circuit by replacing $RV_2$, etc., with a duplicate of the $SW_2 - RV_2$ related circuitry (i.e. all the circuitry to the right of $SW_1$), but with all component values reduced by a factor of ten. This modification enables the unit to read voltages to within the nearest 0.1mV, and to be initially calibrated to 1.0181V. Note that all resistors must be precision-matched against a single 10k reference resistor.

# 5 Basic meter and multimeter circuits

Three major classes of meter are in general use in the electronics world. The oldest of these is the simple electromechanical 'analogue' type, which draws energy from the signal under test and uses it to move a pointer a proportionate (analogue) amount across a calibrated indicator scale; this class of meter is the main subject matter of the present chapter. The two other classes of meter are the electronic analogue and digital types, which are internally powered and absorb negligible energy from the test signal; these are dealt with in detail in Chapters 6 and 7.

## Moving-coil meter basics

A variety of electromechanical moving-pointer meters have been developed over the years, but the most important one in modern use is the moving-coil type. This draws its energizing current from the signal under test and passes it through a coil of fine copper wire, which is carried on an aluminium bobbin that also carries the meter's pointer and is supported on low-friction bearings. This assembly is mounted within the field of a powerful magnet, as shown in *Figure 5.1*, and the signal currents are fed to each end of the coil via a pair of contra-wound springs that are fitted in such a way that their tensions balance out when the meter's pointer is in the 'zero' position. These signal currents generate a magnetic field around the coil, and this interacts with that of the magnet; the resulting torque forces the coil and pointer to rotate until a position is reached where the torque is countered by the force of the two coil springs. The magnitude of this rotational movement is proportional to that of the coil current,

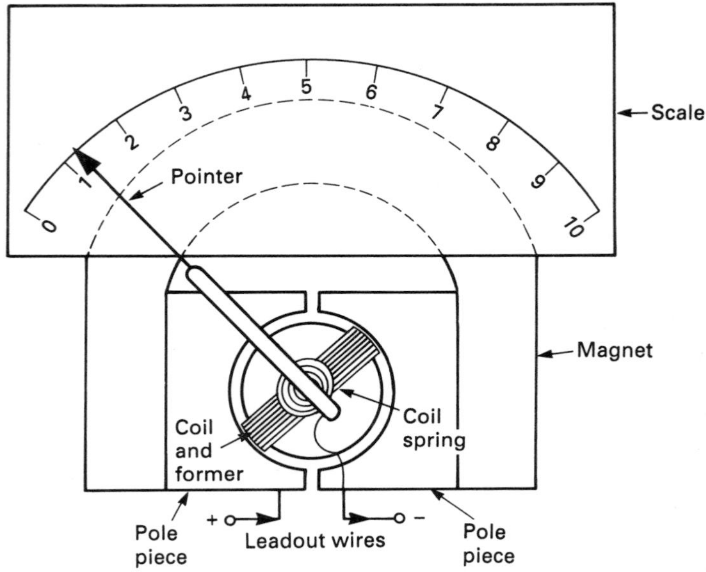


Figure 5.1. *Basic moving-coil meter movement.*

and the meter's scale can thus be directly and linearly calibrated in terms of current.

Most meters have the 'zero' current mark on the left of their scale, as shown in the diagram, but a few (known as 'centre zero' types) have the zero in the centre of the scale, with negative numbers to its left and positive ones to its right. The pointer's 'zero' position is usually trimmable via a screw-headed control on the front of the meter.

All moving-coil meters have their movements or coil units supported on a bearing assembly. If the bearings are of the jewelled type a degree of friction inevitably occurs between the coil pivots and the bearings, and may cause the meter to suffer from a characteristic known as 'stiction', which makes the pointer slow or inaccurate in following current variations, and may even make it jam completely. Some of the more expensive meters have their movements supported on a taut band or rod, which acts rather like a torsion bar and gives friction-free suspension. These 'taut-band suspension' meters do not suffer from stiction problems.

The most important parameter of any moving-coil meter is its **basic** full-scale deflection (F.S.D.) current value, which is usually referred to simply as its 'sensitivity'; most practical meters have a basic sensitivity in the range 50μA to 10mA.

A moving-coil meter is quite a versatile device; it can be made to act as a high-current D.C. meter by wiring a shunt resistor across (in parallel with) its terminals, or as a D.C. voltmeter by wiring a 'multiplier' resistor in series with its terminals, or as an A.C. voltmeter by connecting it into a bridge rectifier that is fed via a suitable multiplier resistor.

Practical moving-coil meters are not guaranteed to have perfect linearity, or to have precisely the indicated value of F.S.D. current sensitivity. Instead, their accuracy is expressed in terms of 'percentage of F.S.D. value' error over the 'effective range' of the instrument. The 'effective range' is defined as 'from 10 to 100 per cent of F.S.D. value' in D.C.-indicating meters, and 'from 25 to 100 per cent of F.S.D. value' in A.C.-indicating meters. Typically, meter accuracies vary from about ±3 per cent of F.S.D. in cheap models, to 2 per cent of F.S.D. in medium-quality ones, to 1 per cent of F.S.D. in high-quality ones. Thus, a medium-quality meter can be expected to be accurate to within ±2 per cent at full-scale, or ±4 per cent at half-scale, or ±20 per cent at $\frac{1}{10}$th-scale, etc.

The meter's coil has a finite resistance, $r$ and this causes a proportionate voltage to be generated or 'lost' across the meter's terminals when it is in use. This loss voltage is typically in the range 50mV to 400mV at F.S.D. *Figure 5.2* lists typical performance details of some popular and readily available 'fixed-value' moving-coil meters.

## Measuring the coil resistance

The most useful moving-coil meter is the multi-range type, which can be made from any meter with an F.S.D. sensitivity of 1mA or less if its coil resistance value ($r$) is known. This value can be measured via the *Figure 5.3* circuit, in which $R_1$ and $RV_1$ have a series value equal to $V_{IN}$ multiplied by $y$, the meter's 'ohms per volt' or $1/I$ sensitivity value, and $R_x$ is either a calibrated variable resistor or a fixed-value precision type roughly equal to the estimated $r$ value. In use, $RV_1$ is first adjusted, with $SW_1$ open, to set

| Meter F.S.D., (indicated) | Coil resistance (typical), OHMS | Volt drop at F.S.D. | Sensitivity, OHMS/volt |
|---|---|---|---|
| 50μA | 2700 – 4300 | 135 – 215mV | 20k/V |
| 50 – 0 – 50μA | 1300 – 3000 | 65 – 150mV | 20k/V |
| 100μA | 1300 – 3750 | 130 – 375mV | 10k/V |
| 100 – 0 – 100μA | 1100 | 110mV | 10k/V |
| 200μA | 750 | 150mV | 5k/V |
| 1mA | 75 – 200 | 75 – 200mV | 1k0/V |
| 100mA | 0.5 – 0.8Ω | 50 – 80mV | N.A. |
| 1A | 0.05 – 0.1Ω | 50 – 100mV | N.A. |
| 5A | 0.01Ω | 50mV | N.A. |
| 10A | 0.005Ω | 50mV | N.A. |
| 5V, 10V, 15V, 100V, 300V at 1k0/V | 75 – 200Ω | 75 – 200mV | 1k0/V |

Figure 5.2. *Typical ranges and performance details of some popular fixed-value moving-coil meters.*

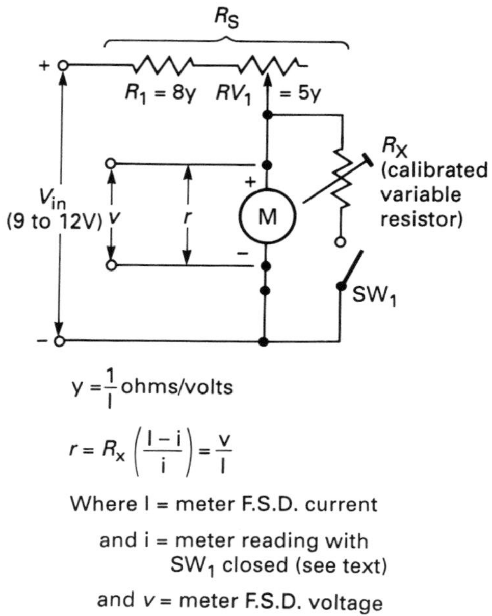


$$y = \frac{1}{I} \text{ ohms/volts}$$

$$r = R_x \left(\frac{I - i}{i}\right) = \frac{v}{I}$$

Where I = meter F.S.D. current

and i = meter reading with $SW_1$ closed (see text)

and $v$ = meter F.S.D. voltage

Figure 5.3. *Circuit for measuring the meter's internal coil resistance,* r.

the meter reading at precisely F.S.D. If a high impedance (at least 1M0) digital voltmeter is available, the $r$ value can then be found by measuring the meter's volt drop, $v$, and calculating $r$ from '$r = v/I$'. Alternatively, if $R_x$ is a calibrated variable type, $r$ can be found by closing $SW_1$ and adjusting $R_x$ to set the meter reading at precisely half-scale value, at which point the $R_x$ value equals $r$. Alternatively, if $R_x$ is a fixed-precision type, simply close $SW_1$, note the change in the meter's current reading, and deduce the $r$ value from

$$r = R_x(I - i)/i$$

where $I$ is the meter's F.S.D. rating, and $i$ is the meter's new reading.

Manufacturers often quote the nominal value of a meter's coil resistance in the instrument's specification sheet, or mark it on the meter's dial; note, however, that these quoted values usually have a precision in the range ±5 to ±15 per cent, and (since the coil is made of copper wire) have a temperature coefficient of +0.4 per cent/°C at temperatures in the region of +20°C. Thus, the resistance of a coil that measures 1000Ω at 20°C rises to about 1040Ω at 30°C, etc.

## Designing D.C. voltmeters

A moving-coil meter can be made to indicate values of D.C. voltages by feeding them to it via a series 'multiplier' resistor, as in *Figure 5.4*, so that the meter current is proportional to the applied voltage. The appropriate multiplier resistance value equals $V/I$, where $V$ is the desired F.S.D. voltage reading and $I$ is the meter's F.S.D. current value. Meter sensitivity is often expressed in terms of 'ohms per volt', where the 'ohms' value equals $1/I$, so a 1mA meter has a sensitivity of 1k0/V and can be used to read 10V F.S.D. by using 10k of multiplier resistance, and a 100μA meter has a sensitivity of 10k/V and can read 10V F.S.D. by using a 100k multiplier, etc. Note, however, that multiplier values include $r$, the meter's coil resistance, and the actual value of external multiplier resistance, $R_m$, needed to give a desired F.S.D. voltage value is thus given by

$$R_m = (V/I) - r.$$

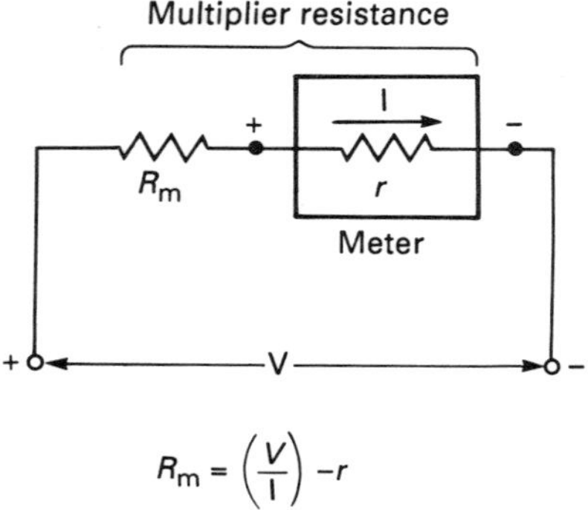


Figure 5.4. *Basic D.C. voltmeter circuit.*

To take two examples in the use of this formula, assume that a 100μA meter has an $r$ value of 2k0 and is to be used to measure (a) 3V and (b) 30V F.S.D. The following results are obtained:

(a) $R_m$ = 30k − 2k0 = 28k.
(b) $R_m$ = 300k − 2k0 = 298k.

Note that the exclusion of $r$ from the calculation would result in a final error of 6.6 per cent in the case of (a), but of only 0.66 per

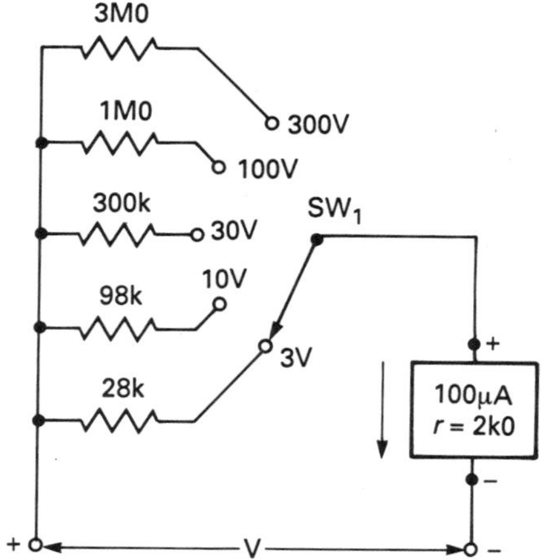


Figure 5.5. *Five-range D.C. voltmeter using individual multiplier resistors.*

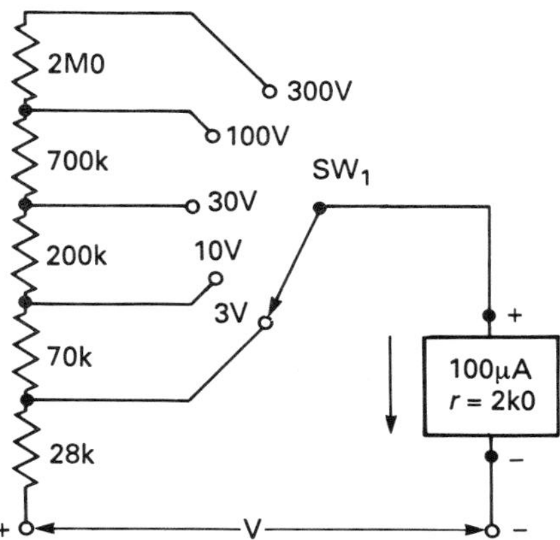


Figure 5.6. *Five-range D.C. voltmeter using series-wired multiplier resistors.*

cent in the case of (b). In practice, $r$ can usually be ignored in cases where $R_m$ is at least 100 times greater than $r$.

*Figures 5.5* and *5.6* show two alternative ways of using the above 100μA meter to give F.S.D. voltage ranges of (a) 3V, (b) 10V, (c) 30V, (d) 100V, and (e) 300V. In each circuit, the total multiplier resistance needed on each range is (a) 30k, (b) 100k, (c) 300k, (d) 1M0, and (e) 3M0. Note in the *Figure 5.5* circuit that the effect of $r$ has to be allowed for on both of the lower ranges, and that if any range resistor develops a short circuit the meter may burn out when it is switched to that range. In the *Figure 5.6* circuit the effect of $r$ needs to be allowed for on the lowest range only, and (except in the case of the lowest range) the meter is unlikely to burn out if any resistor develops a short circuit. The *Figure 5.6* type of circuit is widely used in good-quality multimeters.

## Extending current ranges

The effective current range of a basic meter can be extended by connecting a 'shunt' resistor across the basic meter, as in *Figure 5.7*, so that a known fraction of the total current passes through the shunt and the remainder passes through the meter, which can be calibrated in terms of 'total' current. The relative values of

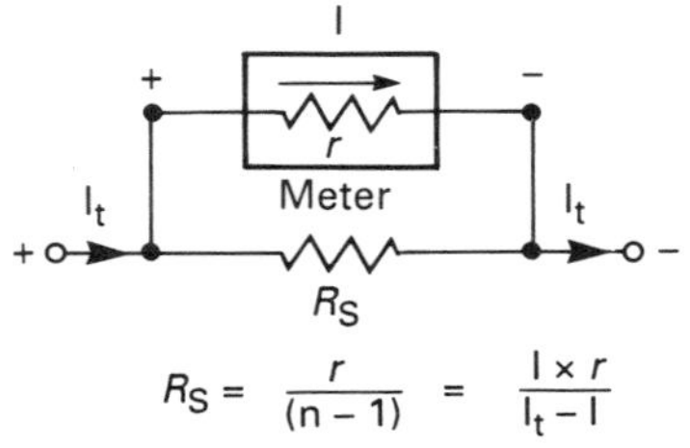


Figure 5.7. *Basic D.C. current meter circuit.*

shunt and meter currents is set by the relative values of the coil and shunt resistances, and the value of shunt resistor, $R_s$, needed to give a particular F.S.D. current reading ($I_t$) is given by

$$R_s = r/(n - 1) \text{ or } (I\ r)/(I_t - I)$$

where $n = I_t/I$, the number of times by which the desired meter range is greater than the basic range. Thus, to convert the 100μA, 2k0 meter to read 100mA F.S.D., $R_s$ needs a value of 2000/(1000 − 1) = 2.0Ω.

In a practical extended- or multiple-range current meter the shunt resistors should be either permanently wired or screwed into place, and should *never* be switched into position using a circuit of the type shown in *Figure 5.8*, because if this switch accidentally goes open-circuit the entire test current will flow through the meter and possible burn it out. If the meter is to be used as a switched multi-range current meter its circuitry must be designed around a so-called 'universal' shunt network.

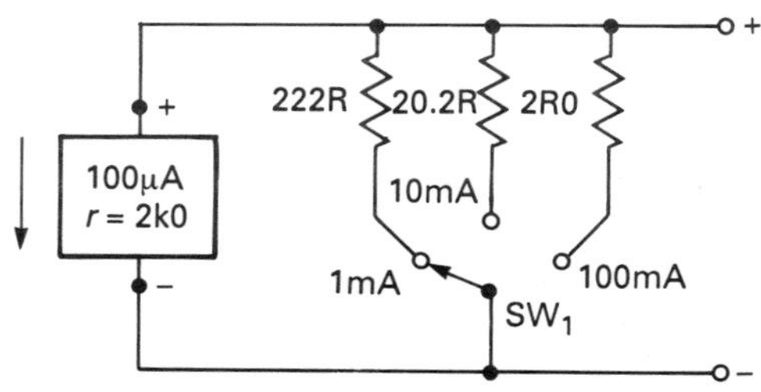


Figure 5.8. *Classic example of how* not *to use shunt switching in a multirange current meter.*

## The universal shunt circuit

*Figure 5.9* shows the practical circuit of a 100μA, 2k0 meter fitted with a universal shunt that gives d.c. current ranges of 1mA, 10mA and 100mA. The three series-connected range resistors are permanently wired across the meter, and range changing is achieved by switching the test current into the appropriate part of the series chain; the meter's accuracy is thus not influenced by variations in $SW_1$'s contact resistances. Note that, since the meter is shunted on all ranges, the lowest effective current range is greater than that of the basic meter.

The procedure for designing a universal shunt follows a logical sequence. The first step is to determine the **total** resistance ($R_t$) of the $R_1-R_2-R_3$ shunt chain, which sets the F.S.D. value of the lowest (1mA) current range, using the formula

$$R_t = r/(n - 1)$$

where $r$ is the meter's coil resistance and $n$ is the current multiplication factor. In the example shown $R_t = 2000/9 = 222.2\Omega$.

The next design step is to find the value of the *highest* current shunt ($R_1$), using the formula:

$$R_s = (r + R_t)/n$$

which in this case gives a value of $2222.2/1000 = 2.22\Omega$ for $R_1$. The same formula is used to find the values of all other shunts, and on the 10mA range gives 22.22Ω, but since this shunt comprises $R_1$ and $R_2$ in series, the $R_2$ value $= 22.2 - 2.2\Omega = 20\Omega$. Similarly, the shunt value for the 1mA range is 222.2Ω, but is made up of $R_1$, $R_2$ and $R_3$ in series, so $R_3$ needs a value of 200Ω. That completes the design procedure.

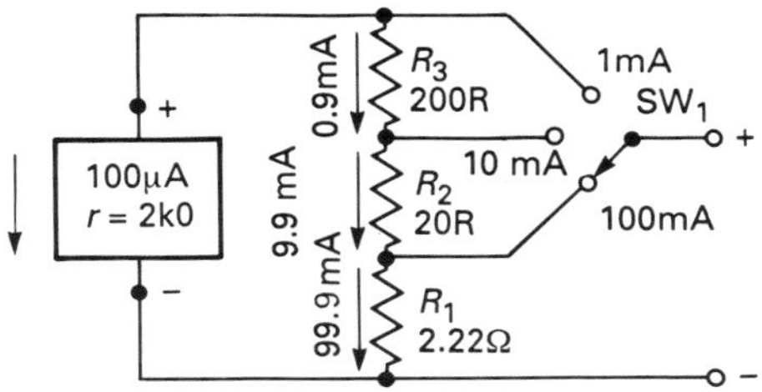


Figure 5.9. *Worked example of a three-range universal shunt circuit.*

Note that, since the total resistance in series with the meter depends on the shunt range setting, the circuit's F.S.D. voltage sensitivity varies between ranges; in the example shown, the F.S.D. sensitivity is 200mV on the 1mA range, 210mV on the 10mA range, and 211mV on the 100mA range. Also note that it is normal practice on commercial instruments to make all current ranges above 1A accessible via screw terminals wired directly into the universal shunt, rather than via a range switch, thus eliminating the need to use switches with very high current ratings.

## The swamp resistor

It has already been noted that the coil resistance ($r$) values of identical models of meter may vary by as much as ±15 per cent when the meters are new (and even more when they are old) and have a temperature coefficient of +0.4 per cent/°C. Thus, if a brand new meter with a ±15 per cent $r$ value is used in the three-range circuit of *Figure 5.9*, its current reading errors could be as high as 15 per cent at +20°C and 19 per cent at +30°C, and readings may vary by up to 30 per cent between individual meters.

An obvious solution to the above problem, which is used in all commercial multimeters, is to wire a 'swamp' resistor in series with the basic meter and trim its value to give a precise $R_{TOTAL}$ ($= r + R_{SWAMP}$) value, which is designed to match into a standard universal shunt network, as shown in the six-range current meter circuit of *Figure 5.10*. If $R_{SWAMP}$ is a carbon film resistor, its temperature coefficient (which has a typical value of −0.25 per cent/°C) will effectively nullify that of the coil; if (for example) $r$ and $R_{SWAMP}$ have similar values at 20°C, their combined temperature coefficient will be only +0.075 per cent/°C, and meter readings will vary by only 0.75 per cent between 20°C and 30°C.

The swamp resistor thus converts the ordinary and troublesome moving-coil meter into a truly useful and semi-precision measuring instrument. Note, however, that the penalty paid for this precision is an increase in the effective F.S.D. voltage value of the meter, i.e., a meter that has a normal F.S.D. sensitivity of 100mV will have one of 200mV if $R_{SWAMP} = r$, etc. To put this into perspective, note that the *Figure 5.9* circuit has an F.S.D. sensitivity of 100mV on its most sensitive (1mA) range but may have shockingly bad precision, while the *Figure 5.10* circuit has an F.S.D. sensitivity

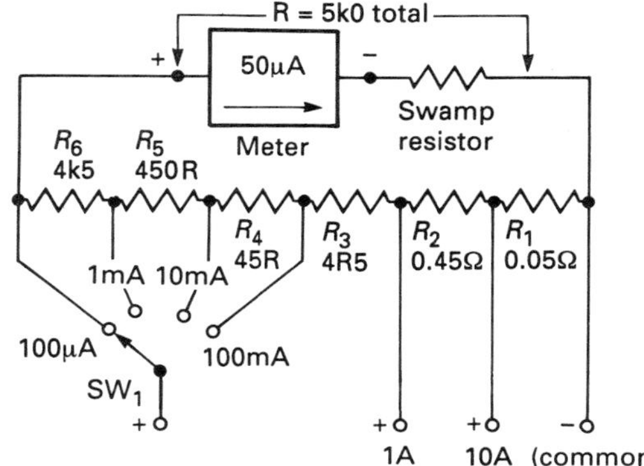


Figure 5.10. *Example of a swamp resistor used in a six-range D.C. current meter.*

of 250mV on its most sensitive (100μA) range but has excellent precision. Note in *Figure 5.10* that the 1A and 10A ranges are selected via screw terminals, and that the F.S.D. sensitivity rises to 500mV on the 10A range.

## A.C. voltmeters

A moving-coil meter inherently reads only mean values of D.C. currents. It can not respond directly to A.C., but can be made to act as an A.C. voltmeter by feeding the voltage to it via a suitable rectifier and voltage multiplier resistor. The rectifier is usually of the full-wave bridge type, in which case the voltmeter is calibrated to read r.m.s. values of a sine-wave input on the assumption that the resulting meter current is 1.11 times greater than the simple D.C. equivalent current; such a voltmeter uses the basic circuit and formulae of *Figure 5.11*. Note that the $R_m$ value is approximately equal to $(V/I) \times 0.9$, but that the precise design formula is complicated by the fact that the forward volt drop of the bridge rectifier ($2V_f$) must be deducted from the effective $V$ value, and that the value of the meter's coil resistance ($r$) and the bridge's forward impedance ($2Z_f$) must be deducted from the simplified $R_m$ value.

In practice, the $V_f$ and $Z_f$ characteristics of diodes are highly non-linear, and an A.C. voltmeter consequently gives a reasonable linear scale reading only if the measured voltage is large relative

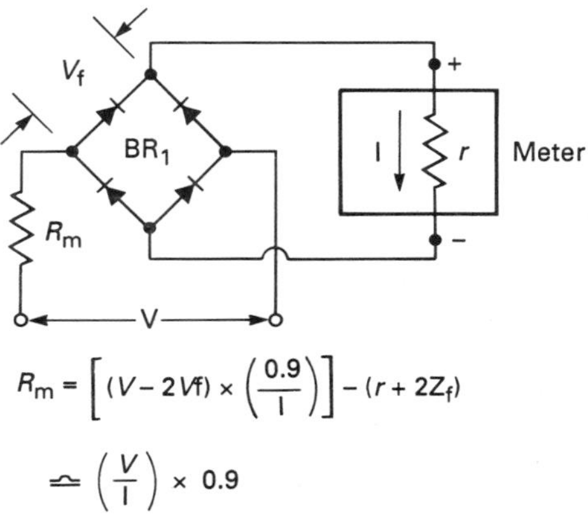


$$R_m = \left[(V - 2V_f) \times \left(\frac{0.9}{I}\right)\right] - (r + 2Z_f)$$

$$\simeq \left(\frac{V}{I}\right) \times 0.9$$

Note: $Z_f$ = impedance of forward-biased diode.

Figure 5.11. *Basic A.C. voltmeter using a bridge rectifier.*

to $V_f$, and the $R_m$ value is large relative to $Z_f$. For this reason, bridge-rectifier types of A.C. voltmeter usually have a maximum useful F.S.D. sensitivity of about 10V.

The bridge rectifier should ideally give a low forward volt drop, so silicon diodes are not really suitable for this application. Old-style (pre-1970) instruments often used a special copper oxide bridge rectifier to meet this ideal, but these suffered from high reverse leakage currents; to overcome this snag, the meters were usually operated at an F.S.D. current of 900μA (to give a high forward/reverse current ratio), and this resulted in the typical circuit of *Figure 5.12*, which has a basic A.C. sensitivity of 1k0/V. By contrast, most modern meters use a bridge rectifier made of either Schottky diodes or germanium diodes that are pre-tested for low reverse-leakage currents, and are able to give a sensitivity of up to 10k/V, as in the case of the circuit of *Figure 5.13*.

A minority of A.C. voltmeter circuits (including the classic old 'Avo Minor' multimeter) use half-wave (rather than full-wave) A.C. rectifier circuits of the type shown in *Figure 5.14*, in which the $V_f$ voltage losses are only half as great as in the bridge type, but in which A.C. sensitivity is unfortunately also halved. *Figure 5.15* shows an example of a multi-range A.C. voltmeter using this technique; here, the meter is shunted (by $R_6$) to give an effective F.S.D. sensitivity of 450μA, enabling the multiplier resistor ($R_1$ to $R_5$) values to be chosen on the basis of 1k0/V.

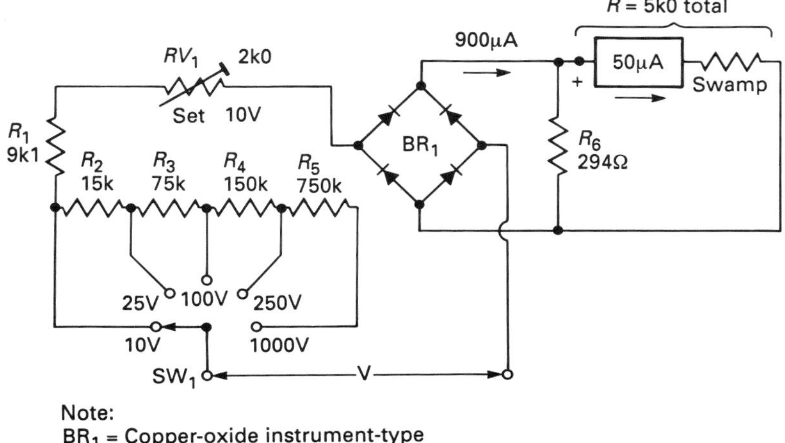


Figure 5.12. *Old-style A.C. voltmeter with a sensitivity of 1k0/V.*

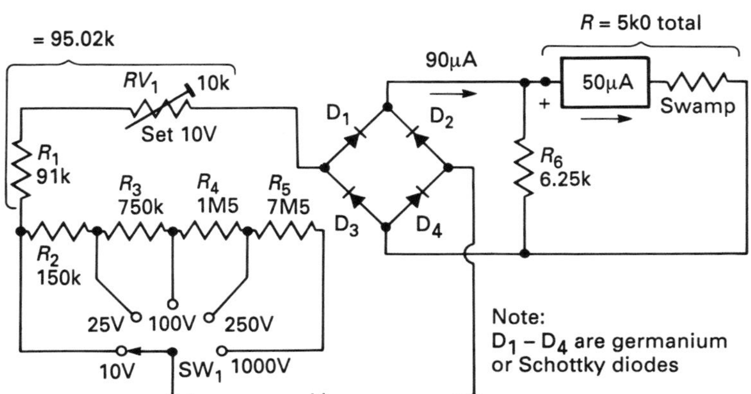


Figure 5.13. *Modern-style A.C. voltmeter with a sensitivity of 10k/V.*

Simple A.C. voltmeters become non-linear when measuring low voltages, so commercial multimeters rarely have F.S.D. A.C. ranges lower than 10V. A few models (including the famous Avo 8) use a step-up autotransformer to boost the input from a 2.5V a.c. range to a higher voltage that is fed to the meter via the rectifier network, thus overcoming the non-linearity problem.

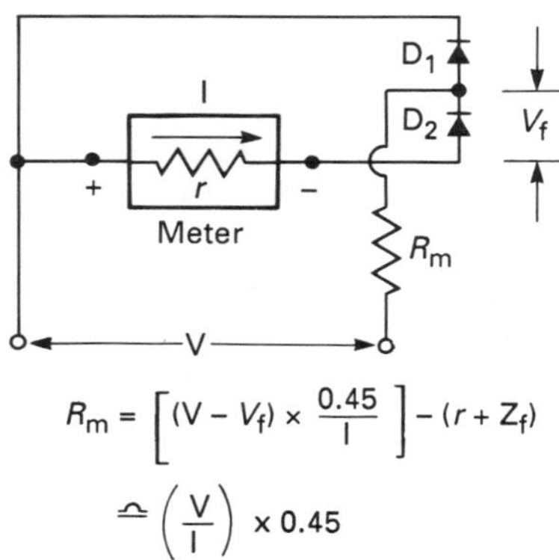


Figure 5.14. *Basic A.C. voltmeter using half-wave rectification.*

A better solution is to use an electronic meter for low-voltage measurements.

When considering the construction of the *Figure 5.11* to *5.15* circuits, note that most resistors have maximum voltage breakdown values of about 200V, so the multiplier resistances on ranges above 100V should be made of several resistors wired in series, to give even voltage distribution. Also note (particularly in *Figure 5.13*) that the multiplier networks are not frequency compensated, and (except on the 10V ranges) are accurate at low frequencies only.

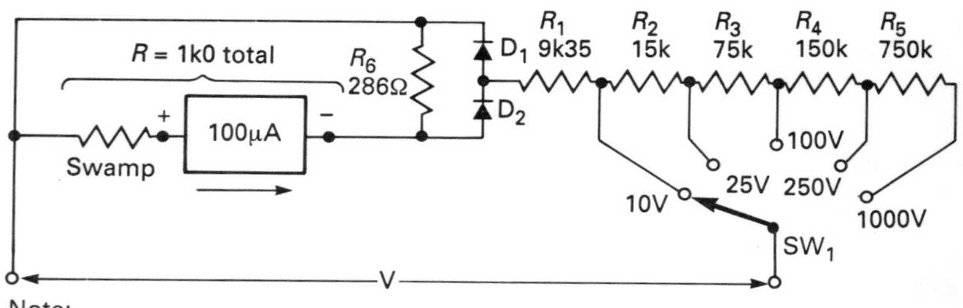


Figure 5.15. *A.C. voltmeter using half-wave rectification; sensitivity = 1k0/V.*

## A.C. current measurement

Alternating current is difficult to measure with a moving-coil meter, and few commercial multimeters have provision for such measurements. One exception is the Avo 8, which has A.C. current ranges of 100mA, 1A, 2.5A, and 10A, and uses an autotransformer to couple the 'transformed' (voltage-boosted and current-divided) A.C. signals to the rectifier and meter network; *Figure 5.16* shows its basic circuit on the 100mA range.

*Figure 5.17* shows an alternative A.C. current meter circuit. Here, the shunt resistor values ($R_1$ to $R_3$) ensure that 500mV is

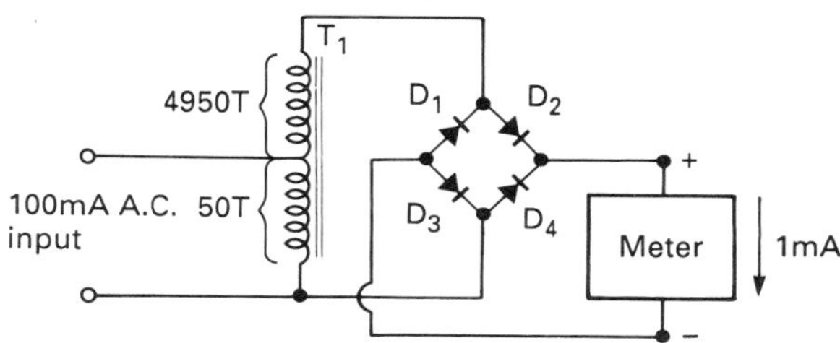


Figure 5.16. *A step-up autotransformer circuit used to give a linear A.C. current reading.*

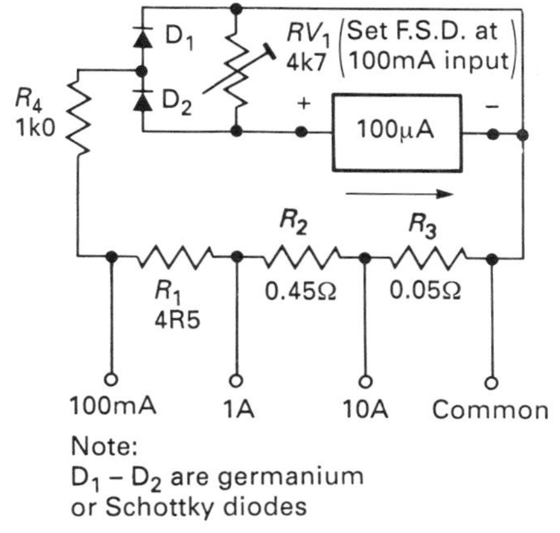


Figure 5.17. *Three-range A.C. current meter using half-wave rectification.*

generated across each set of input terminals at its designated F.S.D. current value, and this voltage is fed to the meter circuitry via $R_4$. The meter circuitry is configured as a half-wave A.C. voltmeter (as in *Figure 5.14*) with an F.S.D. sensitivity of 500mV (set via $RV_1$). Meter readings are not perfectly linear, but are sufficiently so for most practical purposes; if perfect accuracy is important, the scale can be hand calibrated. To initially calibrate this circuit, simple feed an accurate 100mA A.C. current into the '100mA' terminals and trim $RV_1$ for a full-scale reading (the meter has an effective F.S.D. sensitivity of about 180μA under this condition).

## Which rectifier diodes?

A 'perfect' rectifier diode generates zero forward volt drop ($V_f$) and has zero forward impedance ($Z_f$) and infinite reverse impedance ($Z_r$). All practical diodes fall short of these ideals, in varying degrees. Three basic types of diode are presently in use as low-level rectifiers, these being the germanium, silicon, and Schottky types. *Figure 5.18* lists the typical characteristics of some popular examples of these diodes; this data is derived from

| Test current | Germanium diodes (0A91, IN34, etc) | | Silicon diodes (IN914, IN4148, etc) | | Schottky diodes (BAT85, etc) | |
|---|---|---|---|---|---|---|
| $I_f$ | $V_f$ | $Z_f$ | $V_f$ | $Z_f$ | $V_f$ | $Z_f$ |
| 10mA | 1291mV | 63R5 | 797mV | 14R | 310mV | 5R1 |
| 1mA | 424mV | 190R | 633mV | 50R | 232mV | 27R |
| 100μA | 185mV | 655R | 516mV | 450R | 172mV | 255R |
| 10μA | 77mV | 3k35 | 411mV | 4k0 | 114mV | 2k35 |
| 1μA | 20mV | 15k5 | 305mV | 42k | 57mV | 23k5 |
| 0.1μA | 2.2mV | 35k | 201mV | 460k | 17.5mV | 115k |
| $I_r$ | $V_r$ | $Z_r$ | – | – | $V_r$ | $Z_r$ |
| –0.1μA | –1.7mV | 40k | n.a. | n.a. | –53mV | 3M0 |
| –1μA | –49mV | 500k | n.a. | n.a. | > –7V | n.a. |
| –10μA | > –7V | n.a. | n.a. | n.a. | > –7V | n.a. |

Figure 5.18. *Measured* $V_f$ *and* $Z_f$ *characteristics of germanium, silicon, and Schottky 'signal' diodes at various test currents.*

an extensive series of test made in the author's own laboratory, at a measurement temperature of 20°C.

Note from *Figure 5.18* that the germanium diode gives a very inferior performance at test currents much above 1mA, and (since it passes significant current when reverse biased) is almost useless as a rectifier at currents below 1μA; the device is most useful over the 5μA to 2.5mA current range.

The major disadvantages of the silicon diode is its relatively high $V_f$ value, which precludes its use in most simple A.C. voltmeter circuits; its big advantages are its relatively low $Z_f$ and very high $Z_r$ values, which make the device very useful in high-voltage and 'electronic' A.C. voltmeter circuits.

The best of all diodes are the Schottky types, which offer delightfully low values of $V_f$ and $Z_f$, and high value of $Z_r$, and outperform germanium and silicon types in almost all respects; they also offer a superb high-frequency or fast-switching action, which enables them to outperform both other types by factors of tens or hundreds in these respects.

It has already been noted that, because of non-linearity problems, simple A.C. voltmeters have minimum useful F.S.D. sensitivities of about 10V, but, to help emphasize the relative merits of various types of diode, *Figures 5.19* and *5.20* show the

| Input volts | Indicated volts, using the following types of bridge diode | | |
|---|---|---|---|
| | Germanium | Silicon | Schottky |
| 5 | 5.00V | 5.00V | 5.00V |
| 4.5 | 4.45V | 4.37V | 4.47V |
| 4 | 3.92V | 3.79V | 3.95V |
| 3.5 | 3.40V | 3.18V | 3.42V |
| 3 | 2.87V | 2.57V | 2.90V |
| 2.5 | 2.34V | 1.97V | 2.35V |
| 2 | 1.81V | 1.39V | 1.83V |
| 1.5 | 1.30V | 0.84V | 1.30V |
| 1 | 0.79V | 0.35V | 0.80V |
| 0.5 | 0.34V | 0.10V | 0.33V |
| $R_m$ value | 39k9 | 33k9 | 41k1 |

Figure 5.19. *Measured performance of a 5V A.C. voltmeter using a 100μA, 1200Ω meter and various types of bridge rectifier diode.*

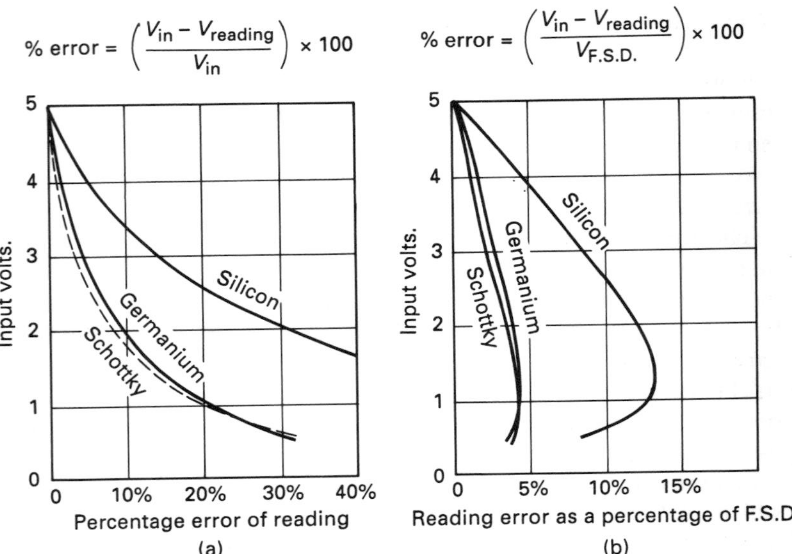


Figure 5.20. *The data of* Figure 5.19 *translated into terms of (a) percentage error of reading and (b) reading error as a percentage of F.S.D.*

results of a series of tests made at 20°C on three voltmeters of the *Figure 5.11* type, each using a 100μA, 1200Ω meter and scaled to read precisely 5V F.S.D., but each using a different type of bridge rectifier diode. *Figure 5.19* presents the results of these tests in tabular form, and *Figure 5.20* translates these into graph form to show each meter's errors in terms of (a) per centage error of reading and (b) reading error as a per centage of F.S.D.

By convention, an analogue A.C. meter's precision is regarded as 'good' if better than 1 per cent of F.S.D. as 'O.K.' at about 2 per cent of F.S.D., and as 'useless' if worse that 3 per cent of F.S.D. If, on this basis, the lowest useful value is accepted as 2.5 per cent of F.S.D., it can be inferred from *Figure 5.20b* that (in the *Figure 5.11* circuit's case) the meter readings become unacceptably non-linear at below 4.5V in the case of silicon diodes, at 3.1V in the case of germanium, and 2.7V in the case of Schottky types.

## The series-type ohmmeter

There are several ways of using a moving-coil meter to read resistance values. The best known of these uses the basic 'series connected' ohmmeter circuit of *Figure 5.21a*, which is used in most commercial analogue multimeters. This battery-powered circuit has a variable shunt wired across the meter and has a range-setting resistor wired in series with the combination. In use, the $X$ terminals are first shorted together, causing a current ($I$) of $V/R_{\text{RANGE}}$ to flow in the meter, and the variable shunt is then trimmed to bring the meter pointer to F.S.D.; since zero ohms are connected across the $X$ terminals under this condition, this is called the 'set zero' operation. The unknown resistor ($R_x$) is then connected 'in series' with $R_1$ by fitting it across the $X$ terminals, and the new current reading ($i$) noted; the value of $R_x$ can then be calculated from

$$R_x = R_{\text{RANGE}}([I/i] - 1)$$

Quite obviously, if $R_x$ has the same value as $R_{\text{RANGE}}$, the $i$ value

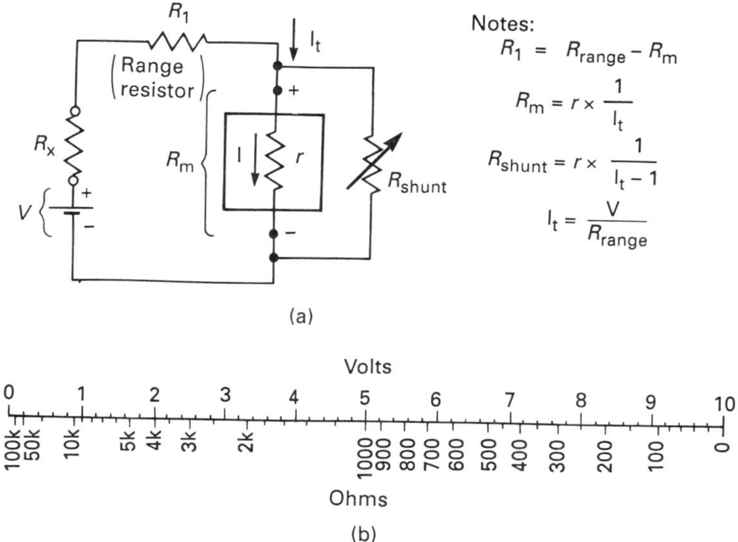


Figure 5.21. *(a) Basic circuit and formulae, and (b) standard calibration scale (compared to a linear voltage scale) of a series-type ohmmeter.*

will equal $I/2$, and the meter will give a centre-scale reading. Consequently, when designing such meters, the $R_{RANGE}$ value is used to set the instrument's centre-scale value.

All meters of the *Figure 5.21* type generate a scale shape of the exact form shown in *Figure 5.21b*, with a zero to the right, with the 'range' value in the dead-centre of the scale, and with '×10 and '×0.1' values at 9 per cent and 91 per cent of F.S.D. respectively. Consequently, this scale can be applied to any series-type ohmmeter, provided that its values are all multiplied by an appropriate amount. For example, the old Avo minor used a centre-scale value of 113Ω, and the Avo 8 uses a centre-scale value of 2000Ω, and many other meters use centre-scale values of 285Ω, but all use the precise scale shape shown in *Figure 5.21b*.

Superficially, the *Figure 5.21a* circuit looks easy to design, but in practice matters are complicated by the facts that the design must allow for large variations in battery voltage and $R_{SHUNT}$ (and thus $R_m$) values, and by the fact that the circuit's mid-scale value is set by the combined values of the fixed $R_1$ and the variable $R_m$. *Figure 5.22* shows how the voltage of a 1.5V zinc carbon cell varies with usage; clearly, an ohmmeter designed for operation from such a cell should have its component values optimized for operation at 1.4V, but should be capable of operating over the range 1.1 to 1.5V.

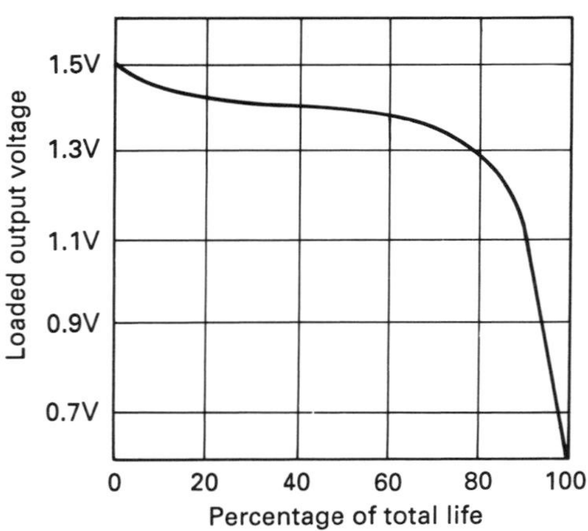


Figure 5.22. *Chart showing how the output voltage of a lightly loaded 1.5V zinc carbon cell varies over its working life.*

To design a circuit of the *Figure 5.21* type, the meter's basic sensitivity and *r* value must first be known and the battery voltage and mid-scale 'range' resistance decided on; the circuit's component values can then be calculated. *Figure 5.23* shows a practical three-range series-type ohmmeter, designed around a 50μA, 3k0 meter; on each range, $SW_{1a}$ selects the range resistor and battery, and $SW_{1b}$ selects the zero-setting $R_{SHUNT}$ resistors; note that the circuit uses a 10.5V supply on the '×100' range, and that all shunts are wired in series across the meter.

*Figure 5.24* lists the full set of calculations made while converting the basic circuit of *Figure 5.21* into the practical design of *Figure 5.23*. Thus, on the '×1' (1k0) range, the design is first optimized for 1.4V operation (using the formulae of *Figure 5.21*); at 1.4V the meter needs an F.S.D. value of 1400μA, so $R_{SHUNT}$ ($= R_s + RV_3$) needs a value of 111.1Ω, and $R_m$ equals 107.1Ω; consequently, $R_1$ ($= R_3$ of *Figure 5.23*) needs a value 893Ω. Once the $R_1$ value has been settled, new sets of calculations must be made for 1.5V, 1.2V, and 1.1V operation, to enable the spread of $R_{SHUNT}$ values and percentage mid-scale errors to be determined, as shown. Thus, $R_{SHUNT}$ must be variable between at least 103 and 143Ω, and the circuit's mid-scale reading is 0.7 per cent low (at 993Ω) at 1.5V and 2.9 per cent high (at 1029Ω) at 1.1V. Similar sets of calculations are made on the '×10' and '×100' ranges; the '×100' range design is optimized for 10V operation.

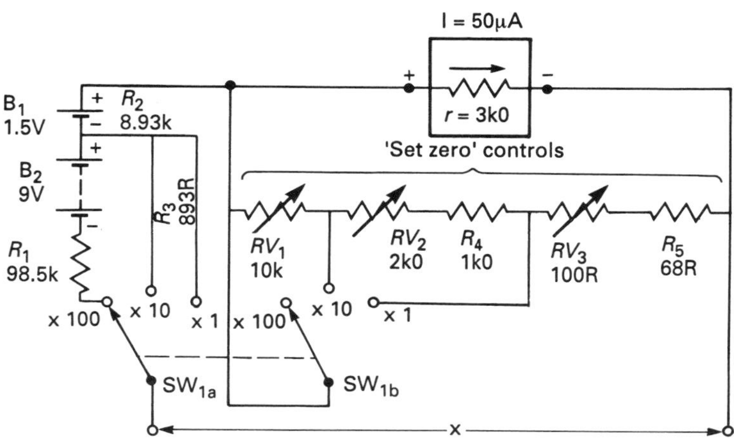


Figure 5.23. *This ohmmeter spans 100R to 1M0 in three ranges.*

| Range | Battery voltage | Mid-scale range value | Meter F.S.D. current | $R_{shunt}$ value | $R_m$ value | Nominal '$R_1$' value | Mid-scale error |
|---|---|---|---|---|---|---|---|
| 'x 1' (1k0) range | 1.5V | 1k0 | 1500μA | 103.5Ω | 100Ω | 900Ω | −0.7% |
| | 1.4V | " | 1400μA | 111.1Ω | 107.1Ω | 893Ω | 0% |
| | 1.2V | : | 1200μA | 130.4Ω | 125Ω | 875Ω | +1.8% |
| | 1.1V | : | 1100μA | 142.8Ω | 136.4Ω | 864Ω | +2.9% |
| 'x 10' (10k) range | 1.5V | 10k | 150μA | 1500Ω | 1000Ω | 9000Ω | −0.7% |
| | 1.4V | " | 140μA | 1667Ω | 1071Ω | 8930Ω | 0% |
| | 1.2V | : | 120μA | 2143Ω | 1250Ω | 8750Ω | +1.8% |
| | 1.1V | : | 110μA | 2500Ω | 1364Ω | 8636Ω | +2.9% |
| 'x 100' (100k) range | 11V | 100k | 110μA | 2500Ω | 1364Ω | 98.64k | −0.14% |
| | 10V | " | 100μA | 3000Ω | 1500Ω | 98.50k | 0% |
| | 9V | " | 90μA | 3750Ω | 1667Ω | 98.33k | +0.17% |
| | 8V | " | 80μA | 5000Ω | 1875Ω | 98.12k | +0.37% |
| | 7V | " | 70μA | 7500Ω | 2143Ω | 97.86k | +0.64% |

Figure 5.24. *Design-calculation chart for the three-range ohmmeter.*

## The parallel-type ohmmeter

Another well-known ohmmeter is the parallel (shunt) type, which can be used to measure low values of resistance. *Figure 5.25* shows the basic circuit; in use, $SW_1$ is first closed and the meter

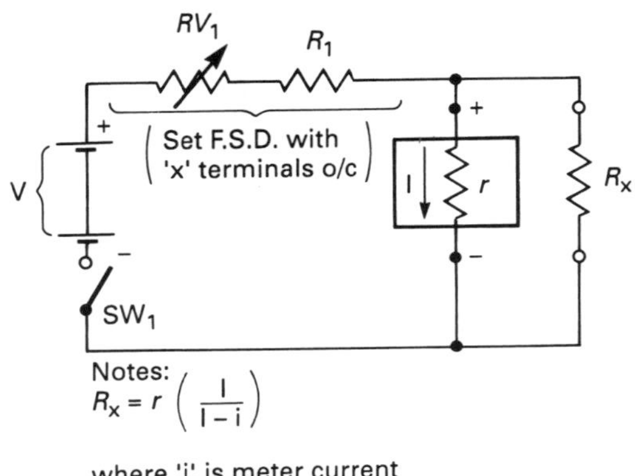


Figure 5.25. *Basic circuit of the parallel-type ohmmeter.*

calibrated by trimming $RV_1$ to set the meter to read F.S.D. *with the X terminals open circuit*, under this condition the meter current equals $I$, and the effective F.S.D. 'resistance' value equals $r$. The unknown resistor ($R_x$) is then connected across the $X$ terminals, so that it shunts the actual meter and reduces its current reading to '$i$'. $R_x$ can then be calculated from

$$R_x = r \times (I/[I - i])$$

Thus, the meter reads half-scale when $R_x = r$. In practice, the effective $r$ value can be varied by wiring a shunt across the meter, and the circuit can be used to measure very low values of resistance. Nowadays this circuit is obsolete, and it is presented here purely as a matter of technical interest.

## Meter overload protection

Moving-coil meters are delicate instruments and can easily be damaged by large overload currents. If the meter is used in conjunction with a swamp resistor, excellent overload protection can be gained by connecting a pair of silicon diodes as shown in *Figure 5.26*. Here, the swamp resistor is split into two parts ($R_1$ and $R_2$), with $R_2$'s value chosen so that 200mV is generated across the diodes at F.S.D.; at overloads in excess of twice the F.S.D. value the diodes start to conduct, and thus limit the meter's overload current; $R_1$'s value is chosen to limit the diode overload currents to no more than a few milliamperes.

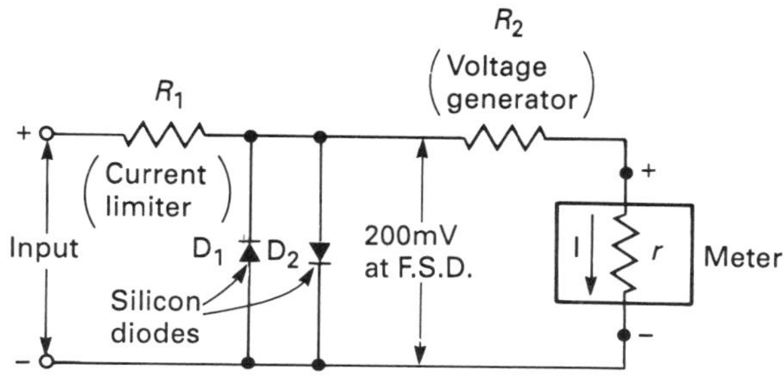


Figure 5.26. *Meter overload protection given via silicon diodes.*

## Multi-function meters

A single moving-coil meter is often built into an item of test gear and used as a multi-function 'volts and current' meter. The designing of such meters is usually quite easy, the basic principle being that all multiplier and shunt resistors are permanently wired into circuit, the meter simply being switched in series or parallel with the appropriate element. Thus, if a common measuring point can be found the switching can be made via a single-pole switch, as in the *Figure 5.27* circuit, which uses one meter to monitor the output voltage and current of a regulated power-supply unit. If a common measuring point cannot be found, the switching must be done via a two-pole multi-way switch, as in the circuit of *Figure 5.28*, which can monitor several independent D.C. voltage and current values.

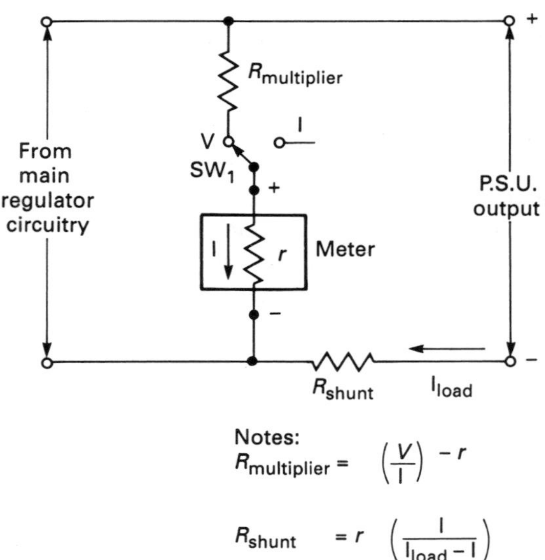


Figure 5.27. *Example of a single meter used to read both* V *and* I *in a P.S.U.*

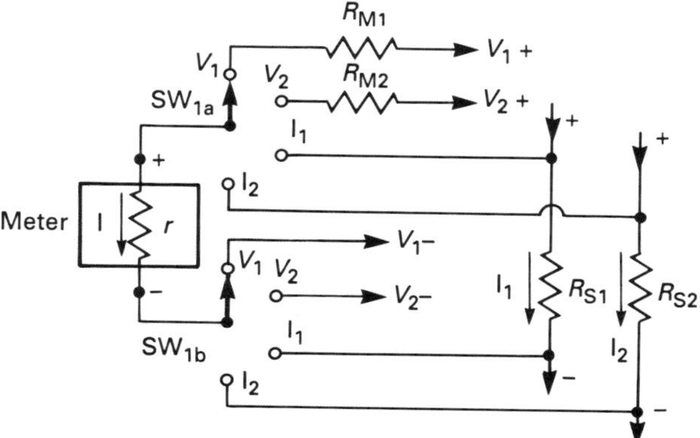


Figure 5.28. *A single meter used to monitor two* V *and two* I *ranges in an instrument.*

## Analogue multimeters (VOMs)

Modern analogue multimeters (called volt–ohm meters, or VOMs, in the USA) have a good selection of ohm and A.C. and D.C. volt and current ranges, and are usually such excellent value for money that it is simply not cost-effective for the amateur to consider building, rather than buying, a multimeter. This situation has obtained for at least twenty years. *Figure 5.29*, for example, shows the circuit of a popular medium-priced British-built eighteen-range instrument of the 1970s, the Avo Multiminor Mark 5. This ancient and obsolescent instrument uses half-wave rectification on its A.C. voltage ranges (as in *Figure 5.15*), and has a basic sensitivity of 1k0/V on the A.C. ranges and 10k/V on its D.C. voltage ranges. Even so, note that it uses a special moving-coil meter which, with a swamp resistor fitted, has an F.S.D. sensitivity of 100mV, and uses a purpose-built two-pole eighteen-way range switch that can handle currents up to 1A and has 1kV of insulation between switch contacts. Also note that it uses a variety of odd-valued precision resistors, and that the 7M5 resistor needs an insulation rating of at least 750V. The amateur has no chance of buying such components at an affordable price.

Modern multimeters are an even greater challenge: they use the latest technology, usually have between eighteen and forty ranges, and typically cost less than half as much as it would cost

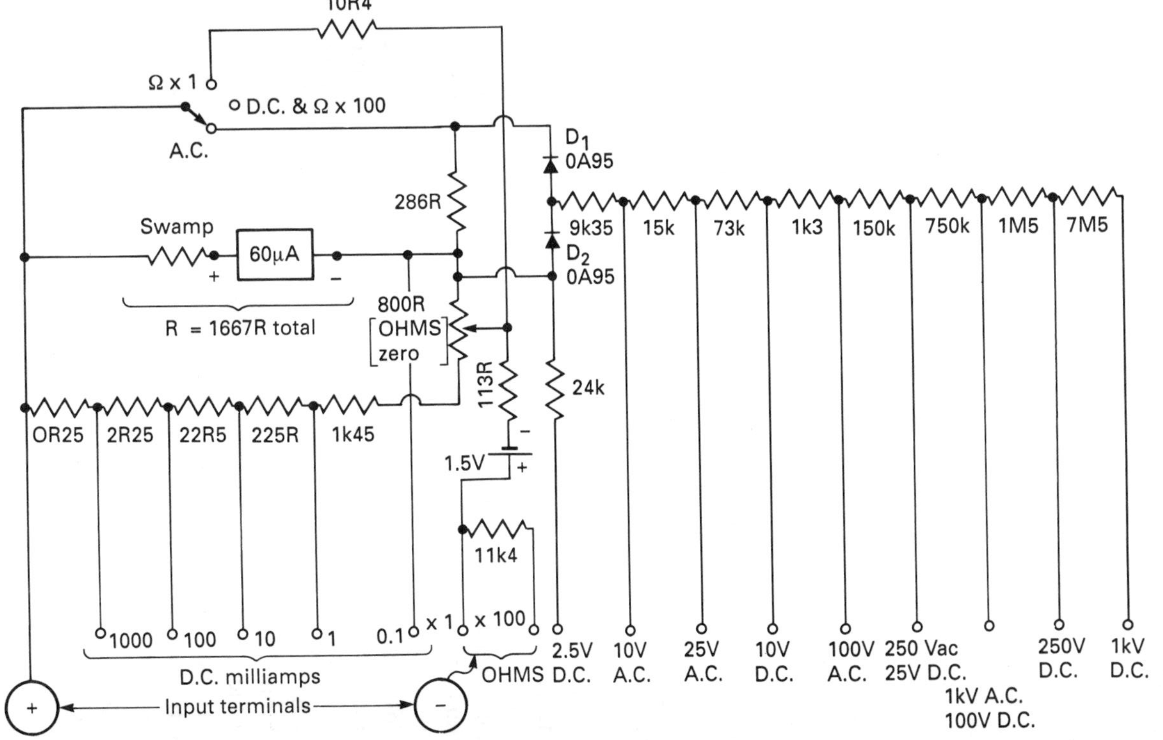


Figure 5.29. *Circuit of the eighteen-range Avo Multiminor Mark 5 of the 1970s era (reproduced by courtesy of Avo Limited, Dover, UK).*

the amateur to make a home-built (and usually ugly and awkward) meter with a similar specification. There are occasions, however, when it is worth while building a multimeter; these are usually when a meter with special ranges is required, or when a use is wanted for a spare meter, or when the need is felt for a challenging or educational construction project. In such cases the 'do-it-yourself' eighteen-range meter of *Figure 5.30* may be considered; it uses a readily-available 50μA meter, which is protected by a couple of silicon diodes, and has a sensitivity of 10k/V on its A.C. voltage ranges and 20k/V on its D.C. voltage ranges.

The reader should have little difficulty in following the circuit of *Figure 5.30*. The multimeter's D.C. current circuitry is derived from *Figure 5.10*, its A.C. voltage section from *Figure 5.13*, and its ohms section from *Figure 5.23*. No attempt has been made to provide the reader with a rigid range-switching diagram, but switching problems have been eased by providing separate terminals for the 1A and 1kV inputs, so range switches need maximum current ratings of only 100mA and contact insulation ratings of 250V.

## Using a multimeter

Analogue multimeters are fragile and easily damaged instruments; when using them, always remember the following basic rules.

(1) Most analogue multimeters are designed to operate with their faces in one specific physical orientation, usually horizontal. If such meters are sloped at an angle or are placed vertically when in use, measurement accuracy may be impaired.

(2) When measuring an unknown voltage or current, always set the meter to its highest range and then work down the ranges until the right one is found.

(3) When measuring an in-circuit voltage, connect the meter across the voltage source, as shown in *Figure 5.31a*. Always remember that the voltmeter's input impedance (the product of its *V* range value and its ohms-per-volt sensitivity) will shunt any resistance that it is connected to and will thus reduce the apparent value of its generated voltage; allow for this 'disturbence' effect when taking measurements.

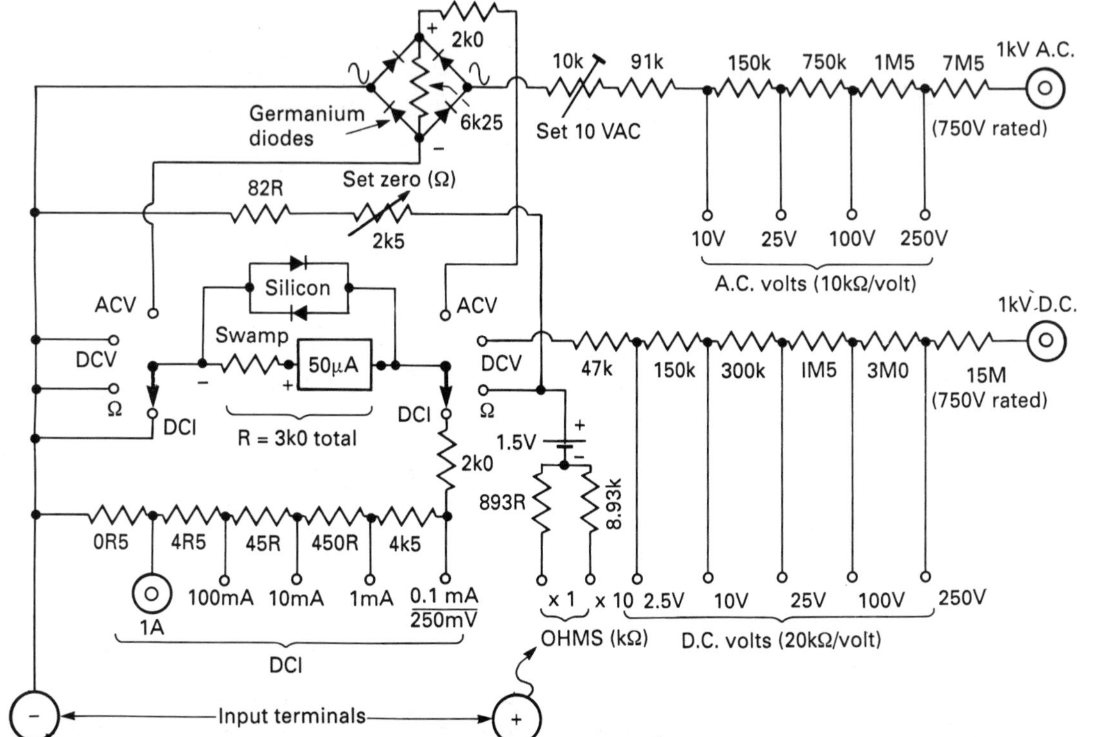


Figure 5.30. *Eighteen-range multimeter suitable for home construction.*

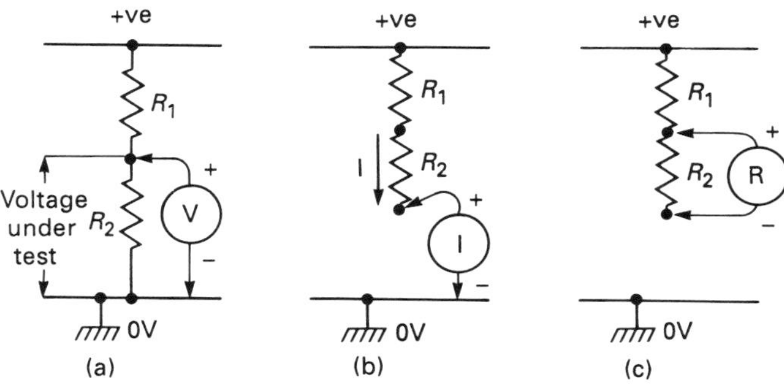


Figure 5.31. *Correct ways to use a multimeter to measure in-circuit (a) voltage, (b) current, and (c) resistance.*

(4) When measuring an in-circuit current, connect the meter in series with the current source, as shown in *Figure 5.31b*. Always remember that the current meter will generate a significant volt drop (usually between 100mV and 500mV at F.S.D.), and that if it is used in low-voltage circuits its presence may have a disturbing effect on the magnitude of the test currents.

(5) When measuring an in-circuit resistance, always isolate the resistance from all other circuitry and then connect the meter across the resistor, as shown in *Figure 5.31c*. Never try to measure the value of a resistance that has a voltage source applied to it. Always remember that the ohmmeter is itself a voltage generator, and that when connected to a semiconductor junction its readings may depend on the polarity of connection; thus, a diode may give a low reading in one direction and a high reading in the other.

## Special types of meter

Simple volt–current–ohm moving-coil meters are the most widely used types of electromechanical analogue meter used in electronics, but they are not the only ones. The following list gives brief details of a few other popular variations and types worthy of mention:

### *dB meters*

In a.c. signal-voltage measurement, the decibel (dB) is used to describe the relative ratios of signal strengths, a value of 1dB representing a ratio of 1.122. Thus, a signal that is 1dB up on a 10V reference has a strength of 10 × 1.122 = 11.22V, and one that is 1dB down on the same reference has a strength of 10/1.122 = 8.91V. The scale of any linear a.c. voltmeter can be scaled in decibels by selecting an arbitrary '0dB' reference voltage and then calculating the appropriate positions for the decibel graduation marks. *Figure 5.32* shows an example of such a scale applied to the 10V range of a meter; in this case 7.94V has been selected as the '0dB' reference value, because it is precisely 2dB down in 10V and thus enables the meter's F.S.D. point to be used as the '+2dB' point. The table lists the positions for the dB graduation points in terms of percentage of F.S.D.

### *Wattmeters*

A true wattmeter makes independent measurements of a load's voltage and current, and gives an output reading that is equal to their product and is independent of variations in load resistance. Such meters are expensive. If power measurements are to be made into a fixed load resistance, however, an inexpensive pseudo-wattmeter can be made by simply using an a.c. voltmeter to monitor the resistor's output voltage, as shown in *Figure 5.33*,

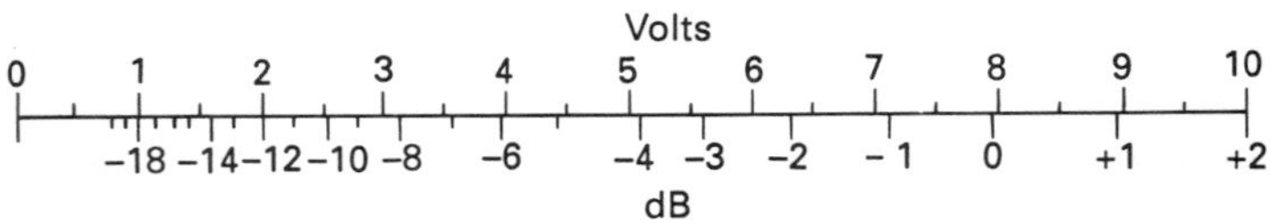


| % F.S.D. | dB | % F.S.D. | dB | % F.S.D. | dB |
|---|---|---|---|---|---|
| 100 | +2 | 50.1 | −4 | 25.1 | −10 |
| 89.1 | +1 | 44.7 | −5 | 20.0 | −12 |
| 79.4 | 0 | 39.8 | −6 | 15.9 | −14 |
| 70.8 | −1 | 35.5 | −7 | 12.6 | −16 |
| 63.1 | −2 | 31.6 | −8 | 10.0 | −18 |
| 56.2 | −3 | 28.2 | −9 | 7.9 | −20 |

Figure 5.32. *A dB volts scale compared with a linear 10V scale, using 7.94V as a '0dB' reference, to give a value of +2dB at F.S.D.*

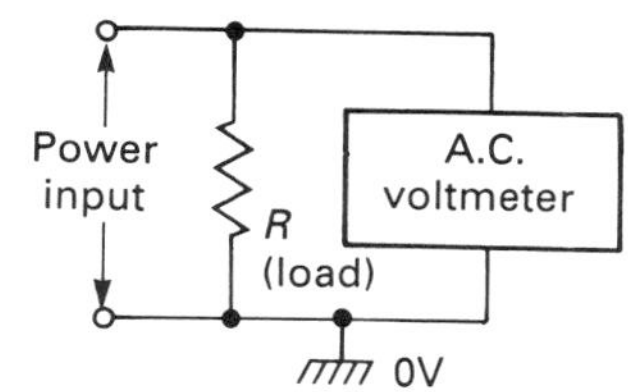


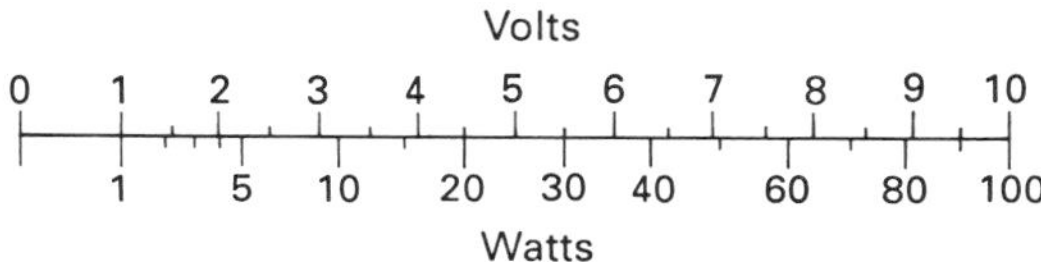


Figure 5.33. *Basic circuit and typical non-linear scale of a simple pseudo-wattmeter.*

and calibrating the meter scale on a basis of $W = (V^2)/R$. Such a meter has a non-linear scale, as shown, since its voltage reading is proportional to the square root of power.

## *Thermocouple meters*

Thermocouple meters are often used as R.F. current or power indicators at frequencies up to hundreds of megahertz, or as wideband a.c./d.c. transfer standards in electrical calibration work. They consist of a thermocouple (a junction of two wires made from dissimilar metals, which generates a cross-junction voltage when heated) that is connected directly to a moving-coil meter, and an externally energized 'heater' that is in thermal contact with the thermocouple. When an external current is fed through this second pair of wires it causes the thermocouple to heat up and generate a proportionate current in the moving-coil meter. This current is proportional to the true r.m.s. input current, and is not influenced by the shape or frequency of the waveform, and such meters can thus be used at frequencies from D.C. to hundreds of megahertz. These meters have a square-law scale. The thermocouples are very fragile and easily burnt out.

## *Moving-iron meters*

These meters are widely used as A.C. or D.C. volt or current meters in low-accuracy applications, etc. They have a fixed coil (through which the measured current flows) and a balanced iron vane that carries a pointer and deflects when the coil is externally energized. Such meters are cheap and robust but have a low sensitivity. They respond equally well to A.C. and D.C.; their scales are non-linear, and are cramped at the low end.

### *Electrostatic meters*

These are usually built to read voltages in the 1kV to 30kV range. In essence, they act as one fixed and one movable set of capacitive vanes; a pointer is fixed to the movable vane, which is deflected electrostatically when an external voltage is applied. Such meters respond to both D.C. and A.C. voltage (they draw zero current from D.C. sources and a frequency-dependent current from A.C. sources). Their meter scales are non-linear, and are cramped at the low end. Such meters were once widely used for high-voltage measurement, but they are now rarely used.

# 6 Electronic analogue meter circuits

The effective performance of a moving-coil meter can be greatly enhanced by combining it with one or more transistors, FETs, or ICs; such circuits can be made to act as sensitive a.c. or d.c. current meters, or as high-impedance volt or millivolt meters, or as linear-scale ohmmeters, etc. This chapter takes an in-depth look at a variety of electronic analogue meter circuits of these basic types. A variety of other types of analogue meter, including ones that read capacitance or give a 'dot-graph' or 'bar-graph' type of readout on a line of LEDS, etc., are described in Chapter 11.

## FET voltmeters

A true voltmeter consumes zero input current and has an infinite input impedance. A reasonable approximation to this ideal can be obtained by driving a simple moving-coil voltmeter via a FET voltage-following buffer stage, as shown in the basic circuit of *Figure 6.1*. Here, $Q_1$ is an enhancement-mode JFET and generates a positive source voltage when the input voltage is zero; the moving-coil meter is set to read 0.5V F.S.D. and is wired between the source and an offset compensation voltage point which equals the zero-input source voltage; the meter thus reads zero when the input voltage is zero, and reads F.S.D. with an input of +0.5V. Note that the JFET's source resistor ($R_2$) is taken to a negative supply voltage to enhance circuit linearity, and that a 10M resistor is connected across the JFET's input to prevent the build-up of static charges when the input is open circuit.

*Figures 6.2* and *6.3* show practical three-range versions of the above circuit, designed to give F.S.D. voltage ranges of 0.5V,

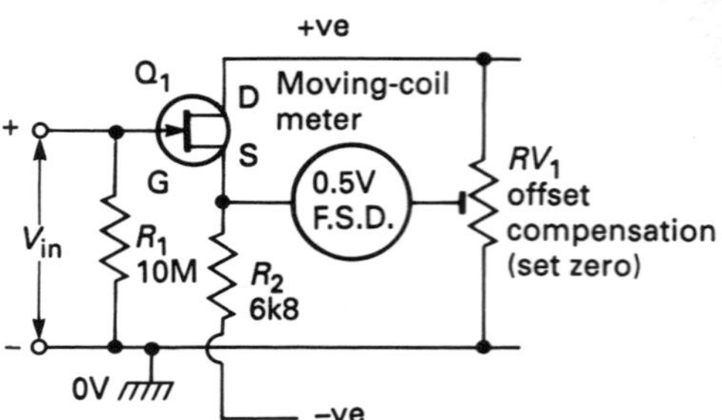


Figure 6.1. *Basic FET voltmeter circuit.*

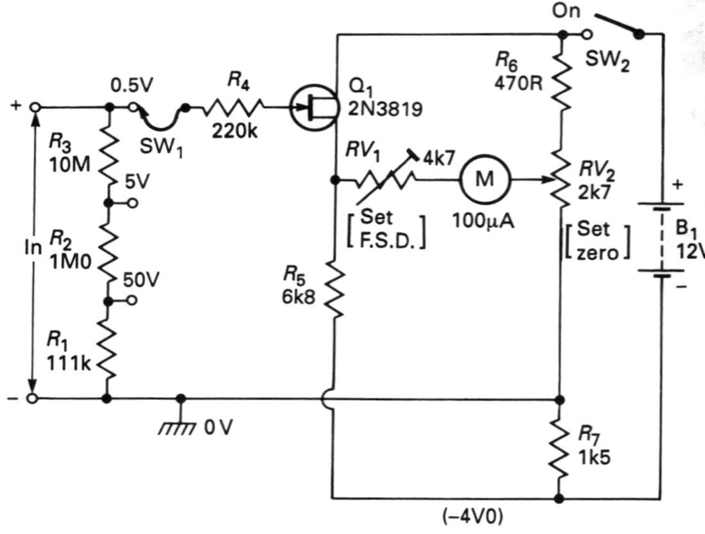


Figure 6.2. *Simple three-range FET voltmeter.*

5V and 50V; each circuit is protected from input overload damage via $R_4$. In each case, $RV_1$ is used to set the meter's basic F.S.D. sensitivity on the 0.5V range, and $RV_2$ is used as the meter's **set zero** control.

The *Figure 6.2* circuit is similar to that already described, but uses the simple $R_6$–$RV_2$–$R_7$ potential divider to give offset (**set zero**) compensation and to generate a −4V rail from the single

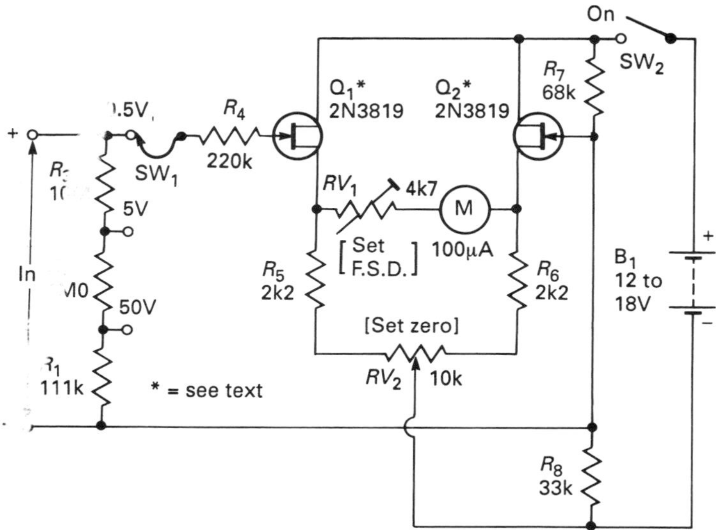


Figure 6.3. *Low-drift three-range FET voltmeter.*

supply battery; this circuit is consequently prone to zero-point drift with changes in temperature and supply voltage and needs frequent set-zero control re-trimming; drift can be greatly reduced by using a regulated 12V supply.

*Figure 6.3* is a low-drift version of the circuit. Here, $Q_1$ and $Q_2$ are wired as a voltage-following differential amplifier in which any drift occurring on one side of the circuit is automatically countered by a similar drift on the other side, thus giving good overall stability. Note that $Q_1$ and $Q_2$ must be selected JFETs, with their $I_{dss}$ values matched to within 10 per cent. The circuit can be used with any supply in the 12 to 18V range.

## Basic op-amp D.C. meter circuits

The best way to make a precision electronic analogue d.c. meter is to wire the moving-coil meter into the feedback loop of a modified op-amp d.c. voltage follower (unity-gain non-inverting amplifier), as shown in the basic circuit of *Figure 6.4*. Note here that $V_{out} = V_{in}$, that $R_x$ represents the series value of $R_3$ and the

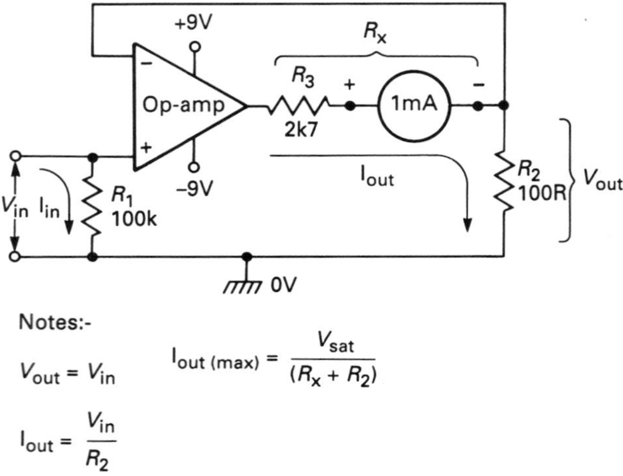


Notes:-

$V_{out} = V_{in}$

$$I_{out\,(max)} = \frac{V_{sat}}{(R_x + R_2)}$$

$$I_{out} = \frac{V_{in}}{R_2}$$

Figure 6.4. *Basic d.c. current meter circuit has an F.S.D. input sensitivity of 1µA at 100mV.*

meter's internal resistance, and that $I_{out} = V_{in}/R_2$ and is independent of the $R_x$ value (provided that the sum of the $R_x$ and $R_2$ volt drops is less than the op-amp's positive saturation voltage. Thus, when $R_2$ has the 100R value shown the 1mA meter reads F.S.D. at an input of 100mV, and (since a current of only 1µA flows in the 100k input resistor $R_1$ under this condition) the overall circuit has an F.S.D. input sensitivity of 1µA at 100mV. Also note that $R_3$ (together with the series resistances of $R_2$ and the meter's coil) limits the maximum output current to less than 3mA when the op-amp output is saturated, and thus provides the meter with automatic overload protection by limiting its maximum current to less than treble its F.S.D. value.

The basic *Figure 6.4* circuit can, by suitable choice of the $R_2$ and $R_3$ values, be used to raise the effective sensitivity of any 50µA to 2.5mA moving-coil meter to 1µA at 100mV, irrespective of the meter's internal resistance value, and gives that meter automatic overload protection. In practice, the op-amp must be a FET type, so that its input impedance does not significantly shunt $R_1$, and must be provided with facilities such as input-overload protection, set-zero control, and stability enhancement. *Figure 6.5* shows a practical version of such a circuit.

The *Figure 6.5* circuit uses a 3140 MOSFET op-amp, and has

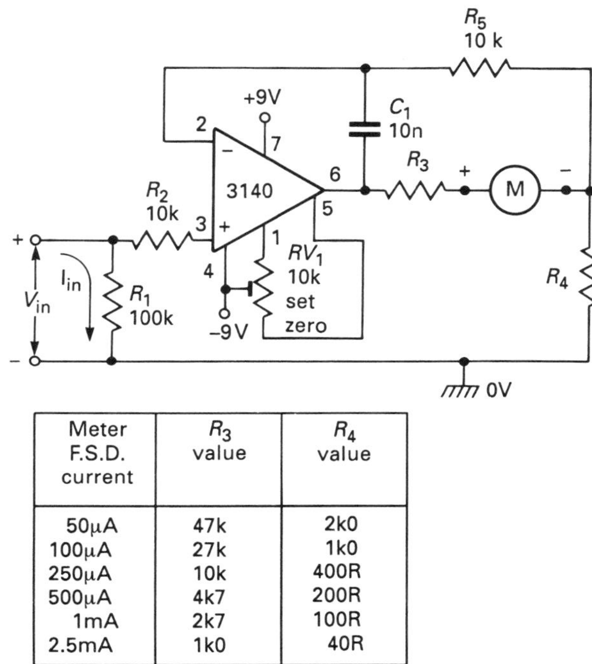


| Meter F.S.D. current | $R_3$ value | $R_4$ value |
|---|---|---|
| 50µA | 47k | 2k0 |
| 100µA | 27k | 1k0 |
| 250µA | 10k | 400R |
| 500µA | 4k7 | 200R |
| 1mA | 2k7 | 100R |
| 2.5mA | 1k0 | 40R |

Figure 6.5. *This circuit gives any of the listed current meters an effective F.S.D. input sensitivity of 1µA at 100mV.*

input overload protection provided via $R_2$ and set-zero offset nulling provided via $RV_1$ (which should ideally be a multi-turn potentiometer). The 3140 (like most wideband op-amps) tends to be unstable when used in the voltage follower mode, so $C_1$–$R_5$ are used to enhance its operating stability. The table shows suitable $R_3$ and $R_4$ values for use with meters having standard sensitivities in the 50µA to 2.5mA range. The circuit consumes about 2.6mA from a ±9V supply when its output is set to zero.

*Figure 6.6* shows how the above circuit (a 1mA version is shown here) can be used as a single-range d.c. volt or current meter. $R_1$'s value is zero in the 'current meter' mode, and $R_2$ is used as a shunt that generates 100mV at the desired F.S.D. current value; in the 'voltmeter' mode $R_1$ and $R_2$ are used as a potential divider that gives a 100mV output at the desired F.S.D. input voltage value.

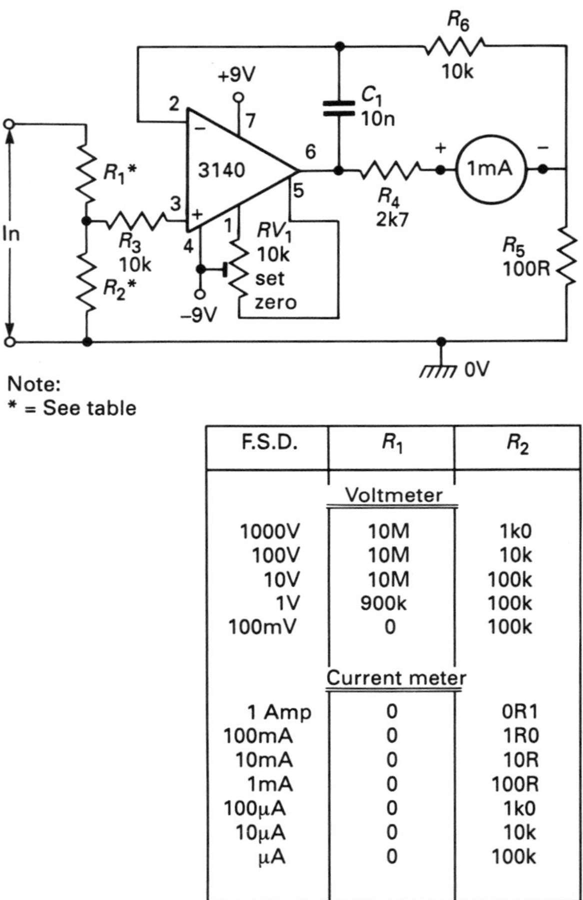


| F.S.D. | $R_1$ | $R_2$ |
|---|---|---|
| | Voltmeter | |
| 1000V | 10M | 1k0 |
| 100V | 10M | 10k |
| 10V | 10M | 100k |
| 1V | 900k | 100k |
| 100mV | 0 | 100k |
| | Current meter | |
| 1 Amp | 0 | 0R1 |
| 100mA | 0 | 1R0 |
| 10mA | 0 | 10R |
| 1mA | 0 | 100R |
| 100μA | 0 | 1k0 |
| 10μA | 0 | 10k |
| μA | 0 | 100k |

Figure 6.6. *A fixed-range d.c. volt or current meter.*

## Multi-range D.C. meter circuits

*Figure 6.7* shows the *Figure 6.6* circuit modified to act as a 12-range d.c. voltmeter that spans 100mV to 500V. $SW_1$ provides four ranges of decade switching (×1, ×10, ×100 and ×1000), and $SW_2$ provides three alternative values of range multiplication (×1, ×2.5 or ×5) by setting the circuit's basic F.S.D. sensitivity to either 100mV (= ×1), 250mV (= ×2.5) or 500mV (= ×5).

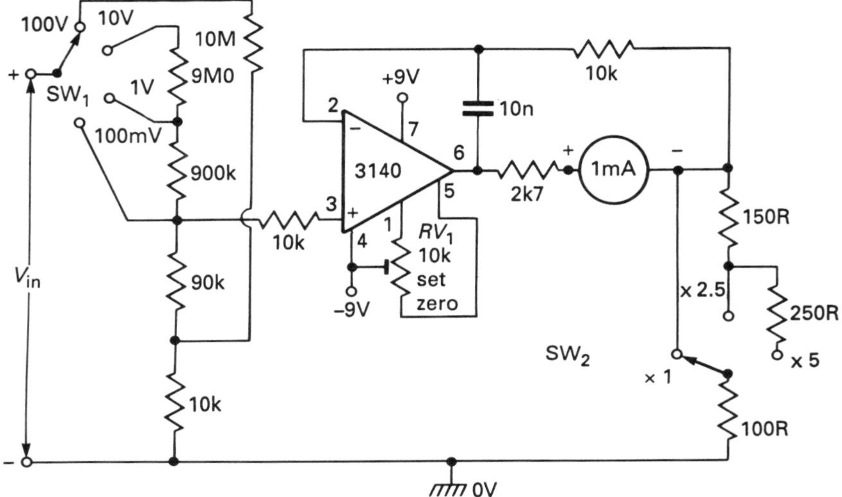


Figure 6.7. *This 12-range d.c. voltmeter spans 100mV to 500V F.S.D.*

The $SW_1$ ranging is achieved by switching the input voltage to various points on the decade attenuator network, which keeps the op-amp's input permanently grounded via 110k of fixed resistance.

*Figure 6.8* shows a multi-range d.c. voltmeter with an input impedance of 10MΩ on all ranges. Here, the input voltage is permanently connected to the top of the decade attenuator chain, and ranging is achieved by switching the op-amp's input to various tapping points on the attenuator via $SW_1$ (which must be a make-before-break switch). Note that the op-amp's input is grounded by 10MΩ of resistance when $SW_1$ is set to the '100mV' position, and that under this condition the circuit is highly susceptible to HF instability and to the disturbing effects of leakage resistance between its pin-3 input terminal and the adjacent pin-4 negative supply rail terminal; a mere 10 000MΩ of resistance between these points will give the meter a negative offset of 9mV (= 9 per cent of F.S.D.).

The above circuit's HF instability problem is overcome by wiring the $C_1 - R_1$ network between the op-amp's pin-3 and ground, to restrict the circuit's frequency response. The leakage resistance problem is overcome by careful design and construction of the

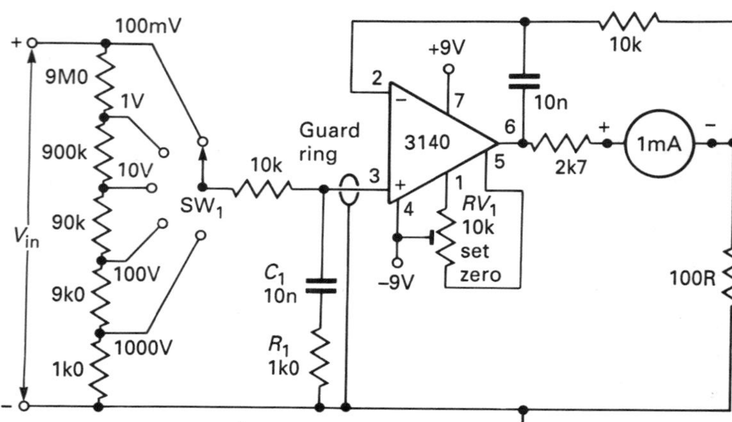


Figure 6.8. *Five-range d.c. voltmeter with 10MΩ input impedance.*

circuit's printed circuit board (PCB), in which the PCB area surrounding pin-3 of the op-amp is given a grounded 'guard ring', as shown in *Figure 6.9.*

*Figure 6.10* shows how the basic *Figure 6.6* circuit can be modified for use as a d.c. current meter that spans 1μA to 1A in seven decade ranges. Note that this circuit can be made to span 1μA to 5A in twenty-one ranges by modifying its output to give

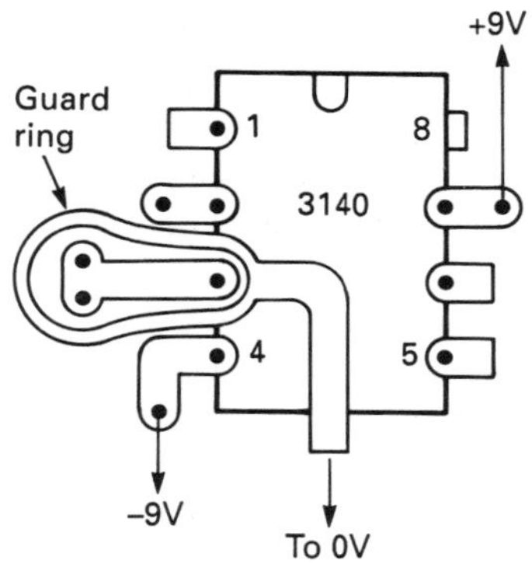


Figure 6.9. *Guard ring etched on a PCB, viewed through the top of the board.*

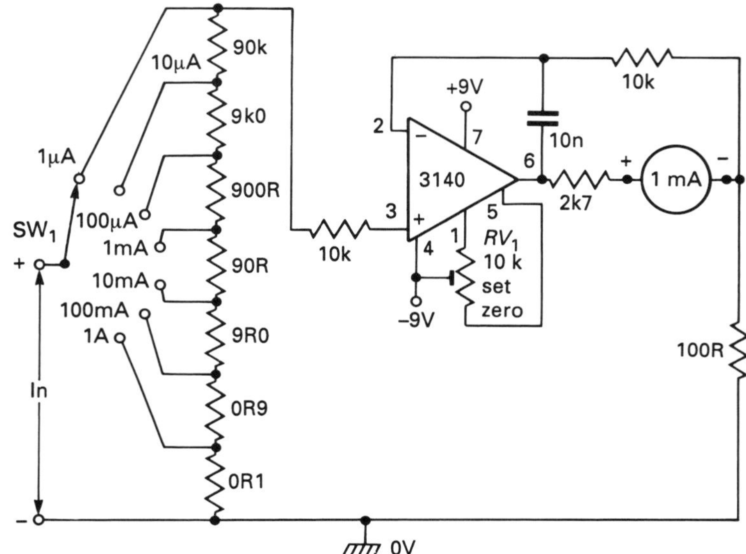


Figure 6.10. *Seven-range d.c. current meter with 100mV F.S.D. sensitivity.*

×1, ×2.5 and ×5 range multiplication, as in the *Figure 6.7* circuit.

Finally, *Figure 6.11* shows how the circuits of *Figures 6.8* and *6.10* can be combined to make a d.c. meter that spans 1µA to 5A and 100mV to 500V in thirty ranges. Note that the 'decade multiple of 9' resistors used here (and in some other circuits) can be made by either wiring two '18R' types in parallel or by wiring a '6R8' and a '2R2' type in series, e.g. a 9k0 resistor can be made from two 18k types in parallel or from a 6k8 and a 2k2 value in series.

## D.C. millivoltmeter circuits

The basic *Figure 6.5* 'd.c. meter' circuit is a unity-gain non-inverting amplifier with an F.S.D. sensitivity of 100mV. *Figure 6.12* shows how the circuit can be modified to act as a d.c. millivoltmeter with a maximum F.S.D. sensitivity of 1mV by

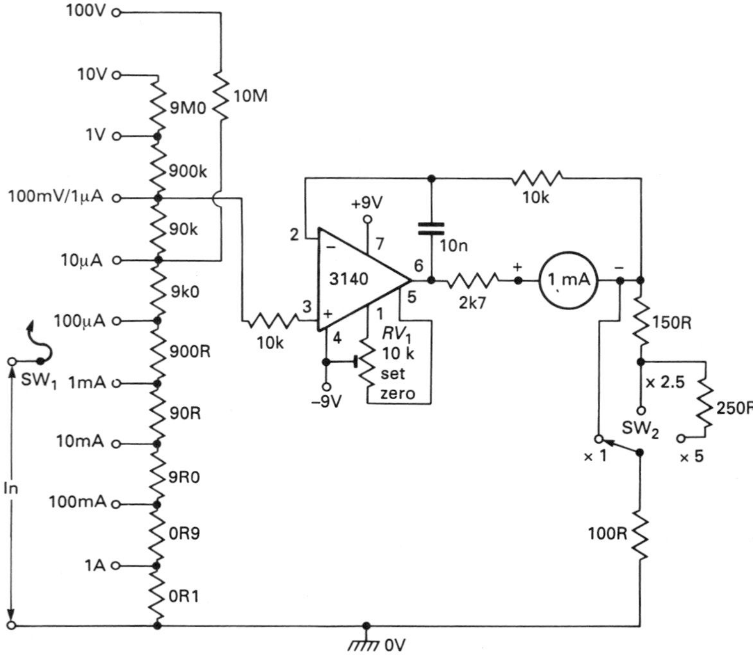


Figure 6.11. *Thirty-range (1μA to 5A and 100mV to 500V) d.c. volt/current meter.*

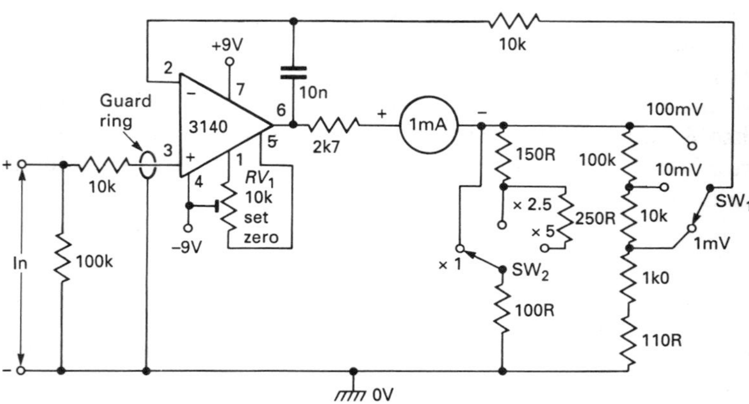


Figure 6.12. *Nine-range (1mV to 500mV) d.c. millivoltmeter.*

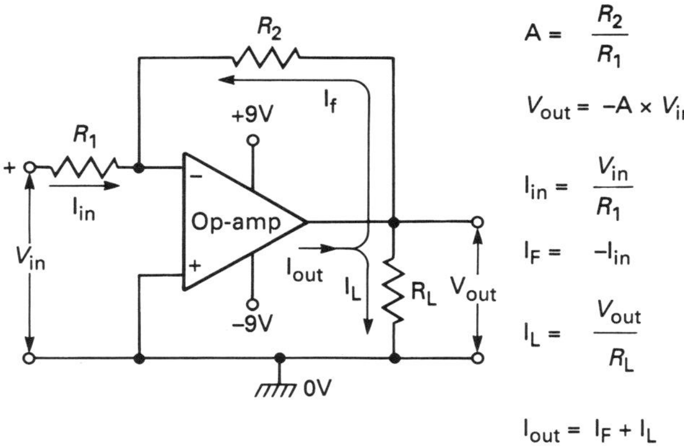


Figure 6.13. *Basic inverting d.c. amplifier circuit.*

making the circuit's gain variable between unity (at 100mV F.S.D.) and ×100 (at 1mV F.S.D.) via $SW_1$. Note that the sensitivity is so high on the 1mV range (it reads F.S.D. with an input current of only 10nA) that the use of a PCB guard ring and a multi-turn **set zero** ($RV_1$) control is mandatory; even so, the circuit's balance is prone to drift on this 1mV range and needs frequent re-trimming.

An alternative way of making a d.c. millivoltmeter is via the basic op-amp inverting d.c. amplifier circuit of *Figure 6.13*, which gives a voltage gain ($A$) equal to the $R_2/R_1$ ratio and generates an output voltage ($V_{out}$) of $-A \times V_{in}$. Note that the op-amp's output current is equal to the sum of the currents flowing in $R_2$ (= $I_F$) and $R_L$ (= $I_1$), and that if $R_2$ is at least 100 times greater than $R_L$ the $I_{out}$ value will, for most practical purposes, equal $I_L$. In this latter case the circuit can be used as a d.c. millivoltmeter by connecting it as shown in *Figure 6.14*.

In *Figure 6.14* the 1mA meter is wired in series with the op-amp output and made to read F.S.D. at an output of 100mV via $R_4$, and is given overload protection via $R_3$; the circuit can thus be given an overall F.S.D. sensitivity of 1mV, 10mV or 100mV, etc., by choosing the $R_2/R_1$ values to give a voltage gain of ×100, ×10 or ×1, etc., as shown in the table.

Alternatively, *Figure 6.15* shows how the basic inverting amplifier can be used as a converter that enables any 1V F.S.D.

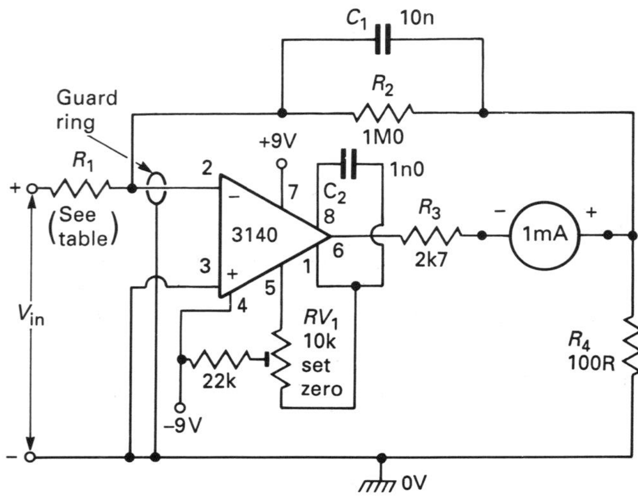


| $V_{F.S.D.}$ | $R_1$ |
|---|---|
| 1V | 10M |
| 100mV | 1M0 |
| 10mV | 100k |
| 1mV | 10k |

Figure 6.14. *Practical d.c. millivoltmeter circuit.*

meter with a sensitivity of 1mA or better to read values in the range 1mV to 10V F.S.D., at a basic sensitivity of 1M0 per volt. The voltage range is set by $R_1$, as shown in the table. Note that this circuit's accuracy is not influenced by the relative impedances of $R_2$ and the meter.

When the *Figures 6.14* and *6.15* circuits are used on the 1mV range they are highly sensitive to the effects of op-amp noise, leakage impedances, and thermoelectric action in the input circuitry. To help overcome these problems, each circuit must be provided with an input guard ring, must have its bandwidth reduced via $C_1$ and $C_2$, and must have its **set zero** control enhanced by the addition of a 22k resistor between the $RV_1$, slider and pin-4 of the op-amp, as shown.

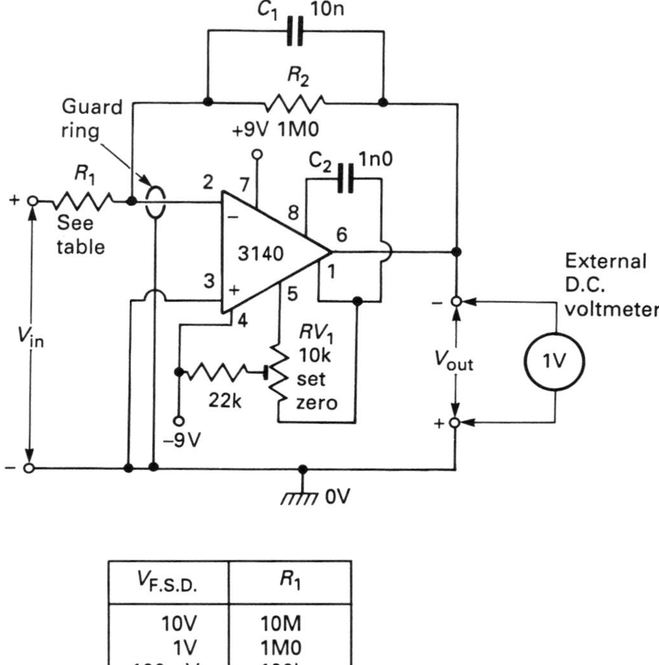


| $V_{F.S.D.}$ | $R_1$ |
|---|---|
| 10V | 10M |
| 1V | 1M0 |
| 100mV | 100k |
| 10mV | 10k |
| 1mV | 1k0 |

Figure 6.15. *Volt/millivolt d.c. voltmeter converter.*

## A.C. voltmeter basics

A moving-coil meter inherently reads mean values of D.C. current, but can be persuaded to respond to A.C. voltages by feeding them to the meter via a suitable rectifier network and voltage multiplier resistor. The most popular circuit of this type is the well-known bridge-rectifier one of *Figure 6.16a*, which has already been described in Chapter 5. One major attraction of this circuit is that (unlike many half-wave types of rectifier) it presents the same input impedance on both the positive and negative halves of the input signal; it thus does not cause unbalanced loading of the voltage source, and can be a.c.-coupled to the source.

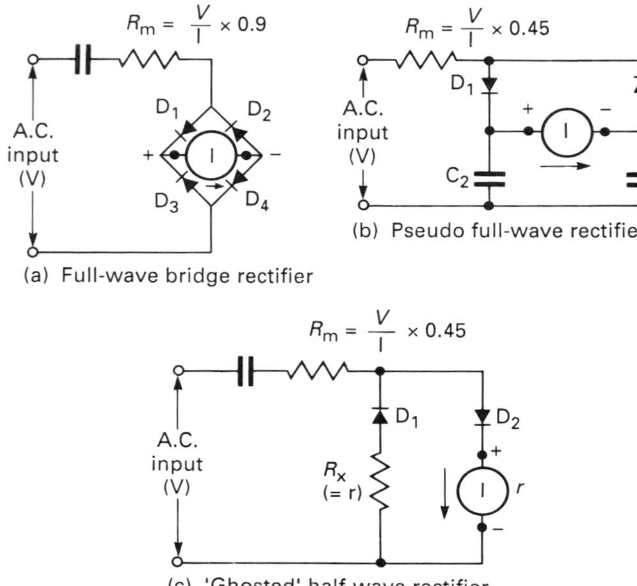


Figure 6.16. *These meter-driving rectifier circuits each have a symmetrical input impedance.*

Diode rectifiers are very non-linear devices, and cause simple rectifier-type A.C. voltmeters to have a highly non-linear scale response to low-value (less than a few volts) inputs. This problem is particularly acute with the *Figure 6.16a* bridge circuit, since two diodes are in series with the meter on each half-cycle ($D_1-D_4$ on positive half-cycles, $D_2-D_3$ on negative ones). *Figures 6.16b* and *6.16c* show alternative meter-driving rectifier circuits which have symmetrical input impedances but have only one active diode in series with the meter and thus have improved linearity.

The *Figure 6.16b* design is a widely used one that gives a pseudo full-wave rectifier action; on positive half-cycles current flows via $Rm-D_1$, and then divides, part flowing via $C_2$ and part flowing via the meter and $C_1$; on negative half-cycles the current flows via $D_2-R_m$, partly via $C_1$ and partly via $C_2$ and the meter; the circuit's conversion efficiency equals that of a half-wave rectifier, as indicated by its $R_m$ formula.

The *Figure 6.16c* circuit gives unashamed half-wave rectifier action, with current flowing through the meter via $R_m$ and $D_2$ on positive half-cycles only; on negative ones the current flows via $R_x$ and the $R_m - D_1$ 'ghosting' network, thus maintaining the input impedance symmetry. Note that the $R_m$ formula is the same as that of *Figure 6.16b*. Ideally, $R_x$ should have the same value as the meter's coil resistance, $r$, but in practice can be shorted out if $R_m$ is very large relative to $r$.

It is important at this stage to understand that simple meters of the *Figure 6.16* type *can* be used at fairly low voltages (possible down to less than 1V F.S.D.) and that in such cases there is not the slightest difficulty in getting them to operate with an F.S.D. frequency response that extends to tens or hundreds of MHz. Their major problem is that they have a very non-linear scale response at low voltages, and this is the major area where electronics can be used to enhance their performance.

To give a linear scale response, an A.C. meter's instantaneous current must be directly proportional to the instantaneous input voltage; in a conventional meter this action occurs when $R_m$ is very large relative to the rectifier's impedance and the input voltage is very large relative to the rectifier's forward volt drop. Typically, linearity is about 3 per cent of F.S.D. in a 10V meter, and about 1 per cent in a 100V meter. Thus, one obvious way to make a highly linear meter with an F.S.D. sensitivity of 1V is to connect the basic meter to read 100V F.S.D. (to give the desired linearity) and then drive it via a ×100 (= +40dB) amplifier, so that it reads F.S.D. with an a.c. input of 1V as shown in *Figure 6.17*.

The crude technique of *Figure 6.17* has obvious drawbacks in terms of power-supply requirements, but it does serve to illustrate the fundamental fact that a meter's scale response can be linearized with the aid of amplifier gain. Rough rules of thumb for the minimum required gain factors are as follows:

**Gain factor** for 3 per cent linearity $= 10/V_{F.S.D.}$
**Gain factor** for 1 per cent linearity $= 100/V_{F.S.D.}$

Thus, to make a 100mV meter with 1 per cent linearity, a gain of at least ×1000, or 60dB, is needed. In reality, a far more practical way of using this gain to linearize a meter is to use it to subject the meter circuitry to negative feedback, as in the case of *Figure 6.18*, in which the basic meter is designed to read 1V F.S.D. but is linearized by subjecting it to 40dB of negative feedback via the unity-gain input amplifier.

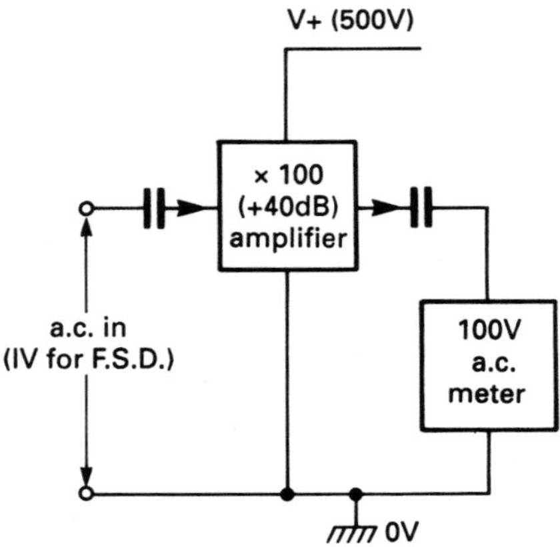


Figure 6.17. *A crude but effective way of making a 1V a.c. meter with 1 per cent linearity.*

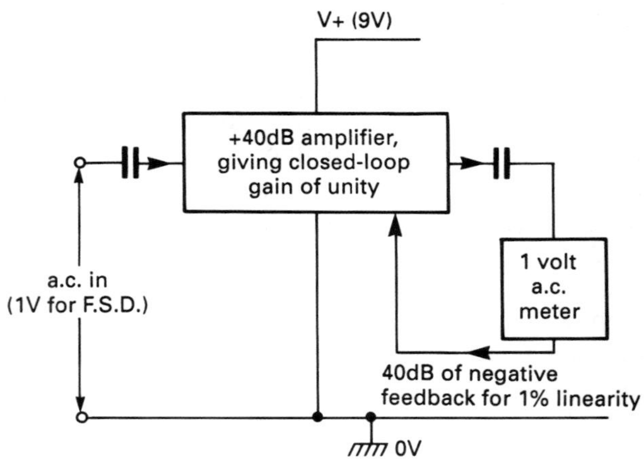


Figure 6.18. *A more practical way of making a 1V a.c. meter with 1 per cent linearity.*

## Transistor A.C. meter circuits

*Figure 6.19* shows a practical example of a 1V F.S.D. a.c. meter using the feedback linearizing technique on a bridge rectifier type of meter network. This simple circuit draws a quiescent current

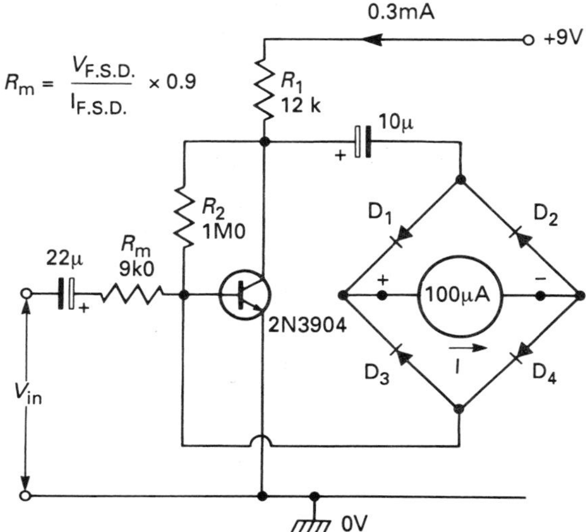


Figure 6.19. *The frequency response of this 1V a.c. meter is flat to above 150kHz.*

of about 0.3mA, has an F.S.D. frequency response that is absolutely flat from below 15Hz to above 150kHz, and has 1 per cent linearity up to 100kHz when using IN4148 silicon diodes, or to above 150kHz when using BAT85 Schottky types. The $R_1$ value of this circuit is chosen to give a quiescent current about three times greater than the meter's F.S.D. value, to give the meter automatic overload protection.

*Figures 6.20* and *6.21* show 'pseudo full-wave' and 'ghosted half-wave' versions of the above circuit. Note that diode $D_3$ is sometimes used in these circuits to apply slight forward bias to $D_1$ and $D_2$ and thus help improve linearity, but this often causes the meter to pass a 'standing' current when no a.c. input is applied; this practice is thus not recommended.

The diodes used in these and all other electronic 'a.c. meter' circuits should normally be silicon (IN4148, etc.) types, or Schottky types if an exceptionally good performance is needed (because of the high sensitivity of these, the circuit may need screening, to exclude unwanted R.F. pick-up). Germanium diodes are generally not suitable for use in negative feedback circuits, due to their relatively low values of reverse impedance.

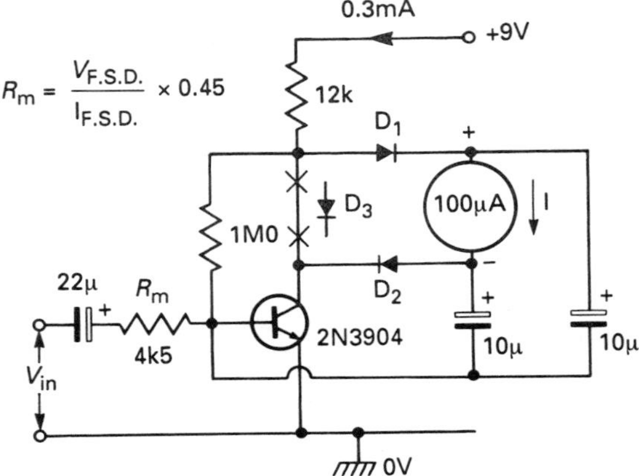


Figure 6.20. *'Pseudo full-wave' version of the 1V a.c. meter.*

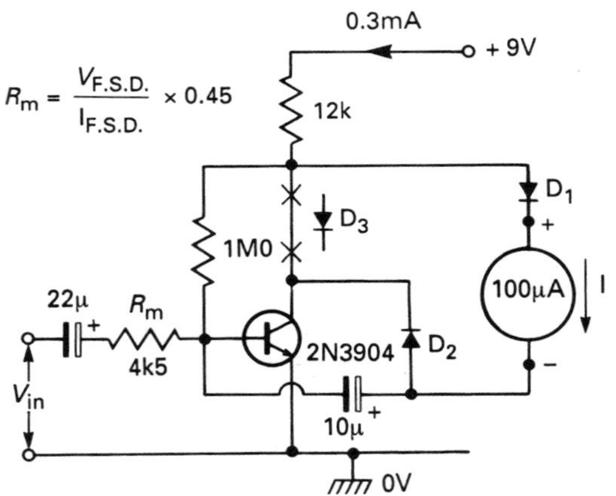


Figure 6.21. *'Ghosted' half-wave version of the 1V a.c. meter.*

In the *Figures 6.19* to *6.21* circuits the transistor is used in the common-emitter mode; in this mode a single transistor's open-loop gain is rarely much greater than 40dB, so these circuits cannot give an F.S.D. input sensitivity greater than 1V without incurring a loss of meter linearity. Reduced sensitivity can be obtained by simply increasing the $R_m$ value, e.g. by a factor of ten for 10V F.S.D., etc., (note in all cases that the circuit's input impedance equals the $R_m$ value).

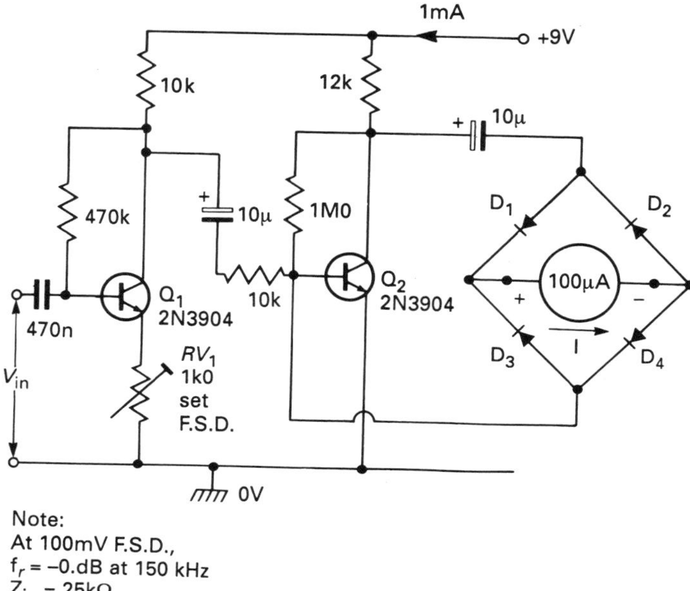


Figure 6.22. *This a.c. voltmeter can be set to give F.S.D. sensitivities in the range 20mV to 200mV.*

If greater F.S.D. sensitivity is wanted from the above circuits it can be obtained by applying the input signal via a suitable pre-amplifier, i.e. via a +60dB amplifier for 1mV sensitivity, etc. *Figure 6.22*, for example, shows a simple way of modifying the *Figure 6.19* circuit to make the F.S.D. sensitivity variable between roughly 20mV and 200mV (via $RV_1$) via a single additional common-emitter amplifier stage. With the sensitivity set at 100mV F.S.D. this circuit has an input impedance of 25k and a bandwidth that is flat within 0.5dB (about 5 per cent) to 150kHz.

## Op-amp A.C. meter circuits

The general principles outlined above can be applied to any type of amplifier device, including op-amps, and *Figure 6.23* shows a type-741 op-amp used as a direct equivalent of the *Figure 6.19*

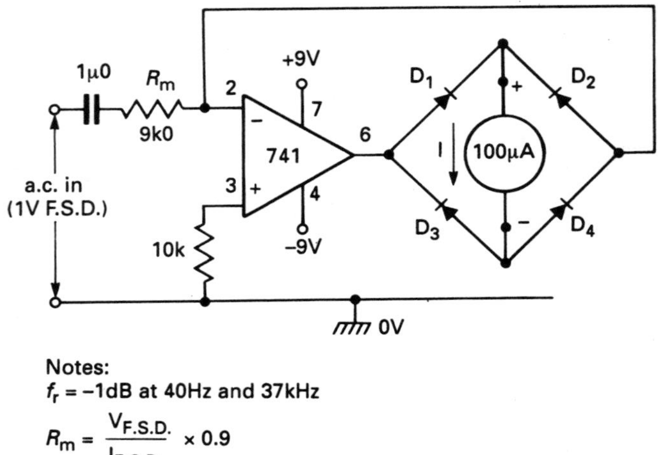


Notes:
$f_r = -1$dB at 40Hz and 37kHz

$$R_m = \frac{V_{F.S.D.}}{I_{F.S.D.}} \times 0.9$$

Figure 6.23. *Simple op-amp 1V a.c. meter circuit.*

circuit, with the meter network wired directly between the op-amp's output and its inverting input. This circuit gives excellent linearity, but its frequency response is severely limited (to 37kHz at −1dB) by the op-amp's slew rate limitations, and this design offers no real advantage over the simple transistor circuit of *Figure 6.19*.

*Figure 6.24* shows an improved version of the above design. In this case the meter network is wired between the op-amp's output and ground via $R_m$ (which sets the meter's basic F.S.D. sensitivity at 1V), and the rectifier network is linearized by feeding $R_m$'s output voltage back to the inverting input terminal via the $R_1$−$R_2$ network, which set the circuit's overall (input-to-$R_m$) gain at unity. With the component values shown the circuit thus has an F.S.D. sensitivity of 1V; note, however, that the circuit's input impedance (100k) is determined by $R_1$ and is independent of the meter's value, and that the meter does not have to be a particularly sensitive type.

In the *Figure 6.24* design $R_3$ is used to give the meter overload protection, and (in conjunction with $R_m$) limits its peak current to about treble the F.S.D. value. This protection is gained at the expense of reduced bandwidth, which is typically about 15kHz at the upper −1dB point when using a 741 op-amp (the bandwidth

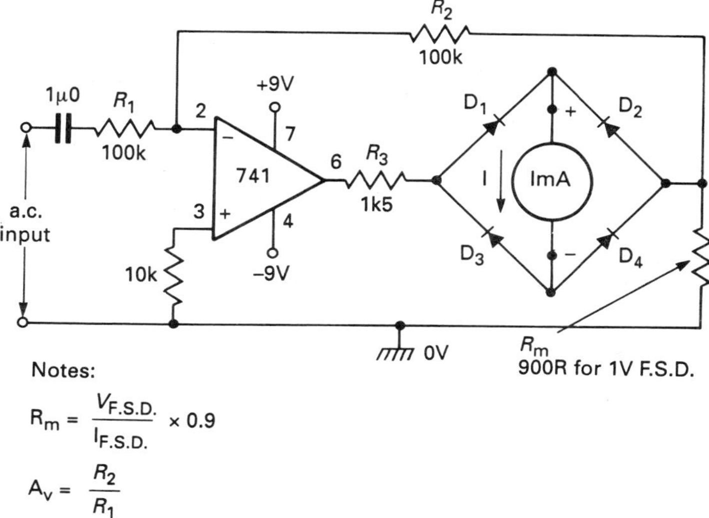


Figure 6.24. *The input impedance of this circuit is independent of meter sensitivity.*

can easily be extended by a factor of ten, to about 150kHz, by using a 'fast' op-amp such as a 3140, etc.). Note that the effective F.S.D. sensitivity of this circuit can be increased to 100mV by reducing the $R_1$ value to 10k (to give an overall gain of ×10, or 20dB), but in this case the bandwidth falls to only 6kHz at the upper −1dB point.

*Figure 6.25* shows an a.c. voltmeter circuit that is a great improvement over the previous two types. The meter network is again wired between the op-amp output and ground via $R_m$, which thus sets the meter's basic F.S.D. sensitivity, but in this case the circuit is wired as a unity-gain non-inverting amplifier or voltage follower and gives an input impedance equal to the $R_1$ value. The op-amp is provided with input overload protection via $R_2$, and with meter overload protection via $R_3$; when wired as a 1V meter the circuit's bandwidth reaches 15.5kHz at the upper −1dB point if the meter protection facility is used, but extends to 27kHz if $R_3$ is shorted out.

This circuit's sensitivity can be increased by reducing the $R_m$ value, but at the expense of reduced bandwidth, as indicated in

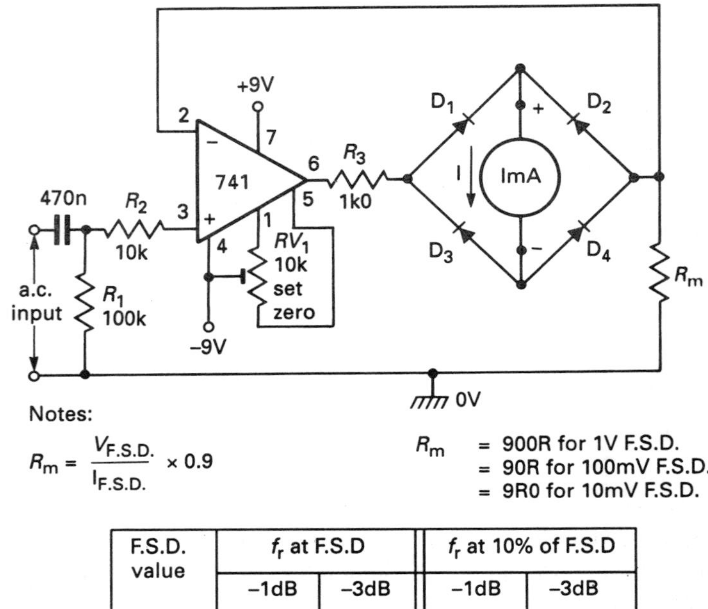


Notes:

$$R_m = \frac{V_{F.S.D.}}{I_{F.S.D.}} \times 0.9$$

$R_m$ = 900R for 1V F.S.D.
= 90R for 100mV F.S.D.
= 9R0 for 10mV F.S.D.

| F.S.D. value | $f_r$ at F.S.D | | $f_r$ at 10% of F.S.D | |
|---|---|---|---|---|
| | −1dB | −3dB | −1dB | −3dB |
| 1V0 | 15.5kHz | 23kHz | 15kHz | 32kHz |
| 1V0* | 27kHz | 36kHz | 40kHz | 85kHz |
| 100mV | 10kHz | 17kHz | 1.5kHz | 4kHz |
| 10mV | 1kHz | 2.2kHz | 40Hz | 270Hz |

*performance with $R_3$ s/c

Figure 6.25. *This a.c. voltmeter offers a high input impedance.*

the table, which lists the circuit's performance details both at F.S.D. and at 10 per cent of F.S.D. Thus, at 10mV sensitivity, the upper −1dB point occurs at 1kHz at F.S.D. and at 40Hz at 10 per cent of F.S.D. This abysmal performance is attributable to inherent limitations of the 741 op-amp.

## Op-amp limitations

The performance of the *Figure 6.25* circuit is actually limited by the op-amp's output slew rate and $f_T$ or 'gain/bandwidth' characteristics. The 741 op-amp's slew rate limit is about 0.5V/μS, and

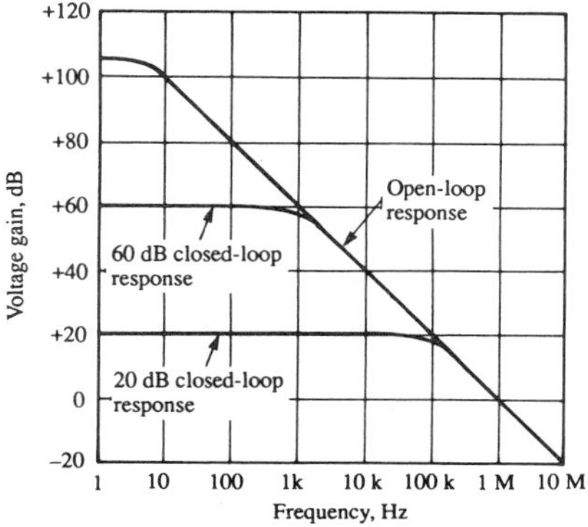


Figure 6.26. *Typical 'small signal' response curve of the 741 op-amp.*

its $f_T$ value is 1MHz. *Figure 6.26* shows the 741's typical 'small signal' output characteristics; its maximum voltage gain is 105dB, but is frequency dependent and falls off at a 20dB/decade rate and equals unity at 1MHz.

Returning to *Figure 6.25*, note the following points from the measured performance data:

(1) When the meter is scaled to read 1V F.S.D., with $R_3$ shorted out, the F.S.D. performance is limited mainly by the op-amp's slew rate, and is 1dB (about 10 per cent) down at 27kHz and 3dB down at 36kHz; its $\frac{1}{10}$th of F.S.D. 'linearity' performance is limited mainly by the op-amp's $f_T$ characteristics, and falls by 3dB at 85kHz as the available 'linearizing' gain falls to about 20dB.
(2) When the meter is scaled to read 1V F.S.D. with $R_3$ in place, the slew rate limitations increase and affect the '$\frac{1}{10}$th of F.S.D.' readings; the −3dB points then occur at 23kHz at F.S.D. and at 32kHz at $\frac{1}{10}$th of F.S.D.
(3) When the meter is scaled to read 100mV F.S.D. the basic sensitivity is increased by 20dB, and available bandwidths are reduced by a combination of slew rate and $f_T$ limitations; the −3dB points occur at 17kHz at F.S.D. and 4kHz at $\frac{1}{10}$th of F.S.D.
(4) When the meter is scaled to read 10mV F.S.D. the basic sensitivity is increased by a further 20dB, and the available

bandwidths are reduced by a proportionate amount; the −3dB points occur at 2.2kHz at F.S.D and at 270Hz at $\frac{1}{10}$th of F.S.D.

The important thing to note from the above data is the point already made in the 'A.C. voltmeter basics' section, namely, that the op-amp gain factor needed to give 1 per cent linearity = $100/V_{F.S.D.}$, i.e. +40dB at 1V F.S.D., +60dB at 100mV, and +80dB at 10mV, etc., and that linearity and F.S.D. accuracy start to decline when the available gain falls below the required 'critical' value. Thus, on the 10mV range the 741's open-loop gain starts to fall below the critical +80dB level at about 100Hz, and the meter's low-level linearity starts to decline as the gain falls below this value, and is 3dB down at 270Hz; the F.S.D. precision starts to collapse after a further decline of about 20dB (and is 3dB down at 2.2kHz in this example). Thus, a combination of wide bandwidth and high F.S.D. sensitivity can only be obtained by using a 'fast' op-amp, or by cascading a number of op-amps to give the desired gain−bandwidth product.

## Circuit variations

The *Figure 6.25* circuit is, allowing for the limitations mentioned above, really an excellent one and can, by using suitably 'fast' op-amps, give a good performance to well above 100kHz. The basic circuit can be subjected to a number of useful modifications, and a few of these are shown in *Figures 6.27* to *6.29*, which are all shown using a medium-speed LF355 JFET op-amp.

*Figure 6.27* shows how the input impedance of the basic circuit can be raised to about 200MΩ by using $R_1$ and $R_2$ as input-grounding resistors and bootstrapping their junction via $C_2$, so that identical signal voltages appear at each end of $R_1$, which thus passes near-zero signal current and appears as a near-infinite impedance.

*Figure 6.28* shows the basic circuit modified to give an F.S.D. sensitivity of 100mV by subjecting the inverting terminal's a.c. feedback signal to 20dB of attenuation via the $R_4$−$C_2$−$R_3$ 'divider' network, so that the op-amp acts as a '×10' amplifier feeding a linearized 1V meter. The meter's basic '1V' sensitivity is set via $R_m$, but this is shunted by the impedance of the $R_4$−$C_2$−$R_3$

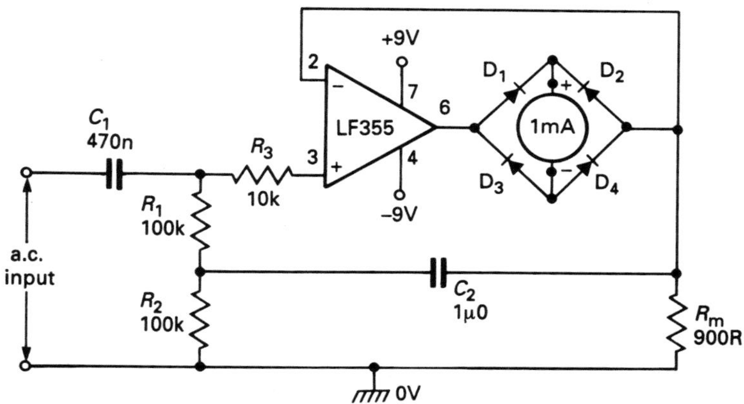


Figure 6.27. *'Bootstrapped' 1 volt a.c. meter with 200MΩ input impedance.*

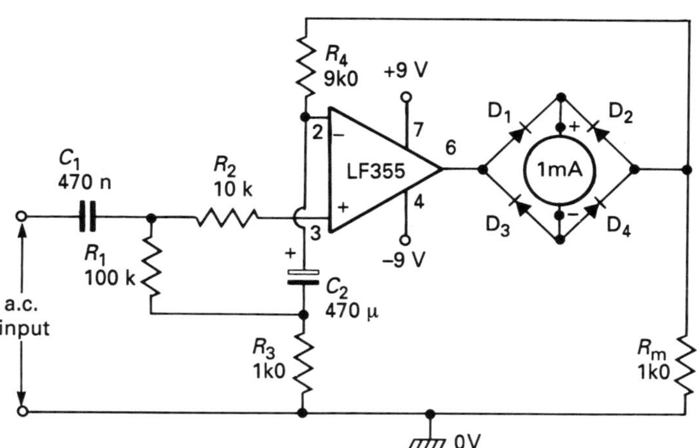


Figure 6.28. *Bootstrapped 100mV a.c. meter.*

feedback network and is thus given an actual value of 1k0 to set its shunted impedance close to the ideal '900Ω' value (a variable resistor can be used to precisely set the F.S.D. sensitivity, if preferred). Note in the diagram that input resistor $R_1$ is bootstrapped via $R_3$, thus giving the circuit a 100MΩ input impedance.

*Figure 6.29* shows the above circuit modified for use with a 100μA moving-coil meter, which needs an $R_m$ value of 9k0 to give an F.S.D. sensitivity of 1V. In this case $R_m$ serves a dual purpose, and forms part of the $R_m$–$C_2$–$R_3$ feedback network that sets the op-amp's closed-loop gain at ×10, to give 100mV overall F.S.D. sensitivity. $R_1$ is again bootstrapped, to give a 100MΩ input impedance.

Three design points are worth noting about these circuits. The first of these concerns the 'frequency' performance of the *Figures 6.28* and *6.29* '100mV' designs, and is that when used with Schottky diodes and a 3140 op-amp they maintain 1 per cent linearity down to 10 per cent of F.S.D. up to 70kHz, and down to 25 per cent of F.S.D. to well above 100kHz. The second point concerns $C_2$ in these two circuits; this component affects low-frequency response, which starts to fall off when the $C_2$ impedance becomes significant relative to $R_3$; $C_2$ thus needs a large value and, since it operates with zero bias, can be an electrolytic type of capacitor.

The final design point concerns all three circuits, and is that each of them operates with such heavy d.c. negative feedback between the output and the inverting input terminal that a **set zero** balance control is not needed (on the LF355, such a control

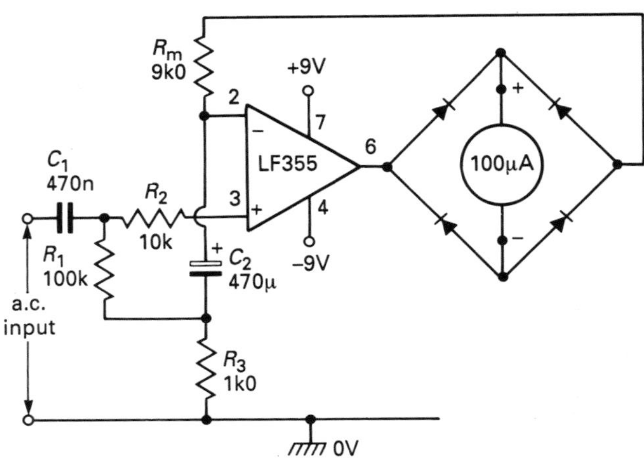


Figure 6.29. *Bootstrapped 100mV meter, using a 100μA movement.*

takes the form of a 25k potentiometer wired between pins 1 and 5, with the potentiometer slider taken to the positive supply rail).

## Multi-range A.C. meters

The bootstrapped 100mV a.c. voltmeter circuits of *Figures 6.28* or *6.29* can easily be converted into a multi-range voltage or current meter. *Figure 6.30* shows a basic circuit that gives conversion into a five-range a.c. voltmeter. Input signals are fed to the multi-decade attenuator via d.c.-blocking capacitor $C_1$, and the attenuator is frequency compensated by $C_2$, $C_3$ and $C_4$. Range switch $SW_1$ feeds the attenuator output to the a.c.-coupled input of the 100mV a.c. voltmeter.

*Figure 6.31* shows a switched shunt circuit that gives conversion into a five-range a.c. current meter. In this case it is not feasible to block d.c. currents from the shunts, but d.c. components are automatically blocked from the meter circuit's input via its a.c.-coupler, so the meter reads a.c. currents only.

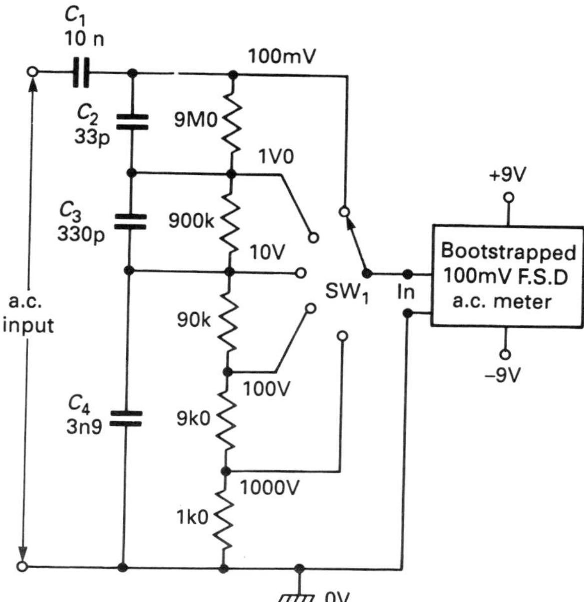


Figure 6.30. *Basic five-range a.c. voltmeter circuit.*

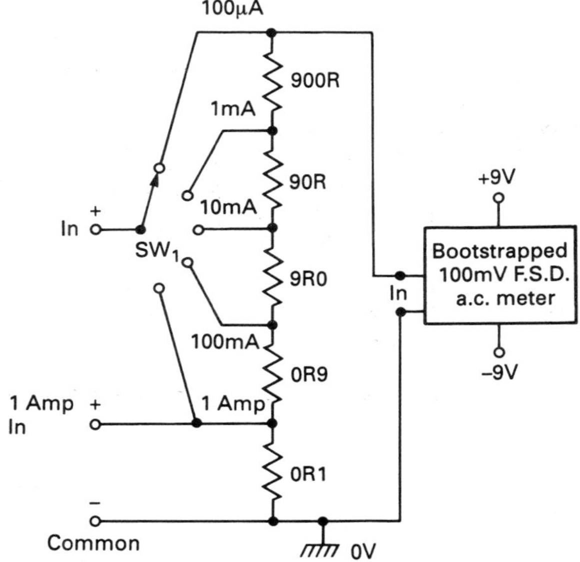


Figure 6.31. *Basic five-range a.c. current meter circuit.*

## A.C./D.C. converter circuits

All the 'a.c. voltmeter' circuits shown so far in this chapter use their electronic circuitry to drive the meter via a direct a.c. input. *Figure 6.32* shows an alternative type of metering system, in which the a.c. input is fed directly to a precision a.c./d.c. converter which then drives a precision d.c. voltmeter, which thus gives an accurate but indirect reading of the a.c. input voltage. This system has considerable merit, since it enables d.c. circuitry to handle tasks such as meter overload protection and inter-decade ranging, etc., and leaves the a.c. circuitry to take care of the relatively simple problem of a.c./d.c. conversion. This basic system is used in all modern digital multimeter circuits.

*Figures 6.33* to *6.38* show examples of some well-known types of op-amp-based a.c./d.c. converter circuit. All of these designs are shown using a 741 op-amp and IN4148 silicon diodes, but for the very best high-frequency and linearity performance a high-frequency op-amp and Schottky diodes should be used.

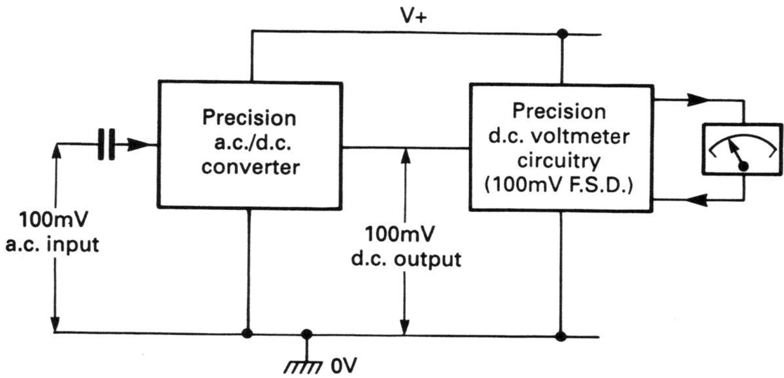


**Figure 6.32.** *Basic a.c. voltmeter using a precision a.c./d.c. converter and d.c. voltmeter.*

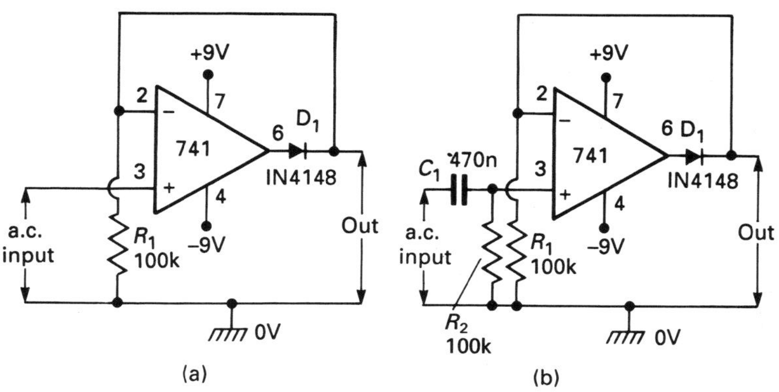


**Figure 6.33.** *Simple half-wave rectifier circuits using (a) direct-coupled and (b) a.c.-coupled inputs.*

*Figure 6.33* shows a simple precision half-wave rectifier circuit, based on a unity-gain voltage follower and having a high input impedance; the circuit gives a positively rectified output, but can be made to give a negatively rectified one by reversing $D_1$. The circuit can be used to accept direct-coupled or a.c.-coupled input signals by using the connections shown in (a) or (b) respectively. *Figure 6.34* shows how the basic circuit can be modified to act as a peak-voltage detector with a buffered output.

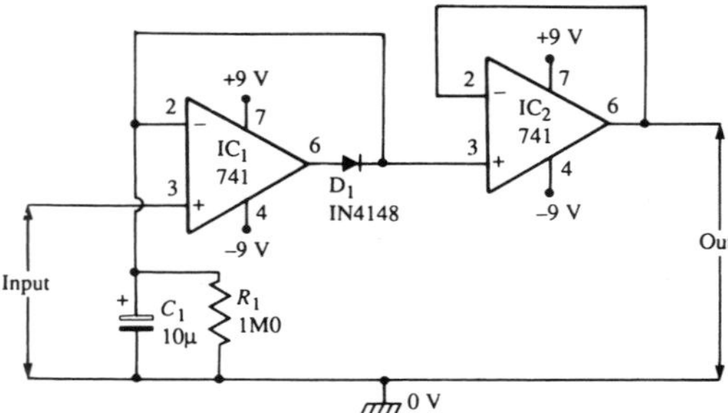


Figure 6.34. *Peak voltage detector with buffered output.*

*Figure 6.35* shows an alternative version of the precision half-wave rectifier, which gives improved linearity and frequency response, but at the expense of a reduced input impedance (equal to $R_1$). In this case the op-amp is wired as an inverting amplifier; when the input signal goes positive the op-amp output tries to go negative, but is effectively prevented from doing so by $D_2$; when the input goes negative the op-amp output goes positive and forward biases $D_1$, which then sets the circuit's voltage gain at unity via $R_1 - R_2$. The circuit's output thus consists of positive half-cycles only. *Figure 6.36* shows how this circuit can be used as a true a.c./d.c. voltage converter by increasing the value of $R_2$ to 22k2 to give form-factor correction, and by using $C_1$ (in conjunction with $R_2$) to integrate the output waveform and convert it to d.c.; note that this circuit has a high output impedance, and must be buffered if fed to a low-impedance load.

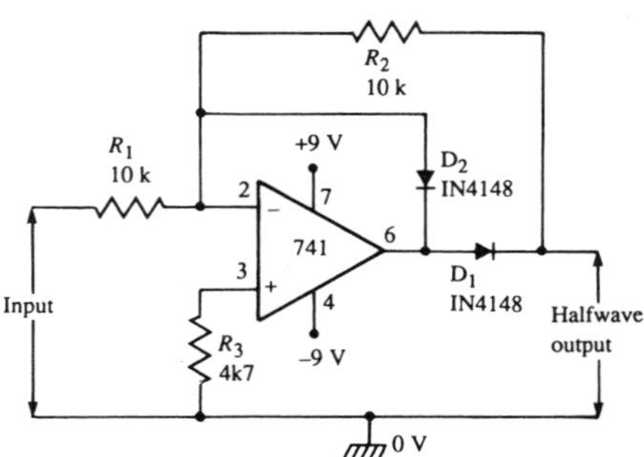


Figure 6.35. *Precision half-wave rectifier.*

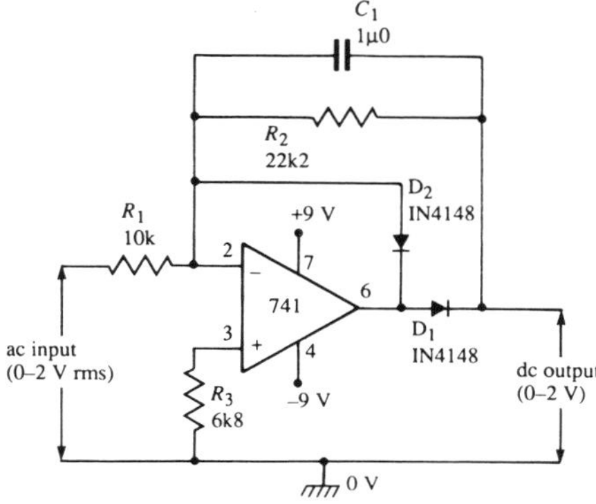


Figure 6.36. *Precision half-wave a.c./d.c. converter.*

*Figure 6.37* shows how a negative-output version of the *Figure 6.35* circuit can be combined with an inverting adder to make a precision full-wave rectifier. Here, $IC_2$ inverts and gives ×2 gain (via $R_3 - R_5$) to the half-wave rectified signal of $IC_1$, and inverts and gives unity gain (via $R_4 - R_5$) to the original input signal ($E_{in}$). Thus, when a negative input is applied the output of $IC_1$ is zero, so $IC_2$'s output equals $+E_{in}$. When positive inputs are applied $IC_1$ gives a negative output, so $IC_2$ generates an output of $+2E_{in}$ via $IC_1$ and $-E_{in}$ via the original input signal, thus giving

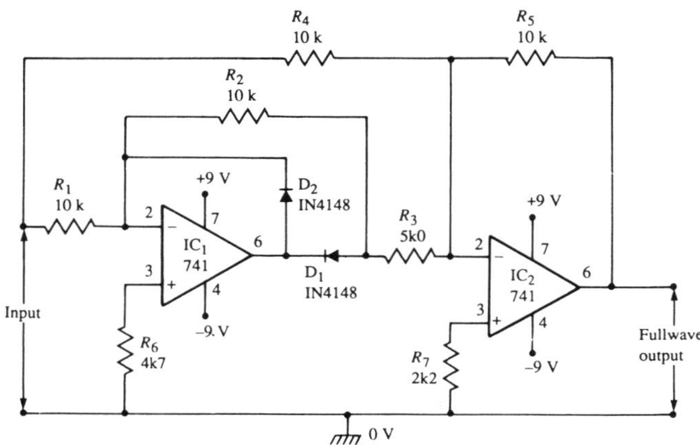


Figure 6.37. *Precision full-wave rectifier.*

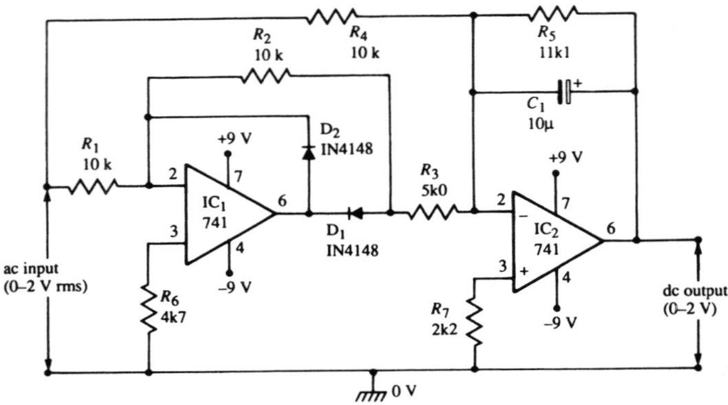


Figure 6.38. *Precision full-wave a.c./d.c. voltage converter.*

an actual output of $+E_{in}$. The final output is thus a full-wave rectified, unity-gain, version of the input signal. *Figure 6.38* shows how this circuit can be used as a precision a.c./d.c. voltage converter by giving $R_5$ a value of 11k1 to give form-factor correction, and by using $C_1-R_5$ to give waveform integration; note that this circuit has a low output impedance.

## Special A.C./D.C. converters

The precision rectifier and converter circuits of *Figures 6.35* to *6.38* offer good linearity but have relatively low values of input impedance. In recent years, mainly as a result of developments in the digital multimeter field (see Chapter 7), a demand has grown for a really good and inexpensive a.c./d.c. voltage converter with excellent linearity and a very high input impedance. This demand has largely been met by the 'standard' circuit of *Figure 6.39*.

In *Figure 6.39* the op-amp is used as a non-inverting amplifier with d.c. biasing applied by $R_1$ and $R_2$, with $D_1-D_2-R_3-R_4$ and $R_5-RV_1$ acting as a 'ghosted' half-wave rectifier that is a.c. coupled into the circuit's negative feedback path. The op-amp's basic action is such that pin-2's a.c. signal intrinsically 'follows' the input voltage ($e$) of pin-3, and (since $R_5-RV_1$ are a.c.-coupled between pin-2 and ground) this causes a current ($i$) of $e/(R_5 + RV_1)$ to flow in $R_5-RV_1$. This current is derived from the op-amp's output and flows via $D_1-R_4$ on positive half-cycles and via

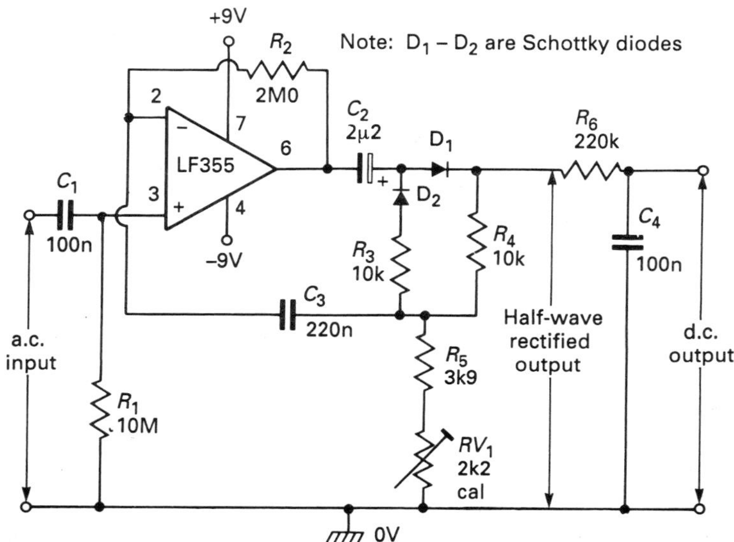


Figure 6.39. *Precision high-impedance a.c./d.c. voltage converter.*

$D_2-R_3$ on negative ones, and generates near-perfect half-wave rectified positive waveforms across $R_4$, and near-perfect negative ones across $R_3$. The output signal generated between the $D_1-R_4$ junction and ground is thus a near-perfect positively rectified half-wave superimposed on a duplicate of the a.c. input signal; when this signal is integrated via $R_6-C_4$ the a.c. element is eliminated, and the rectified portion of the signal is converted into d.c.; $RV_1$ enables the $R_4$ to $R_5-RV_1$ ratio to be set to give perfect sinewave form-factor correction, enabling the circuit to give precision a.c./d.c. voltage conversion.

The *Figure 6.39* circuit has a useful a.c./d.c. conversion range (with excellent linearity) from greater than 1V to less than 10mV. Precision falls off at low values of input, and the output is typically 1mV down with a 10mV input, i.e. linearity is typically 1 per cent of a 100mV F.S.D. value, or 0.1 per cent of a 1V F.S.D. value. The circuit's input impedance is slightly less than the $R_1$ value of 10MΩ.

*Figure 6.40* shows a high-performance version of the a.c./d.c. converter. Its input impedance is raised to about 100MΩ by bootstrapping $R_1$ via $R_7-RV_1$, and the op-amp is given input

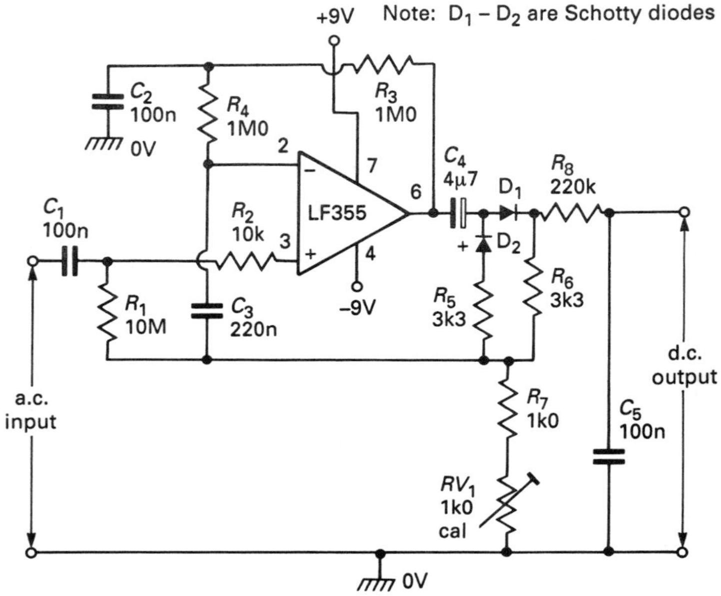

Figure 6.40. *Bootstrapped precision a.c./d.c. voltage converter.*

overload protection via $R_2$. The circuit's linearity is enhanced by trebling the forward operating currents of $D_1$ and $D_2$ (to peak values of about 100μA at 100mV) to give improved forward/reverse current ratios, and by a.c.-decoupling the $R_3-R_4$ d.c.-biasing network so that it does not significantly shunt the $D_1-D_2-R_5-R_6$ feedback network; these simple measures improve linearity by some 300 per cent, to give d.c. errors of only 0.3mV at 10mV input, and a linearity factor of 0.3 per cent of a 100mV F.S.D. input value. $D_1$ and $D_2$ should be BAT85 Schottky diodes, in which case (when using an LF355 op-amp) the circuit maintains its linearity to within 1 per cent of a 500mV F.S.D. value to above 150kHz, or to within 1 per cent of a 100mV F.S.D. value to about 40kHz.

*Figure 6.41* shows, in basic form, how an a.c./d.c. converter of the above type can be used in conjunction with a compensated input attenuator (see *Figure 6.30*) and a simple d.c. voltmeter (see *Figure 6.7*) to make a precision 30-range a.c./d.c. voltmeter; in a practical instrument the converter should be disabled by breaking its supply connections when it is not in use.

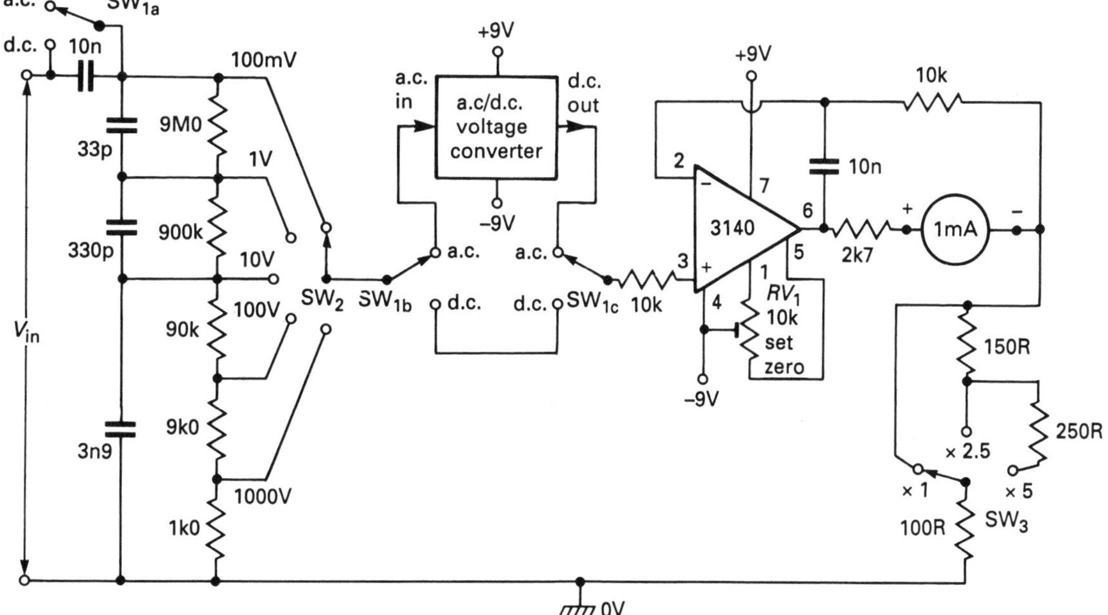


Figure 6.41. *Basic thirty-range a.c./d.c. voltmeter using a precision a.c./d.c. converter.*

## True-r.m.s. converters

All the a.c. voltmeter and a.c./d.c. converter circuits shown so far in this chapter give an output reading in terms of r.m.s. voltage on the assumption that their a.c. inputs have a pure sinewave form; if these circuits are driven from impure waveforms,

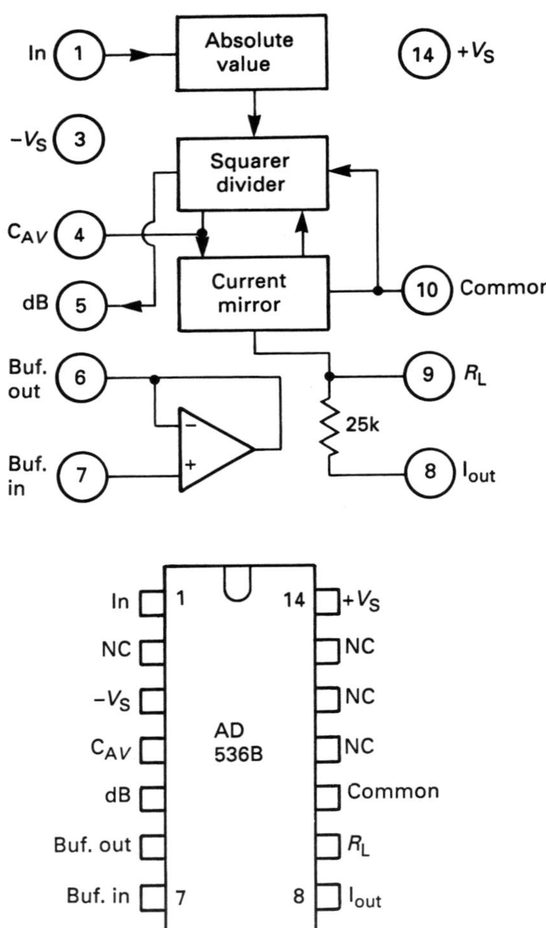


Figure 6.42. *Outline and equivalent circuit of the AD536B r.m.s.-to-d.c. voltage converter IC.*

their outputs may in fact differ greatly from the true r.m.s. value of the input signal.

There are many applications in which it is necessary to be able to read the true r.m.s. value of an input voltage irrespective of waveform shape, and a number of dedicated (but usually rather expensive) r.m.s.-to-d.c. voltage converter ICs are available for this purpose. The best known of these is the AD536A, which is manufactured by Analogue Devices; *Figure 6.42* shows the outline, pin notations, and basic equivalent circuit of this IC.

The AD536A uses its internal components to make an analogue computation of the true r.m.s. value of any input waveform, almost irrespective of its form or crest factor, and presents its output in the form of an equivalent d.c. voltage. The device can operate from zero to 2MHz, can use dual supplies in the ±3V to ±18V range or single-ended ones in the +5V to +36V range, and consumes a typical quiescent current of 1mA; its precision is such that errors rise by only 1 per cent even when measuring pulse or noise waveforms with crest factors (peak/r.m.s. voltage) as high as seven. A useful additional feature of the IC is an auxiliary output voltage that is proportional to the logarithm of the r.m.s. output, thus providing decibel conversion; this facility has a useful dynamic range of 60dB.

*Figure 6.43* shows the AD536A's basic application circuit, using ±12V supplies, and *Figure 6.44* shows the circuit modified to minimize (trim) measurement errors (to set up this circuit, short the input and trim $RV_2$ for zero output, then apply a known input voltage (a.c. or d.c.) and trim $RV_1$ for an equal d.c. output voltage). Note that these two circuits can be used to measure both d.c. and a.c. input signals; they can be modified to measure only a.c. signal components by simply connecting the inputs via a

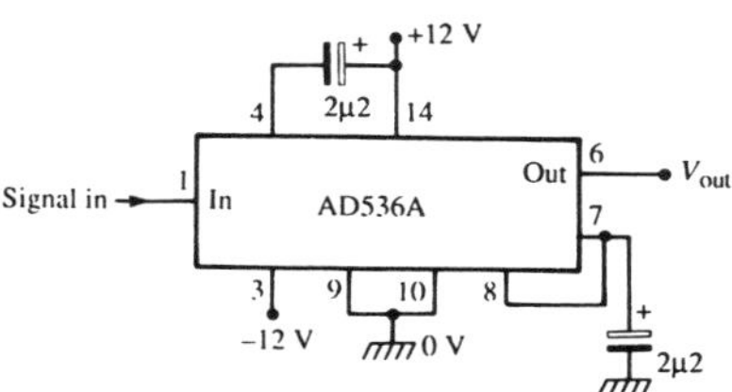


Figure 6.43. *Basic split-supply AD536A r.m.s.-to-d.c. voltage converter circuit.*

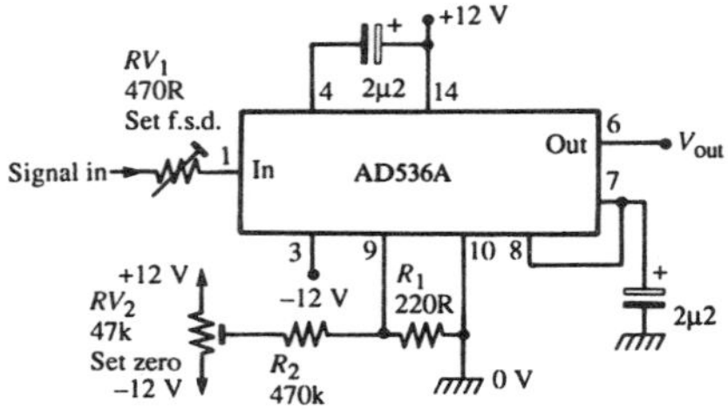


Figure 6.44. *r.m.s.-to-d.c. converter with error-trim facilities.*

blocking capacitor. *Figure 6.45* shows how the basic AD536A circuit can be used with a single-ended power supply; this circuit can be used to measure a.c.-coupled input voltages only.

Another of Analogue Devices' useful r.m.s.-to-d.c. converter ICs is the AD636JH (see *Figure 6.46*), which is similar to the AD536A but is housed in a 10-pin metal package and is specifically designed to give a full-scale output of 200mV, making it compatible with modern digital voltmeters, etc. This IC gives a

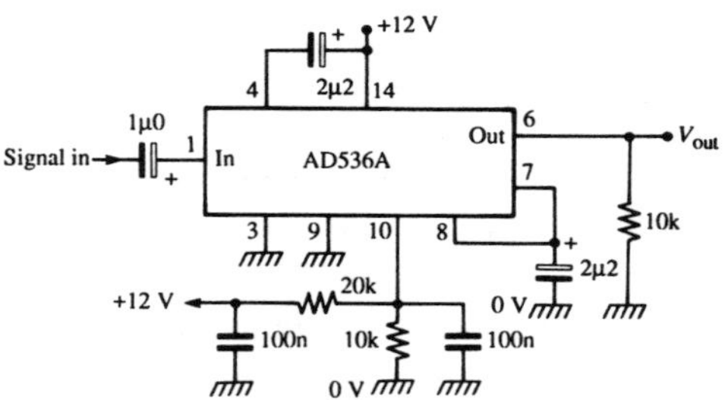


Figure 6.45. *r.m.s.-to-d.c. converter using single ended supply.*

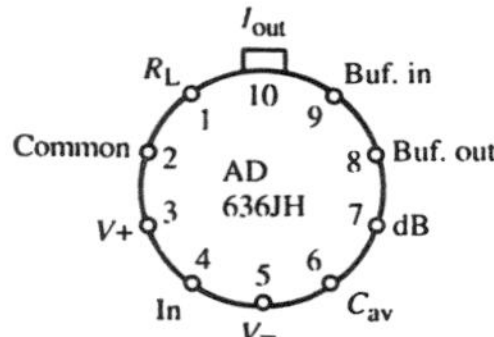


Figure 6.46. *Outline and pin notations of the AD636JH low-level r.m.s.-to-d.c. voltage converter IC.*

useful performance up to 1.3MHz, and can handle crest factors up to six with less than 1.5 per cent total error. The IC can use split supplies in the ±2V to ±12V range, or single-ended ones in the +5V to +24V range, and consumes a quiescent current of 1mA maximum.

*Figures 6.47* to *6.49* show practical examples of basic, error-trimmed, and single-ended supply circuits using the AD636JH; these circuits are similar to those shown for the AD536A, except for changes in pin numbering and component values.

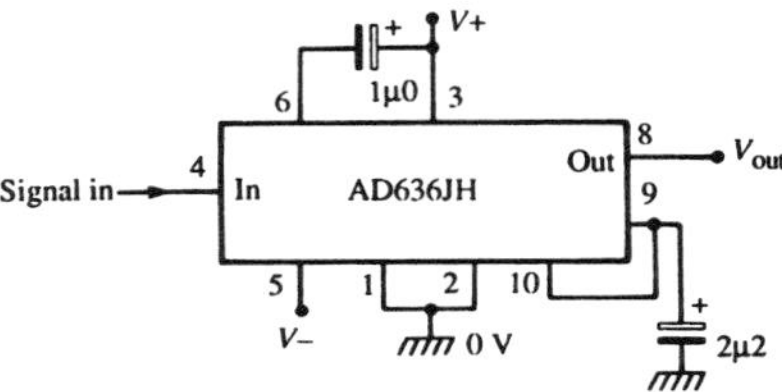


Figure 6.47. *Basic split-supply AD636JH r.m.s.-to-a.c. converter circuit.*

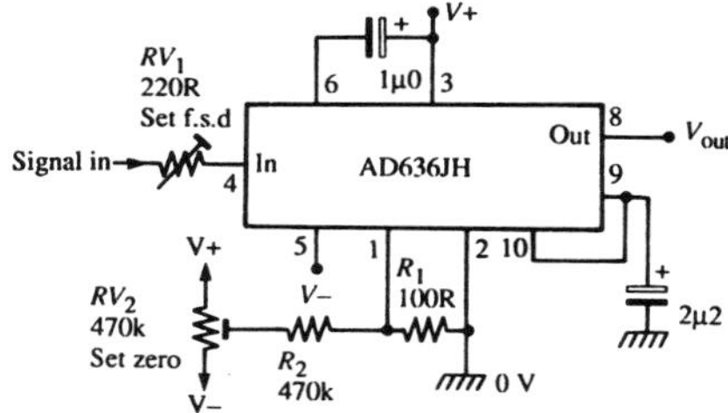


Figure 6.48. *r.m.s.-to-d.c. converter with error-trim facilities.*

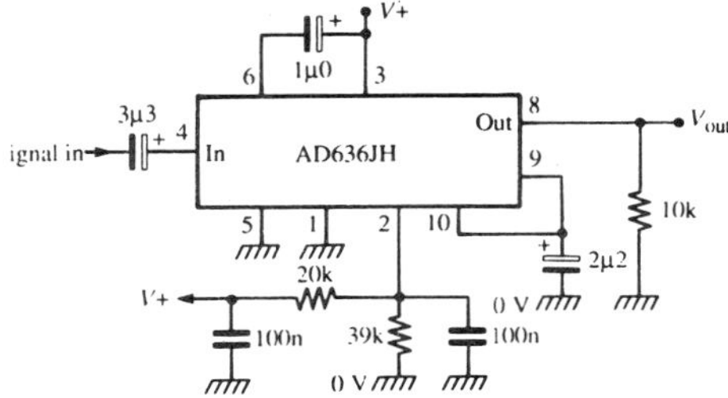


Figure 6.49. *r.m.s.-to-d.c. converter using single-ended supply.*

## A.C. millivoltmeter circuits

Most of the a.c. meter circuits shown so far have a basic F.S.D. sensitivity of 100mV. If greater sensitivity is needed it can easily be obtained by coupling the a.c. input signal to such a meter via a suitable pre-amplifier stage, i.e. by a ×10 type for 10mV sensitivity, or ×100 for 1mV sensitivity, etc. If a wide bandwidth (up to hundreds of kHz) is required it is best obtained by using transistor (rather than op-amp) circuitry.

The maximum voltage gain available from two cascaded common-emitter transistor stages is about 80dB, so the highest useful F.S.D. sensitivity they can give (with good linearity and gain stability) is 10mV. *Figure 6.50* shows an excellent two-transistor circuit that gives F.S.D. sensitivities in the range 10mV to 100mV (set via $R_x$). This circuit uses $D_1$ and $D_2$ in the

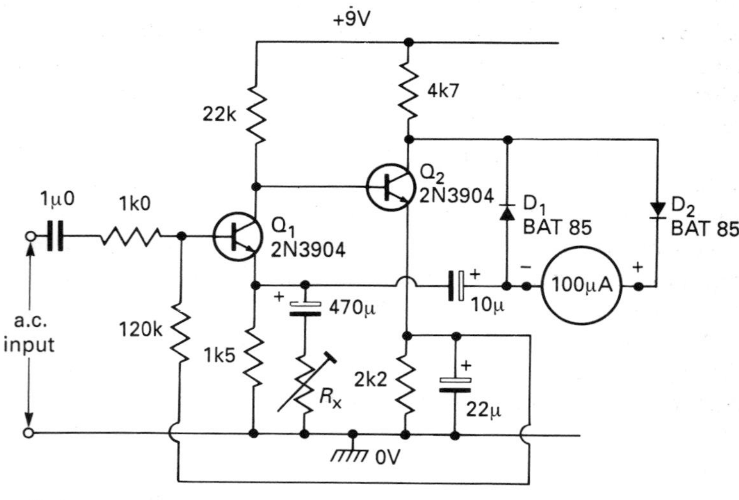


Notes:-
$D_1 - D_2$ = Schottky diodes
$R_x \simeq$ 470R at 100mV F.S.D.
" $\simeq$ 47R at 10mV F.S.D.
$f_r$ > 150kHz (±0.5dB)
$Z_{in}$ (at 100mV F.S.D.) = 120kΩ
$Z_{in}$ (at 10mV F.S.D.) = 90kΩ at 15kHz
" " " = 56kΩ at 150kHz

Figure 6.50. *Wideband a.c. millivoltmeter with F.S.D. sensitivity variable from 10mV to 100mV via $R_x$.*

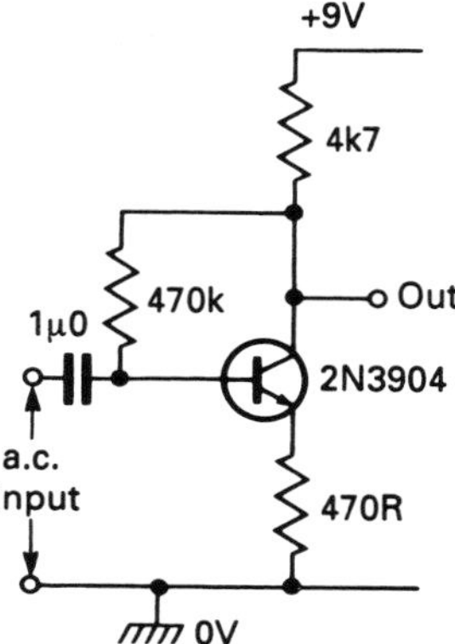


Figure 6.51. *This ×10 wideband preamplifier can be used to boost an a.c. millivoltmeter's sensitivity.*

'ghosted half-wave' configuration, and its response is flat within 0.5dB to above 150kHz; the circuit's input impedance is about 110k when set to give 100mV F.S.D. sensitivity ($R_x$ = 470R); when set to give 10mV sensitivity ($R_x$ = 47R) the input impedance varies from 90k at 15kHz to 56k at 150kHz.

*Figure 6.51* shows a simple ×10 pre-amplifier that can be used to boost the above circuit's F.S.D. sensitivity to 1mV; this circuit has an input impedance of 45k and has a good wideband response. Note when building highly sensitive a.c. millivoltmeters that great care must be taken to keep all connecting leads short, to prevent unwanted RF pickup.

A wide-range a.c. volt/millivolt meter can be made by feeding the input signals to a sensitive a.c. meter via suitable attenuator circuitry. To avoid excessive attenuator complexity, the technique of *Figure 6.52* is normally adopted. Here, the input is fed to a high-impedance unity-gain buffer, either directly (on millivolt ranges) or via a compensated 60dB attenuator (on volt ranges), and the buffer's output is fed to the basic millivolt meter (with 1mV F.S.D. sensitivity) via a low-impedance (3k0 in this case) attenuator that does not require frequency compensation. In the diagram this second attenuator is shown with 1–3–10, etc., ranging, but if the meter is fitted with a dB scale it is more usual to give the attenuator 1–3.16–10, etc., ranging, to give accurate 10dB range stepping.

*Figure 6.53* shows a useful variation of the above technique. In

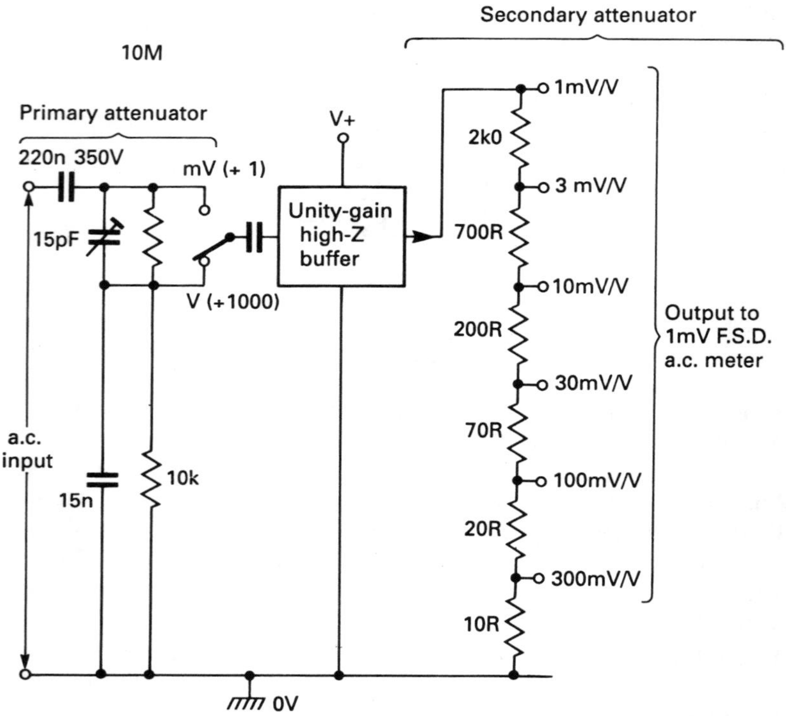

Figure 6.52. *Basic multi-range a.c. volt/millivolt meter circuit.*

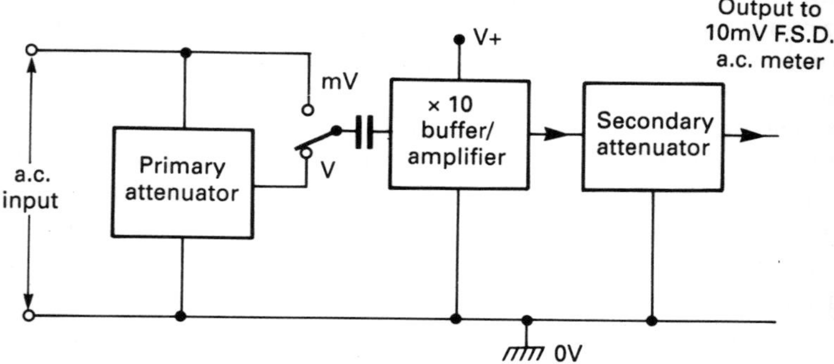


Figure 6.53. *A useful a.c. volt/millivolt meter circuit variation.*

this case the input buffer also serves as a ×10 amplifier, and the secondary attenuator's output is fed to a meter with 10mV F.S.D. sensitivity, the net effect being that a maximum overall sensitivity of 1mV is obtained with a minimum of complexity.

*Figures 6.54* and *Figure 6.55* show input buffers suitable for

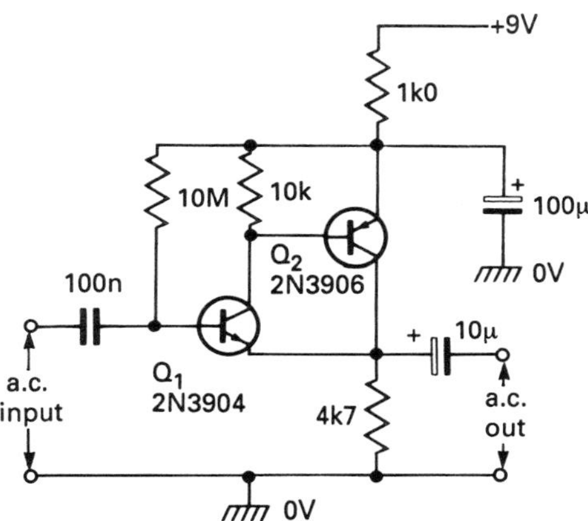


Figure 6.54. *Unity-gain input buffer.*

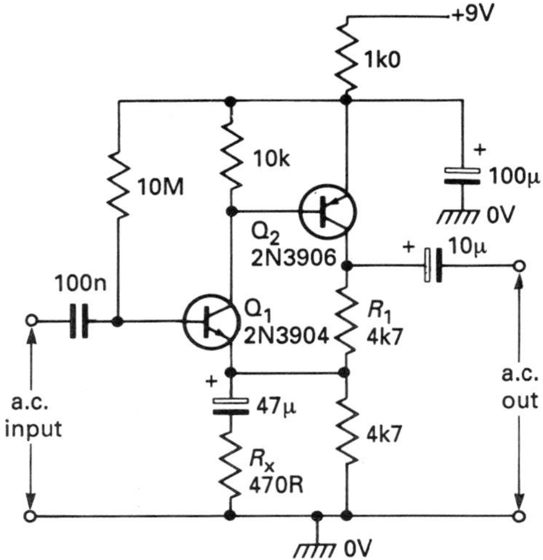


Figure 6.55. *Buffer with ×10 gain.*

use with the above types of multi-range circuit. The *Figure 6.54* design is that of a unity-gain buffer; it gives an input impedance of about 4M0. The *Figure 6.55* buffer gives a ×10 voltage gain (set by the $R_1/R_x$ ratio) and has an input impedance of 1M0.

## Linear-scale ohmmeter basics

One popular application of the electronic analogue meter is as a linear-scale ohmmeter. This type of meter is not without its disadvantages, however, as is made clear by *Figure 6.56*, which shows such a scale marked in the widely used E12 set of values (which have nominal increments of 20 per cent) over the range 10–100Ω. Note that the scale's value resolution is excellent above 40 per cent of F.S.D. but is very poor below 20 per cent of F.S.D.; to be of real value, the meter must thus provide two or three F.S.D. scale values (i.e. ×1 and ×3, or ×1, ×2.5, and ×5, etc.) per resistance decade.

There are three alternative ways of making a linear-scale ohmmeter. The most useful of these uses the basic circuit of *Figure 6.57*, in which a regulated voltage and a precision reference resistor ($R_{ref}$) are used to drive a resistance-to-voltage (*R*-to-*V*) converter that generates an output voltage that is directly proportional to the $R_x$ value and is read on an analogue voltmeter. This type of circuit gives accurate reading of resistance values from about 1Ω to 50MΩ. Its *R*-to-*V* converter is based on the simple inverting amplifier circuit of *Figure 6.13*, with $R_{ref}$ and $R_x$ taking the places of $R_1$ and $R_2$.

*Figure 6.58* shows another type of a linear-scale ohmmeter; here, a known value of 'constant-current' is fed through $R_x$, which thus generates an output voltage that is directly proportional to its resistance and is read on a d.c. voltmeter. This type of

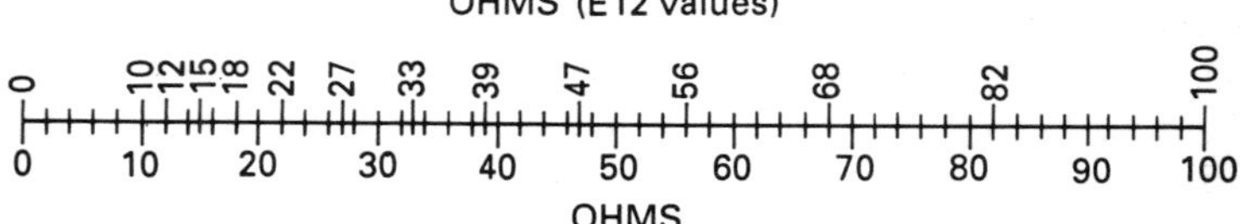


Figure 6.56. *The resolution of a linear-scale ohmmeter is excellent above 40 per cent of F.S.D. but very poor below 20 per cent of F.S.D.*

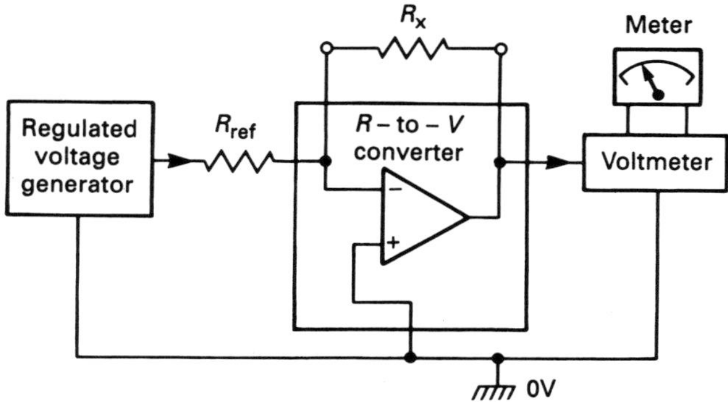


Figure 6.57. *Basic linear-scale ohmmeter using resistance-to-voltage converter.*

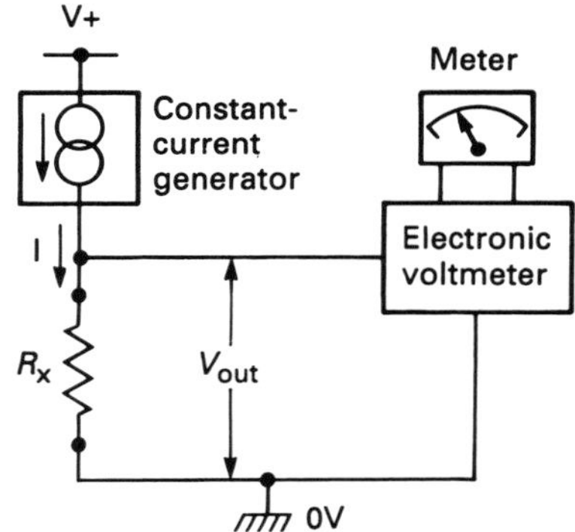


Figure 6.58. *A linear-scale ohmmeter using a constant-current generator.*

circuit gives accurate readings of resistance from about 1Ω to 50k; the upper limit is set by the difficulty of accurately generating suitable low-value 'constant-currents' and by the shunting effects of the voltmeter; the lower limit is set by the interfering and often unpredictable effects of wiring and terminal-contact resistances, etc. This once-popular type of circuit is inferior to that of *Figure 6.57*, and is now rarely used.

Finally, *Figure 6.59* shows a circuit that is ideal for measuring low-value resistances. Here, the constant-current generator and voltmeter are separately powered, and a 'four-terminal' measurement technique is used in which the $R_x$ voltage is read directly

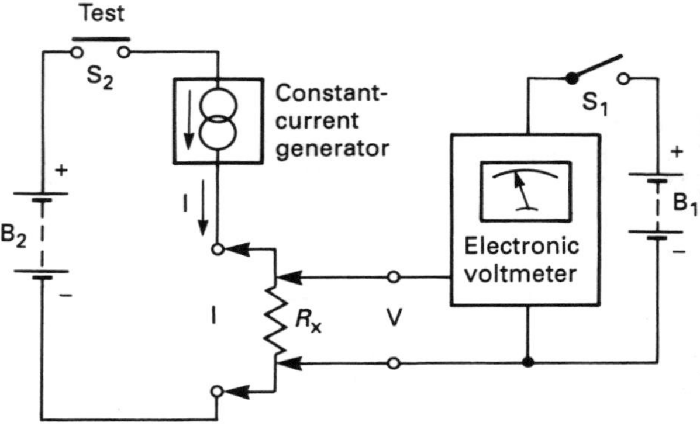


Figure 6.59. *Basic 'four-terminal' low-value linear-scale ohmmeter using individually powered constant-current generator and voltmeter.*

across $R_x$, rather than across the '$R_x$' terminals, thus eliminating the interfering effects of wiring and contact resistances, etc. This type of circuit can accurately measure resistance down to a few milliohms (using a 100mA test current and a meter with 0.1mV resolution).

## An 18-range ohmmeter circuit

*Figure 6.60* shows a practical eighteen-range linear-scale ohmmeter of the *Figure 6.57* type; it gives accurate resistance readings from a few ohms up to a maximum of 50MΩ. In this circuit $IC_1$ acts as a precision voltage regulator that gives a stable −1V output, and $IC_2$ acts as a precision resistance-to-voltage converter, with its output driving a d.c. voltmeter with 1V0, 2V5, and 5V0 ranges; the converter acts as follows. $IC_2$ is an inverting amplifier, and its pin-2 input terminal forms a virtual ground (zero volts) point; consequently, the regulated −1V output of $IC_1$ causes a current of $-1/R_{ref}$ to flow in whatever 'reference' resistor is selected by $SW_1$; the natural action of $IC_2$ is such that its output automatically endeavours to generate a phase-inverted but otherwise identical feedback current via $R_x$, and $IC_2$ thus generates an output voltage that is directly proportional to the $R_x/R_{ref}$ ratio, and equals 1V when $R_x$ equals $R_{ref}$. Note that the $R_x$ terminals thus provide the action of a constant-current generator, with the current variable

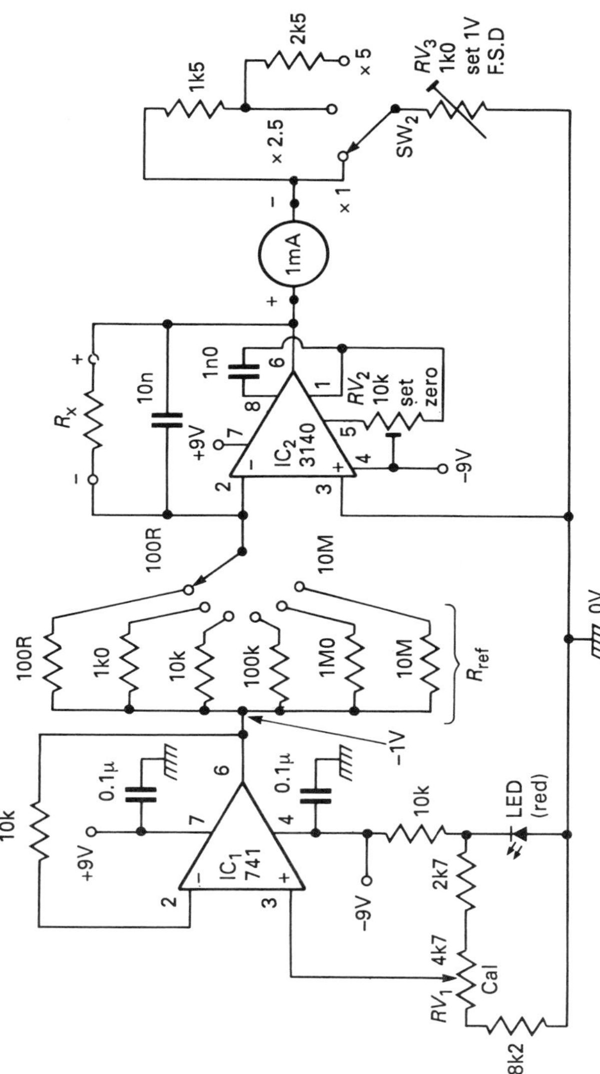


Figure 6.60. *This eighteen-range linear-scale ohmmeter spans 100R to 50M F.S.D.*

in decade steps between 0.1μA (on the 10M range) and 10mA (on the 100R range).

The red LED is used in *Figure 6.60* as a precision voltage reference, operated at a nominal 0.7mA. A red LED operating under this condition generates a forward volt drop of about 1.5V (which is tapped down to 1V via $RV_1$, and fed to the input of the $IC_1$ voltage follower), and has a typical temperature coefficient of −1.2mV/°C (= −0.08 per cent/°C) and a dynamic impedance of 40Ω, and thus gives better thermal stability and regulation than most Zener diodes. Once this ohmmeter circuit has been initially calibrated, a ±10°C change in the LED's ambient temperature causes a typical change of only 0.8 per cent in the meter's F.S.D. accuracy (this error can be eliminated by simply retrimming the 'CAL' control).

To initially calibrate the *Figure 6.60* circuit, first short its $R_x$ terminals together, set $SW_1$ to the '1k0' position and set $SW_2$ to '×1', and then adjust $RV_1$ to give an output of −1.000V between $IC_1$'s output and ground; now trim $RV_2$ to give zero output from $IC_2$. Finally, remove the short from the $R_x$ terminals, insert a precision 1k0 resistor in its place, and trim $RV_3$ to set the meter reading to F.S.D. Calibration is then complete. When using the meter, occasionally recheck its F.S.D. accuracy and re-trim $RV_1$ if necessary.

## A 21-range multi-function ohmmeter

*Figure 6.61* shows a precision twenty-one-range linear-scale ohmmeter that can be built as either an add-on unit for use with an existing d.c. meter with 100mV F.S.D. sensitivity, or as a self-contained unit. The voltage regulator ($IC_1$) section of this unit is similar to that described above except that the red LED is replaced with a precision bandgap reference ($IC_3$) with a typical temperature coefficient of 0.005 per cent/°C, thus eliminating the need for an adjustable CAL facility. This circuit also provides an extra decade of resistance measurement (down to 10R F.S.D.), which is achieved by using $SW_{1b}$ to set the meter's sensitivity so that (with $SW_2$ in the '×1' position) it reads F.S.D. when $IC_2$'s output is 100mV (rather than 1V, as on all other basic ranges).

The basic action of the *Figure 6.61* circuit is such that a constant current is generated between its two '×' terminals, and the meter

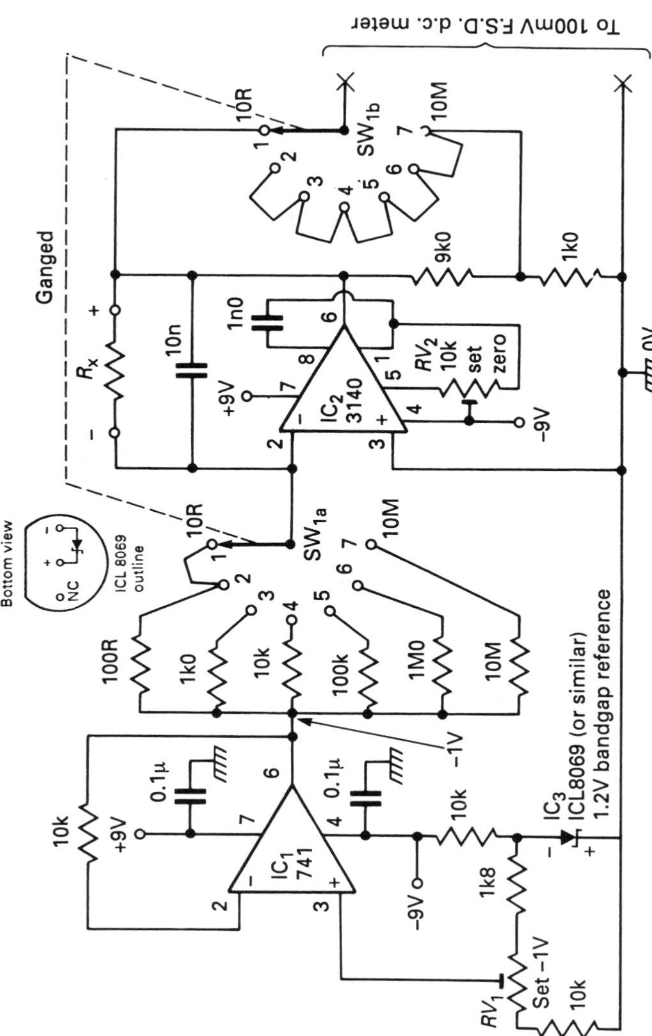


Figure 6.61(a). *This precision 21-range multi-function 'ohmmeter' can be built as either an add-on* (Figure 6.61a only) *or a self-contained* (Figure 6.61a + b) *unit.*

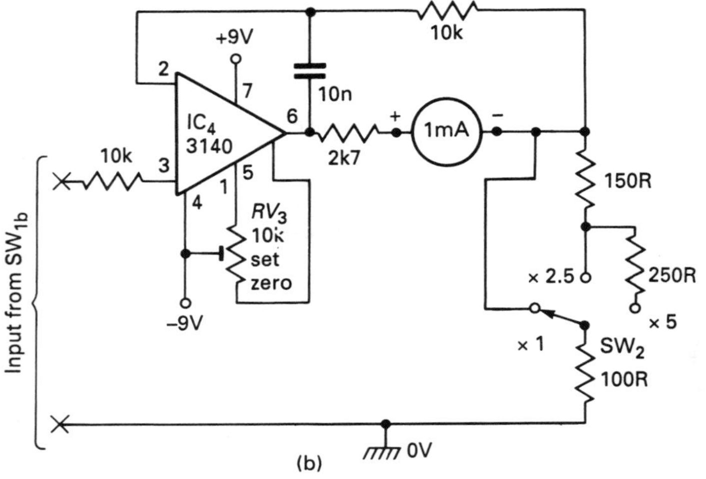


Figure 6.61(b). *100mV F.S.D. d.c. meter for use with the* Figure 6.61a *circuit.*

gives a reading of the volt drop between these terminals. By using the connections shown in *Figure 6.62a* the meter can thus be used to measure the forward or reverse volt drops (up to a maximum of 5V) of diodes, LEDs, or zeners, etc., at a variety of set test currents, as listed in *Figure 6.63*.

The *Figure 6.61* circuit can, by using the connections shown in *Figure 6.62b*, also be used to measure values of capacitance in the range 100nF to 3F; in this case (when $S_1$ is open) the constant current causes the capacitor's voltage to rise at a steady rate that is directly proportional to the values of test current and capacitance; by measuring the time, $t$, (in seconds) taken for the meter reading to reach F.S.D. on any given range, the capacitor's value can be deduced by simply multiplying $t$ by an appropriate factor, as shown in the table of *Figure 6.63*. Thus, with $SW_1$ on range 4 and with $SW_2$ on '×5', if the meter reading reaches F.S.D. 16s after $S_1$ is opened, the '$C_x$' value equals 16 × 20μF, or 320μF, etc.

## An electronic analogue multimeter

The multi-function ohmmeter circuit of *Figure 6.61a* is an outstandingly useful design, and *Figure 6.64* shows how it and the

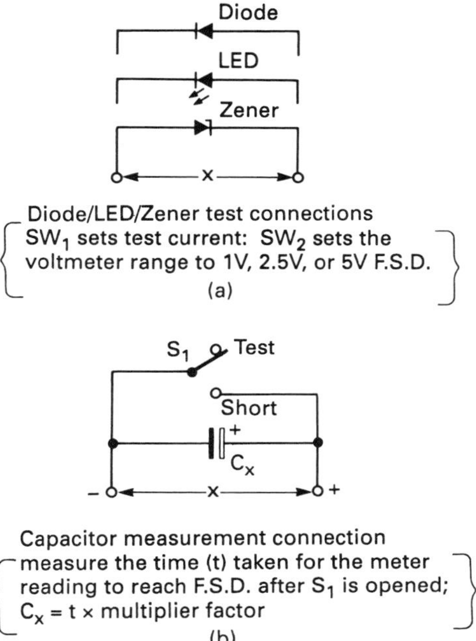


Figure 6.62. *The precision twenty-one-range multi-function ohmmeter can also be used to make useful tests on diodes, LEDs, and Zeners (a), and to measure the values of capacitors in the range 100nF to 3F (b).*

a.c./d.c. voltage converter of *Figure 6.40* can be combined with a few other circuit elements and a d.c. voltmeter to make a superb general-purpose electronic multimeter that, as well as offering twenty-four voltage ranges, thirty-six current ranges, twenty-one resistance ranges, three temperature (°C) ranges, and forty-two ranges of 'diode test' and capacitance measurement, also has facilities for testing its own battery voltages, for reversing its meter connections, and for giving a precision d.c. output voltage to an external 0–200mV d.c. digital voltmeter.

In this circuit, $SW_1$ selects voltage or current ranges via the input attenuator network, $SW_3$ selects either an a.c.- or d.c.-coupled input connection on the voltage ranges, and $SW_{2a}$ and $SW_{2b}$ feed the attenuators output to the $IC_1$ three-range d.c. voltmeter, either directly or via the precision a.c./d.c. converter. $SW_{2b}$ enables the voltmeter's input to be derived from either the

| Switch settings | | Resistance range, F.S.D. | Diode tests | | Capacitor measuring 'multiplier' factor |
|---|---|---|---|---|---|
| $SW_1$ | $SW_2$ | | Voltmeter range, F.S.D. | Test current | |
| 1 | × 1 | 10R | 100mV | 10mA | 0.1 F/sec |
| " | × 2.5 | 25R | 250mV | " | 0.04 "/" |
| " | × 5 | 50R | 500mV | " | 0.02 "/" |
| 2 | × 1 | 100R | 1V | 10mA | 10,000μF/sec |
| " | × 2.5 | 250R | 2.5V | " | 4000 "/" |
| " | × 5 | 500R | 5V | " | 2000 "/" |
| 3 | × 1 | 1k0 | 1V | 1mA | 1000μF/sec |
| " | × 2.5 | 2k5 | 2.5V | " | 400 "/" |
| " | × 5 | 5k0 | 5V | " | 200 "/" |
| 4 | × 1 | 10k | 1V | 100μA | 100μF/sec |
| " | × 2.5 | 25k | 2.5V | " | 40 "/" |
| " | × 5 | 50k | 5V | " | 20 "/" |
| 5 | × 1 | 100k | 1V | 10μA | 10μF/sec |
| " | × 2.5 | 250k | 2.5V | " | 4 "/" |
| " | × 5 | 500k | 5V | " | 2 "/" |
| 6 | × 1 | 1M0 | 1V | 1μA | 1μF/sec |
| " | × 2.5 | 2M5 | 2.5V | " | 0.4 "/" |
| " | × 5 | 5M0 | 5V | " | 0.2 "/" |
| 7 | × 1 | 10M | 1V | 0.1μA | 100nF/sec |
| " | × 2.5 | 25M | 2.5V | " | 40 "/" |
| " | × 5 | 50M | 5V | " | 20 "/" |

Figure 6.63. *Complete range of measurements of the multi-function 'ohmmeter' circuit.*

*V/I* inputs or via the seven-decade ohmmeter or the external temperature sensor ($IC_2$); $SW_{2c}$ and $SW_{2d}$ connect the power supply to the operative circuit elements. $SW_5$ enables the 1mA meter's connections to be reversed; this facility enables the meter to measure its own negative battery voltages.

## A low-value ohmmeter

To conclude this chapter, *Figure 6.65* shows a practical version of the basic 'four-terminal' low-value ohmmeter of *Figure 6.59*. This particular unit has four ranges, giving F.S.D. values of 100R, 10R, 1R0, and 0R1, and is capable of measuring resistances as low as a few milliohms on its most sensitive range. The voltmeter

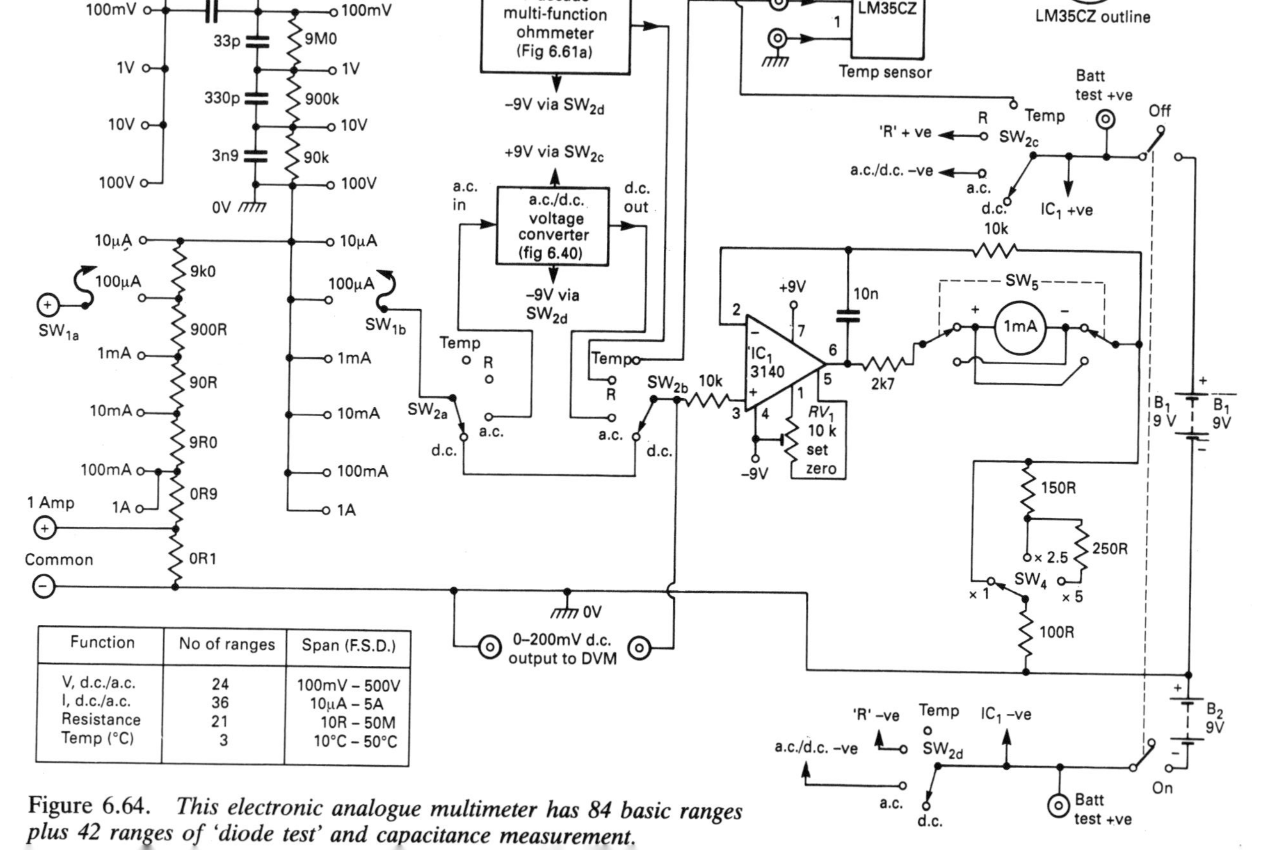


| Function | No of ranges | Span (F.S.D.) |
|---|---|---|
| V, d.c./a.c. | 24 | 100mV – 500V |
| I, d.c./a.c. | 36 | 10μA – 5A |
| Resistance | 21 | 10R – 50M |
| Temp (°C) | 3 | 10°C – 50°C |

Figure 6.64. *This electronic analogue multimeter has 84 basic ranges plus 42 ranges of 'diode test' and capacitance measurement.*

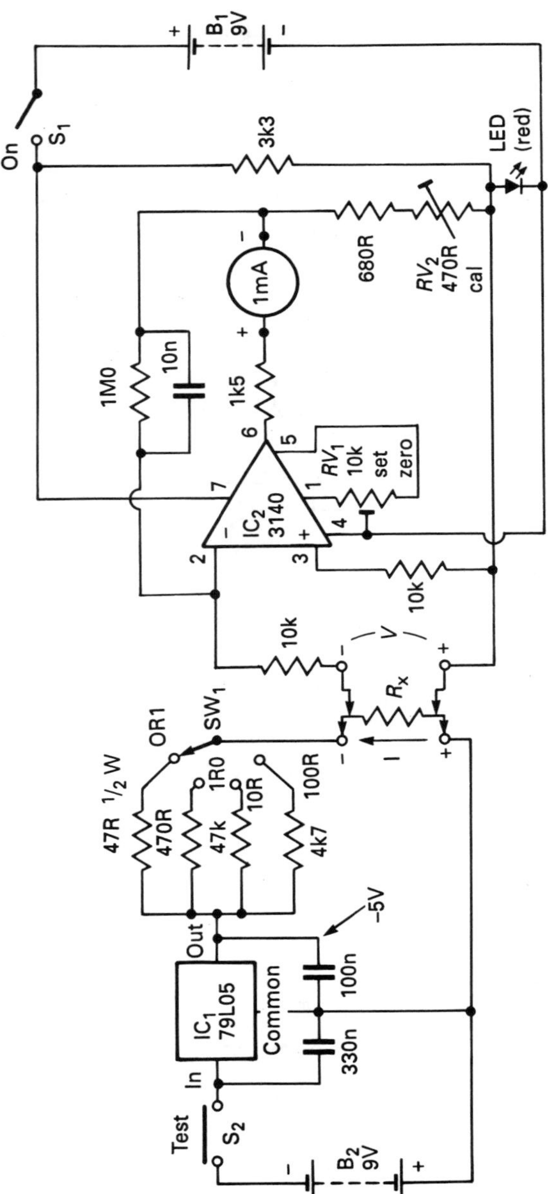


Figure 6.65. *This four-range 'four-terminal' low-value ohmmeter measures resistance from 100Ω down to a few milliohms.*

section of the unit reads F.S.D. with an $R_x$ input voltage of only 10mV, so very little power is dissipated in $R_x$.

The 'constant-current' generator part of the circuit is very simple. $IC_1$ is a −5V voltage regulator, and the output test current ($I$) is determined by the range resistor selected via $SW_1$; on each range the value of this resistor is very large relative to $R_x$, and the −5V supply is very large relative to the 10mV F.S.D. sensitivity of the unit's voltmeter; consequently, at meter readings below F.S.D., the output current on each range is effectively 'constant' and is independent of variations in the $R_x$ value.

The d.c. millivoltmeter (designed around $IC_2$) is a fairly conventional 'inverting' design with full overload protection. It uses a 3140 op-amp, which can respond to d.c. inputs down to zero volts. To enable the output to go slightly negative (for zero-setting purposes) a −1.5V rail is generated via the LED and 3k3 resistor.

To initially set up and calibrate this circuit, first short out the $V$ terminals, close $S_1$, and carefully trim $RV_1$ (which should be a multi-turn preset) to give zero reading on the meter. Now remove the short, switch $SW_1$ to the '100R' range, fit an accurate 100R resistor in the $R_x$ position, close **test** switch $S_2$ and trim $RV_2$ for an F.S.D. reading on the meter. The calibration is then complete, and the unit is ready for use. To use the unit, simply connect $R_x$ in place between the $I$ terminals, connect the $V$ leads directly across $R_x$ and, after selecting the appropriate range via $SW_1$, close $S_2$ to read the true value of $R_x$.

# 7 Digital panel meter circuits

Modern LCD digital panel meter modules are versatile units that can easily be used to accurately measure voltage, current, resistance, capacitance, frequency, temperature, and a whole lot more. This chapter explains how they work and how to use them.

## Digital panel meter basics

Modern digital panel meter (DPM) modules are basically sensitive high-resolution d.c. voltmeters that can be used to replace moving-coil meters in virtually all precision 'analogue' measuring applications. They combine a special A-to-D converter chip and an LCD readout unit and a few other components into a compact module that consumes less than 1mA from a 9V supply and costs little more than a good-quality moving-coil meter. Usually, these modules provide a $3\frac{1}{2}$-digit readout and have a basic full-scale measurement sensitivity of ±199.9mV, with 100μV (2000-count) resolution and typical calibrated precision of 0.1 per cent ±1 digit, but can be made to read any desired current or voltage range by connecting suitable shunts or dividers to the input terminals. When connected to suitable external circuitry the modules can also be made to indicate a.c. voltage or current, resistance, capacitance, frequency, or any other parameter that can be converted onto a linear analogue voltage or resistance.

DPM modules can be home-built with little difficulty, but the effort is scarcely worth while since compact and attractive commercially manufactured $3\frac{1}{2}$-digit ones are readily available at very economical prices. Most of these modules are designed around a GE/Intersil ICL7106, 7126, or 7136 A-to-D converter chip. *Figures 7.1* and *7.2* show the outline and basic usage diagram that is

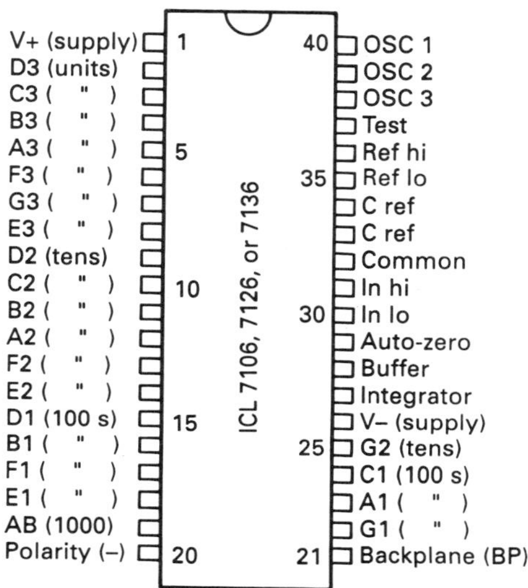


Figure 7.1. *Outline and pin notations of the ICL7106/7126/7136 LCD-driving DPM IC.*

common to all three of these ICs. Each of these low-power CMOS ICs houses a precision A-to-D converter and LCD drive circuitry, etc., in a 40-pin package. The A-to-D converter uses the dual-slope integration technique, with its inherent advantages of high noise rejection, near-perfect conversion linearity, and non-critical clock frequency. The IC accepts a true differential input voltage and provides digital conversion accurate to within ±1 count over the entire ±2000 count readout range; an auto-zero function ensures a zero reading at 0V input, and polarity indication is automatic. The ICL7106 typically consumes 1mA from a 9V supply; the 7126 and 7136 typically consume only 70μA of operating current.

All of the ICL7106/7126/7136 internal action is controlled via clock signals derived from a built-in oscillator, which (in *Figure 7.2*) is set to operate at about 48kHz via $R_1-C_1$. This frequency is divided by four and then used to control a three-phase (signal integrate, reference de-integrate, and auto-zero) conversion cycle which occupies 16000 oscillator cycles, thus giving the DPM about three reading updates per second. $R_3$ and $C_4$ set the integration time constant, and $C_5$ enhances the auto-zero circuitry's

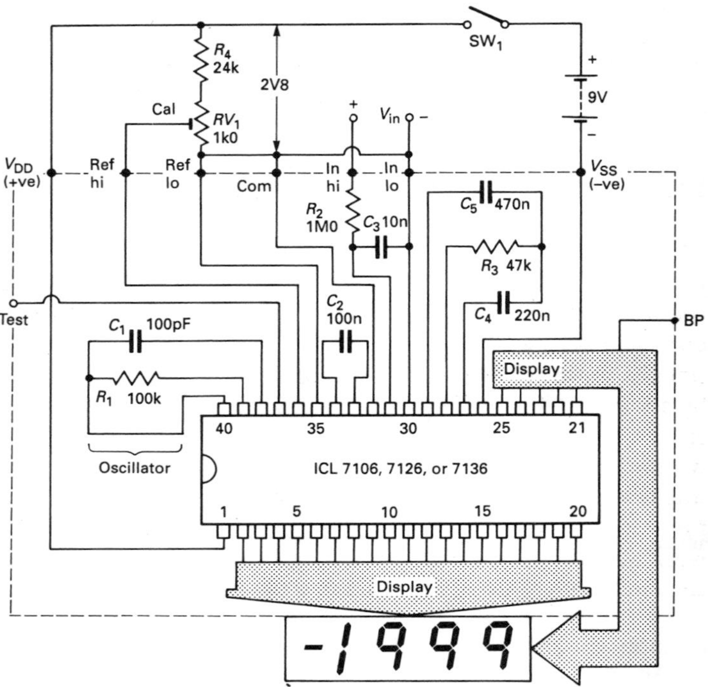


Figure 7.2. *Basic usage diagram of the ICL7106/7126/7136 as a 0–199.0mV d.c. meter.*

noise immunity. $R_2$ and $C_3$ form an input low-pass filter and overload protection network.

In *Figure 7.2* all of the above components are shown within the dotted lines, which enclose the IC's minimal operating circuitry. In action, the IC actually measures and compares the relative values (ratios) of its $V_{in}$ and $V_{ref}$ inputs and produces an LCD display of $1000 \times V_{in}/V_{ref}$. Thus, to make the circuit function as a 0 to 200mV d.c. voltmeter, the REF LO, IN LO, and COMmon terminals must be shorted together as shown, the input (test) voltage must be applied between the IN LO and IN HI terminals, and a 100mV reference voltage must be applied between the REF HI and REF LO terminals. The IC houses a zener regulator that generates a stable 2.8V between the COM and $V_{DD}$ terminals, and in the diagram this voltage is tapped down via $R_4$–

$RV_1$ and used to generate the 100mV REF HI to REF LO reference voltage. The *Figure 7.2* circuit thus functions as a basic 0 to 200mV d.c. voltmeter; it gives an over-range indication by blanking the three least significant digits of its display.

## Practical DPMs

The simple circuit of *Figure 7.2* makes a useful single-range voltmeter, but is too crude to make a really useful DPM. It has, for example, no facility for driving LCD decimal points or legends/annunciators, which must be driven via an inverted backplane signal. In practice, however, this problem can easily be overcome by adding a CMOS digital gate IC, worth a few cents, to the basic circuit. For a few cents more a one-transistor **low battery volts** warning unit can be added to the designs, and for just an extra dollar or two the circuit can be provided with a really stable precision 'bandgap' voltage reference. At that stage you end up with a standard and highly versatile commercial-grade DPM that can, in essence, be represented by the diagram of *Figure 7.3*.

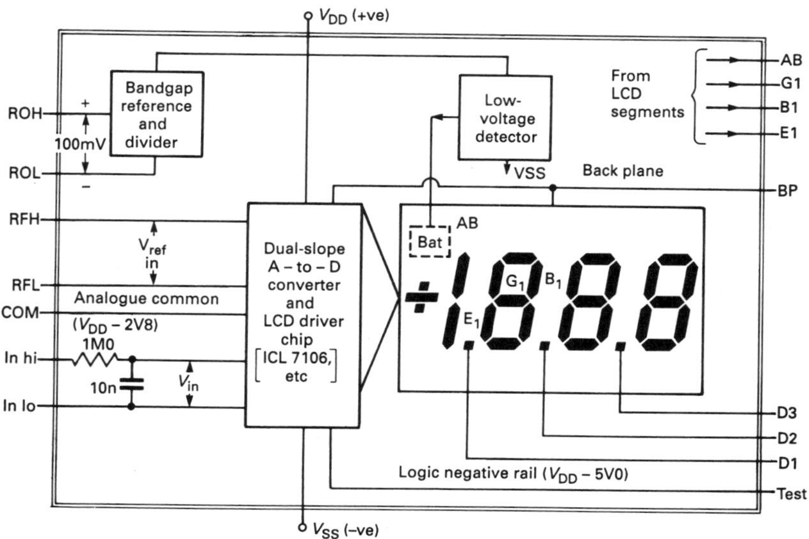


Figure 7.3. *Block diagram and 'user view' of a typical $3\frac{1}{2}$-digit DPM.*

$3\frac{1}{2}$-digit LCD DPMs of the *Figure 7.3* type are manufactured by dozens of companies, but normally differ only in minor details of their internal circuitry and displays, and in the number and notations of their user-available terminals. *Figures 7.4* and *7.5* show examples of the face appearance and rear-panel terminal notations of old-style and modern-style DPMs that are very typical of the genre; *Figure 7.6* lists the main parameters and features typical of modern DPMs. The main points to note from these diagrams are as follows:

DPMs are normally designed to be powered from a 9V battery connected between the $V_{DD}$ ($V+$) and $V_{SS}$ ($V-$) terminals. DPMs

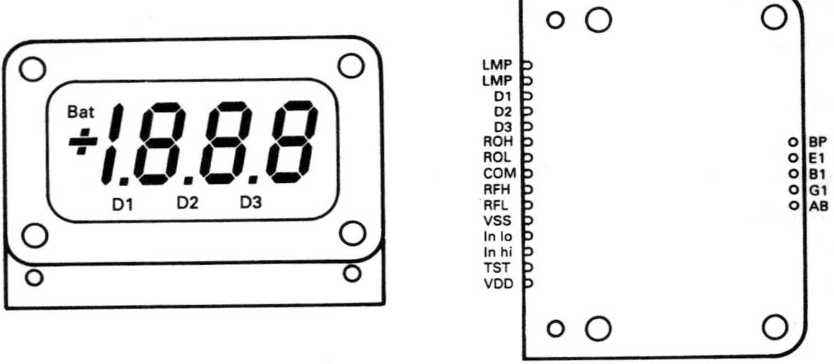


Figure 7.4. *Typical face and rear-panel terminal notations of an old-style or 'simple' DPM.*

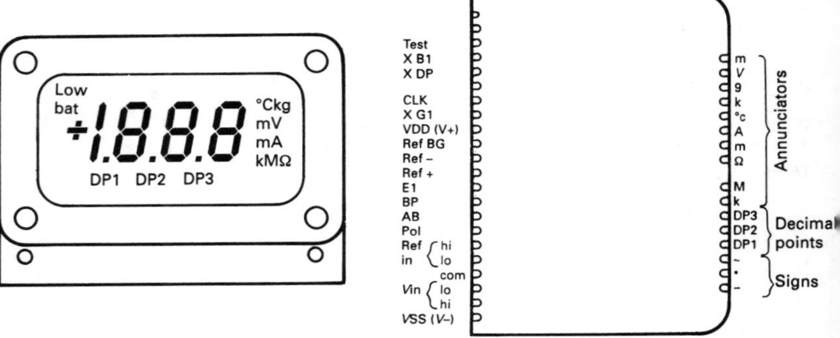


Figure 7.5. *Typical face and rear-panel terminal notations of a modern DPM.*

| Characteristic | Data (at 25°C) |
|---|---|
| Display | $3^1/_2$-digit LCD. |
| Full-scale sensitivity | ± 199.9mV |
| Power supply voltage | 7V to 10V DC (9V nominal) |
| Supply current | 1mA typ, on ICL7106-based units (70μA typ on 7126/7136-based units) |
| Initial calibration accuracy | ± 0.1% ± 1 count |
| Zero-input reading | ± 000.0 typ. |
| Display resolution | 1 count = 100μV |
| Input leakage current ($V_{in}$ = 0) | Less than 10pA |
| Operating temperature range | 0°C to +50°C |
| Input impedance (min) | 100MΩ |
| Clock frequency | 40kHz – 50kHz |
| Sample rate | 2.5 to 3 readings/second |
| 'Low battery' indication voltage | 7.2V typ. |

Figure 7.6. *Main parameters and features of a typical modern DPM.*

display the relative **Ratios** of their *input* and *reference-input* voltages; each of these voltages is applied via a **pair** of terminals (RFH [or REF HI] and RFL [or REF LO] for the reference, IN HI and IN LO for the input). These terminals must not vary from the COM terminal by more than ±2V. The terminals have typical input impedances of about 5000MΩ (1000MΩ minimum), and pass typical leakage currents of only a few picoamperes. The IN HI terminal features an internal d.c.-integrating filter.

DPMs usually have two built-in reference-voltage sources. The voltage between the COM and $V_{DD}$ ($V$+) terminals is zener-regulated at 2V8 and has a typical temperature coefficient of 80ppm/°C; any reference voltage below this value can be obtained by wiring a simple potential divider between these two terminals. The DPM also houses a precision 1.2V bandgap reference, and when ROL (REF−) is tied to COM a stable 100mV is generated between ROH (REF+) and ROL (REF−) and has a typical temperature coefficient of 50ppm/°C.

Access to the display's decimal points is externally available on terminals notated $D_1$, $D_2$, $D_3$ (or $DP_1$, $DP_2$, $DP_3$); usually, the left-hand point (or digit) is referred to as '1' and the right-hand one as '3' (as shown in *Figure 7.3*, but in some modules this practice is reversed. Access to all useful signs and annunciators is also externally available (see *Figure 7.5*). Each of these points or symbols can be turned on by connecting it to an inverted backplane (BP) signal, and the DPM invariably houses circuitry that makes this task easy. In old-style DPMs the points can usually be turned on by connecting the point terminal to the $V_{DD}$ ($V+$) terminal; in modern units the points and symbols can be turned on by simply connecting them to the XDP terminal; the manufacturer's leaflet supplied with the DPM explains these options.

The waveforms of the AB (1000 digit), $G_1$, $B_1$ and $E_1$ (hundreds) segments of the LCD display are externally available, either directly or in inverted ($X$) form, and can be used (in conjunction with external circuitry) to detect **under-range** and **over-range** operating conditions in some applications.

## Basic DPM configurations

*Figures 7.7* to *7.10* show four different ways of connecting the DPM's main terminals to give different types of measurement action. *Figure 7.7* shows the connections for making the DPM act as a ratiometric voltmeter, which (ideally) gives a reading of '1000' when two input voltages have identical values, irrespective of the actual values. Note here that the upper diagram (a) shows the notations and point-driving method used in old-style (*Figure 7.4*) DPMs, while the lower diagram (b) shows the connections applicable to a modern-style (*Figure 7.5*) unit, in which the 'mV' sign is activated via the XDP terminal and auto-polarity action is engaged by shorting the '−' and POL terminals. *Note through the rest of this chapter that*, to avoid unnecessary repetition, all remaining diagrams use the basic notations of *Figure 7.7a*, but show the modern (via XDP) method of driving the decimal points; in these diagrams minor details such as auto-polarity indication and annunciator activation are left to the common sense of the reader.

*Figure 7.8* shows the standard way of using the DPM as a 0 to 199.9mV d.c. meter, using the 100mV bandgap voltage (from ROL and RFL) as a precision reference, and decimal point $D_3$ activated via XDP so that the unit reads '100.0' when 100.0mV as applied between IN HI and IN LO.

*Figure 7.9* shows the DPM connected as a precision ohmmeter. Here, the $R_1-R_2$ divider generates roughly 270mV between the RFH and COM terminals, and this voltage is used to energize the $R_{ref}$-$R_x$ potential divider. Identical currents flow through these

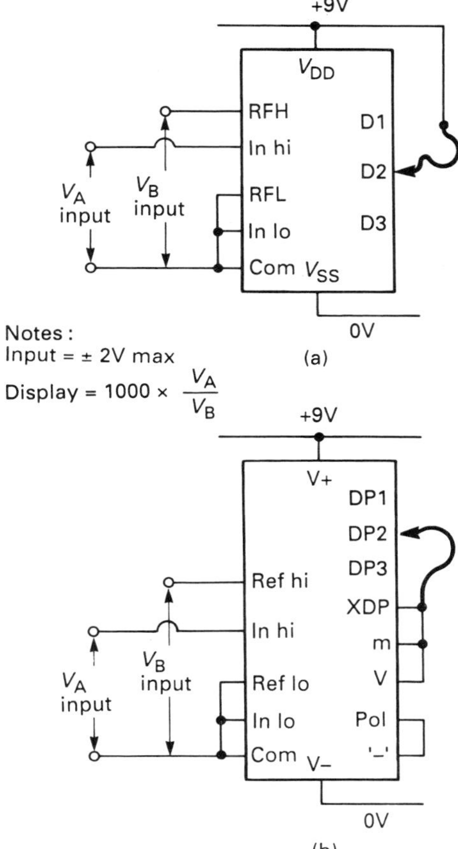


Figure 7.7. *Basic ratiometric voltmeter connections using (a) old-style and (b) modern-style DPMs.*

two resistors, and the generated voltage of $R_{ref}$ is applied across the RFH and RFL reference terminals, and that of $R_x$ is applied across the IN HI and IN LO input; the display reading thus equals 1000 × $R_x/R_{ref}$; if $R_x$ has a decade value (1k0, 10k, etc.) the display gives a direct readout of the $R_x$ value (this reading is independent of the actual value of the $R_2$ energizing voltage.

Finally, *Figure 7.10* shows how an offset voltage can be applied to the basic voltmeter circuit so that the display reads zero when

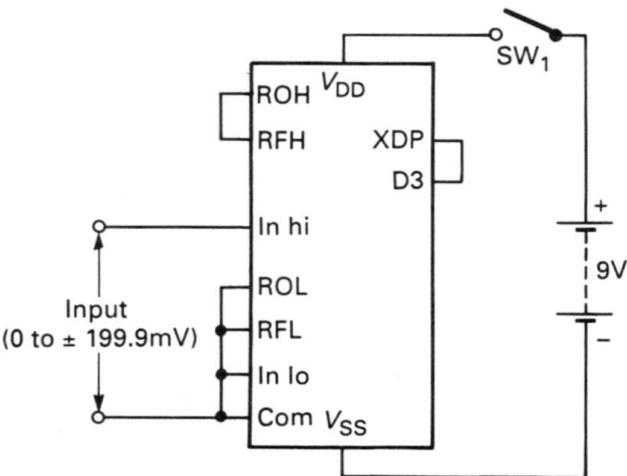


Figure 7.8. *Standard '199.9mV full-scale' connections of a DPM.*

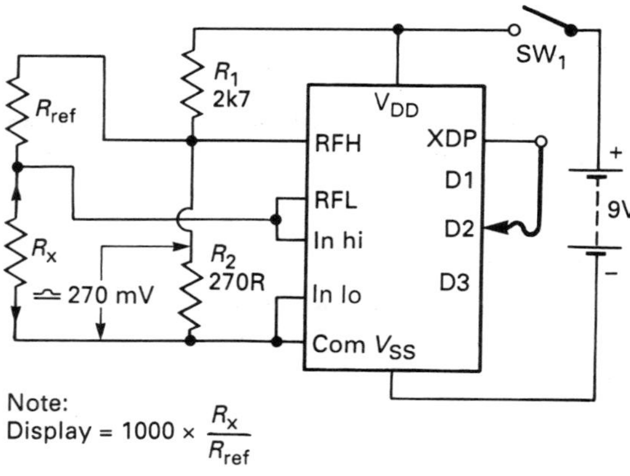


Figure 7.9. *Precision resistance meter, using ratiometric technique.*

the input voltage is at a value other than zero. This facility is useful in, for example, temperature-reading applications in which a sensor IC gives an output of 1mV/°K, thus giving an output of 273.2mV at 0°C and 373.2mV at 100°C. By connecting the sensor IC's output between the COM and IN HI terminals and applying a 273.2mV offset between COM and IN LO the DPM (which reads the *differential* value of input) can be made to give a direct reading of temperature in degrees Celsius.

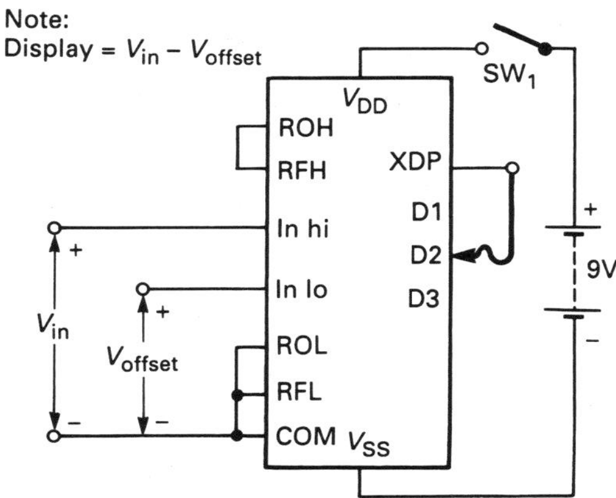


Figure 7.10. *Method of applying zero-offset to the basic '199.9mV d.c.' meter circuit.*

## Some finer points

Readers wishing to make the very best use of a DPM will need to learn a few fine 'usage' points, as detailed under the following set of sub-headings.

### *Calibration accuracy*

As supplied, a DPM module is pre-calibrated to read 199.9mV full scale, with a typical accuracy of ±0.1 per cent of reading ±1 count (at 25°C) when used in the standard configuration of *Figure 7.8*. The best attainable accuracy of a $3\frac{1}{2}$-digit (2000-count) meter is ±1 digit, and this corresponds to an actual reading accuracy of 0.05 per cent at full scale, to 0.5 per cent at 10 per cent of full scale, and to 5 per cent at 1 per cent of full scale.

### *Ratiometric accuracy*

A DPM is a ratiometric unit. If connected as in *Figure 7.11*, with identical voltages applied to the RFH and IN HI terminals, it should ideally read '1000' ±1 count, but in practice usually gives a reading about 0.1 per cent below this figure. This discrepancy is caused by the potential divider action of the internal 1M0 filter resistor and the input impedance of the IN HI line. When the meter is supplied for use in the voltmeter mode it is precalibrated to allow for ratiometric errors.

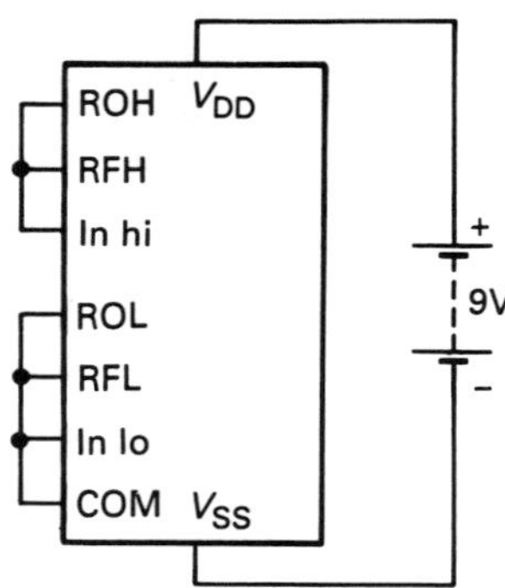


Figure 7.11. *Ratiometric-accuracy test circuit.*

### *Reference accuracy*

The built-in '100 mV' reference (between ROH and ROL) of the DPM is factory-calibrated so that the meter reads '100.0mV' with 100.0mV input applied. This is achieved by adjustment of $V_{ref}$ to compensate for the meter's ratiometric error; if the ratiometric error is 0.1 per cent low (reading 999), $V_{ref}$ is also set 0.1 per cent low (at 999mV) to give the correct 'voltmeter' accuracy. The $V_{ref}$ reference voltage is precisely accurate only when ROL is tied directly to COM (which is normally 2V8 below $V_{DD}$) and when ROH is loaded by an impedance greater than 50MΩ or so. *Figure 7.12* shows the typical circuit of the internal bandgap reference; the circuit's output impedance is about 20k, so an

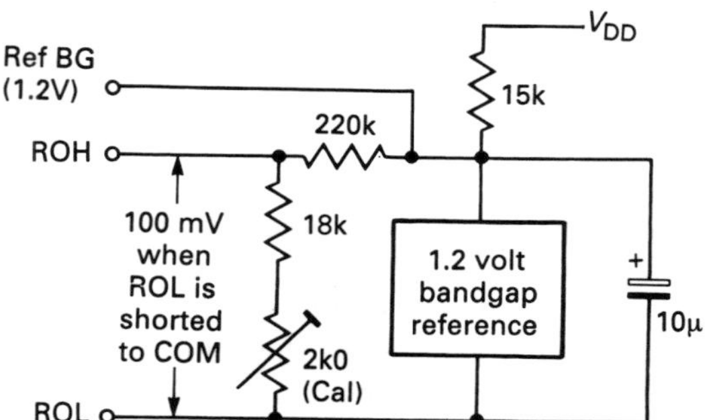


Figure 7.12. *Typical bandgap reference circuit has an output impedance of about 20k.*

external loading of 2M0 introduces an error of 1 per cent and 20M an error of 0.1 per cent; the high input impedance of the RFH input causes zero loading error.

### *Input connections*

All the internal analogue action of the DPM's A-to-D converter IC is referenced to the COM (common) line. In use, the INPUT and REFERENCE inputs should not vary from the COM line by more than ±2V; if the terminals rise beyond these levels the input leakage currents may rise to hundreds of picoamperes, invalidating the auto-zero action of the chip. The IC may be damaged if the terminals rise above $V_{DD}$−0.5V or fall below $V_{SS}$ + 1V.

### *The 'COM' terminal*

The module's COM terminal is connected to the circuit of *Figure 7.13* within the A-to-D chip, and enables the COM terminal to be used as either a precision voltage reference or as an externally-biased analogue reference point. When used as a precision voltage reference, only low (below 100μA) external sink currents must be allowed to flow between $V_{DD}$ and COM; under this condition the module's basic calibration is valid, and the COM terminal is

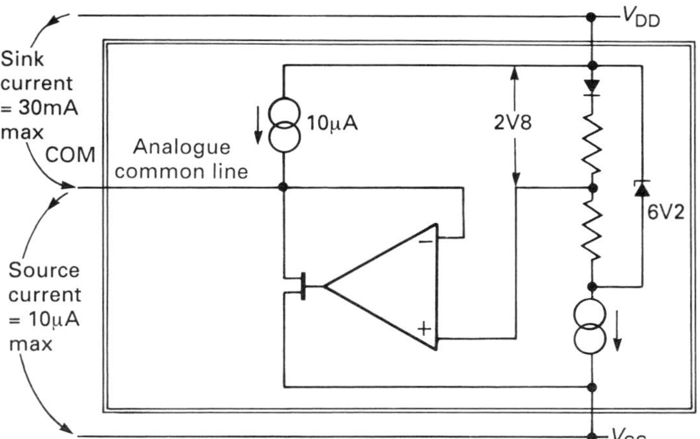


Figure 7.13. *Analogue COMmon line biasing circuit within the A-to-D converter chip.*

about 2V8 below $V_{DD}$ and has a typical temperature coefficient of about 80ppm/°C. Note that external load currents of up to 30mA *can* be allowed to flow between $V_{DD}$ and the COM terminal (which has an impedance of about 15R in this mode), but in this case the module's basic calibration may be invalid, and the RFH and RFL terminals may need to be driven from an external reference.

The COM terminal can source currents up to a maximum of only 10μA; the COM terminal can thus be tied to a value that is more than 2V8 below $V_{DD}$ by simply connecting it to an external bias voltage of the required value (as shown in the example of *Figure 7.15*), but must not be biased more than 4V7 below $V_{DD}$. Note that in this mode the module's basic calibration may be invalid, and the RFH and RFL terminals may have to be driven from an external reference.

***TEST & BP***

The negative or ground rail of the A-to-D converter chip's digital circuitry is internally biased at about 5V below $V_{DD}$ by the circuit of *Figure 7.14* and is coupled to the TEST terminal via a 500R resistor. This terminal can be used as the negative rail of external digital circuitry that is powered from $V_{DD}$, provided that the TEST currents do not exceed 1mA. If TEST is shorted directly to $V_{DD}$ the LCD should read '−1888' (in some models the B and G segments of the left-hand '8' are blanked in this

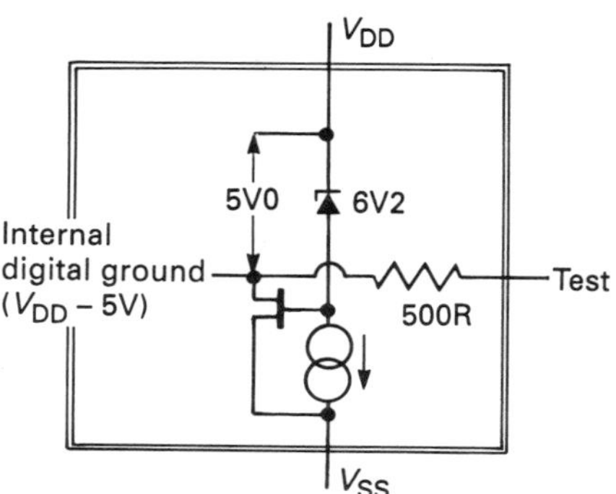


Figure 7.14. *Internal digital ground biasing circuit of the A-to-D converter chip.*

TEST mode); under this condition 10mA flows into the TEST pin and a D.C. voltage is applied to the LCD; this voltage may burn the display if sustained for several minutes.

The back-plane (BP) drive signal to the display switches fully between TEST and $V_{DD}$ at a rate of about 50 to 60Hz; the actual frequency is not critical, but equals the oscillator frequency divided by 800.

### *Power supplies*

In most application DPMs are simply powered via a 9V battery or a fully-floating 9V single-ended supply connected between the $V_{DD}$ and $V_{SS}$ terminals. A DPM can, however, be built into a piece of equipment and powered from existing 'split' supply rails by using the connections of *Figure 7.15*, in which COM is tied to the existing 'common' rail, $V_{DD}$ is fed from +4V7, $V_{SS}$ from −4V7, and the two sets of input terminals are referenced to the COM terminal; RFH must be driven via an external reference, as shown.

That completes the 'introductory' section of this chapter. The rest of the chapter deals with practical DPM application circuits.

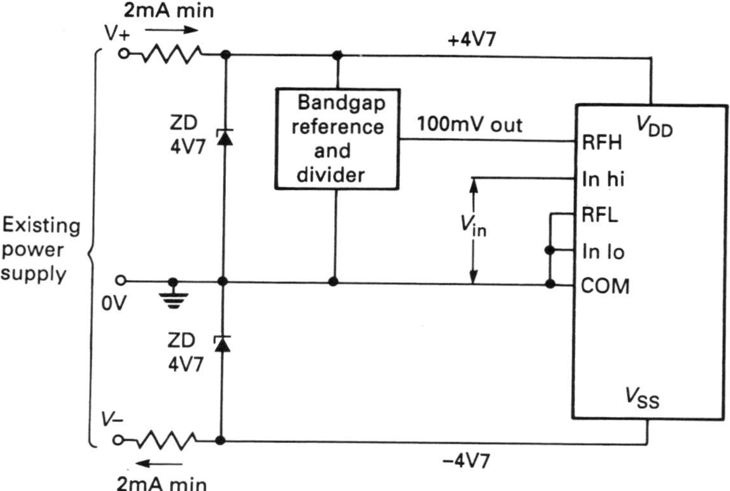


Figure 7.15. *Method of building a DPM module into existing equipment that is powered from split supply rails.*

# Practical DPM applications

## D.C. volt and current meters

A DPM module is usually supplied ready-calibrated to give a full-scale reading of ±199.9mV d.c. It can be made to give alternative full-scale d.c. voltage readings by connecting the input voltage to the module via a decade potential divider, as shown in *Figure 7.16*, or can be made to act as a d.c. current meter by wiring a suitable shunt resistor across the input terminals, as shown in *Figure 7.17*. Note in both diagrams that the appropriate decimal point of the display must be activated, as shown.

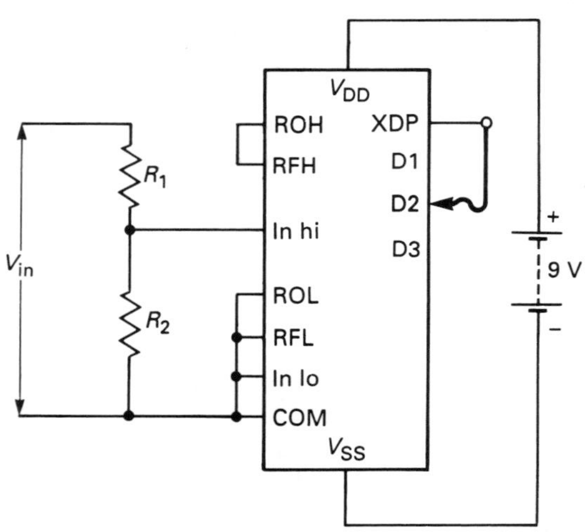


| $R_1$ | $R_2$ | $V_{full\ scale}$ | Decimal point high |
|---|---|---|---|
| 0 | 10M | 199.9mV | D3 |
| 9M0 | 1M0 | 1.999V | D1 |
| 9M9 | 100k | 19.99V | D2 |
| 10M | 10k | 199.9V | D3 |
| 10M | 1k0 | 1.999kV | D1 |

Figure 7.16. *A DPM can read alternative D.C. voltage ranges by connecting the input via a potential divider.*

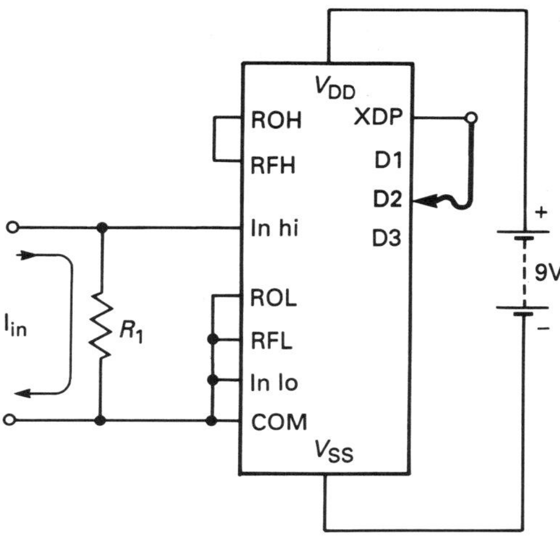


| $R_1$ | $I_{full\ scale}$ | Decimal point high |
|---|---|---|
| 10k | 19.99μA | D2 |
| 1k0 | 199.9μA | D3 |
| 100R | 1.999mA | D1 |
| 10R | 19.99mA | D2 |
| 1R0 | 199.9mA | D3 |
| 0R1 | 1.999A | D1 |
| 0.01R | 19.99A | D2 |

Figure 7.17. *A DPM can be made to read D.C. current by connecting a shunt resistor across its input.*

The module can be used as a five-range d.c. voltmeter by using the connections shown in *Figure 7.18*; the table shows alternative potential-divider component values to give input impedances of either 10 or 11.11MΩ. All multi-range circuits should ideally be fitted with some form of overload protection, and in the diagram this is given via fuse $F_1$ and a voltage-dependent resistor (VDR) or 'transient suppressor' across the divider; note on the '1.999kV' range that the maximum input is actually limited to 700V by the VDR.

The DPM module can be used as a five-range d.c. current meter by using the connections shown in *Figure 7.19*; the generated

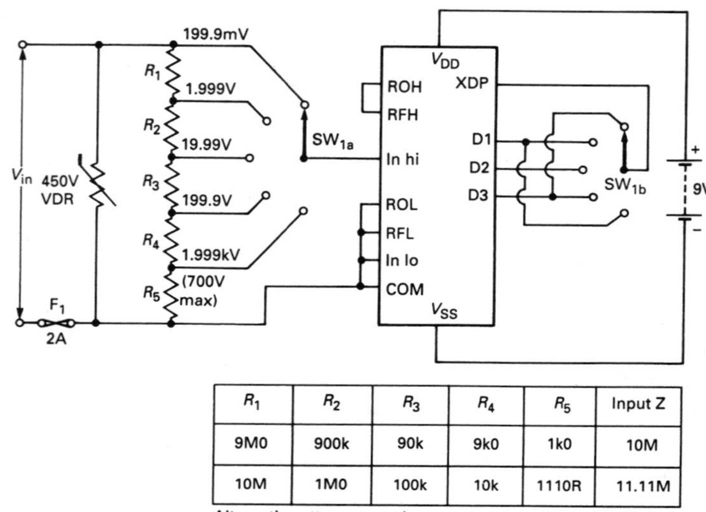


| $R_1$ | $R_2$ | $R_3$ | $R_4$ | $R_5$ | Input Z |
|---|---|---|---|---|---|
| 9M0 | 900k | 90k | 9k0 | 1k0 | 10M |
| 10M | 1M0 | 100k | 10k | 1110R | 11.11M |

Alternative attenuator valves

Figure 7.18. *Five-range D.C. voltmeter.*

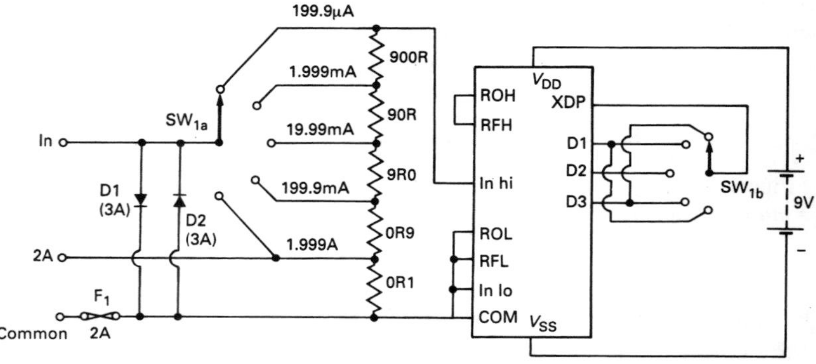


Figure 7.19. *Five-range D.C. current meter.*

voltages of the shunts are directly read by the module, and variations in the switch resistance of $SW_{1a}$ have no effect on the accuracy of measurement. Note that a separate input terminal is used for the '2A' measurement, and that overload protection is provided via $D_1$–$D_2$ and $F_1$.

## A.C. volt and current meters

*Figure 7.20* shows how the *Figure 7.18* circuit can be modified to act as a five-range a.c. voltmeter with a frequency response that is flat within 1dB to about 120kHz. Input signals are fed to the attenuator via d.c.-blocking capacitor $C_1$, and the attenuator is frequency-compensated by $C_2$ to $C_4$. The attenuator output is fed to the input of the DPM via a precision a.c./d.c. converter, which gives a d.c. voltage output equal to the r.m.s. value of a sine-wave input.

*Figure 7.21* shows how the *Figure 7.19* circuit can be similarly modified to act as a five-range a.c. current meter. In this case it is not feasible to prevent d.c. currents feeding into the shunts: instead, d.c.-blocking is done at the output of the shunts via $C_1$–$R_1$, and the resulting a.c. signals are fed to the input of the DPM via a precision a.c./d.c. converter. Input protection is via $F_1$ and two pairs of series-connected diodes.

*Figure 7.22* shows the circuit of the precision a.c./d.c. converter recommended for use with the above two circuits; the design is based on that of *Figure 6.40*, which is fully described in Chapter 6, and uses BAT85-type Schottky diodes as signal rectifiers. The gain of the converter can be set to precisely 2.2 via $RV_1$, to give a

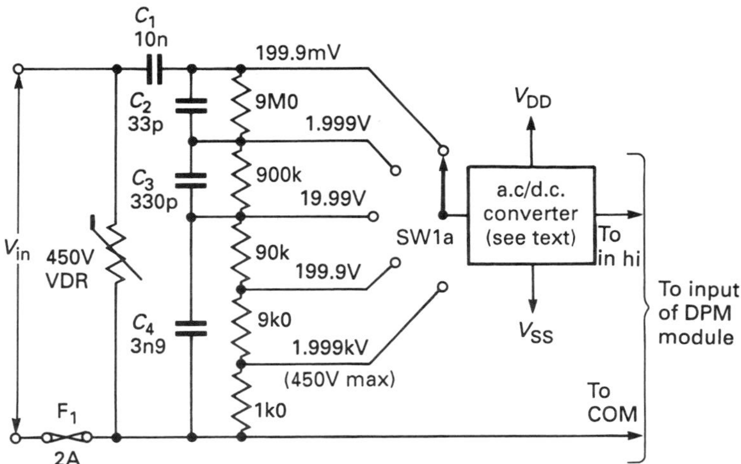


Figure 7.20. *Modification of the* Figure 7.18 *circuit, to act as a five-range A.C. voltmeter.*

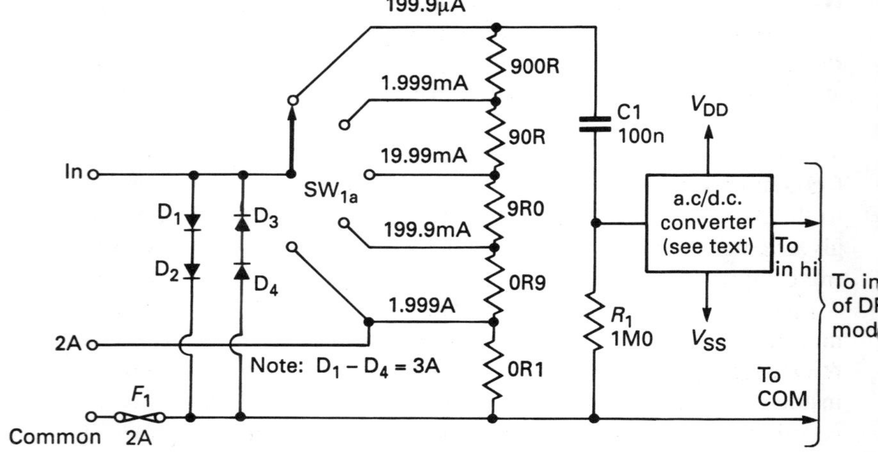


Figure 7.21. *Modification of the* Figure 7.19 *circuit, to act as a five-range A.C. current meter.*

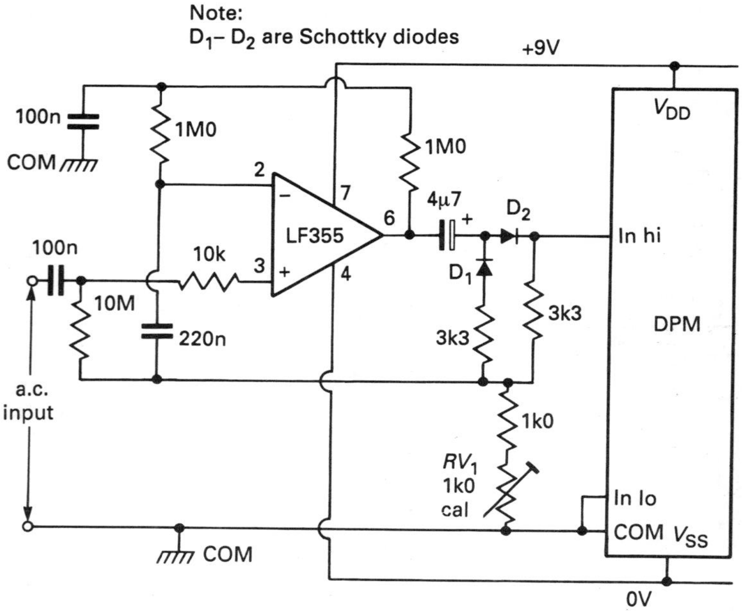


Figure 7.22. *Precision a.c./d.c. converter.*

d.c. output that is equal to the r.m.s. value of a sine-wave input. The converter is powered from the DPM's supply rails and is designed around an LF355 op-amp, which can operate well from the 2V8 between $V_{DD}$ and COM.

## Ohmmeters

The easiest and best way to use a DPM as a resistance (ohm) meter is to use it in the ratiometric configuration of *Figure 7.9*. This technique has two major advantages. First, it is very stable and inherently self-calibrating, the meter reading being equal to $R_x \times (\text{rat}/R_{ref})$, where 'rat' is the DPM's ratiometric value when used in the *Figure 7.11* test circuit: 'rat' is typically only 0.1 per cent low (0.1 per cent below unity), so measurement accuracy is determined primarily by $R_{ref}$. The second advantage is that very low test voltages are generated across $R_x$, at maximum being two thirds of the energizing voltage (typically 100 to 300mV at full scale). *Figure 7.23* shows how a DPM can be connected as a practical five-range ohmmeter.

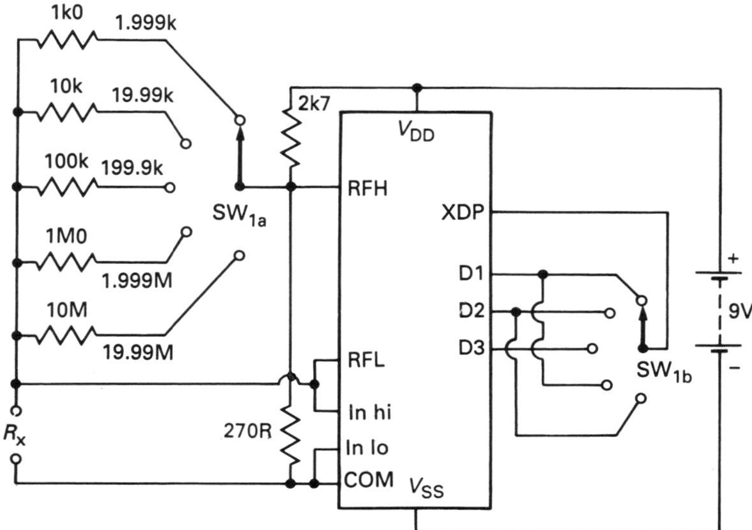


Figure 7.23. *Five-range digital ohmmeter.*

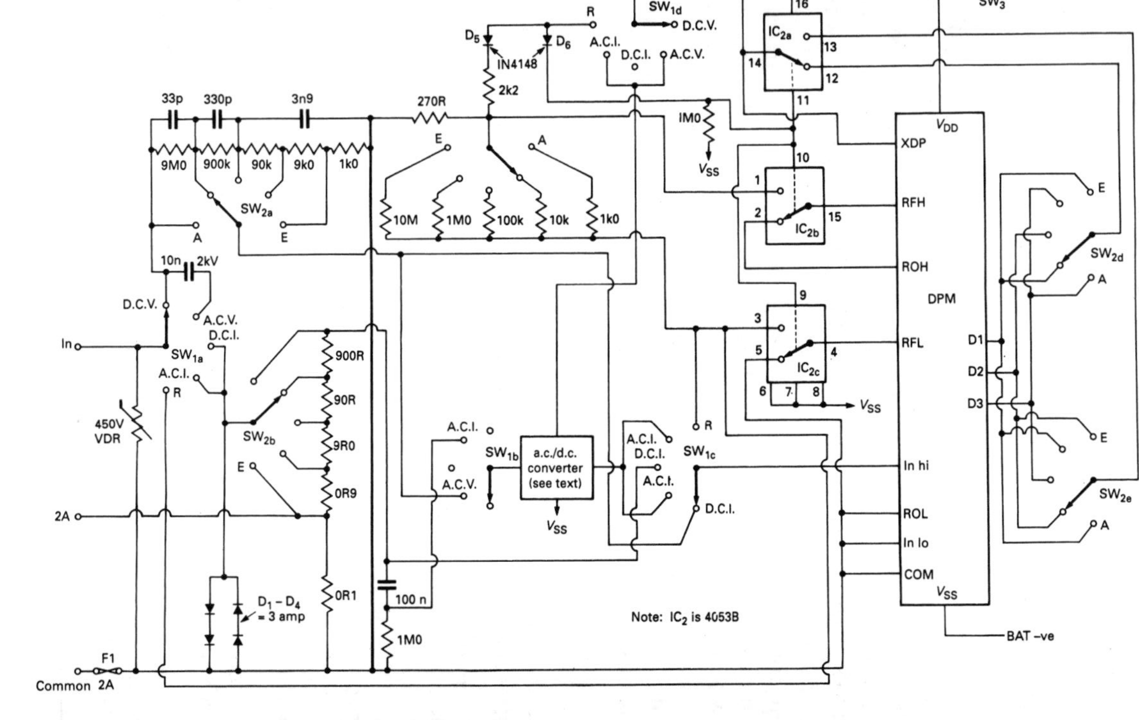


Figure 7.24. *Complete five-function 25-range multimeter.*

## A 25-range digital multimeter (DMM)

*Figure 7.24* shows how the circuits of *Figures 7.18* to *7.23* can be joined together to make a complete five-function 25-range digital multimeter, or DMM, and the table of *Figure 7.25* lists the ranges and functions of the meter.

The reader should have little difficulty in following the *Figure 7.24* circuit. Functions are selected by $SW_1$, ranges by $SW_2$. $SW_{1a}$ connects the inputs to the voltage, current, or resistance measuring networks, and $SW_{1d}$ activates the a.c./d.c. converter (which is the same as in *Figure 7.22*) or energizes the 'ohms' circuitry when necessary. Voltage ranges are selected by $SW_{2a}$, current ranges by $SW_{2b}$, and resistance ranges by $SW_{2c}$. $SW_{2d}$ and $SW_{2e}$ control the decimal point position on each range, the approriate switch being selected automatically via $IC_{2a}$. $IC_{2b}$ and $IC_{2c}$ control the basic configurations of the DPM module. $IC_2$ (a triple two-way analogue switch) is activated via $SW_{1d}$.

## Digital thermometers

A DPM module can be made to act as a wide-range (−50°C to + 150°C) digital thermometer by feeding the output of a linear voltage-generating temperature sensor to its inputs. Two types of sensor are readily available, the first being an ordinary bipolar silicon transistor, and the second being a dedicated IC. In either

| Mode ($SW_1$) | Range ($SW_2$) | | | | |
|---|---|---|---|---|---|
| | A | B | C | D | E |
| DCV | 199.9mV | 1.999V | 19.99V | 199.9V | 1.999kV [700Vmax] |
| ACV | 199.9mV | 1.999V | 19.99V | 199.9V | 1.999kV [450V max] |
| DCI | 199.9μA | 1.999mA | 19.99mA | 199.9mA | 1.999A |
| ACI | 199.9μA | 1.999mA | 19.99mA | 199.9mA | 1.999A |
| R | 1.999kΩ | 19.99kΩ | 199.9kΩ | 1.999MΩ | 19.99MΩ |

Figure 7.25. *Table of ranges and functions of the 25-range multimeter.*

case the resulting digital thermometer has a temperature discrimination of 0.1°C; linear accuracy varies from 0.5°C to 1.5°C, depending on the type of sensor and circuitry used.

Because of its low mass, a transistor sensor has a thermal response time some 10 to 100 times faster than a normal mercury thermometer. When used to measure sharp changes in the temperature of free air, a transistor-sensor circuit typically settles to within 0.1°C of the new temperature within one minute; a mercury thermometer takes some 20 minutes to attain the same accuracy.

## Transistor-sensor circuits

When an ordinary npn silicon transistor is connected as in *Figure 7.26a* and driven via a constant-current source it generates an output voltage that is directly proportional to the transistor's temperature; this voltage has a temperature coefficient of about −2mV/°C, and typically varies from about 600mV at 0°C to about 400mV at 100°C, as shown in the idealized graph of *Figure 7.26b*.

In practice the 'straight line' of the *Figure 7.26b* graph is linear, within about 1mV, over the full '0°C to 100°C' temperature range, but the precise voltage generated at any given temperature depends on the individual transistor and its operating current; errors due to self-heating effects are negligible at operating currents below 100μA; *Figure 7.26c* shows the typical voltage variation (at 25°C) over the 10 to 40μA operating current range.

*Figure 7.27* shows a practical example of a simple digital thermometer that uses a transistor sensor and gives a direct readout in °C, and has a linear accuracy within 1.5°C over the 0°C to 100°C range. A stable 2V8 is generated between $V_{DD}$ and COM of the DPM module, so $R_1$ drives the sensor transistor with a current of 22μA at 0°C, rising to about 24μA at 100°C (this current variation causes most of the 1.5°C linear error of the circuit). The sensor's output is fed directly to the DPM's IN LO terminal, and a 600mV (nominal) offset voltage (equal to the sensor voltage at 0°C) is fed to IN HI, and a 200mV (nominal) reference voltage (equal to the difference between the generated 0°C and 100°C voltages) is fed to the DPM's RFH terminal. Thus (since the DPM responds to the differential or 'IN HI minus IN LO' of its input), at 0°C the meter sees an input of 600mV −

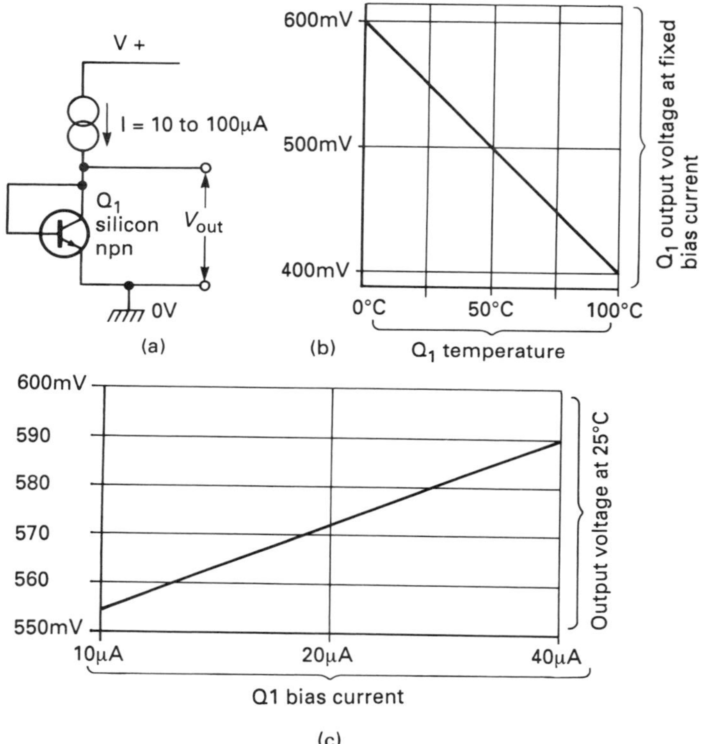


Figure 7.26. *When a transistor is connected as in (a) its output voltage varies by about −2mV/°C, as shown in (b). The output voltage also varies with drive current, as shown in (c).*

600mV = 0mV, and gives a reading of '00.0°C', but at 100°C it sees an input of 600mV − 400mV = 200mV and (since 200mV is applied to RFH) gives a reading of '100.0°C'.

*Figure 7.28* shows a 'precision' version of the above thermometer circuit. This design has a linear accuracy of about 0.5°C, and its transistor sensor is energized at about 20μA via constant-current generator $Q_1$, which is temperature compensated by $Q_2$. Here, the $R_3$–$R_4$ divider (wired between $V_{DD}$ and COM) generates voltage $V_t$ (about 1V) across $R_3$, and this voltage is 'followed' by $Q_2$ and causes voltage $V_b$ (equal to $V_t + V_{be2}$) to appear on $Q_1$ base. The '$V_e$' voltage appearing on the emitter of $Q_1$ is thus

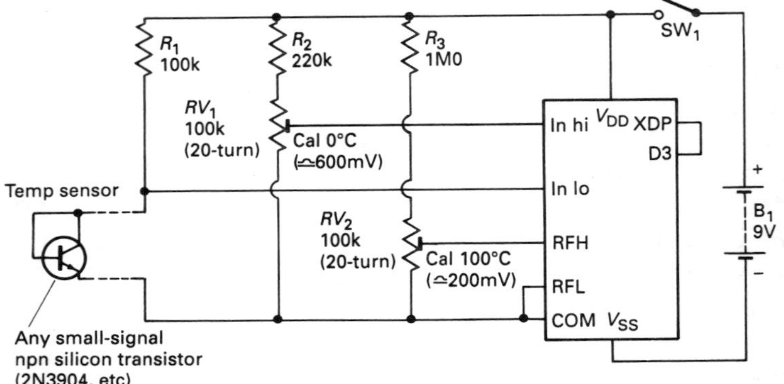


Figure 7.27. *Simple digital thermometer using a transistor sensor. Linear accuracy is about 1.5°C.*

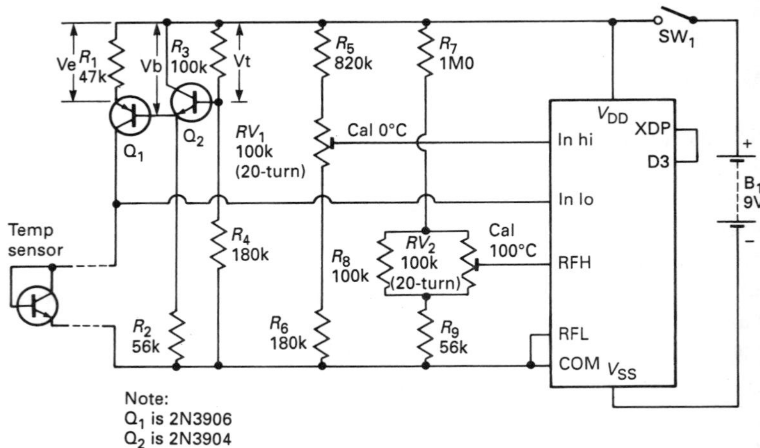


Figure 7.28. *Precision digital thermometer using a transistor sensor. Linear accuracy is 0.5°C.*

equal to $V_t + V_{be2} - V_{be1}$; note, however, that since $Q_1$ and $Q_2$ operate at near-identical temperatures and at similar current levels, the $V_{be1}$ and $V_{be2}$ values cancel out at all operating temperatures, and $V_e$ thus equals $V_t$. The constant-current output of $Q_1$ thus equals $V_t/R_1$, and is independent of variations in ambient temperature, etc.

## Calibration procedure

To calibrate the above two 'thermometer' circuits, first make up the transistor sensor and its flexible leads, then coat all sensitive parts with insulating varnish. When the varnish has dried, mix a quantity of crushed ice and cold water in a tumbler (to act as a '0°C' standard), immerse the sensor in the tumbler, and adjust $RV_1$ to give a '00.0' reading on the DPM. Finally, remove the sensor from the tumbler and immerse it in gently simmering boiling water (to act as a '100°C' standard), then adjust $RV_2$ to give a meter reading of '100.0'. Basic calibration is then complete. If the meter is to be used mainly around some nominal value, such as 25°C, etc., $RV_1$ can (after initial calibration) be used to set the meter 'spot on' at that value by immersing the probe and a standard thermometer in a liquid that is raised to the desired temperature.

## IC-sensor circuits

Several companies manufacture dedicated temperature-sensor ICs suitable for use in DPM-based digital thermometers. One such device is the GE/Intersil AD590; essentially a two-pin IC (but with a third pin shorted to its case), it gives an output current of 1μA/°K which, when fed through a 1k0 resistor, gives an output of 1mV/°K. The uncalibrated 'spot' accuracy of the AD590 varies from 0.5°C to 10°C, and linearity error from 0.3°C to 1.5°C, depending on the device's 'grade' (indicated by a suffix number); the 590kH version of the IC has a 'spot' accuracy of ±2.5°C at 25°C and can be used over the −55°C to +150°C temperature range. *Figure 7.29* shows how an AD590 can be used with a DPM module.

The AD590 needs a supply of at least 4V, and this is obtained by wiring the IC between $V_{DD}$ and TEST (which is internally set at 5V below $V_{DD}$) via $D_1$, which biases the COM terminal about 600mV above TEST. $R_1$ is wired in series with the AD590 and generates approximately 1mV/°K (= 273.2mV at 0°C, 373.2mV at 100°C), and this voltage is fed to the IN HI terminal. Bandgap reference $IC_2$ generates a stable 1V2, which is divided down via $R_3$−$RV_1$−$R_4$ to give a 'SET 0°C' offset voltage of 273.2mV nominal at IN LO. The bandgap reference voltage is also divided

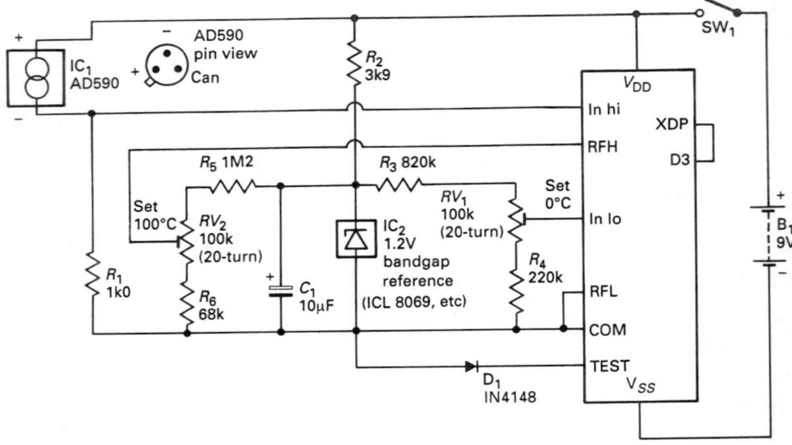


Figure 7.29. *Digital thermometer based on the AD590 temperature-sensor IC.*

down by $R_5$–$RV_2$–$R_6$ to provide a 'SET 100°C' scaling voltage of 100mV nominal at RFH. The circuit must be calibrated in the way already described for the *Figure 7.27* and *7.28* designs.

An even more useful temperature sensor IC is the LM35CZ, from National Semiconductors. This three-terminal IC is housed in a plastic TO-92 package and gives a linear output voltage of 10mV/°C, with a typical accuracy of ±0.4°C at 25°C, and can be used over the −40°C to +110°C temperature range. The IC must be powered from a voltage in the 4 to 30V range, typically consumes 90μA at 5V, has a very low output impedance (typically 0.4Ω at 1mA load), and needs no external calibration. *Figure 7.30* shows the IC's outline and basic application circuits; note that if the IC is to be used to indicate sub-zero temperatures '*R*' must be connected to its output (pin-2) and taken to a negative supply rail.

The major feature of the LM35CZ is that it needs no external calibration, and the best way to use it in DPM applications is as an add-on accessory for use with an existing DPM voltmeter. In this case the IC should be used as a 'stand-alone' independently powered unit as shown in *Figure 7.31*, with its output taken (when needed) to the '200mV d.c.' input of the DPM via the 10:1 $R_1$–$R_2$ attenuator.

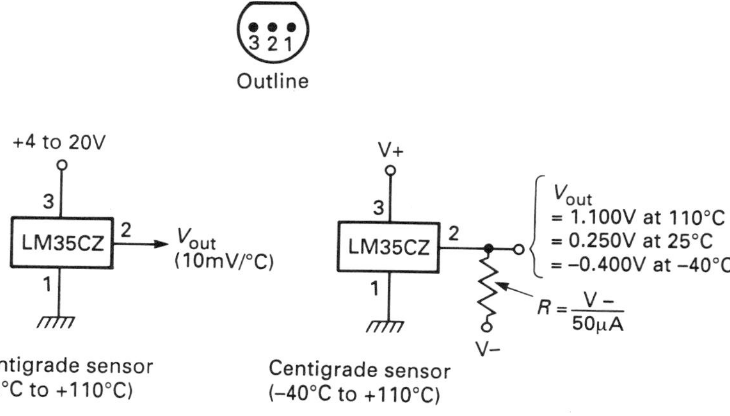


Figure 7.30. *LM35CZ outline and basic application circuit.*

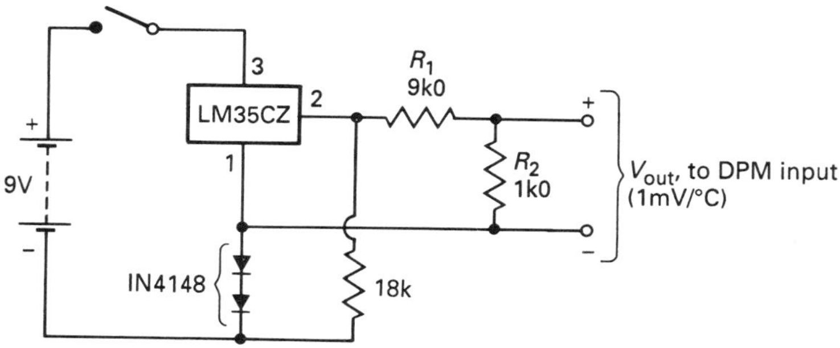


Figure 7.31. *'Stand-alone' IC temperature converter, for use with a 0–200mV d.c. DPM.*

## Digital capacitance meter basics

A DPM can be made to read capacitance ($C$) values by connecting the unknown $C_x$ to it via a linear $C$-to-$V$ converter. One way to make such a converter is to use $C_x$ and a standard resistor ($R_x$) as the timing elements in a precision monostable that generates an output pulse with a width ($W$) linearly proportional to the $C_x$–$R_x$ product, as shown in *Figure 7.32*. This monostable is triggered at

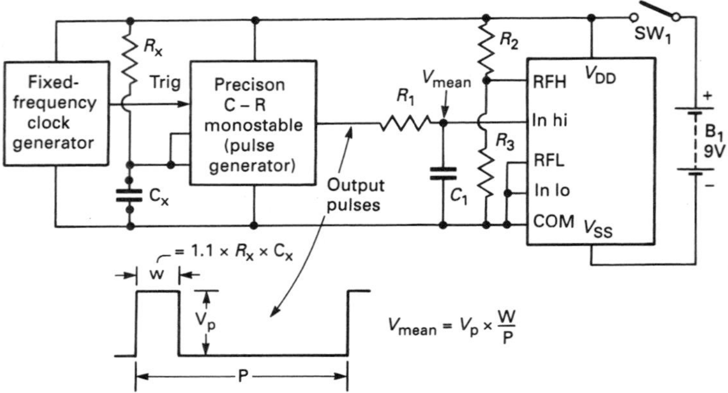


Figure 7.32. *Basic operating principle and circuit of a digital capacitance meter.*

a fixed frequency or repetition period, $P$, and its output is converted to a mean d.c. value via a $C$–$R$ integrator; this mean value equals the peak pulse amplitude multiplied by $W/P$ and, since $R_x$ and $P$ are fixed, is directly proportional to $C_x$; the DPM thus acts as a digital capacitance meter when this voltage is fed to its input.

In *Figure 7.32* the DPM's reference (RFH) voltage is derived from the monostable's supply rail via divider $R_2$–$R_3$, so (since the DPM reads the *ratio* of the input and reference voltages) the unit's calibration is independent of variations in supply rail voltage but can be varied by altering the $R_2$–$R_3$ ratio. The circuit can be made to read different capacitance ranges by switching $R_x$ in decade multiples.

## A practical capacitance meter

*Figure 7.33* shows a practical example of the basic *Figure 7.32* circuit. It uses a 7555 timer IC (a CMOS version of the 555) as its precision monostable, with decade values (1k0 to 10M) of $R_x$ used for range selection. This monostable generates a pulse width of $1.1 \times C \times R$, thus giving a full-scale pulse width (at '1999' on the DPM) of 22ms with $C$ and $R$ values of 1999pF and 10M, or

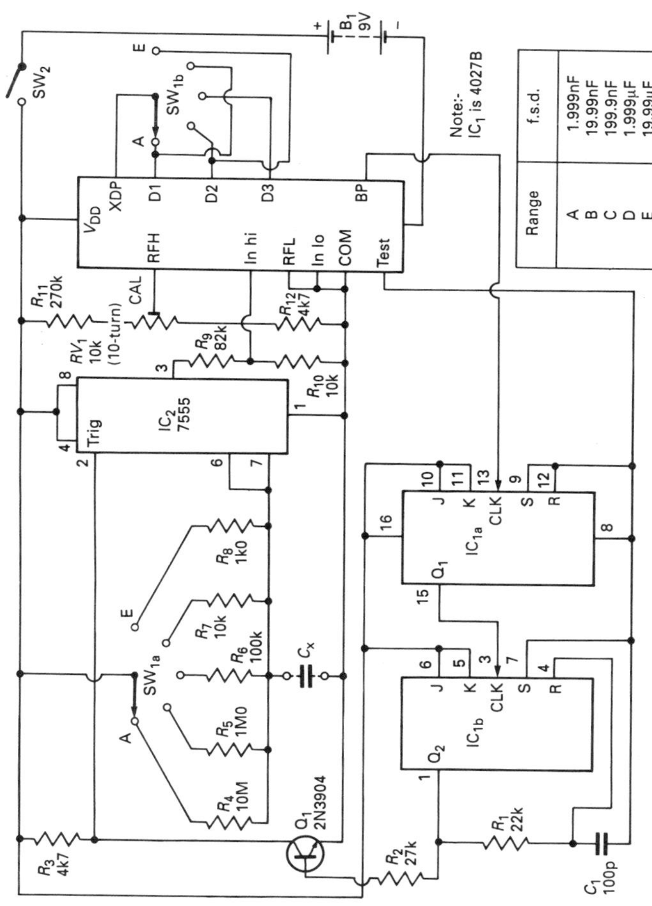


| Range | f.s.d. |
|---|---|
| A | 1.999nF |
| B | 19.99nF |
| C | 199.9nF |
| D | 1.999μF |
| E | 19.99μF |

Figure 7.33. *Digital capacitance meter.*

19.99μF and 1k0, etc. To give the 7555 adequate recovery time between pulses the clock period must be at least 50 per cent longer than the maximum pulse width; it must be at least 33ms.

The 7555 monostable is triggered by pulling pin-2 of the IC low, and for correct operation the trigger pulse must be shorter than the minimum required output pulse. In this particular application the shortest pulse width that can be indicated by the DPM module is 22ms/2000 = 11μs. Thus, in this circuit the trigger pulse needs to be a negative-going one with a width less than 11μs and with a repetition period greater than 33ms. In *Figure 7.33* these requirements are met as follows.

In the DPM module the TEST terminal is internally biased at about 5V below $V_{DD}$, and the BP (backplane) terminal switches between TEST and $V_{Dd}$ at about 50Hz, giving a period of 20ms. In *Figure 7.33*, $IC_1$ is powered via the TEST terminal, and the BP signal is divided-by-2 by flip-flop $IC_{1A}$; the resulting 25Hz (40ms) signal clocks $IC_{1b}$, which is configured as a monostable and generates (via $R_1$ and $C_1$) positive-going output pulses of 2μs width. These pulses are inverted and level shifted via $Q_1$, to produce negative-going 2μs trigger pulses with periods of 40ms on the pin-2 TRIG terminal of monostable pulse generator $IC_2$.

$IC_2$'s pulse width is controlled by $C_x$ and range resistors $R_4$ to $R_8$; its output is attenuated by $R_9$−$R_{10}$ to give a mean value of about 100mV at the mid-scale ('1000') setting of the DPM, and the resulting signal is fed to the DPM's IN HI terminal, where it is integrated by its internal 1M0−10nF filter. Divider $R_{11}$−$RV_1$−$R_{12}$ feeds 100mV nominal to the RFH terminal of the DPM, and $RV_1$ is used to adjust the precise calibration of the capacitance meter.

The precision of the *Figure 7.33* circuit is determined mainly by its $R_4$ to $R_8$ range resistors, which should be 1 per cent or better types. To calibrate the circuit, simply connect a precision capacitor (say 100nF) in place as $C_x$, switch to the appropriate range, and trim $RV_1$ for the appropriate meter reading. Calibration is then valid on all ranges.

## A precision capacitance meter

The *Figure 7.33* circuit suffers from two minor defects. The first is that the periods of its BP-derived 40ms clock signals (and thus the circuit's calibration accuracy) drift by as much as 0.5 per cent with variations in temperature and battery voltage. The second snag is that the circuit reads *all* capacitance, including residuals, appearing between its $C_x$ terminals, and these total about 32pF with no external $C_x$ connected; these residuals are too small to be read on ranges *C* to *E*, but (for maximum accuracy) must be subtracted from all readings obtained on ranges *A* and *B*.

*Figure 7.34* shows how the circuit can be modified so that residual capacitance is effectively cancelled out and the meter reads zero on all ranges when no external capacitance is connected to the $C_x$ terminals. In this case the BP-derived signal is used to synchronously trigger *two* 7555 monostables, and their outputs are EX-ORed via $IC_4$ to give a pulse equal to the *difference* between their pulse widths, and this 'difference' pulse is fed to the DPM module's IN HI terminal. Monostable $IC_2$ is connected to the $C_x$ terminals (which are shunted by an additional 10pF), and monostable $IC_3$ is 'timed' via trimmer capacitor $C_2$; during calibration, $C_2$ is adjusted so that both monostables generate identical pulse widths with no external $C_x$ connected, and zero 'difference' pulse are fed to the DPM; the circuit's residuals are thus effectively cancelled, and the meter responds to *externally* connected $C_x$ values only. Note that $IC_3$ is range-switched in parallel with $IC_2$ via $SW_{1c}$; precise ganging is provided on ranges *A*, *B* and *C* only; on all other ranges the residuals are too small to influence the meter readings.

## Frequency measurement

A DPM can be made to read frequency by connecting the unknown frequency to its input via an f-to-V converter; a suitable converter can be made by using a 7555 monostable in the manner shown in *Figure 7.35*. Here, the input signals are fed through a trigger-pulse generator that triggers the fixed-period 7555 monostable pulse generator on the arrival of each new input cycle, and these monostable pulses are integrated via $R_1-C_2$ and fed to the input of the DPM module, which is scaled via $R_3-R_4$. The integrated mean-d.c. value of these pulses equals $V_p$ (their peak amplitude) multiplied by *W* (their width) and *f* (the input frequency); $V_p$ and *W* have fixed values, however, so the d.c. signal reaching the DPM is directly proportional to *f*. Thus, when the DPM is suitably

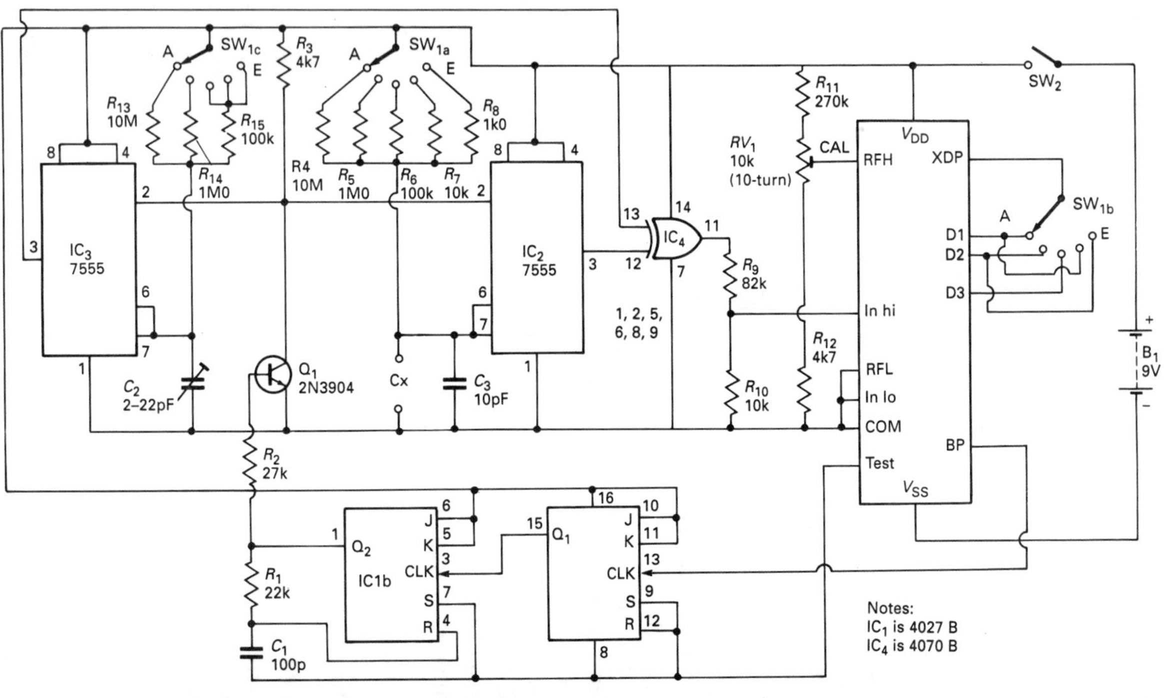


Figure 7.34. *Precision capacitance meter with zero residual reading.*

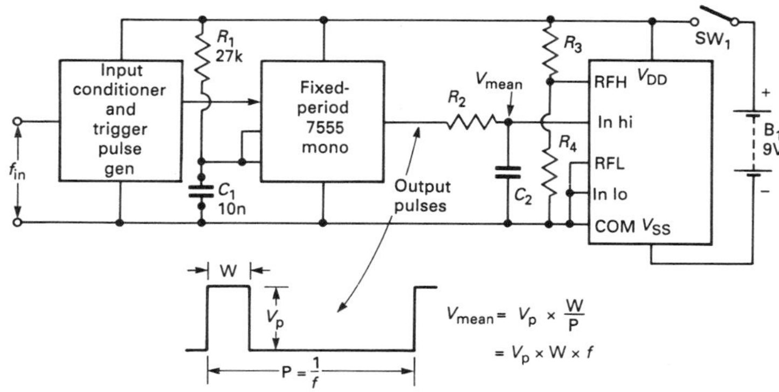


Figure 7.35. *Basic method of using a DPM module as a frequency meter.*

scaled via $R_3$–$R_4$ it acts as direct-reading digital frequency meter, or DFM.

In practice, the lowest convenient full-scale range of a DPM-based $3\frac{1}{2}$-digit DFM is 1.999kHz, and this corresponds to a pulse period of 500μs. For maximum accuracy, the pulse width must be less than two-thirds of $P$, so a width ($W$) of about 300μs is needed and can be obtained from the 7555 by using $R_1$ and $C_1$ values of 27k and 10nF respectively.

*Figure 7.36* shows how the basic *Figure 7.35* circuit can be modified to act as a multi-range DFM. In this case the input signal is fed to an input conditioner and Schmitt trigger, and the Schmitt output is used to ripple-clock four decade dividers. The 7555 300μs monostable is provided with a trigger generator that can be fed from the output of the Schmitt or from any of the dividers. Thus, when the 7555 is triggered directly from the Schmitt the DPM reads 1.999kHz full scale, and when fed from the output of the last divider reads 19.99MHz full scale.

## Practical frequency meters

Standard CMOS counter ICs need supplies of at least 3V, so when a DPM is used as a DFM sharing supplies that are common with those of the CMOS divider stages it must be used in the 'split-supply' mode, with its COM terminal pulled below the

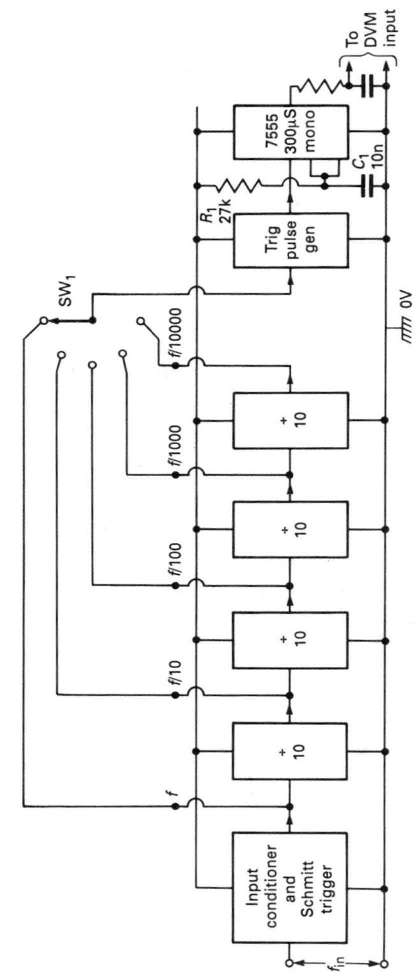


Figure 7.36. *Basic method of using a DPM as a multi-range frequency meter.*

normal '$V_{DD}$ − 2V8' value by external circuitry, i.e. with COM at 0V and $V_{DD}$ and $V_{SS}$ at values of about +4V5 and −4V5 respectively. *Figure 7.15* shows one way of obtaining these supplies; alternatively, *Figure 7.37a* shows how the supplies can be obtained from a stack of six 1V5 cells, or *Figure 7.37b* shows how they can be obtained from a single 9V battery via an op-amp supply-splitter. The supply-splitter of *Figure 7.37b* adds a quiescent current consumption of about 2mA to the DPM circuit, but can supply additional currents of tens of milliamperes to circuitry connected between +4V5 and 0V.

*Figure 7.38* shows the practical circuit of a DPM-based DFM that reads up to 19.99MHz full-scale in five decade ranges. When used with the *Figure 7.37b* power supply the circuit consumes about 3mA quiescent from a 9V battery, rising to 4mA at 1MHz, and (when calibrated) has a reading accuracy of ±1 digit. The circuit accepts input signals in the range 200mV to 5V0 r.m.s., and operates as follows.

Input signals are fed, via $C_1$−$R_1$, to the input of $IC_{1a}$, a very fast Schmitt trigger, which is biased at half-supply volts via $R_2$−$R_3$. The Schmitt output is used to ripple-clock four decade-divider stages; ordinary CMOS dividers operate up to maximum speeds of only 1MHz when operated from 4V5 supplies, so to give the required fast operating speeds 'HC' types of silicon-gate CMOS counters are used in the first two ($IC_2$ and $IC_3$) counter positions; on the prototype unit these operate well up to about 18MHz.

The outputs of the $IC_{1a}$ Schmitt and the four divider stages are fed to range-selector $SW_{1a}$ and passed on to 4μs trigger-pulse generator $C_4$−$R_4$−$IC_{1b}$−$IC_{1c}$ which triggers the 7555 monostable via $Q_1$. The output of the 7555 is fed to IN HI of the DPM via $R_8$−$R_9$, and a calibration 'reference' voltage is fed to RFH via $RV_1$. The circuit is calibrated by feeding in a signal of known frequency, switching to the appropriate range, and trimming $RV_1$ for the appropriate reading on the DPM module. Once the initial calibration is complete, subsequent accuracy is influenced only by variations in the 7555's pulse width, caused by thermal variations in the values of $R_7$ and $C_5$; for optimum calibration stability, $R_7$ should be a highly stable metal-glaze resistor, and $C_5$ a polycarbonate capacitor.

The *Figure 7.38* circuit can be modified in a variety of ways, to satisfy individual needs. *Figure 7.39* shows a 1MHz crystal calibration oscillator, designed around one section of a 4007UB

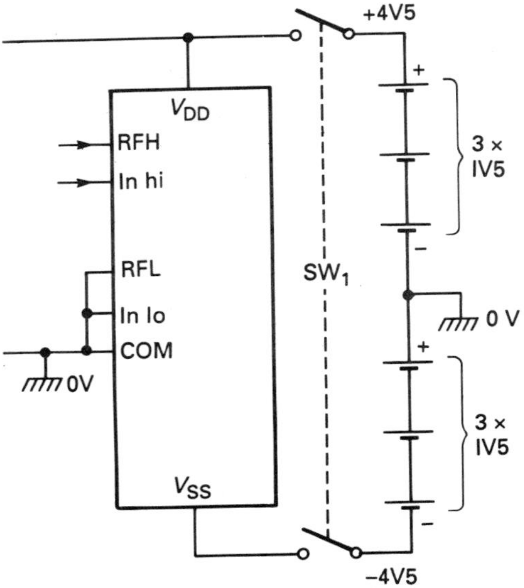

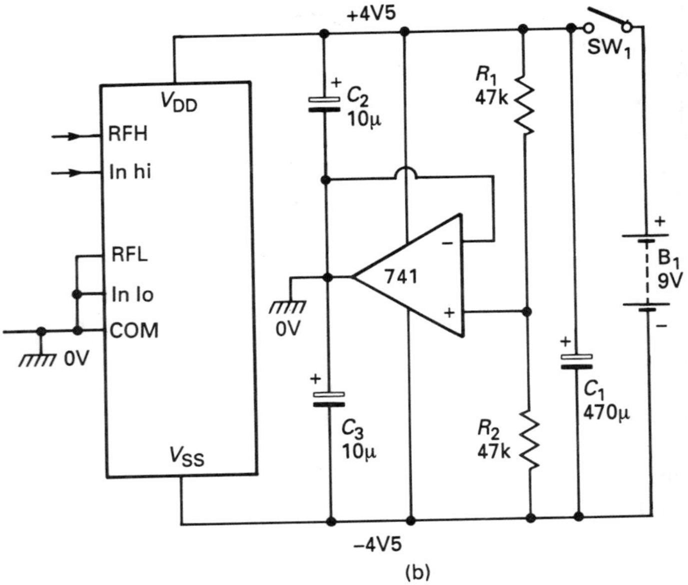

(a)

(b)

Figure 7.37. *A DPM frequency meter needs split supplies. These can be obtained from either a stack of 1V5 cells (a), or from a single 9V battery and an op-amp supply-splitter (b).*

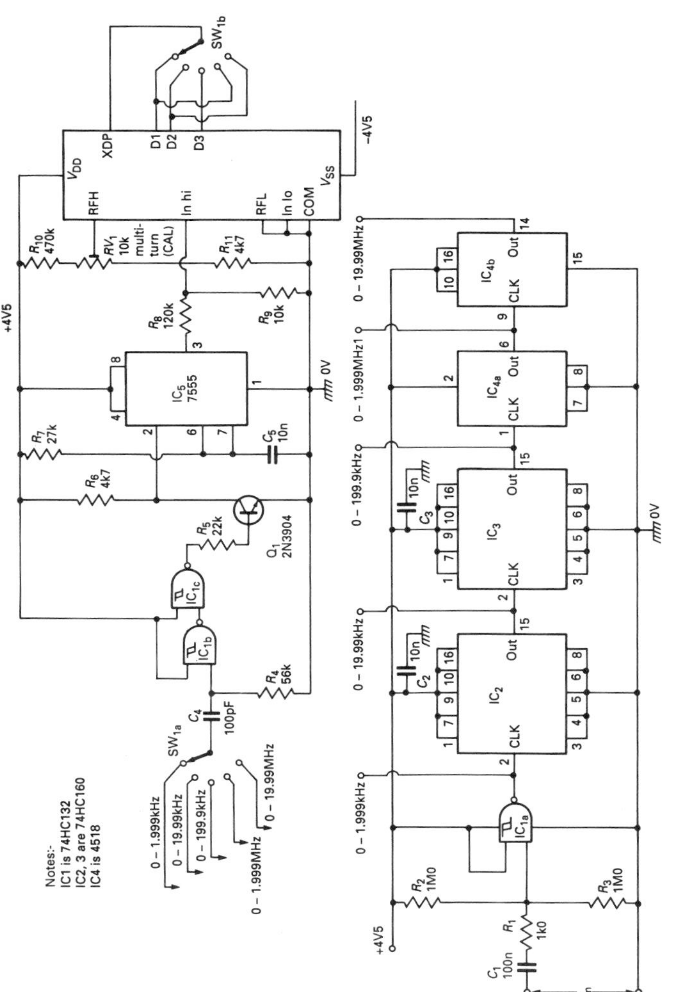


Figure 7.38. *Digital frequency meter, reading 0 to 19.99MHz in five decade ranges.*

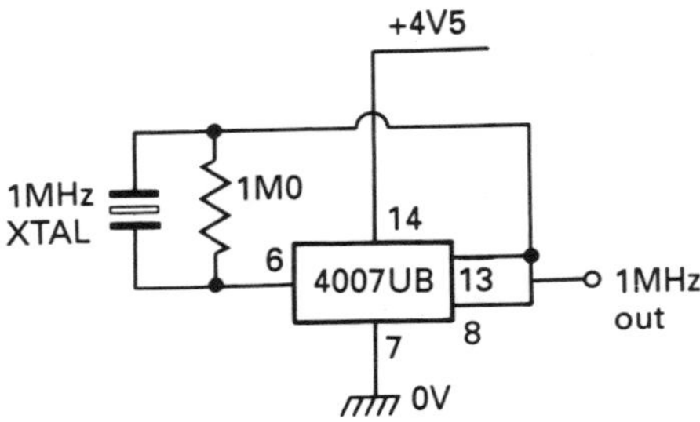


Figure 7.39. *This 1MHz crystal calibration oscillator can easily be added to the DFM circuit.*

CMOS IC, which can easily be added to the DFM and consumes a mere 300μA when active. *Figure 7.40* shows two simple pre-amplifiers that can be used to improve the basic sensitivity of the meter. The *Figure 7.40a* design, based on one section of a 4007UB, has an input impedance of about 1M0 and improves sensitivity by about 20dB (to 20mV) at audio frequencies, but is useful to only a few hundred kilohertz. The simple *Figure 7.40b* design also gives a gain of about 20dB at low frequencies, but has a low input impedance (about 2k2) and is useful to several megahertz. Each circuit consumes a couple of mA.

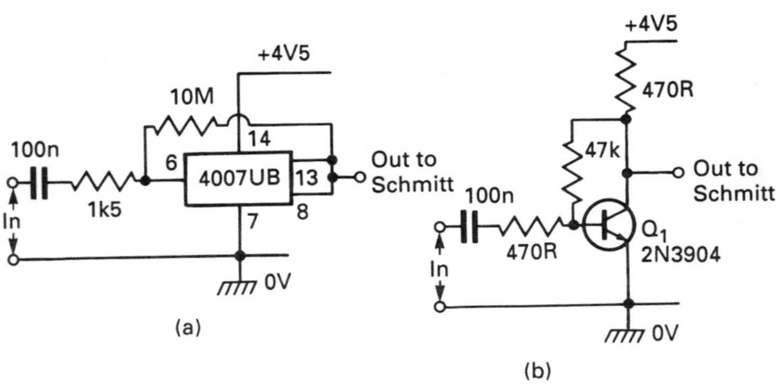


Figure 7.40. *Two simple pre-amplifiers that can be used with the frequency meter.*

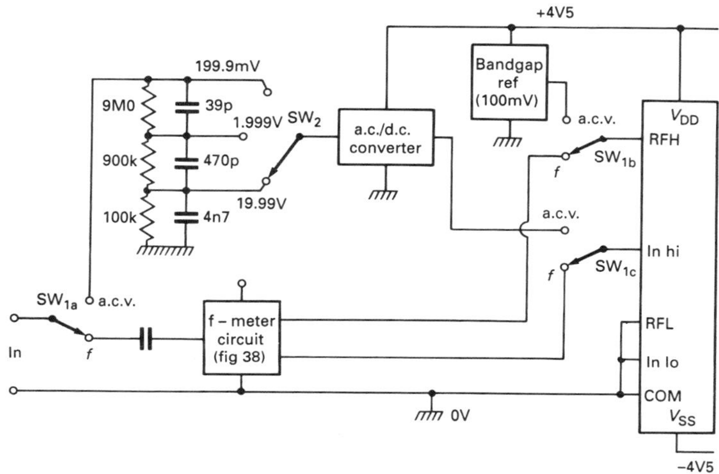


Figure 7.41. *Combined frequency/acv meter (basic circuit).*

*Figure 7.41* shows, in basic form, how the DPM module can be used to read both frequency and a.c. volts (or any other desired parameter). With $SW_1$ switched to '*f*', the input is switched to the input of the *f*-meter circuit, and IN HI and RFH of the DPM are switched to the circuit's output. When $SW_1$ is set to 'acv', the input is switched to the input of the frequency-compensated attenuator, which has its output fed to IN HI via $SW_2$ and a precision a.c./d.c. converter (see *Figure 7.22*), and RFH is switched to a 100mV standard voltage derived from a bandgap reference.

## Miscellaneous applications

DPM modules can be used to indicate the value of any parameter that can be converted into a predictable (linear or log) voltage, current, or resistance. Linear transducers are readily available for measuring values of pH, light intensity, and radiation, etc.

Cyclic parameters such as r.p.m. and heart-beat rate, etc., can be measured by adapting the frequency meter technique already

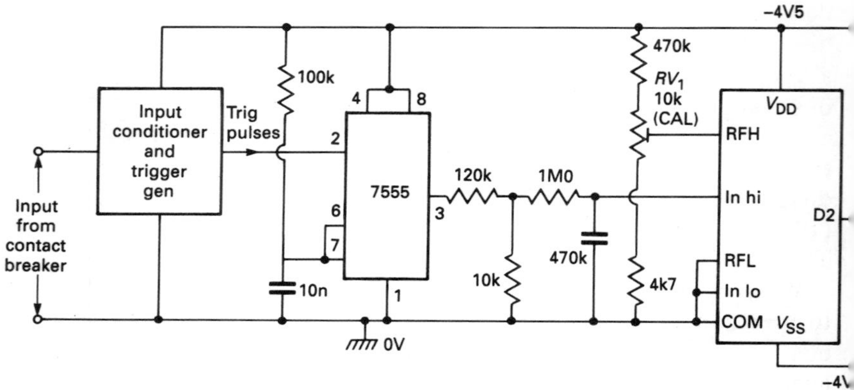


Figure 7.42. *Basic r.p.m. meter, reading 19 990 rpm full-scale from a four-cylinder four-stroke petrol engine.*

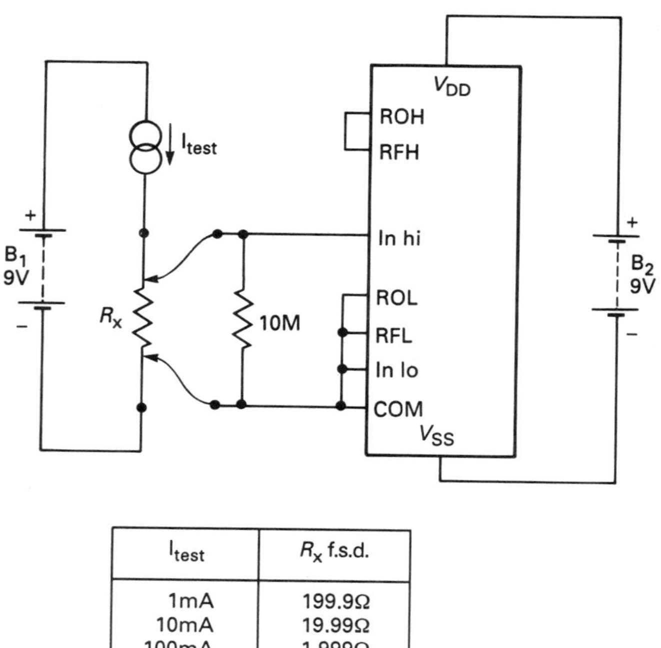


| $I_{test}$ | $R_x$ f.s.d. |
|---|---|
| 1mA | 199.9Ω |
| 10mA | 19.99Ω |
| 100mA | 1.999Ω |

Figure 7.43. *Basic milli-ohmmeter, using four-terminal measurement technique.*

described. The r.p.m. of a petrol-powered engine, for example, is directly proportional to its contact-breaker (CB) frequency, $f$. On a four-stroke engine, $f = N \times$ r.p.m./120, where $N$ is the number of cylinders. Thus, on a single-cylinder engine 10 000r.p.m. gives a CB frequency of 83.3Hz, and on a four-cylinder engine a frequency of 333.3Hz. *Figure 7.42* shows the basic circuit of a digital r.p.m. meter, designed to read 19 990r.p.m. full-scale (10 000r.p.m. at mid-scale) on a four-cylinder four-stroke engine. The 7555 monostable gives an output pulse width of about 1ms.

When measuring low values of resistance, care must be taken to ensure that the resistive effects of range switches and terminals, etc., are excluded from the measurement results. The best way of achieving this is to use the four-terminal technique of *Figure 7.43*, which uses two independent circuits. The unknown resistor is connected between the $R_x$ terminals and fed with a constant current from $B_1$, and the volt drop *directly across* $R_x$ is measured via a 199.9mV full-scale d.c. voltmeter powered from $B_2$; thus, when 10mA is fed through $R_x$, the DPM indicates 19.99Ω full scale.

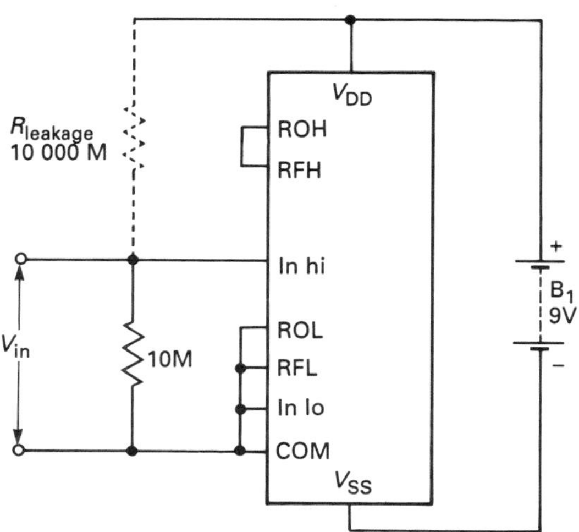


Figure 7.44. *In this 199.9mV d.c. voltmeter circuit, PCB or module leakage resistance causes the meter to indicate 28.0mV with no external input applied.*

## Constructional notes

When using DPM modules, two vital usage points must be noted; the first arises from the DPM's high sensitivity, and is illustrated in *Figure 7.44*, where the DPM is wired as 199.9mV d.c. voltmeter with a 10M input resistance. Thus, if a leakage resistance of 10 000MΩ appears between $V_{DD}$ and IN HI the meter will read 28.0mV with no external input applied. Leakage resistance of this magnitude can be caused by minute amounts of moisture, dirt, or oil, etc., between the tracks of the module's PCB, and to exclude this effect the PCB and its terminals must, after project construction is complete, be coated with a good-quality insulation varnish.

The final point concerns the use of external components, which in all cases must be high-stability types; all resistors should be metal-glaze types; critical capacitors should be polycarbonate types.

# 8 Sine-wave generator circuits

A wide variety of waveform types are used in modern electronics, and the most basic of these is the sine wave. Sine waves can be produced directly from suitable $C-R$ or $L-C$ oscillators, or can be synthesized via special waveform generator ICs, etc. This chapter looks at sine-wave generators of all these types.

## Oscillator basics

Two basic requirements must be satisfied to make a simple sine-wave oscillator, as shown in *Figure 8.1*. First, the output of an amplifier ($A_1$) must be fed back to its input via a frequency-selective network ($A_2$) in such a way that the sum of the amplifier

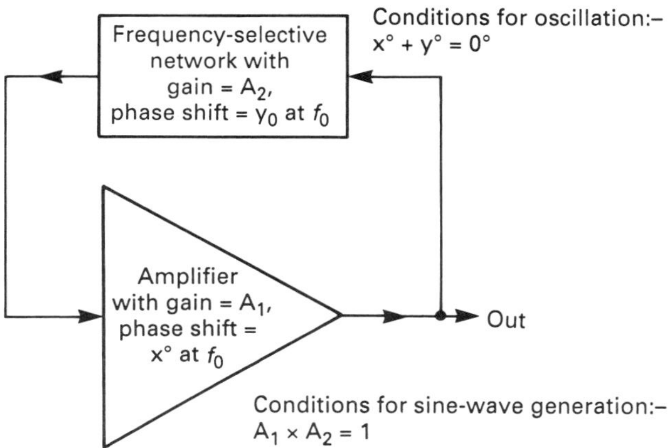


Figure 8.1. *Basic circuit and conditions needed for sine-wave generation.*

and feedback network phase-shifts equals zero degrees at the desired oscillation frequency, i.e. so that $x° + y° = 0°$. The second requirement is that the gain of the amplifier must exactly counter the attenuation (loss) of the feedback network at the desired oscillation frequency, to give an overall system gain of exactly unity, e.g. $A_1 \times A_2 = 1$. If the system gain is less than unity the circuit will not oscillate, and if greater than unity the system will be over-driven and will produce distorted (non-sinusoidal) waveforms.

The frequency-selective feedback network used in a sine-wave oscillator usually consists of either a $C-R$ (capacitor–resistor) or an $L-C$ (inductor–capacitor) filter network. $C-R$ networks are generally used at frequencies ranging from a few hertz to about 150kHz; $L-C$ networks are generally used at frequencies ranging from 50kHz upwards; naturally, there is some overlap between these general frequency limits. Regarding $C-R$-based sine-wave oscillators, the two most widely used types of frequency-selective $C-R$ networks used in modern circuits are the Wien bridge and the Twin-T types; note that the once-popular 'phase-shift' type of oscillator (see *Figures 3.3* and *3.4* in Chapter 3) is now obsolescent and rarely used.

## Wien bridge oscillator basics

The best and easiest ways of making an $R-C$-based sine-wave oscillator is to connect an amplifier and a frequency-selective Wien network in the basic configuration shown in *Figure 8.2*, in which the Wien network (formed by $R_1-C_1$ and $R_2-C_2$) is symmetrical, so that $C_1 = C_2 = C$, and $R_1 = R_2 = R$. The main feature of this Wien network is that (as is fully explained in Chapter 3) the phase relationship of its output and input signals varies from −90° to +90°, and is precisely 0° at a centre frequency ($f_0$) of $1/2\pi CR$; at this frequency the network has a voltage 'gain' of ×0.33. Thus, in *Figure 8.2* the Wien network is connected between the output and input of a non-inverting amplifier with a voltage gain of ×3, so that the circuit gives zero overall phase shift and unity loop gain at $f_0$, and thus satisfies the basic requirements for sine-wave oscillation.

The above is, inevitably, a somewhat simplified explanation of circuit operation. In reality the Wien network is, because of

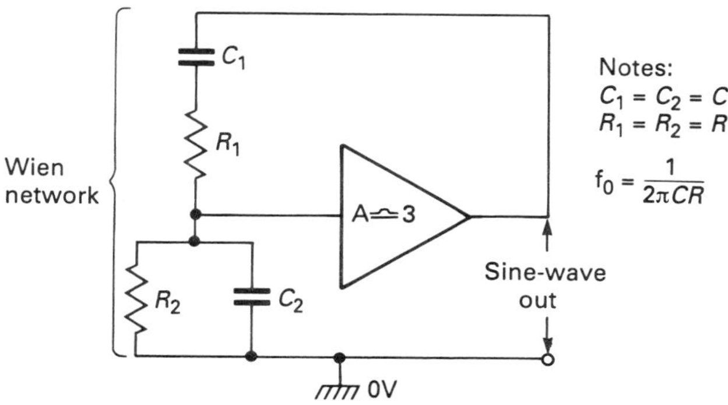


Figure 8.2. *Basic Wien-bridge sine-wave oscillator.*

component working tolerances, rarely precisely symmetrical, and its 'gain' may thus deviate considerably from the ideal ×0.33 value; to compensate for this and enable the oscillator's loop gain to be set at unity, the amplifier's gain must be variable (either manually or automatically) between ×3 and (say) ×5. Also, the loop gain must initially be slightly greater than unity to start off the oscillation process, but must then be reduced (either manually or automatically) to the unity value necessary for low-distortion sine-wave generation.

Another complication arises from the nature of the amplifier's output stage; if this is a simple emitter follower it may not be capable of providing a low-distortion drive to the Wien network. This point can be understood with the aid of *Figure 8.3a*, which shows sine-wave-driven npn emitter follower $Q_1$ driving the input of a Wien network, which is represented by $C_1$ and $Z_L$. On positive-going half-cycles the forward currents of $C_1$ and $Z_L$ are sourced (supplied) by $Q_1$, but on negative-going ones their reverse currents are sunk (absorbed) by $R_L$; if $R_L$ is large relative to $Z_L$ the reverse currents of $C_1$ and $Z_L$ may be too limited to enable the $Z_L$ voltage to correctly 'follow' the negative-going half cycles, with the consequent distortion shown in the diagram.

A similar kind of distortion may occur if the amplifier's output stage takes the form of an npn common emitter amplifier, as shown in *Figure 8.3b*, but in this case the distortion that occurs if $R_L$ is large relative to $Z_L$ appears on the rising parts of the output waveform, since the $C_1$–$Z_L$ source currents flow via $R_L$, and the

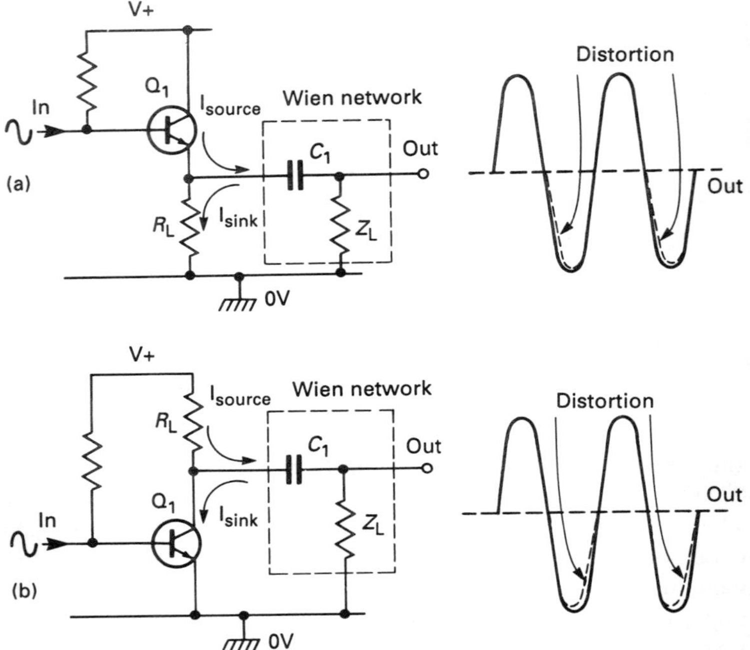


Figure 8.3. *A simple emitter–follower (a) or common emitter amplifier (b) generates a distorted output if* $R_L$ is greater than $Z_L$.

sink ones flow via $Q_1$. Note that these 'distortion' problems do not occur if the amplifier's output takes the form of a complementary emitter follower, since such a circuit can source or sink high output currents with equal ease.

## Transistor oscillator circuits

*Figure 8.4* shows the practical circuit of a simple transistor-based 1kHz Wien oscillator that consumes 1.8mA from a 9V supply and has an output amplitude that is fully variable up to 6V peak-to-peak via $RV_2$. The circuit operates as follows:

$Q_1$–$Q_2$ is a direct-coupled complementary feedback pair of common emitter amplifiers, and gives a very high input impedance to $Q_1$ base, a low output impedance from $Q_2$ collector, and a

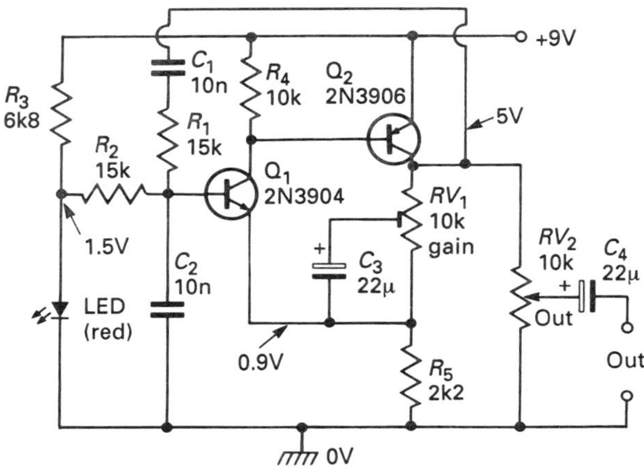


Figure 8.4 *1kHz Wien-bridge sine-wave generator with variable-amplitude output.*

non-inverted d.c. voltage gain of ×5.5 (= $[RV_1 + R_5]/R_5$) and an a.c. voltage gain that is variable from unity to ×5.5 via $RV_1$; $Q_2$'s collector load impedance (formed by $RV_1$, $RV_2$ and $R_5$) is about 5k0. The red LED is driven via $R_3$ and used to generate a low-impedance 1.5V bias source that is fed to $Q_1$ base via $R_2$ and thence biases $Q_2$'s output to a quiescent value of +5V. The Wien network (formed by $R_1-C_1$ and $R_2-C_2$ and connected between $Q_2$'s output and $Q_1$'s input) has an active impedance of about 15k and is easily driven by $Q_2$'s output. The oscillator's output amplitude is fully variable via $RV_2$.

To set up the *Figure 8.4* circuit, simply connect its output to a 'scope and adjust $RV_1$ so that a stable and visually 'clean' waveform is generated. Under this condition the oscillation amplitude is limited only by the onset of positive-peak clipping as the amplifier starts to run into saturation; this occurs at a peak-to-amplitude of about 6V, and is really a form of distortion-generated automatic gain control (AGC), and reduces the oscillator's loop gain below the critical 'unity' level as the waveform's amplitude reaches a specific peak value. If $RV_1$ is carefully adjusted this clipping can be reduced to an almost imperceptible level, enabling good-quality sine waves, with less than 0.5 per cent THD, to be generated.

The *Figure 8.4* circuit is outstandingly useful and economic in fixed- and switched-frequency applications needing the use of a single-ended supply, provided that the $R_1-R_2$ values are not reduced below 5k0. The $R_1-R_2$ and $C_1-C_2$ values can be varied over a wide range to give alternative operating frequencies; small changes in frequency can be obtained by altering the value of a single component ($R_1$ or $R_2$).

*Figure 8.5* shows a modified version of the above circuit, in which the oscillation frequency is fully variable from 1.5kHz to 15kHz via $RV_1$, and which can serve both as a practical sine-

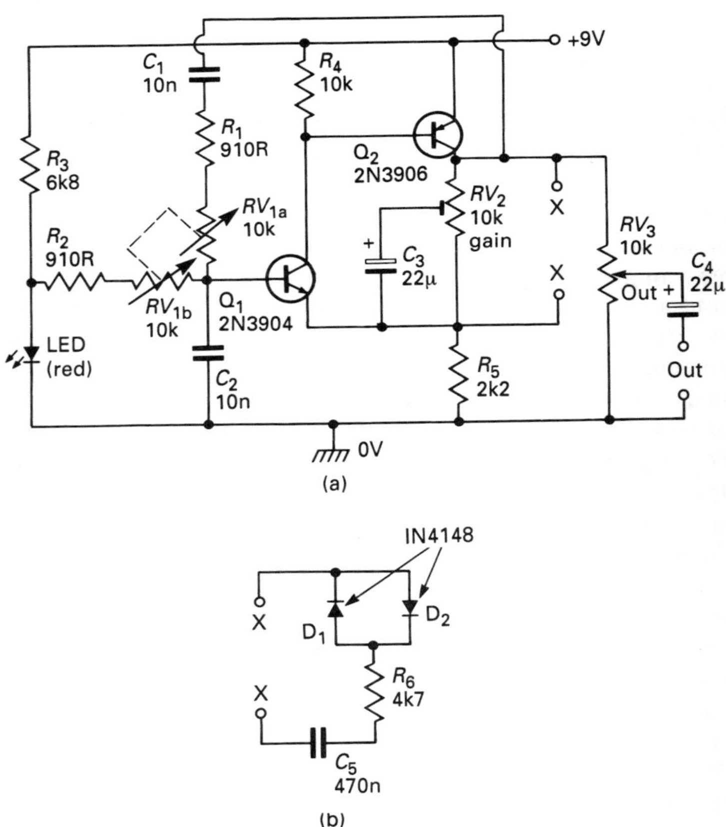


Figure 8.5. *Variable-frequency (1.5kHz to 15kHz) Wien demonstration unit.*

wave generator and as an ideal 'Wien' demonstration unit. The Wien network comprises $C_1-R_1-RV_{1a}$ and $C_2-R_2-RV_{1b}$.

To use this circuit as a Wien demonstrator, simple build it as shown in *Figure 8.5a*, connect its output to a 'scope (with $RV_3$ at maximum output), set $RV_1$ to maximum resistance (i.e. for lowest frequency), and carefully trim $RV_2$ to give a reasonably clean and stable waveform on the 'scope. Under this condition the Wien network presents a fairly high impedance and is easily driven by $Q_2$, so the oscillation amplitude is limited only by the onset of positive-peak clipping at about 6V peak-to-peak amplitude, as already described.

Now progressively increase the operating frequency by reducing $RV_1$'s resistance, retrimming $RV_2$ as necessary to maintain oscillation, until the maximum frequency is obtained. Note under this condition that the waveform's peak-to-peak amplitude falls to about 3V, and that slight distortion is visible on the falling halves of the waveform; what is happening here is that $Q_2$ loses its ability to cleanly drive the Wien network as its impedance falls below a few kilohms, and this results in a form of amplitude-limiting distortion-generated AGC. This problem can be overcome, at the expense of a large increase in the circuit's quiescent current, by simple wiring a 1k5 resistor between $Q_2$'s collector and ground, thus increasing $Q_2$'s output drive capacity; when this modification is made the waveform amplitude is again limited by clipping at about 6V peak-to-peak.

Finally, to complete the use of the demonstration unit, remove the 1k5 resistor from $Q_2$'s collector and connect the $D_1-D_2-R_6-C_5$ network of *Figure 8.5b* across $RV_2$, at the two '×' points. Now vary $RV_1$ across the whole frequency band and trim $RV_2$ to find a position at which a clean sine-wave of about 1.2V peak-to-peak amplitude is produced in all $RV_1$ positions. What happens here is that $R_6$ and the two diodes introduce a form of amplitude-limiting distortion-generated AGC; at the start of each half-cycle the circuit's loop gain is greater than unity, so oscillation starts, but as soon as the waveform amplitude nears a peak value of about 600mV one or other of the diodes starts to conduct and shunt $R_6$ across $RV_2$, thus reducing the loop gain to unity. This particular form of limiting is quite gentle and typically generates less than 1 per cent THD. This version of the *Figure 8.5* circuit thus acts as a cheap but effective variable frequency sine-wave generator; its frequency range can be altered via $C_1$ and $C_2$.

## Op-amp oscillator circuits

An ordinary op-amp, with its complementary emitter follower output stage, is an ideal device for making a Wien-bridge oscillator. *Figure 8.6* shows a simple 1kHz version of such a circuit; $C_1-R_1$ and $C_2-R_2$ form the Wien network, and $RV_1-R_3$ control the op-amp's closed-loop gain. When $RV_1$ is suitably adjusted the circuit oscillates, but the waveform amplitude is limited only by the onset of peak clipping as the op-amp runs into saturation. If $RV_1$ is adjusted with great care this clipping can be reduced to a fairly innocuous level, giving a good sine-wave output, but this technique can only be used in fixed-frequency applications; in all other cases the oscillator must be provided with some form of AGC, to give amplitude limiting with minimal distortion. *Figures 8.7* to *8.11* show practical examples of various types of AGC system.

*Figure 8.7* shows three basic ways of regulating the waveform amplitude by using diodes to provide distortion-generated AGC, as described earlier. The simple IN4148 diode regulator is the cheapest system, but (at low distortion levels) gives a peak-to-peak output of only 1V. The LED and Zener regulators both give excellent results, and deliver peak-to-peak outputs of about 4 and 6V respectively. When using these circuits, simply adjust $RV_2$ to the minimum setting that gives sustained oscillation across

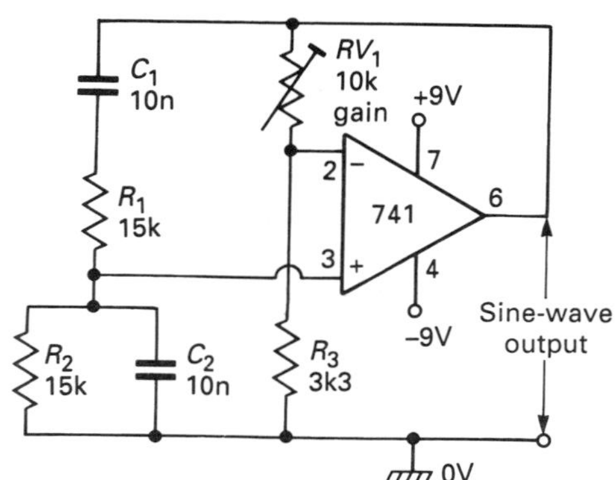


Figure 8.6. *Basic 1kHz Wien op-amp oscillator.*

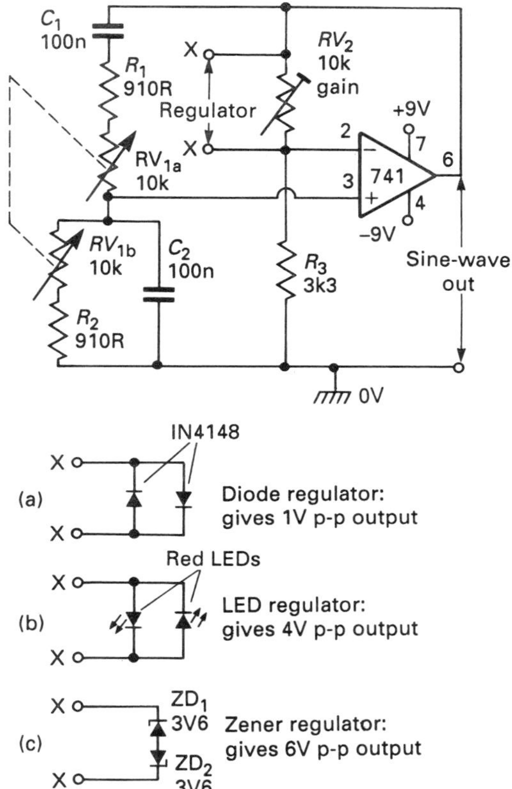


Figure 8.7. *150Hz to 1.5kHz Wien oscillator, with three alternative types of regulator.*

the whole frequency band; if the Wien components are well matched, THD may be less than 0.5 per cent under this condition.

*Figure 8.8* shows a 'diode' regulator variation that gives excellent results in fixed-frequency applications. Here, the Wien-plus-regulator feedback loop is taken from the $R_4-R_5$ junction, rather than directly from the op-amp output, and this simple modification effectively amplifies the diode regulation voltage by a factor of $(R_4 + R_5)/R_5$ to give an output of about 6V peak-to-peak in this case; if $RV_1$ is adjusted with care, THD levels of 0.1 per cent can be achieved.

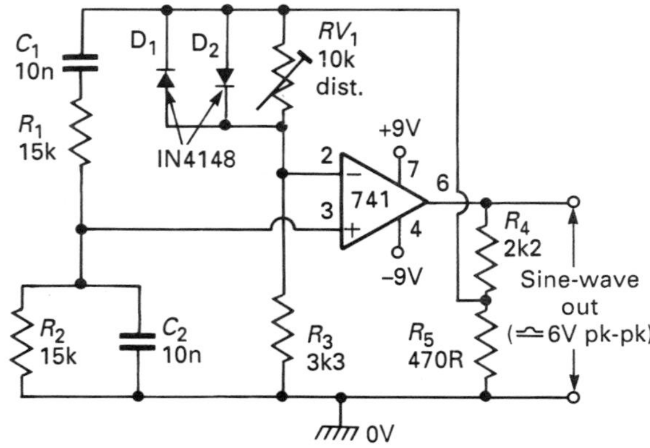


Figure 8.8. *1kHz Wien oscillator with amplified diode regulator.*

## Linear AGC circuits

The oscillators of *Figures 8.6* to *8.8* rely on the use of distortion-generated AGC to control waveform amplitude; such circuits have the great advantage of maintaining a constant and judder-free amplitude as the frequency is swept up and down the available band. There is an alternative control technique that uses automatic 'linear' gain control; such oscillators usually generate negligible distortion, but suffer from amplitude 'bounce' when the frequency is swept up and down the available band, as the AGC system 'hunts' for the correct gain value. *Figures 8.9* to *8.11* show three practical circuits of the latter type.

In the 1kHz oscillator circuit of *Figure 8.9* the output amplitude is stabilized by an RA53 (or similar) negative-temperature-coefficient (ntc) thermistor with a fairly long thermal time constant. $TH_1$ and $RV_1$ form a gain-determining feedback network; $TH_1$ is heated by the output signal's mean power, and at the desired amplitude has a resistance value double that of $RV_1$, thus giving the circuit an overall gain of unity. If the output amplitude starts to rise, $TH_1$'s temperature rises and its resistance falls and thus reduces the gain and restores the original output level; the reverse action occurs if the output starts to fall, and the original output level is again restored. This circuit generates negligible distortion, but the RA53 thermistor is rather expensive.

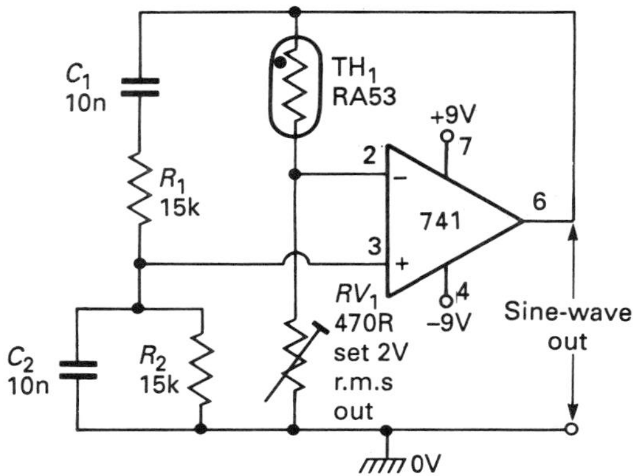


Figure 8.9. *Low-distortion thermistor-regulated 1kHz oscillator.*

*Figure 8.10* shows an alternative method of stabilization, in which a low-current lamp is used as a positive-temperature-coefficient (ptc) thermistor, and is placed in the lower part of the gain-determining feedback network. Thus, if the output amplitude increases, the lamp heats up and increases its resistance, thereby reducing the circuit gain and providing automatic amplitude stabilization, etc. This type of circuit is very popular in the USA.

The above two circuits rely on the heating effects of the oscillator signal, and thus draw fairly high operating currents. *Figure 8.11* shows an alternative system that consumes only a few milliamperes;

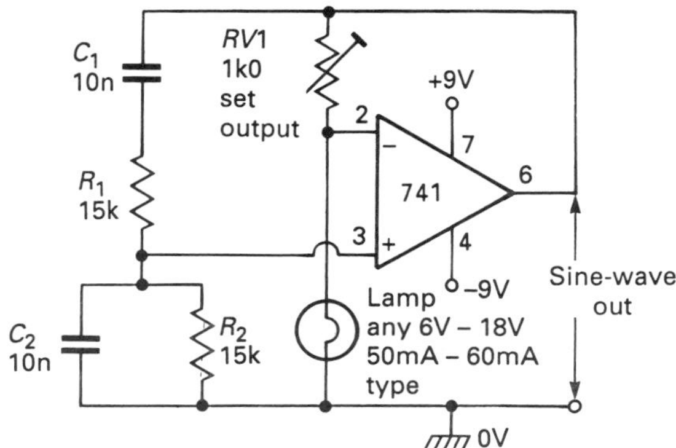


Figure 8.10. *Low-distortion lamp-regulated 1kHz oscillator.*

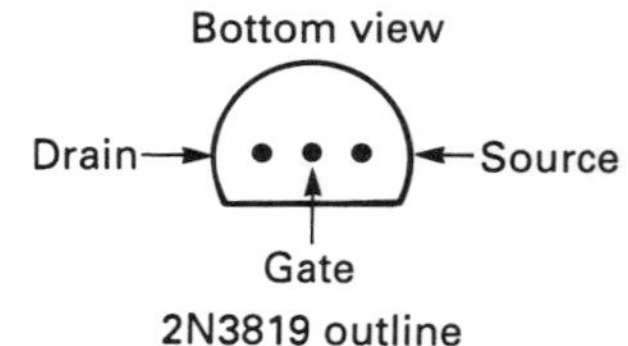


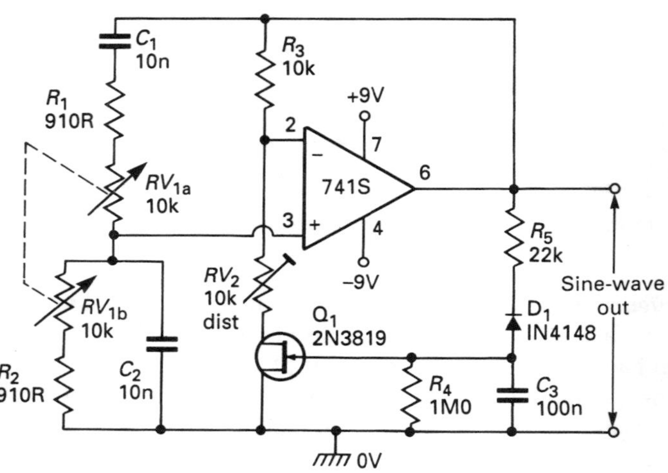


Figure 8.11. *JFET-regulated 1.5 to 15kHz Wien oscillator.*

this circuit uses JFET $Q_1$ as a variable resistance that is voltage-controlled via the oscillator's negative peak amplitude (detected via $R_5-D_1-C_3-R_4$). The JFET's drain-to-source path acts like a low resistance when its gate is biased to 0V, and as a near-infinite one when the gate is biased to a negative 'pinch-off' value of a few volts. When $RV_2$ is suitably adjusted the circuit oscillates and generates a low-distortion output with a peak-to-peak value of $x$ volts; if the output tries to rise above this $x$-value the detected change automatically increases $Q_1$'s resistance value and thus reduces the op-amp's gain, so countering the attempted rise in output; if the output tries to fall below the $x$-value the reverse action takes place, and the gain increases, to maintain a constant output level.

To use the *Figure 8.11* circuit simply connect its output to a 'scope and adjust $RV_2$ to the lowest setting that gives stable oscillation without visible distortion over the whole frequency band; if the Wien components are well matched, THD may be well below 0.1 per cent at 1kHz. The output signal amplitude depends on the 'pinch-off' characteristics of the individual 2N3819 JFET, but is typically in the range 2.5V to 7V peak-to-peak; if desired, the level can be pre-set 8V peak-to-peak by wiring a 10k potentiometer across the op-amp output and feeding $R_5$ from its slider. The AGC system's charge/discharge time constants are controlled by $R_5-C_3$ and $R_4-C_3$; the $R_4-C_3$ time constant must (to give low distortion) be long relative to that of the generated waveform cycle; $C_3$ must be increased to 2μ2 if the circuit is to be used to generate signals down to 15Hz. Note that if $C_3$ is removed, the circuit gives simple distortion-generated AGC via the negative half-cycles.

## Wide-range oscillator circuits

The frequency ranges of the *Figure 8.6* to *8.11* circuits can be changed via the $C_1$ and $C_2$ values; increasing them by a decade reduces the frequency by a decade, etc.; a wide-range multi-decade oscillator can be built by switch-selecting alternative decade-related $C_1$ and $C_2$ values. Note that the maximum useful operating frequency of this type of circuit is restricted by the slew rate limitations of the op-amp; the useful limit is about 20kHz with a 741 op-amp, 80kHz with a 741S, 120kHz with an LF355, and 250kHz with an LF356.

When building variable-frequency Wien oscillators, note that the two tracks of the $RV_1$ frequency-control potentionate must be well matched if a good low-distortion and stable-amplitude performance is to be obtained. In multi-decade oscillators the $C_1$ and $C_2$ values should ideally all be closely matched on all ranges; if these components are not well matched it may be necessary to provide each range with its own switch-selected AGC **gain** or **distortion** control, to ensure a good and stable performance on all ranges.

*Figure 8.12* shows the practical circuit of a variable-frequency Wien oscillator that spans 15Hz to 15kHz in three switched decade ranges. It uses thermistor stabilization and generates a low-distortion output with an amplitude that is fully adjustable via switched and variable attenuators. If desired, the frequency

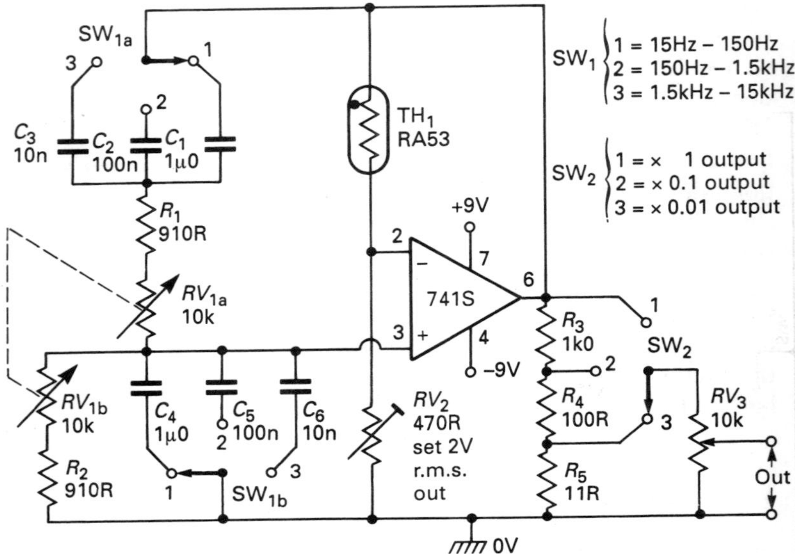


Figure 8.12. *Three-decade (15Hz to 15kHz) Wien oscillator.*

span of this circuit can be raised to 150kHz by replacing the 741S op-amp with a LF356 type and adding a pair of switch-selected 1n0 'range' capacitors.

Finally, to complete this look at Wien oscillators, *Figure 8.13* shows the basic JFET-regulated circuit of *Figure 8.11* modified to make a low-cost sine/square generator that spans 15Hz to 150kHz. $RV_3$ enables the sine-wave's peak-to-peak output level to be pre-set to 8V, as already described. The square-wave generator section consists of common-emitter amplifier $Q_2$ and Schmitt trigger $IC_2$. Note that $Q_2$'s base is driven by the sine-wave output of $IC_1$ via $R_9$, and that $Q_2$'s emitter is biased to about −600mV via $D_2$–$R_{11}$; consequently, $Q_2$ is driven on or off whenever the sine wave swings more than a few millivolts above or below the 0V rail, and $Q_2$ thus generates a good symmetrical square-wave output; $IC_2$ reduces its rise and fall times output to less than 100ns and makes the final square-wave output available via $RV_5$. To conserve battery power, the square-wave generator is switched off (via $SW_{3c}$ and $SW_{3a}$) when not in use.

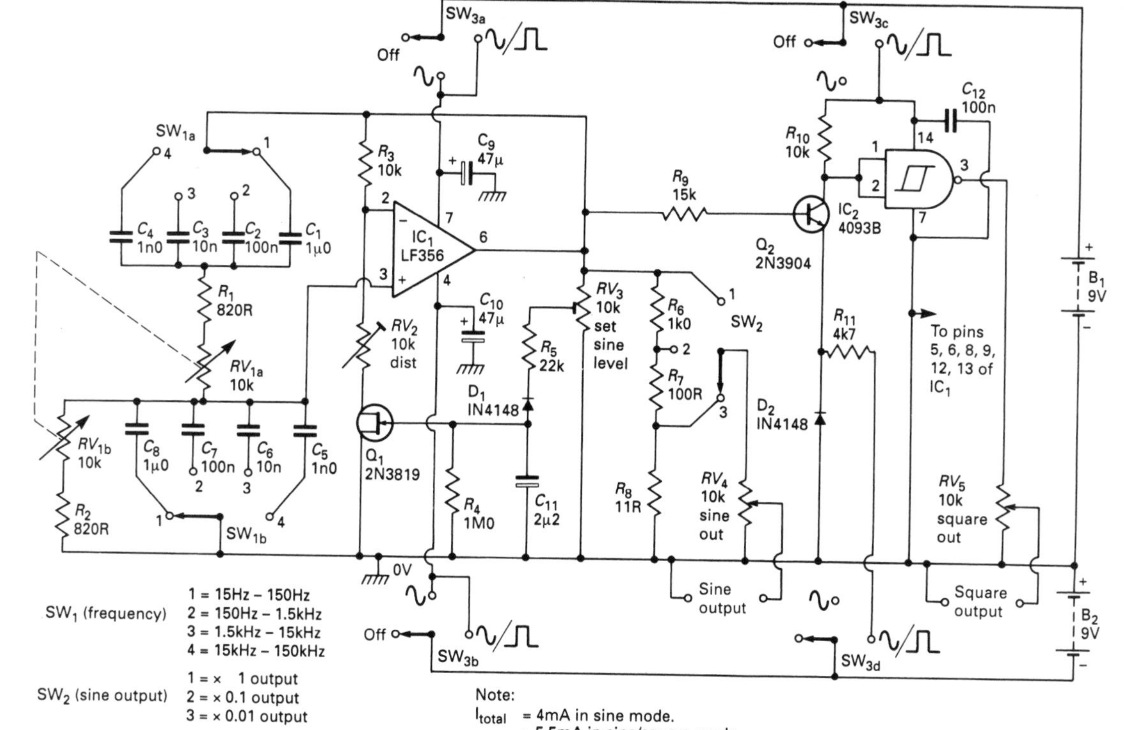


Figure 8.13. *This excellent low-cost sine/square generator spans 15Hz to 150kHz.*

## Twin-T oscillators

It was mentioned earlier that another popular design of $C-R$-based sine-wave oscillator is the Twin-T type. This circuit is useful in fixed-frequency applications, and can be made by wiring a Twin-T network between the output and input of an inverting op-amp, as shown in *Figure 8.14*. The Twin-T network comprises $R_1-R_2-C_3$ and $C_1-C_2-R_3-RV_1$; in a perfectly balanced network these components are in the ratios $R_1 = R_2 = 2(R_3 + RV_1)$, and $C_1 = C_2 = C_3/2$, and give zero output at a centre frequency, $f_0$, of $(1/2\pi)R_1C_1$, and a finite output at all other frequencies. If the Twin-T is imperfectly balanced it gives a slight output at $f_0$, and the output phase depends in the direction of the imbalance; if the imbalance is caused by $(R_3 + RV_1)$ being low in value, the output phase is inverted relative to the input.

In *Figure 8.14* the Twin-T network is critically adjusted via $RV_1$ so that it gives a small phase-inverted output at an $f_0$ of 1kHz; zero overall phase inversion thus occurs around the feedback loop, and the circuit oscillates at 1kHz. In practice, $RV_1$ is adjusted so that oscillation is barely sustained, and under this condition the sine-wave amplitude is limited at about 5V r.m.s. by the onset of op-amp clipping, and the output waveform has less than 1 per cent THD; the output amplitude is fully variable via $RV_2$.

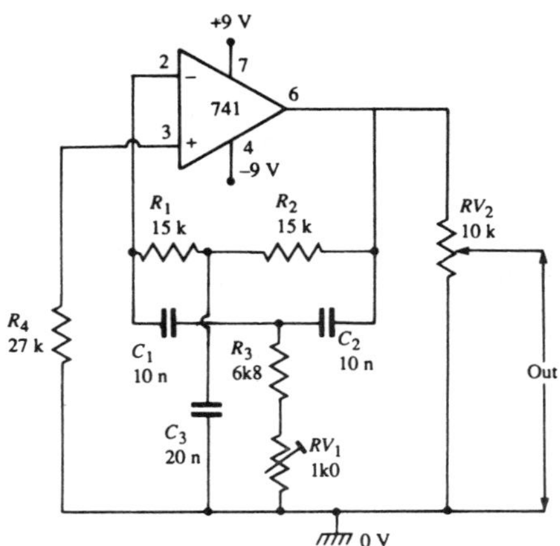


Figure 8.14. *1kHz twin-T oscillator.*

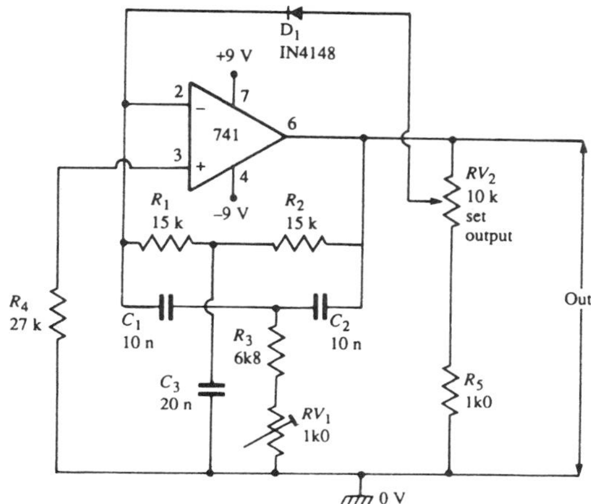


Figure 8.15. *Diode-regulated 1kHz Twin-T oscillator.*

*Figure 8.15* shows a simple Twin-T variant that gives slightly less distortion and uses diode $D_1$ to provide distortion-generated AGC. To set up this circuit, first set $RV_2$ slider to the op-amp output and adjust $RV_1$ so that oscillation is just sustained, giving an output sine wave of about 500mV peak-to-peak. $RV_2$ then enables the output signal to be varied between 170mV and 3V r.m.s.

## Sine-wave synthesizers

All the $C-R$ circuits shown so far are oscillator types that give direct sine-wave generation. Sine waves can, however, also be produced by synthesizing them from either digital or analogue types of waveform. *Figure 8.16* shows how a sine wave can be created digitally by first building up the rough sine-wave shape in a number of digital steps and then removing the digital signal's high-frequency components via a simple filter network. Here, a clock signal is fed to the input of a five-stage walking ring or Johnson counter; four of the counter outputs are added together via a resistor weighing network, to produce a crude sine wave which is then converted into a reasonably pure form via low-pass filter $C_1$. The sine-wave output frequency is one-tenth of that of

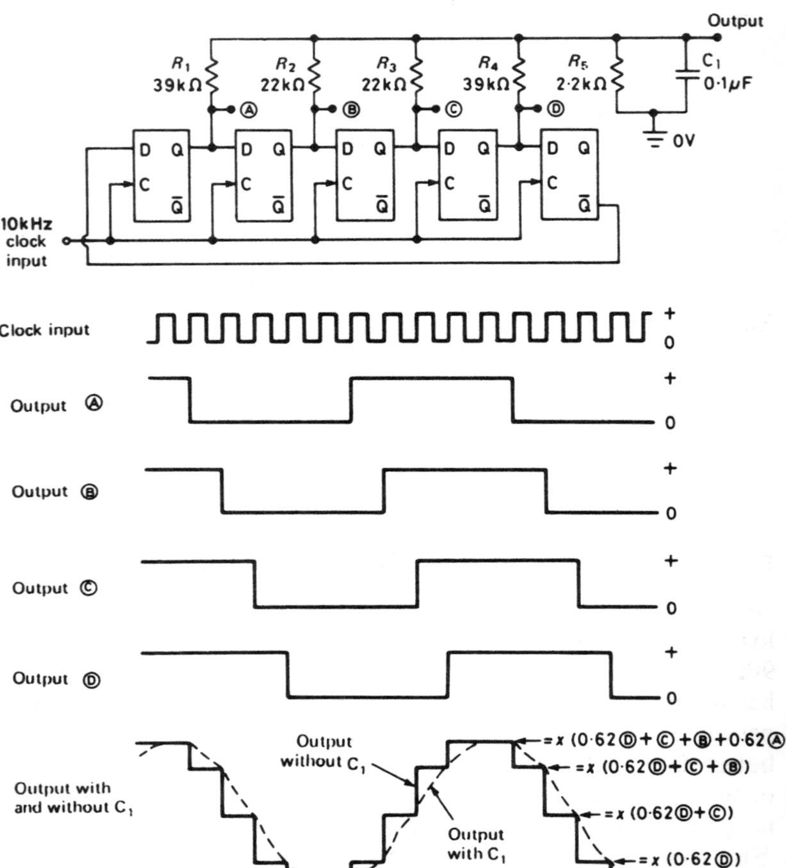


Figure 8.16. *Basic circuit and waveforms of 1kHz digital sine-wave synthesizer.*

the original clock signal; consequently (since digital signals generate only odd harmonics) the lowest harmonic of any consequence to the final sine-wave signal are the 9th, 11th, 19th, 21st, and so on, and these are easily removed via $C_1$.

*Figure 8.17* shows a practical 1kHz digital sine-wave synthesizer of the above type. It is built around a 4018B CMOS presettable divide-by-*N* counter, with transistor $Q_1$ used to convert an external 10kHz input signal into a form suitable for clocking the IC. The

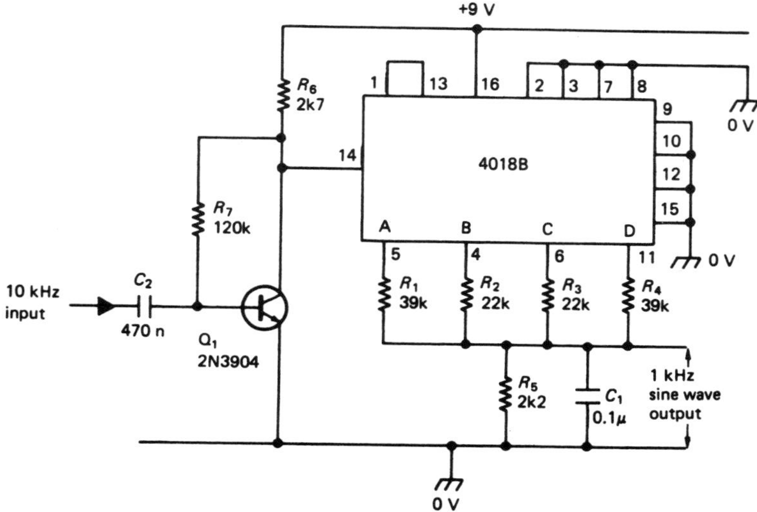


Figure 8.17. *Practical 1kHz digital sine-wave synthesizer.*

lowest significant harmonic of this circuit's 1kHz output is the 9th, at −36dB relative to the fundamental; the sine wave thus has a THD content of about 2 per cent. If a second-order low-pass filter is used in place of $C_1$, all harmonics are reduced to better than 65dB down on the fundamental, giving a THD value of about 0.1 per cent. This circuit thus provides a simple and inexpensive means of generating good-quality sine waves.

Sine waves can also be synthesized from linear 'triangle' waveforms, and a number of manufacturers produce dedicated 'waveform synthesizer' or 'function generator' ICs for this purpose. The best known of these ICs are the ICL8038, which is available from several manufacturers, and the XR-2206, which is produced by Exar Integrated Systems Inc. of America. Both of these ICs work in the same basic way, as shown in *Figure 8.18*. They contain a combined linear-triangle and square-wave generator that has its frequency controlled by a simple $C-R$ network; the generated triangle waveform is shaped into a sine form via an integral non-linear amplifier. Major advantages of these waveform generators are that the frequency is variable via an external voltage or resistor and a single capacitor, that the frequency can be varied from a fraction of a hertz to hundreds of kilohertz, and

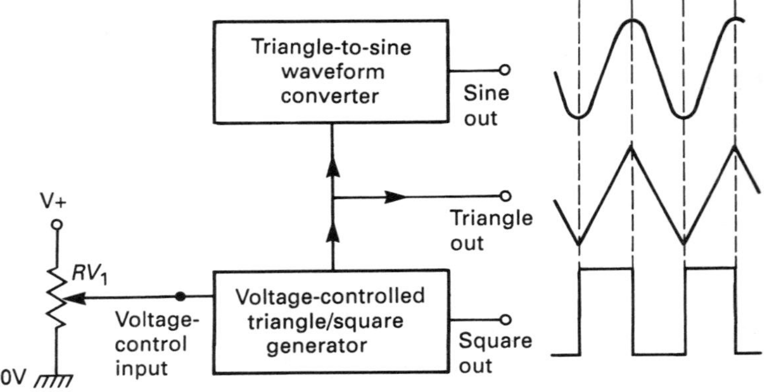


Figure 8.18. *Basic elements of a 'function generator' IC.*

that the waveform is free from 'bounce'. Disadvantages are that the sine waves have typical THD values of 2 per cent in the case of the 8038, or 0.5 per cent in the case of the XR-2206, and that these ICs are fairly expensive.

## ICL8038 basics

The ICL8038 can produce simultaneous sine, square and triangle outputs at frequencies ranging from below 1Hz to above 100kHz. Its output signals can be subjected to frequency sweeping and modulation (FM), and it can be powered via either single-ended supplies in the range 10 to 30V, or split ones in the ±5 to ±15V range. The 8038's is a popular and readily available IC, even though its sine-wave output distortion is fairly high.

*Figure 8.19* shows the outline and pin notations of the 8038, and *Figure 8.20* shows the basic way of using it as a fixed-frequency triangle/sine/square waveform generator that is powered via a single-ended supply. Note in this circuit that the pin-7 FM BIAS terminal is shorted directly to the pin-8 FM SWEEP INPUT terminal, and in this case the 8038's operating frequency is determined by the values of $C$, $R_A$ and $R_B$. These two resistors in fact set the operating values of a pair of internal constant-current generators that alternately charge and discharge the main timing capacitor ($C$).

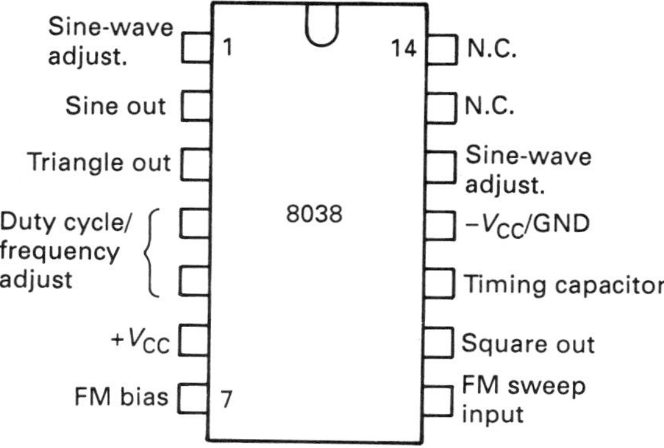


Figure 8.19. *Outline and pin notations of the ICL8038 waveform generator IC.*

The basic action of the *Figure 8.20* circuits is such that $C$ alternately charges linearly at a rate set by $R_A$ until the $C$ voltage reaches two thirds of $+V_{CC}$, at which point a switching action occurs and $C$ starts to discharge linearly at a rate set by $R_B$ until the $C$ voltage drops to one-third of $V_{CC}$, at which point another switching action takes place and the whole process starts to repeat.

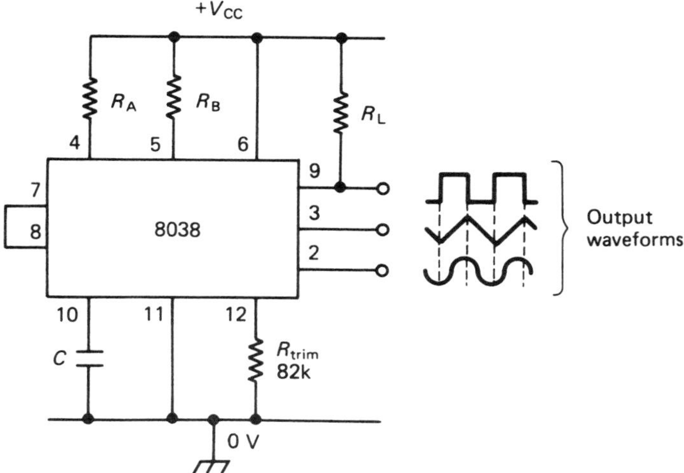


Figure 8.20. *Basic fixed-frequency triangle/sine/square waveform generator.*

$R_A$ and $R_B$ can have any values in the range 1k0 to 1M0; if these components have equal values ($R$) the circuit operates at a frequency of $0.3/(RC)$ and generates a symmetrical linear triangle waveform with a peak-to-peak amplitude of $0.33 \times V_{CC}$ on pin-3, and a square wave with a peak-to-peak value of $V_{CC}$ on pin-9 (which is loaded by $R_L$); the triangle waveform is also fed to an internal triangle-to-sine converter, which produces a fairly good sine-wave output (with a peak-to-peak amplitude of $0.22 \times V_{CC}$) on pin-2 when $R_{TRIM}$ is given a value of 82k as shown.

## Sine-wave distortion

The *Figure 8.20* circuit can be made to generate non-symmetrical output waveforms by simply giving $R_A$ and $R_B$ different values. For best sine-wave purity the circuit must be set to give perfect waveform symmetry, and this can be achieved by modifying the circuit as shown in *Figure 8.21*, which also shows how $R_{TRIM}$ can be made variable and used to trim the sine wave for minimum distortion. In practice, sine-wave THD figures as low as 0.8 per

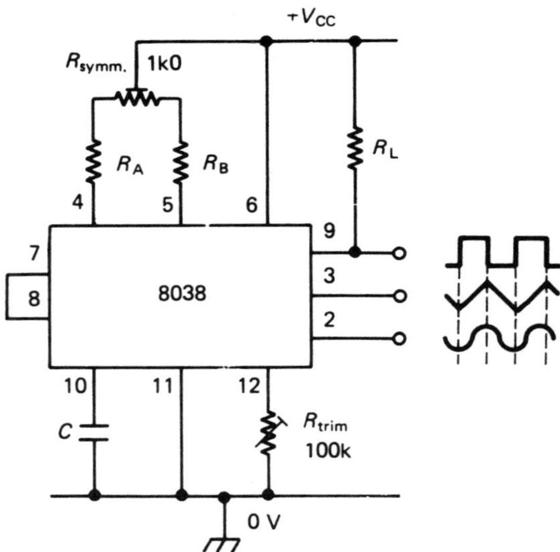


Figure 8.21. *Modified circuit gives perfect symmetry and reduced sine-wave distortion.*

cent can be obtained from the *Figure 8.21* circuit when it is used in fixed-frequency applications below 10kHz; the distortion can be reduced even further (to about 0.5 per cent) by further modifying the circuit as shown in *Figure 8.22* and trimming all three variable components for best performance.

Note that the 8038 rarely maintains perfect symmetry when used in variable-frequency applications, and in such cases may produce worst-case THD figures of several per cent; this is the 8083's greatest fault. The IC consumes a quiescent current of about 12mA at 20V and tends to run warm. In most multi-waveform generator applications the user needs to feed the waveforms to the outside world via some type of buffer circuit, so that the desired waveform can be selected at will and made available at variable amplitude levels.

## Supplies and circuits

The 8038 is shown using single-ended supplies in the circuits of *Figures 8.20* to *8.22*, and in such cases the three output waveforms

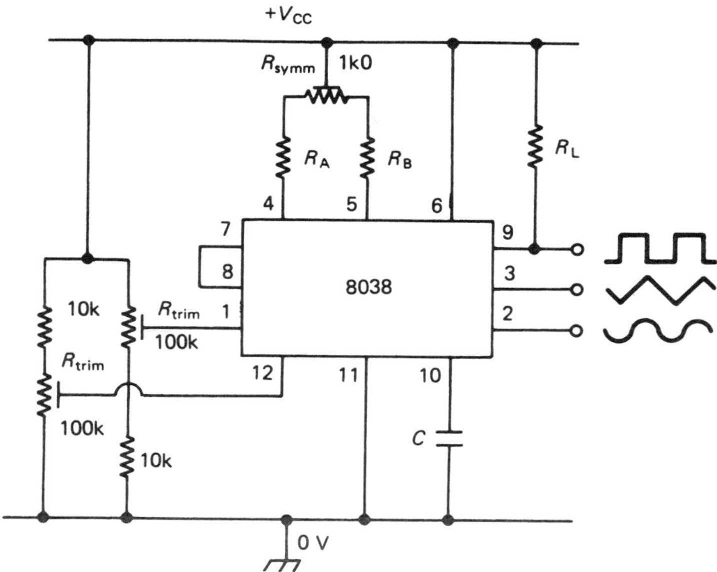


Figure 8.22. *Circuit modified to give minimum sine-wave distortion.*

all swing about (are centred on) the half-supply voltage value. These circuits can be powered via split (dual) supplies by simply using the 'zero' rail as the negative supply line; in this case all output waveforms are centred on the zero or ground line of the split supply. Note in all cases that pin-8 of the IC is susceptible to unwanted signal pick-up, and should be decoupled by wiring a 100nF capacitor between pin-8 and $+V_{CC}$.

The operating frequency of the 8038 is a direct function of the DC voltage applied between pin-8 and the IC's positive supply terminal (pin-6). The frequency can thus be varied or swept by altering this voltage, or can be modulated by feeding a suitable modulation signal to pin-8. An easy way of using the IC as a manually controlled variable frequency waveform generator is to wire it as shown in *Figure 8.23*, with pin-8 connected to a variable control voltage taken from the $RV_1$ slider; this voltage is variable from $V_{CC}$ to two-thirds of $V_{CC}$; the frequency is minimum when the pin-8 voltage equals $V_{CC}$, and is maximum when it equals $(\frac{2}{3}V_{CC} + 2V)$. This simple circuit enables the frequency to be varied over a range of about 1000:1, but to attain this the highest

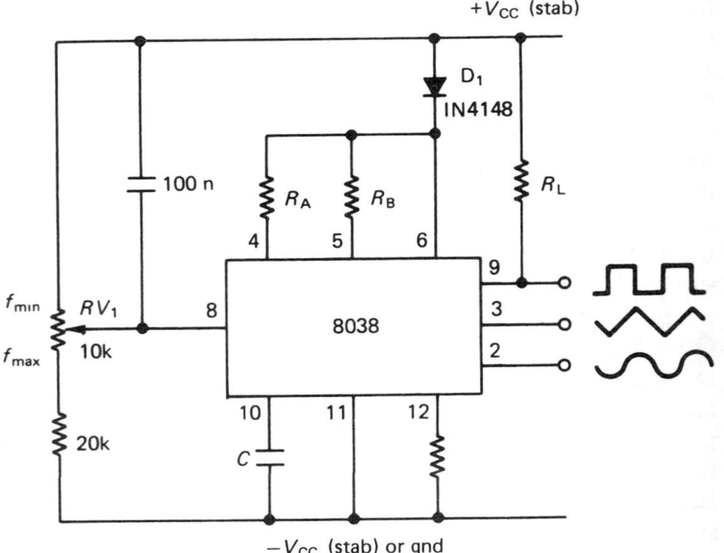


Figure 8.23. *Wide-range variable-frequency waveform generator.*

control voltage on pin-8 must exceed that of pin-6 by a few hundred millivolts; this is achieved by reducing the IC's pin-6 voltage to about 600mV below $+V_{CC}$ via the forward volt drop of $D_1$. Note that, for optimum frequency stability, this circuit's supply voltages must be stabilized.

To complete this look at the ICL8038, *Figure 8.24* shows how it can be used to make a practical wide-range (10Hz to 100Hz) sine/triangle/square waveform generator by combining the circuits of *Figures 8.22* and *8.23* and adding an op-amp buffer stage ($IC_2$). To set up this circuit, first set $RV_4$ to mid-value and $SW_1$ to range-2 and then trim $RV_2$ and $RV_3$ so that the generator spans the 100Hz to 1kHz frequency range via $RV_1$. Next, set $RV_1$ to give 1kHz output and trim $RV_4$ to give a symmetrical square wave output. Re-check the frequency span range. Finally, reset 1kHz and trim $R_5$ and $R_6$ for minimum sine-wave distortion.

## XR-2206 circuits

The XR-2206 is a 16-pin IC capable of generating high-quality sine, square, triangle, ramp and pulse waveforms at frequencies from below 1Hz to hundreds of kilohertz using either resistance or voltage control of frequency, and of generating either FM, AM, or FSK forms of waveform modulation. It can operate from either single-ended or dual power supplies. This excellent IC is more expensive and less readily available than the ICL8038. For our present purpose we are only concerned with using the IC in its most basic modes, and with this in mind *Figure 8.25* shows the IC (plus internal block diagram) connected as a simple sine/square/triangle generator that is powered from a dual power supply. The circuit operates as follows.

The heart of the XR-2206 is a voltage-controlled oscillator (VCO), which is driven via a pair of current switches. The VCO's main timing capacitor, $C$ (1n0 to 100μF), is wired between pins 5 and 6, and its timing resistor, $R$, (4k0 to 200k) is wired between pins 7 and the negative supply line; the VCO generates a linear ramp waveform with a frequency of $1/RC$ Hz. When this ramp is rising $Q_1$ is switched on, and when it is falling $Q_1$ is off; a synchronous square wave output is thus available at pin 11 if it is biased high via a 15k resistor, as shown. The actual ramp waveform is fed into the 'multiplier and sine shaper' block and is

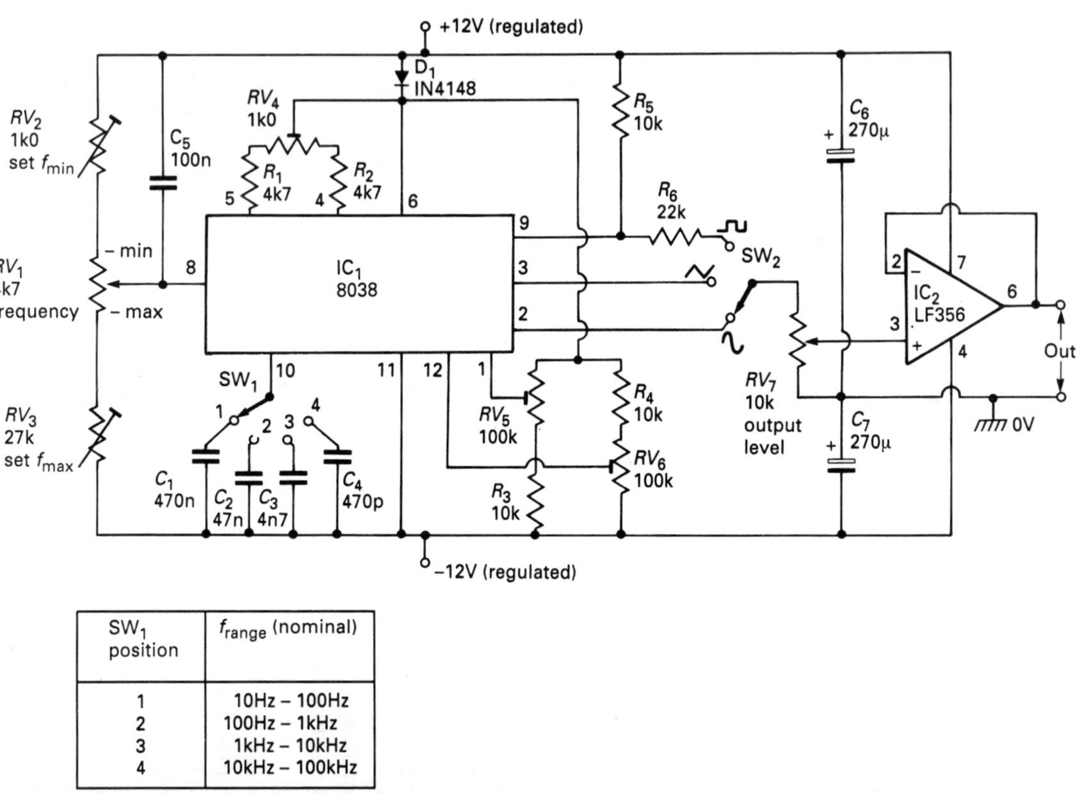


| $SW_1$ position | $f_{range}$ (nominal) |
|---|---|
| 1 | 10Hz – 100Hz |
| 2 | 100Hz – 1kHz |
| 3 | 1kHz – 10kHz |
| 4 | 10kHz – 100kHz |

Figure 8.24. *Wide-range sine/triangle/square waveform generator using dual power supplies*

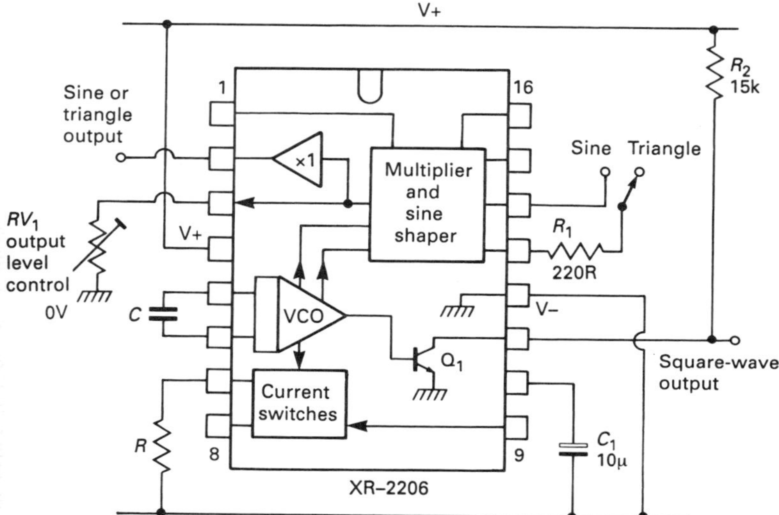


Figure 8.25. *XR-2206 block diagram and basic 'sine/triangle/square' waveform generator connections.*

subsequently made directly available at a high impedance level on pin 3, or in buffered form on pin 2. If pins 13–14 are open circuit this waveform is unmodified and appears as a linear ramp, but if a resistance of about 220Ω ($R_1$) is wired between these pins the 'multiplier and sine shaper' block exponentially reduces the peaks of the input ramp waveform and produces a sine-wave output. This sine-wave has a typical THD of about 2.5 per cent but can be reduced to 0.5 per cent by trimming the $R_1$ value.

*Figure 8.26* shows how the above points can be put to practical use to make a simple but useful variable-frequency multi-waveform generator that uses a single-ended power supply. The operating frequency is inversely proportional to the values of $C_1$ and $R_1$–$RV_1$, and can be varied from 10Hz to 100kHz in four-decade ranges by using the $C_1$ values shown. The amplitude of the sine/triangle output is fully variable via $RV_2$, but can have its maximum value preset via $RV_3$; the sine-wave THD is typically less than 2.5 per cent.

*Figure 8.27* shows how the above circuit can be modified for operation from dual power supplies, and how sine-wave distortion can be reduced to a typical value of 0.5 per cent by adjustment of

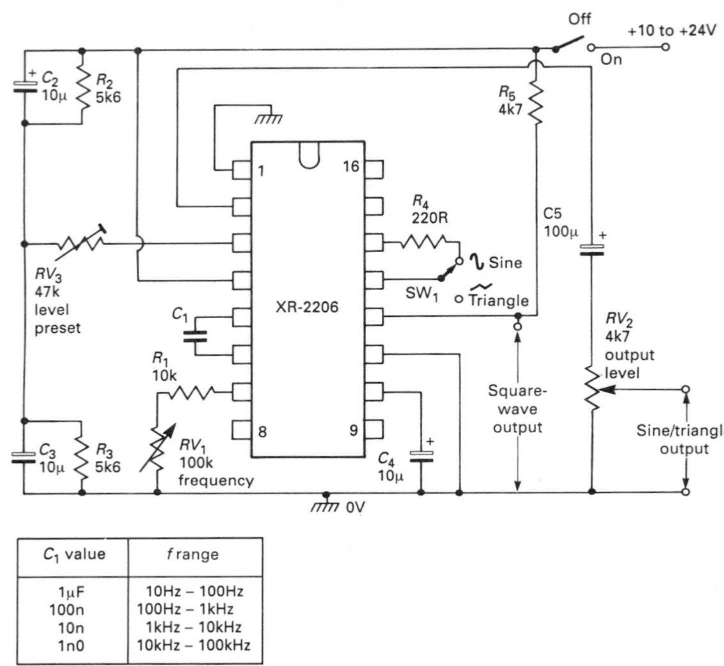


| $C_1$ value | f range |
|---|---|
| 1µF | 10Hz – 100Hz |
| 100n | 100Hz – 1kHz |
| 10n | 1kHz – 10kHz |
| 1n0 | 10kHz – 100kHz |

Figure 8.26. *Simple XR-2206-based wide-range sine/triangle/square generator using a single-ended power supply.*

preset controls $RV_2$ and $RV_4$. These two controls must be adjusted in unison to give minimal distortion when the circuit is first built, and need no further adjustment thereafter. The maximum output level of these circuits can be preset via $RV_3$, which should be set to give a maximum output of less than 2V r.m.s., to prevent excessive distortion.

## *L–C* oscillator circuits

*C–R* sine-wave oscillators are useful for generating signals up to a maximum of several hundred kilohertz only. *L–C* oscillators, on the other hand, can generate signals ranging from a few tens of kilohertz to hundreds of megahertz. *Figures 8.28* to *8.33* show a selection of practical transistor-based *L–C* oscillator circuits.

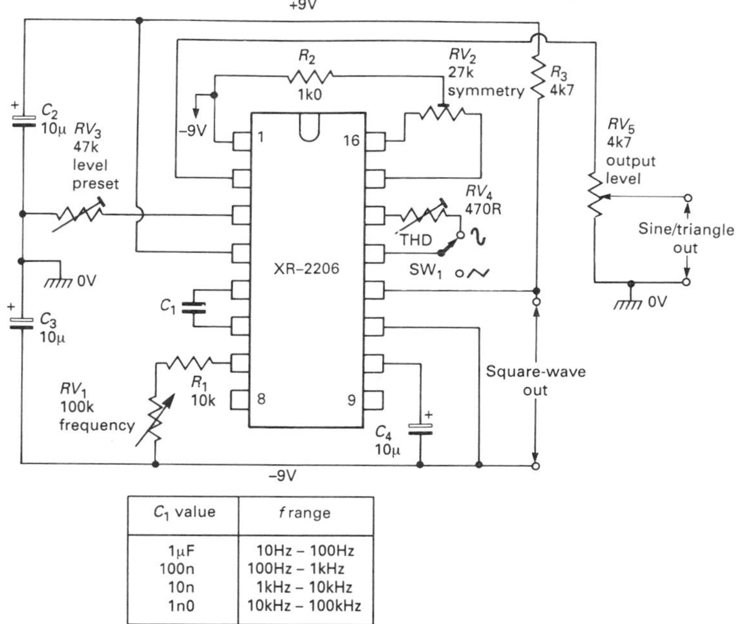


| $C_1$ value | *f* range |
|---|---|
| 1µF | 10Hz - 100Hz |
| 100n | 100Hz - 1kHz |
| 10n | 1kHz - 10kHz |
| 1n0 | 10kHz - 100kHz |

Figure 8.27. *High-performance wide-range sine/triangle/square generator using split power supply.*

A transistor $L-C$ oscillator consists, in essence, of a simple RF amplifier plus a frequency-selective $L-C$ network that gives appropriate feedback between its output and input. $L-C$ networks have inherently high $Q$ or frequency-selectivity, so such oscillators produce reasonably pure sine-wave outputs, even when the oscillator's loop gain is far greater than unity.

There are many different types of the transistor $L-C$ oscillator; the simplest is the tuned collector feedback type, and an example of this is shown in *Figure 8.28*. Here, common emitter amplifier $Q_1$'s base bias is provided via $R_1-R_2$, and emitter resistor $R_3$ is RF-decoupled via $C_2$. $L_1-C_1$ form the tuned collector circuit, and collector-to-base feedback is provided via '$L_2$, which is inductively coupled to $L_1$ and thus provides a transformer action; by selecting the phase of this feedback signal the circuit can be made to give zero loop phase shift at the tuned frequency so that, if the loop gain (determined by $T_1$'s turns ratio) is greater than unity, the circuit will oscillate.

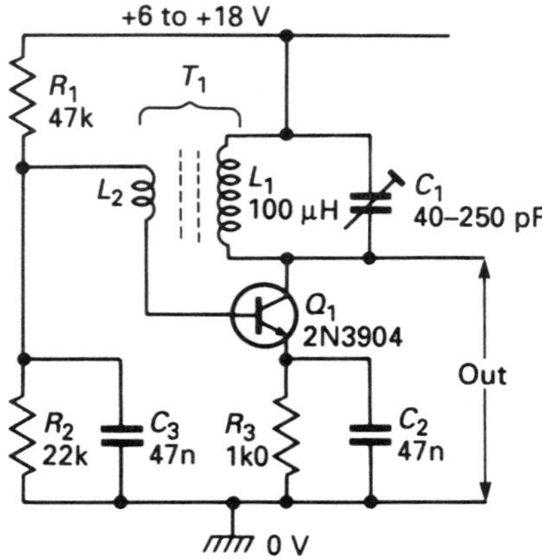


Figure 8.28. *Tuned-collector feedback* L−C *oscillator.*

A feature of any $L-C$ tuned circuit is that the phase relationship between its energizing current and induced voltage varies between $-90°$ to $+90°$, and is zero at a 'centre' frequency ($f$) given by $f = 1/[2\pi \sqrt{(LC)}]$. The *Figure 8.28* circuit gives zero overall phase shift and thus oscillates at this centre frequency; with the component values shown, $f$ can be varied from 1MHz to 2MHz via $C_1$, but the basic circuit can easily be modified to operate at frequencies ranging from tens of hertz (by using a laminated iron-core transformer) up to tens or hundreds of megahertz.

## Circuit variations

*Figure 8.29* shows a simple variation of the *Figure 8.28* design, this particular circuit being known as a Hartley oscillator. Here, collector load inductor $L_1$ is tapped 20 per cent down from its top, and the circuit's positive supply rail is connected to this tap point; $L_1$ thus gives an auto-transformer action in which the signal voltage appearing at the top of $L_1$ is 180° out of phase with that on its low ($Q_1$ collector) end. The signal voltage from the top of the coil (which is 180° out of phase with the collector signal) is coupled to $Q_1$ base via isolating capacitor $C_2$, and the circuit thus oscillates at a centre frequency determined by the $L-C$ values.

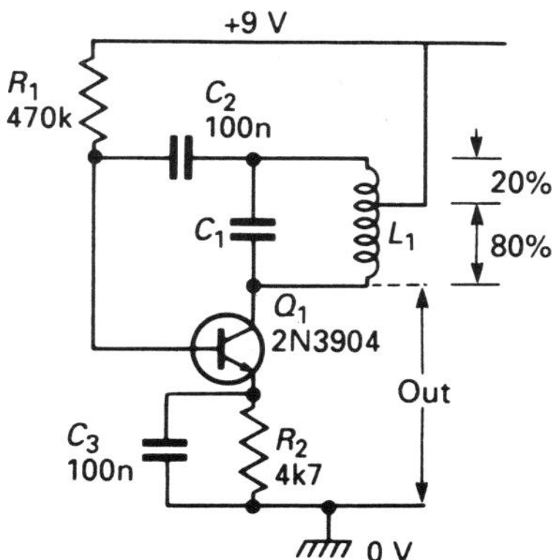


Figure 8.29. *Basic Hartley* L–C *oscillator.*

Note from the above description that oscillator action depends on a 'common signal' tapping point being made into the tuned circuit, so that a phase-splitting autotransformer action is obtained. This tapping point does not in fact have to be made in the actual tuning coil, but can be made into the tuning capacitor, as in the Colpitts oscillator circuit shown in *Figure 8.30*. With the component values shown this particular circuit oscillates at about 37kHz.

Note in *Figure 8.30* that $C_1$ is in parallel with $Q_1$'s output capacitance, and $C_2$ is in parallel with $Q_1$'s input capacitance, and changes in $Q_1$ capacitance (due to thermal shifts, etc.) thus cause

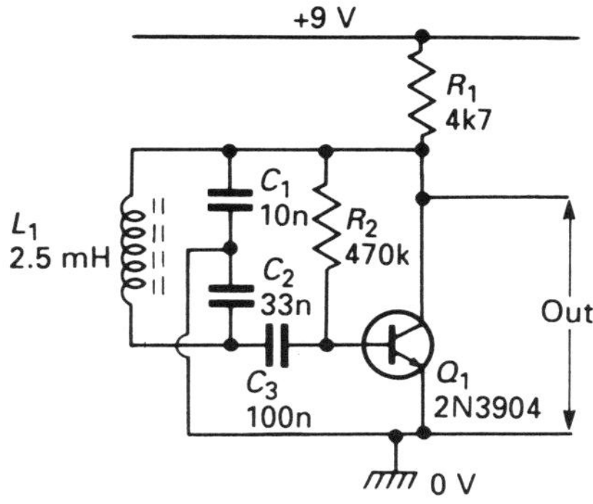


Figure 8.30. *37kHz Colpitts* L–C *oscillator.*

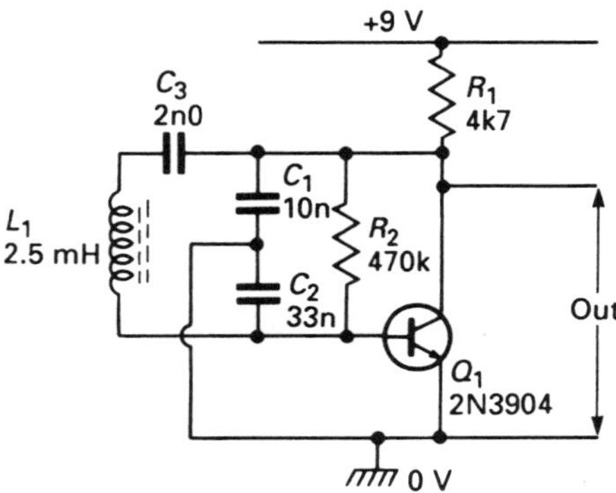


Figure 8.31. *80kHz Gouriet or Clapp* L–C *oscillator.*

a shift in frequency. This effect can be minimized (and good frequency stability obtained) by making $C_1$ and $C_2$ large relative to the internal capacitances of $Q_1$.

A modification of the Colpitts oscillator, known as the Clapp or Gouriet oscillator, is shown in *Figure 8.31*. Here, capacitor $C_3$ is wired in series with $L_1$, and has a value that is small relative to $C_1$ and $C_2$. Consequently, the circuit's resonant frequency is decided mainly by the values of $L_1$ and $C_3$, and is not upset by variations in $Q_1$'s capacitances. This circuit thus gives excellent frequency stability. With the component values shown, it oscillates at about 80kHz.

*Figure 8.32* shows the basic circuit of a so-called Reinartz oscillator, in which the tuning coil has three inductively coupled windings. Positive feedback is obtained by coupling $Q_1$'s collector and emitter signals via windings $L_1$ and $L_2$, which are both coupled to $L_3$, and the circuit oscillates at a frequency set by $L_3$–$C_1$. The diagram shows typical coil–turns ratios for a circuit designed to oscillate at a few hundred-kilohertz.

Finally, to complete this look at basic $L$–$C$ oscillators, *Figure 8.33* shows how the *Figure 8.28* design can be modified so that it acts as a 465kHz beat-frequency oscillator (BFO) that is 'Varicap' tuned via potentiometer $RV_1$. Here, a standard 465kHz transistor IF transformer ($T_1$) is used as the $L$–$C$ tuned circuit, and silicon diode $D_1$ is used as an inexpensive Varicap diode or voltage-variable capacitor.

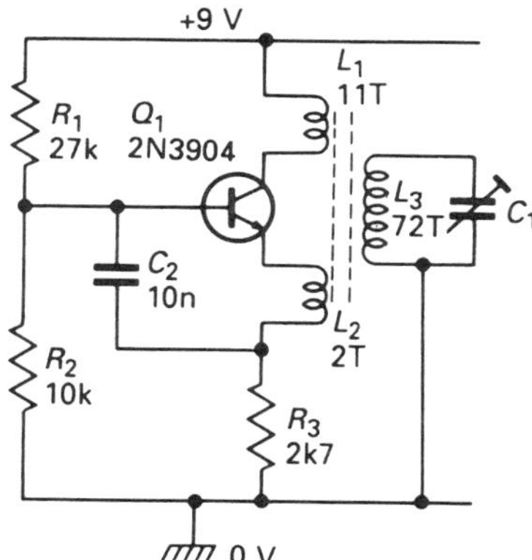


Figure 8.32. *Basic Reinartz* L–C *oscillator.*

When any silicon diode is reverse biased its effective capacitance varies with the applied voltage; it is greatest when the voltage is low, and least when the voltage is high. Varicap diodes are made to exploit this effect, but the ordinary IN4001 diode can be used

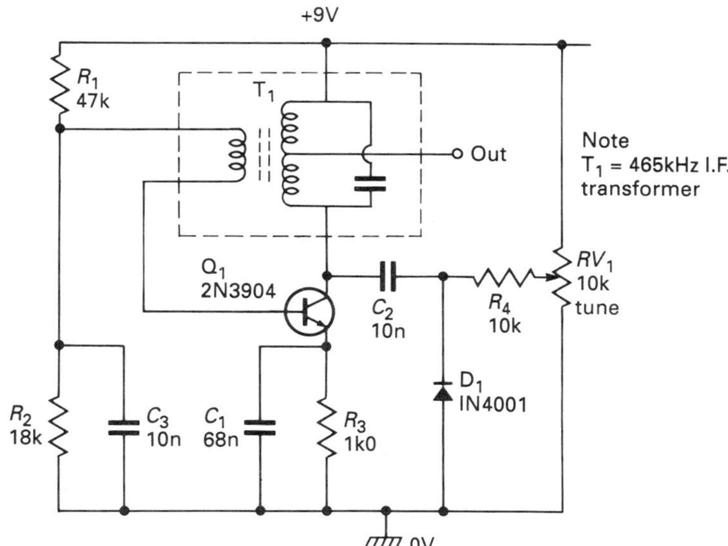


Figure 8.33. *465kHz B.F.O. with Varicap tuning.*

for the same purpose, as in *Figure 8.33*. Here, $C_2$ (which gives D.C. isolation between $Q_1$ and $D_1$) and 'capacitor' $D_1$ are wired in series, and the combination is effectively wired across the $T_1$ tuned circuit (since the circuit's supply rails are shorted together as far as a.c. signals are concerned). Consequently, the oscillator's centre frequency can be varied by altering the capacitance of $D_1$ via $RV_1$.

# 9 Square and pulse waveform generators

A wide variety of non-sinusoidal waveform generator types are used in modern test gear, and the two best known and most widely used of these are the square-wave and the triggered pulse waveform types of generator. Many practical waveform generators of both these types are described in this chapter.

## Square-wave basics

Square-waves are free-running 'pulse' waveforms and can be generated directly or derived (by conversion) from existing waveforms. *Figure 9.1* illustrates the basic parameters of a square-wave; in each cycle the wave first switches from zero to some peak voltage value ($V_{pk}$) for a fixed period, and then switches

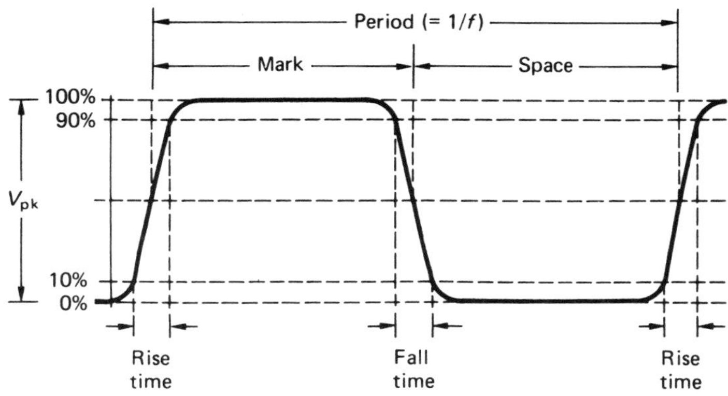


Figure 9.1. *Basic parameters of a square wave.*

low again for a second fixed period. The time taken for the waveform to rise from 10 per cent to 90 per cent of $V_{pk}$ is known as its **rise time**, and that taken for it to drop from 90 per cent to 10 per cent of $V_{pk}$ is known as its **fall time**.

Circuits that produce poor-quality square-waves, with fairly long rise and fall times, are colloquially known as 'squirt' generators; such waveforms are useful in non-critical applications such as relay driving, LED flashing, sound generation, etc. High-quality square-waves have very short rise and fall times, and are produced via so-called 'clock' generators; such waveforms are essential for correctly clocking fast-acting digital counter and divider ICs, etc.

In each square-wave cycle the 'high' part is known as its **mark** and the 'low' part as its **space**. In a symmetrical square-wave (such as *Figure 9.1*) the mark and space periods are equal and the waveform is said to have a 1:1 M–S ratio, or a 50 per cent duty cycle (since the mark duration forms fifty per cent of the total cycle period). Square waves do not have to be symmetrical, however, and their M–S ratios, etc., can be varied over a very wide range, as illustrated in *Figure 9.2*.

Note from *Figure 9.2* that the *mean* output voltage ($V_{mean}$) of each waveform, integrated over a full cycle period, equals $V_{pk}$ multiplied by the percentage duty cycle. Thus, if $V_{pk}$ is 10V, the *Figure 9.2a* waveform (which has a 10 per cent duty-cycle) gives a $V_{mean}$ of 1V, *Figure 9.2b* (which has a 50 per cent duty cycle) gives a $V_{mean}$ of 5V, and *Figure 9.2c* (which has a 90 per cent duty cycle) gives a $V_{mean}$ of 9V. Thus, $V_{mean}$ is fully variable via the M–S ratio or duty-cycle value.

## Sine-to-square conversion

Good-quality square waves can be generated by feeding an existing sine wave through a simple sine-to-square converter, and the easiest way to do this is to use one of the four available gates of a CMOS 4093B quad two-input NAND Schmitt IC, using the connections shown in *Figure 9.3* (the three unused gates can be disabled by grounding their input terminals). This circuit produces an excellent square-wave output, with typical rise and fall times of less than 100ns when the output is loaded by 50pF; the Schmitt's trigger threshold can be set via $RV_1$.

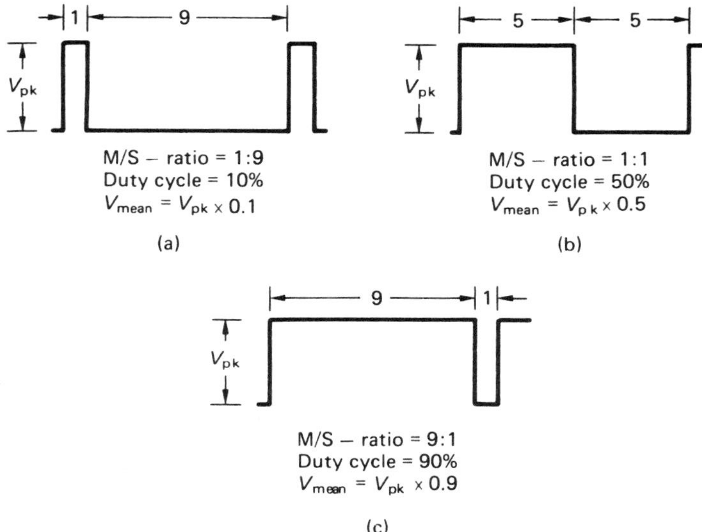


Figure 9.2. *Square waves with various mark–space values.*

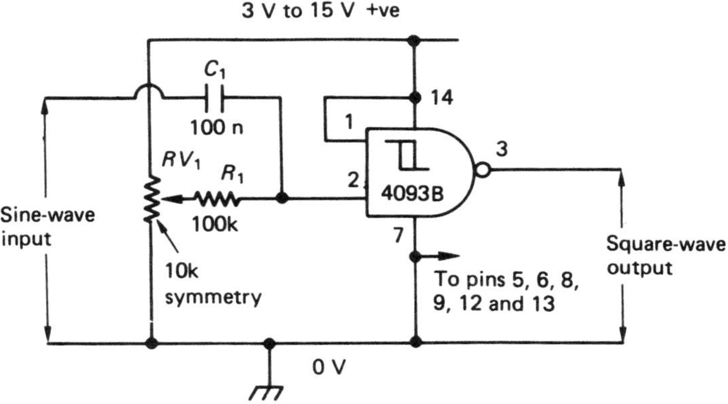


Figure 9.3. *CMOS Schmitt sine–square converter.*

## Transistor astable circuits

One way of directly generating square waves is via a two-transistor astable multivibrator. *Figure 9.4* shows a practical 1kHz version

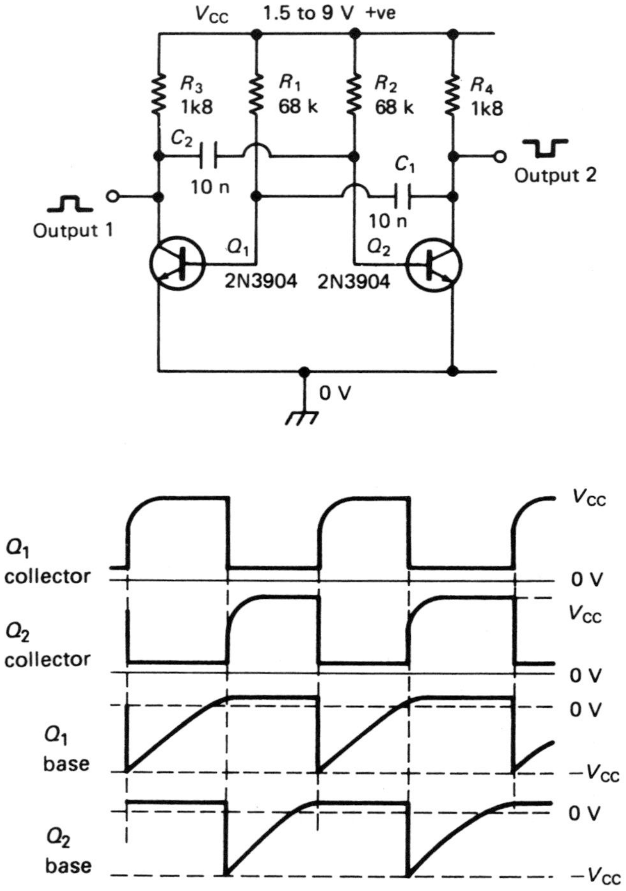

Figure 9.4. *Circuit of basic 1kHz transistor astable multivibrator.*

of this circuit, which can operate with good stability from supplies in the 1.5V to 9V range. It is a cross-coupled oscillator, with its mark and space periods controlled by the $C_1 - R_1$ and $C_2 - R_2$ time constants. If these time constants are equal ($C_1 = C_2$ and $R_1 = R_2$), the circuit generates a symmetrical square-wave output and operates at a frequency of $1/(1.4C_1R_1)$. Thus, frequency can be decreased by raising the $C$ or $R$ values, or vice versa, and can be made variable by using twin-gang variable resistors (in series with 10k limiting resistors) in place of $R_1 - R_2$.

The square-wave outputs of this circuit can be taken from the collector of either transistor, and are in anti-phase; the output waveform leading edges are rounded and have rather long rise times, so this simple astable is really only useful as a crude square-wave 'squirt' generator. There are many variants of this basic circuit, designed to improve its voltage range and/or wave-shape, but if a really good square wave is needed it is best to use a different type of circuit, using either op-amps, CMOS or TTL gates or Schmitts, or a dedicated '555 timer' IC, etc.

## Op-amp square-wave generators

Useful square waves can be generated by using an op-amp in the basic relaxation oscillator configuration of *Figure 9.5*. This circuit's output switches alternately between the op-amp's positive and negative saturation levels; potential divider $R_2-R_3$ feeds a fraction of this voltage back to the op-amp's non-inverting input, to provide the op-amp with an 'aiming' voltage, and feedback components $R_1-C_1$ act as a time-constant network. The circuit operation is such that, when the output is high, $C_1$ charges up via $R_1$ until its voltage reaches the positive 'aiming' value set by $R_2-R_3$, at which point a comparator action occurs and the op-amp output regeneratively switches negative, causing $C_1$ to start to discharge via $R_1$ until its voltage falls to the negative aiming value set by $R_2-R_3$, at which point the op-amp output switches positive again, and the whole sequence repeats *ad infinitum*, generating a symmetrical square wave at the output of the op-amp, and a non-

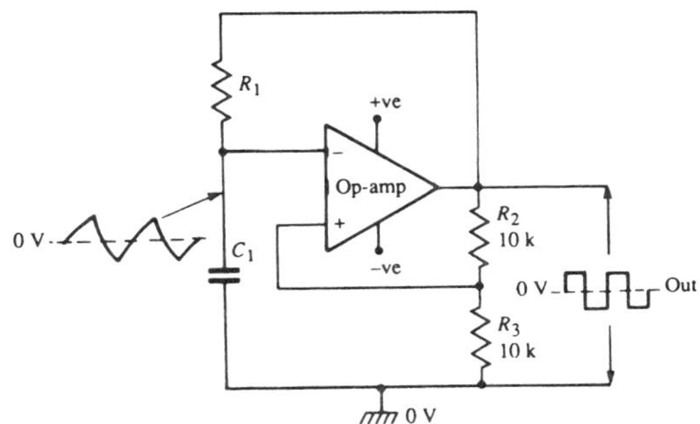


Figure 9.5. *Basic op-amp relaxation oscillator circuit.*

linear triangle waveform across $C_1$. A fast op-amp, such as the CA3140, should be used if good rise and fall times are needed from the square wave.

This circuit's operating frequency can be varied by altering either the $R_1$ or $C_1$ values, or by altering the $R_2$–$R_3$ ratios; the circuit is thus quite versatile. *Figure 9.6* shows it adapted to make a 500Hz to 5kHz square-wave generator, with frequency variation obtained by altering the $R_2$–$RV_1$–$R_3$ attenuation ratio. $RV_2$ can be used to pre-set the range of the $RV_1$ frequency control; $RV_3$ gives output amplitude control.

*Figure 9.7* shows the above circuit modified to make a general-purpose square-wave generator that spans 2Hz to 20kHz in four switched decade ranges. Pre-set pots $RV_1$ to $RV_4$ are used to precisely set the minimum frequency of the 2Hz to 20Hz, 20Hz to 200Hz, 200Hz to 2kHz, and 2kHz to 20kHz ranges respectively.

In the *Figure 9.5* circuit $C_1$ alternately charges and discharges via $R_1$, and the circuit generates a symmetrical square-wave output. It can be made to give a variable-symmetry output by providing $C_1$ with alternate charge and discharge paths, as shown in *Figure 9.8*. Here, the waveform's M–S ratio is fully variable from 11:1 to 1:11 via $RV_1$, and the frequency is variable from 650Hz to 6.5kHz via $RV_2$. The action is such that $C_1$ alternately charges up via $R_1$–$D_1$ and the left-hand side of $RV_1$, and discharges via $R_1$–$D_2$ and the right-hand side of $RV_1$, giving a variable-symmetry output; variation of $RV_1$ has negligible effect on the circuit's operating frequency.

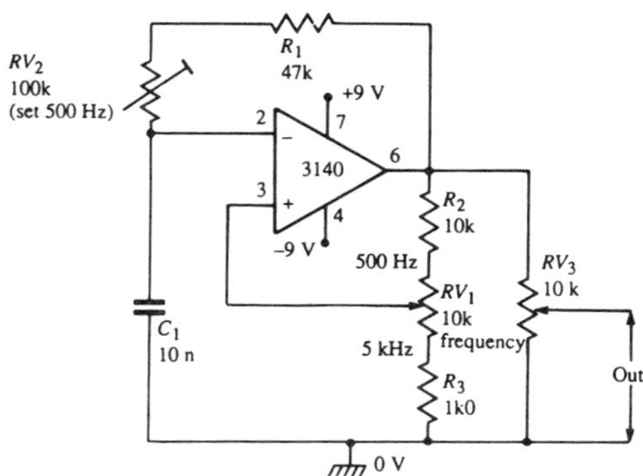


Figure 9.6. *500Hz to 5kHz square-wave generator.*

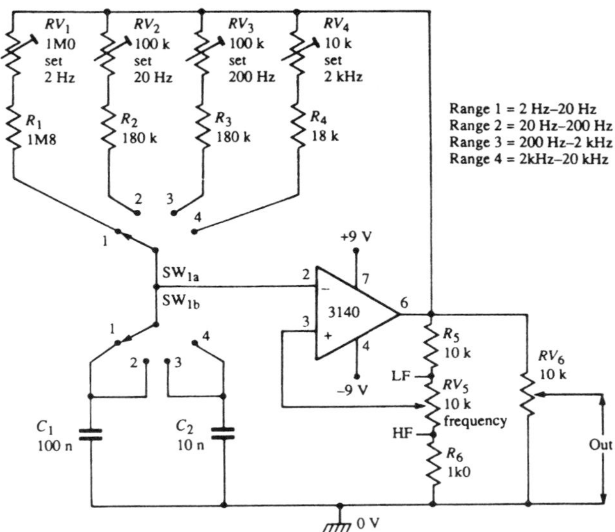


Figure 9.7. *General-purpose four-decade (2Hz to 20kHz) op-amp square-wave generator.*

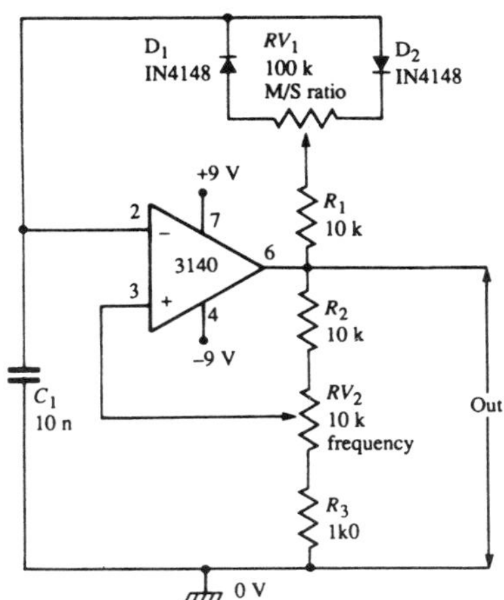


Figure 9.8. *Square-wave generator with variable M–S ratio and frequency.*

## CMOS astable basics

Another way to make a square-wave generator is to use the gates of inexpensive CMOS logic ICs such as the 4001B, 4011B, etc., as simple inverters, which are then wired in the astable multivibrator mode, as in *Figure 9.9a*. This circuit generates a good square-wave output from $IC_{1b}$ (and a not-quite-so-good anti-phase square-wave output from $IC_{1a}$), and operates at about 1kHz with the

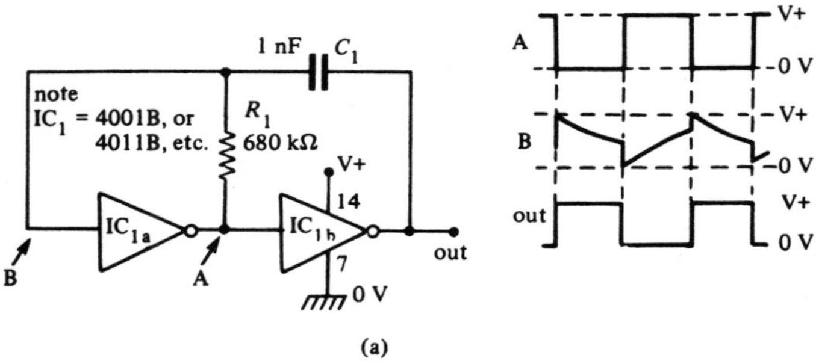


Figure 9.9a. *Circuit and waveforms of basic two-stage 1kHz CMOS astable.*

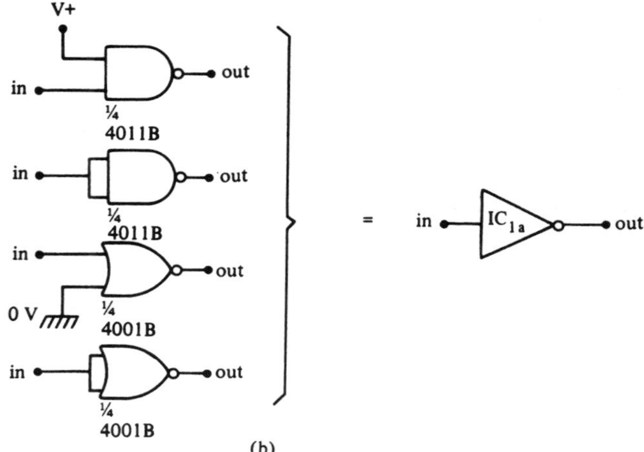


Figure 9.9b. *Ways of connecting a two-input NAND (4011B) or NOR (4001B) gate for use as an inverter.*

component values shown. The circuit is suitable for use in many (but not all) 'clock' generator applications, and operates as follows.

The two inverters are wired in series, and time-constant network $C_1-R_1$ is wired between the outputs of $IC_{1b}$ and $IC_{1a}$, with the $C_1-R_1$ junction fed to the input of $IC_{1A}$. Suppose initially that $C_1$ is fully discharged and the output of $IC_{1b}$ has just switched high; this makes the $C_1-R_1$ junction initially fully positive, thus driving the $IC_{1a}$ output low, but the voltage starts to decay exponentially as $C_1$ charges up via $R_1$, until eventually it falls into the linear 'transfer voltage' range of $IC_{1a}$, making its output start to swing high. This initiates a regenerative action in which $IC_{1b}$ output switches abruptly to the low state (and $IC_{1a}$ output switches high). This switching action makes the charge of $C_1$ try to apply a negative voltage to the $IC_{1a}$ input, but $IC_{1a}$'s built-in input protection diodes prevent this and instead discharge $C_1$.

Thus, at the start of the second cycle, $C_1$ is again fully discharged, so the $C_1-R_1$ junction is initially at 0V (driving $IC_{1a}$ output high), but then rises exponentially as $C_1$ charges up via $R_1$, until eventually it rises into the linear 'transfer voltage' range of $IC_{1a}$, thus initiating another regenerative switching action in which the $IC_{1b}$ output switches high again (and the $IC_{1a}$ output switches low), and $C_1$ is again discharged via the $IC_{1a}$ input protection diodes. The operating cycle then continues *ad infinitum*.

The circuit's operating frequency is inversely proportional to the $C-R$ time constant (the period is roughly $1.4 \times CR$), so can be raised by lowering the values of either $C_1$ or $R_1$. $C_1$ must be non-polarized and can vary from a few tens of picofarads to several microfarads, and $R_1$ can vary from 4k7 to 22M; the astable operating frequency can vary from a fraction of a hertz to about 1MHz. For variable-frequency operation, wire a fixed and a variable resistor in series in the $R_1$ position.

Each of the 'inverters' of the *Figure 9.9a* circuit can be made from a single gate of a 4001B quad two-input NOR gate or a 4011B quad two-input NAND gate, etc., by using the connections shown in *Figure 9.9b*; the inputs of all unused gates in these ICs must be tied to one or other of the supply-line terminals. The CMOS astable can be used with any supplies in the range 3V to 18V; the 'zero volts' terminal goes to pin-7 of the 4001B or 4011B, and the '+ve' terminal goes to pin-14.

The output of the *Figure 9.9a* astable switches between the zero and positive supply rail values, but the $C_1-R_1$ junction voltage is prevented from swinging below zero or above the positive supply-rail levels by the built-in clamping diodes at the input of $IC_{1a}$. This fact makes the operating frequency somewhat dependent on supply-rail voltage; typically, a 10 per cent rise in supply voltage causes a 0.8 per cent fall in frequency. The waveform's frequency and symmetry are also influenced by the 'transfer voltage' value of the individual $IC_{1a}$ inverter/gate (the frequency may vary by as much as 10 per cent between different ICs). These defects are usually of little practical importance.

## Astable variations

Some of the defects of the *Figure 9.9a* circuit can be minimized by using the 'compensated' astable of *Figure 9.10*, in which $R_2$ is wired in series with $IC_{1a}$'s input. This resistor must be large relative to $R_1$, and its main purpose is to allow the $C_1-R_1$ junction to swing freely below the zero and above the positive supply-rail voltages and thus improve the astable's frequency stability and waveform symmetry. Typically, when $R_2$ is ten times the $R_1$ value, the frequency varies by only 0.5 per cent when the supply is varied between 5 and 15V.

The basic and compensated astable circuits of *Figures 9.9a* and *9.10* can be built with several detail variations. *Figure 9.11* shows the basic circuit modified to give a variable-symmetry output; here, $C_1$ charges via $D_1-RV_1-R_1$, to generate the mark part of the waveform, but discharges via $D_2-RV_2-R_1$, to give the space part of the waveform.

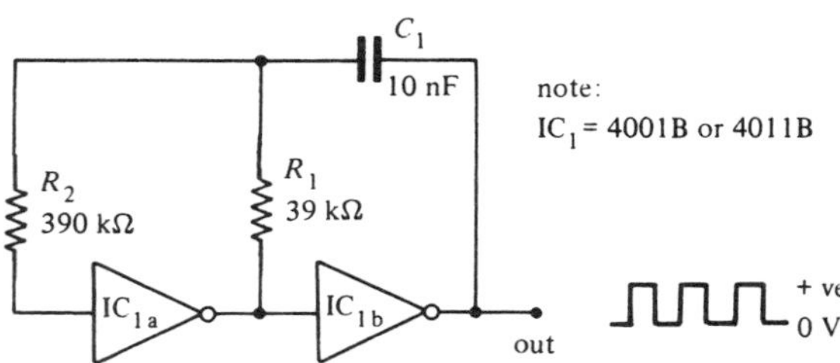


Figure 9.10. *This 'compensated' version of the 1kHz astable has excellent frequency stability.*

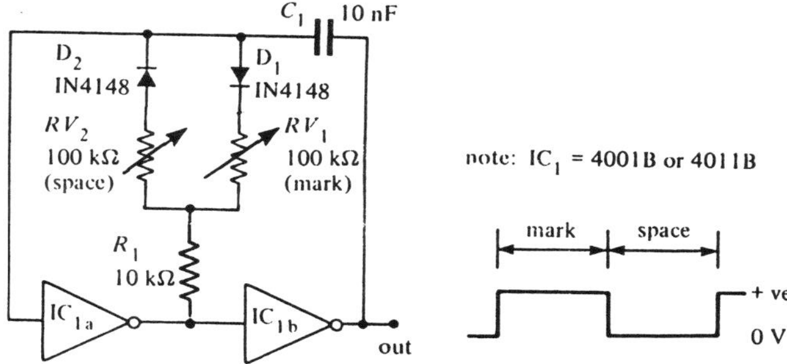


Figure 9.11. *CMOS astable with independently variable **mark** and **space** times.*

## 'Ring-of-three' astable

The two-stage astable circuit is a good general-purpose square-wave generator, but is not always suitable for direct use as a 'clock' generator with fast-acting counting and dividing circuits, since it tends to pick up and amplify any existing supply-line noise during the 'transitioning' parts of its operating cycle and to thus produce output square waves with 'glitchy' leading and trailing edges. A far better type of 'clock' generator circuit is the 'ring-of-three' astable shown in *Figure 9.12*.

The *Figure 9.12* ring-of-three circuit is similar to the basic two-stage astable, except that its 'input' stage ($IC_{1a}-IC_{1b}$) acts as an ultra-high-gain non-inverting amplifier and its main timing components ($C_1-R_1$) are transposed (relative to the two-stage

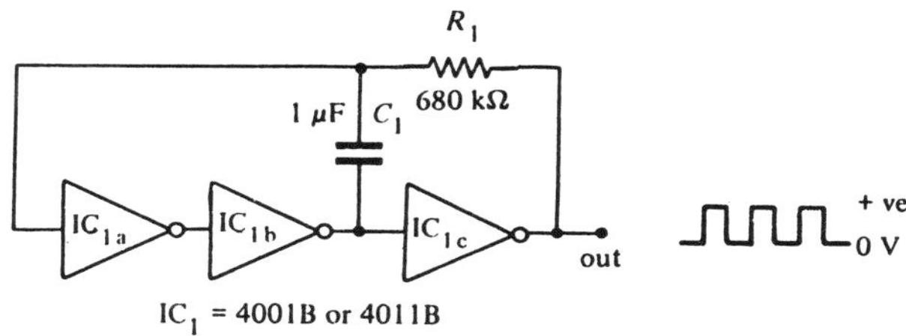


Figure 9.12. *This 'ring-of-three' astable makes an excellent clock generator.*

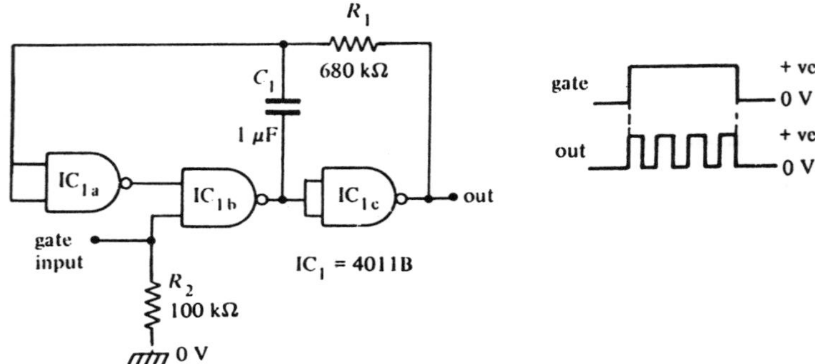


Figure 9.13. *This gated 'ring-of-three' astable is gated by a logic-1 input and has a normally low output.*

astable). Because of the very high overall gain of the circuit, it produces an excellent and glitch-free square-wave output, ideal for clock-generator use.

The basic ring-of-three astable can be subjected to all the design modifications already described for the basic two-stage astable, e.g. it can be used in either basic or compensated form and can give either a symmetrical or non-symmetrical output, etc. The most interesting variations occur, however, when the circuit is used in the 'gated' mode, since it can be gated via either the $IC_{1b}$ or $IC_{1c}$ stages. *Figure 9.13* shows an example of a 'gated' oscillator that is gated on by a logic-1 input signal and has a normally low output.

## The CMOS 'Schmitt' astable

An excellent astable 'clock' generator can also be made from a single CMOS Schmitt inverter stage. Suitable ICs for use here are the 40106B hex Schmitt inverter, and the 4093B quad two-input NAND Schmitt trigger. Each NAND gate of the 4093B can be used as an inverter by simply disabling one of its input terminals as shown in the basic Schmitt astable circuit of *Figure 9.14*. This circuit gives a square-wave output with edges that are unaffected by supply-line ripple and other 'nasties'; its operating frequency is decided by the $C_1$–$R_1$ values, and can be varied from below 1Hz to above 1MHz. The circuit action is such that $C_1$ alternately

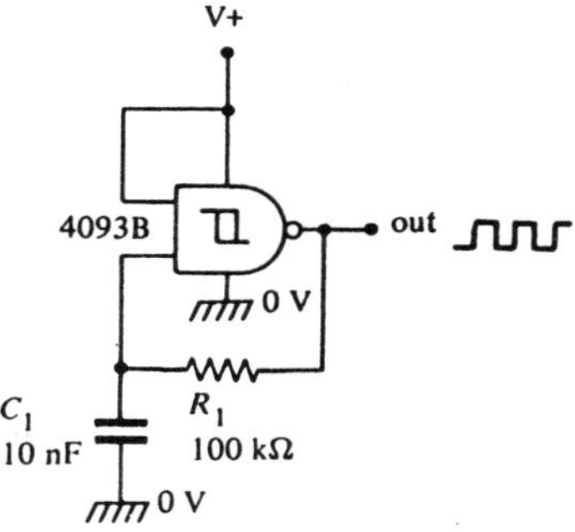


Figure 9.14. *Basic CMOS Schmitt astable.*

charges and discharges via $R_1$, without switching the $C_1$ polarity; $C_1$ can thus be a polarized component.

The *Figure 9.14* circuit can be gated via an external signal by disconnecting the 'spare' input terminal from the positive rail and using it as the gate input terminal; the astable is gated on by a high (logic-1) input to this terminal, but gives a 'high' output when gated off.

## TTL Schmitt astable circuits

Astable square-wave generators can also be built using inexpensive TTL ICs, and one popular way of doing this is to use elements from the 74LS14 hex Schmitt inverter. *Figure 9.15* shows an example of such a circuit, which generates a clean square-wave output with a 2:1 M/S ratio and uses a second Schmitt stage to give a buffered output. The circuit should be used with a fixed 5V supply, and its timing resistance ($R_1$ + $RV_1$) value must be within the 100$R$ to 1k2 range. The circuit's frequency is variable (via $RV_1$) from about 8.2kHz to 89kHz when $C_1$ has a value of 100nF.

## 4046B VCO circuits

One really useful CMOS square-wave 'clock' generator IC is the 4046B phase-locked loop (PLL) IC, which houses (amongst other things) a very useful VCO (voltage-controlled oscillator). This

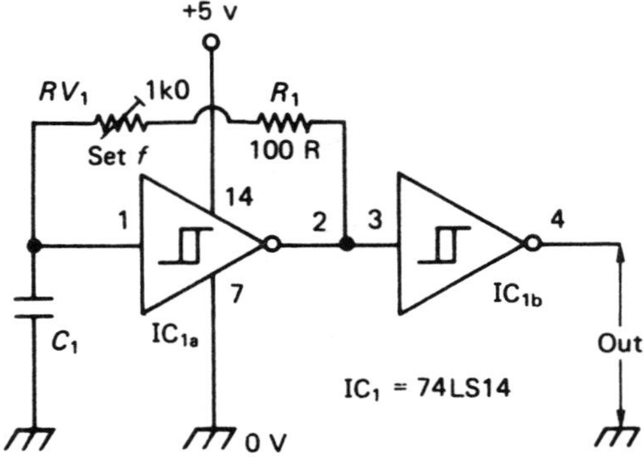


Figure 9.15. *Variable-frequency TTL Schmitt astable.*

VCO is highly versatile; it gives an excellent and symmetrical square-wave output, has a top frequency limit in excess of 1MHz, has a voltage-to-frequency linearity of about 1 per cent and can be 'scanned' through a 1000000:1 range by an external voltage fed to the pin-9 VCO input terminal. The VCO frequency depends on the values of a capacitor (minimum value 50pF) connected between pins 6 and 7 and a resistor (minimum value 10k) wired between pin-11 and ground, and the voltage applied to pin-9.

*Figure 9.16* shows the simplest possible way of using the 4046B as a voltage-controlled square-wave generator. Here, $C_1 - R_1$ deter-

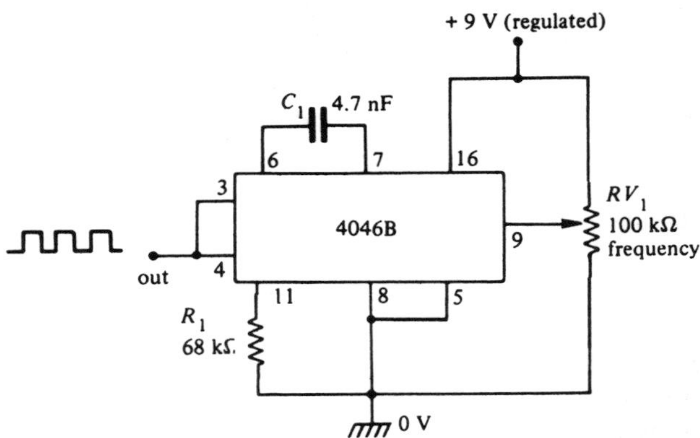


Figure 9.16. *CMOS wide-range VCO, spanning near-zero to 5kHz via* RV*1*.

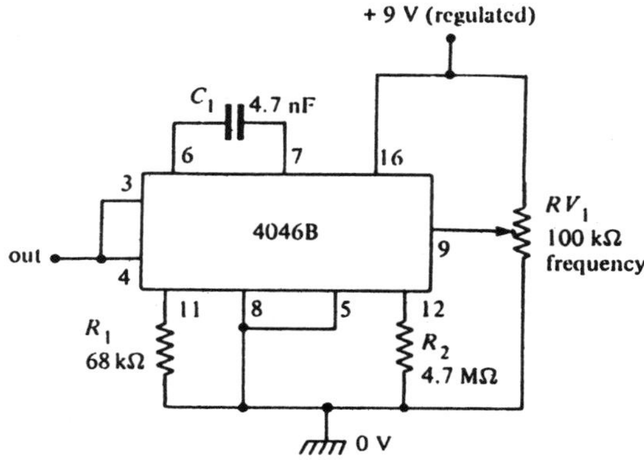


Figure 9.17. *Restricted-range VCO, with frequency variable from roughly 72Hz to 5kHz via* $RV_1$.

mine the maximum frequency that can be obtained (with the pin-9 voltage at maximum) and $RV_1$ controls the actual frequency by applying a control voltage to pin-9: the frequency falls to a very low value (a fraction of a hertz) with pin-9 at 0V. The effective voltage-control range of pin-9 varies from roughly 1V below the supply value to about 1V above zero, and gives a frequency span of about 1 000 000:1. Ideally, the circuit supply voltage should be regulated.

*Figure 9.17* shows the above circuit modified, by wiring a resistor between pin-12 and ground, to set the minimum operating frequency of a restricted-range VCO; $f_{min}$ is determined by $C_1-R_2$, and $f_{max}$ is determined by $C_1$ and the parallel resistance of $R_1$ and $R_2$.

## 555 astable circuits

The 555 timer IC can be used as a free-running astable multivibrator or square-wave generator by using it in the basic configuration shown in *Figure 9.18*, in which **trigger** pin-2 is shorted to the pin-6 **threshold** terminal, and timing resistor $R_2$ is wired between pin-6 and **discharge** pin-7. When power is first applied to this circuit $C_1$ starts to charge exponentially via the series $R_1-R_2$ combination, until eventually the $C_1$ voltage rises to $\frac{2}{3}V_{CC}$, at which point

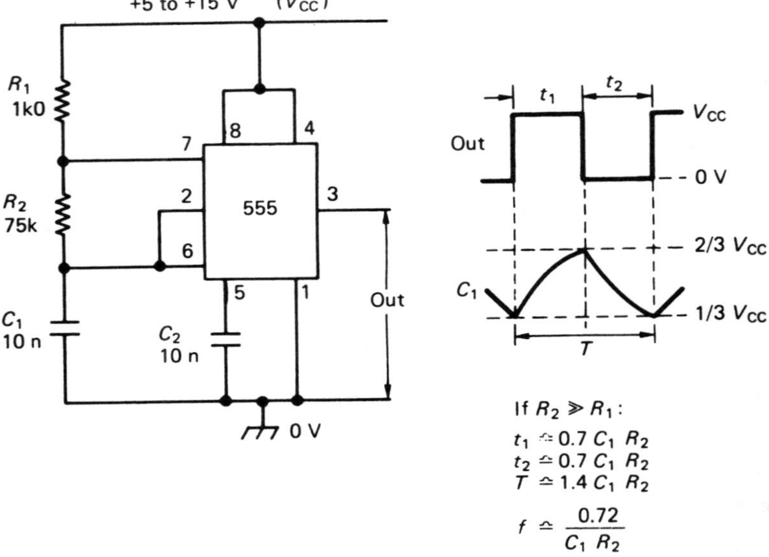


Figure 9.18. *Basic 1kHz 555 astable multivibrator.*

**discharge** pin-7 switches low and starts to discharge $C_1$ exponentially via $R_2$, until eventually the $C_1$ voltage falls to $\frac{1}{3}V_{CC}$, at which point a new timing sequence is initiated, and $C_1$ starts to recharge towards $\frac{2}{3}V_{CC}$ via $R_1$ and $R_2$. The whole sequence then repeats *ad infinitum*, with $C_1$ alternately charging towards $\frac{2}{3}V_{CC}$ via $R_1{-}R_2$ and discharging towards $\frac{1}{3}V_{CC}$ via $R_2$ only.

When $R_2$ is very large relative to $R_1$ the operating frequency is determined mainly by $R_2$ and $C_1$, and an almost symmetrical square-wave output is developed on pin-3 and a near-linear triangle waveform appears across $C_1$. The $R_1$ and $R_2$ values can be varied from 1k0 to tens of megohms; note, however, that $R_1$ affects the circuits current consumption, since pin-7 is effectively grounded during half of each cycle.

*Figure 9.19* shows how the operating frequency of the *Figure 9.18* circuit can be made variable by simply replacing $R_2$ with a series-wired fixed and a variable resistor. With the component values shown the frequency can be varied from about 650Hz to 7.2kHz via $RV_1$; the frequency span can be further increased by selecting alternative values of $C_1$.

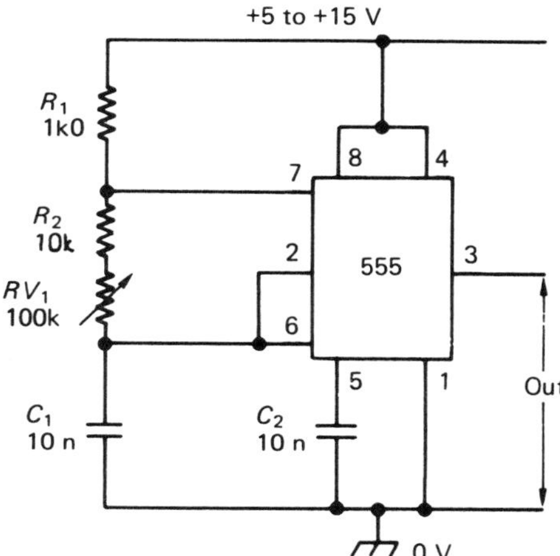


Figure 9.19. *Variable-frequency (650Hz to 7.2kHz) square-wave generator.*

## Mark–space control

In each operating cycle of the *Figure 9.18* circuit $C_1$ alternately charges via $R_1$–$R_2$ and discharges via $R_2$ only; the circuit can thus be made to generate a non-symmetrical waveform with a desired mark–space (M–S) ratio by suitably selecting the $R_1$ and $R_2$ values. *Figures 9.20* and *9.21* show ways of making the M–S ratios fully variable.

*Figure 9.20* shows a way of gaining independent control of the mark and space periods. Here, $C_1$ alternately charges via $R_1$–$D_1$–$RV_1$ and discharges via $RV_2$–$D_2$–$R_2$. $R_2$ protects the IC against damage when $RV_2$ is reduced to zero, and the mark and space periods can each be independently varied over a 100:1 range, enabling the M–S ratio to be varied from 100:1 to 1:100; the frequency varies as the M–S ratio is altered.

*Figure 9.21* shows a way of altering the M–S ratio without significantly altering the operating frequency. Here, $C_1$ alternately charges via $R_1$–$D_1$ and the upper half of $RV_1$ and discharges via $D_2$–$R_2$ and the lower half of $RV_1$, and the action is such that the mark period automatically increases as the space period decreases, and vice versa, so the total period of each cycle is constant. The circuit operates at a nominal 1.2kHz with the $C_1$ value shown.

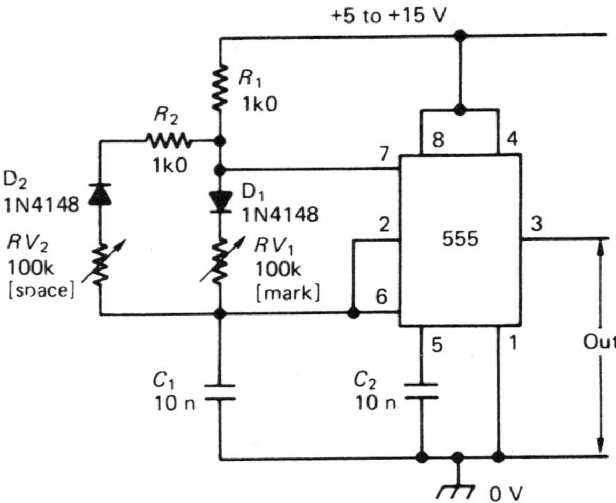


Figure 9.20. *Astable with* **mark** *and* **space** *periods independently variable from 7μs to 750μs.*

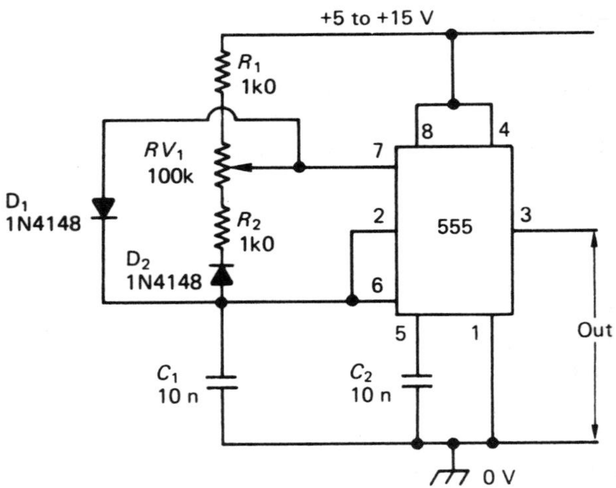


Figure 9.21. *1.2kHz astable multi with duty cycle variable from 1 per cent to 99 per cent.*

The most important waveform feature of this circuit is its 'duty cycle' or relationship between the **on** time and total period of each cycle, which is variable from 1 to 99 per cent via $RV_1$.

## Pulse generator circuits

A pulse generator is a circuit that produces a single or 'one-shot' rectangular output waveform cycle when triggered by a suitable input signal. Such generators may take several basic forms, and can be designed around a variety of semiconductor devices. The rest of this chapter deals with pulse generator principles and circuits.

## Pulse generator basics

Circuit designers often have to devise means of generating pulse waveforms. If the need is to simply generate a pulse of non-critical width on the arrival of the leading or trailing edge of an input square wave, a circuit element known as a 'half-monostable' or edge-detector may be used, as shown in *Figure 9.22*. Alternatively, if the need is to generate a pulse of some specific width on the arrival of a suitable trigger signal, a standard monostable or 'one-shot' multivibrator circuit may be used.

In the standard monostable circuit, the arrival of the trigger signal initiates an internal timing cycle which causes the monostable output to change state at the start of the timing cycle, but to revert back to its original state on completion of the cycle, as shown in *Figure 9.23*.

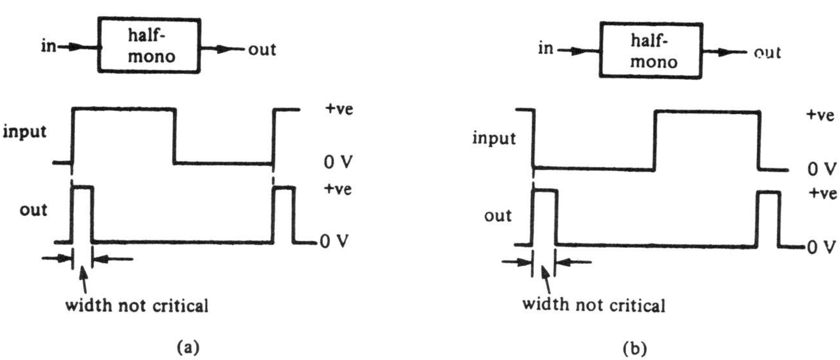


Figure 9.22. *A 'half-mono' circuit may be used to detect (a) the leading or (b) the trailing edge of an input waveform.*

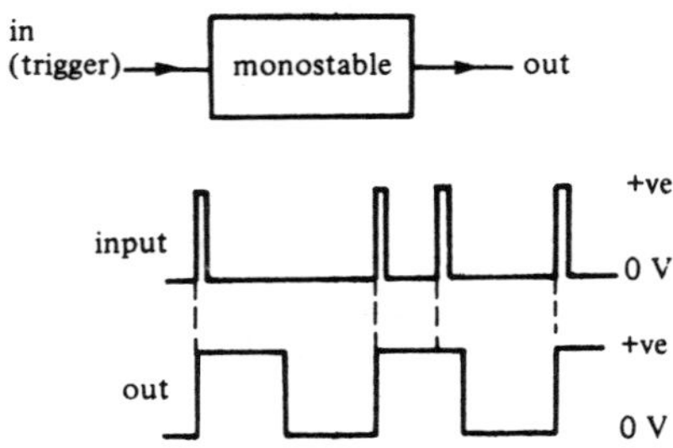


Figure 9.23. *A standard monostable generates an accurate output pulse on the arrival of a suitable trigger signal.*

Note that once a timing cycle has been initiated the standard monostable circuit is immune to the effects of subsequent trigger signals until its timing period ends naturally. This type of circuit can sometimes be modified by adding a **reset** control terminal, as shown in *Figure 9.24*, to enable the output pulse to be terminated or aborted at any time via a suitable command signal.

A third type of monostable circuit is the 'retriggerable' mono. Here, the trigger signal actually resets the mono and then, after a very brief delay, initiates a new pulse-generating timing cycle, as shown in *Figure 9.25*, so that each new trigger signal initiates a new timing cycle, even if the trigger signal arrives in the midst of an existing cycle.

Thus, the circuit designer may use a half-mono, a standard mono, a resettable mono, or a retriggerable mono to generate

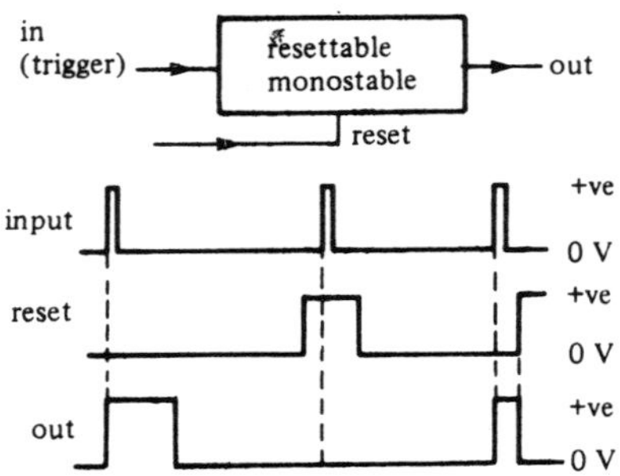


Figure 9.24. *The output pulse of a resettable mono can be aborted by a suitable reset pulse.*

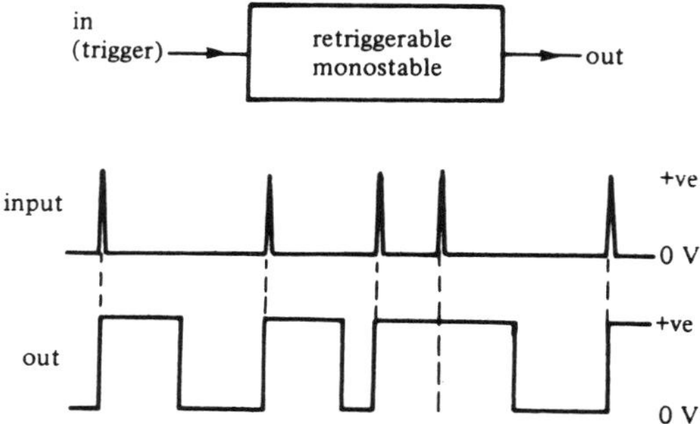


Figure 9.25. *A retriggerable mono starts a new timing cycle on the arrival of each new trigger signal.*

pulses, the 'type' decision depending on the specific circuit design requirements.

The pulse generator may be designed around a variety of types of semiconductor device, or may be designed around a dedicated pulse generator IC; the choice is usually dictated by considerations of economics and convenience, rather than by the actual design requirements.

## 'Half-mono' pulse generator circuits

The simplest of all pulse generators is the 'half-monostable' or 'half-mono' type. One of the most popular applications of this is as an 'edge detector', which generates a simple output pulse on the arrival of the leading or the trailing edge of a rectangular input waveform; the precise width of the output pulse is usually non-critical.

The basic method of making an edge-detector is to feed the rectangular input waveform to a short-time-constant $C-R$ differentiation network, to produce a positive output spike on the arrival of each leading edge and a negative one on each trailing edge, and to then eliminate the unwanted waveform spike with a discriminator diode. The remaining sawtooth-shaped spike is then converted into a clean pulse shape by feeding it through a Schmitt trigger circuit.

The simplest way of making a practical edge-detector is to use a CMOS Schmitt trigger IC, since these incorporate built-in protection diodes on all input terminals, and these can be used to perform the discriminator diode action described above. *Figures 9.27* to *9.29* show a selection of edge-detector designs based on CMOS Schmitt stages. Note that each gate of the popular 4093B quad two-input NOR Schmitt IC can be used as a normal Schmitt inverter by wiring one input terminal to the positive supply rail and using the other terminal as the input point, as shown in *Figure 9.26*, which also shows how a non-inverting Schmitt can be made by wiring two inverting Schmitts in series.

*Figure 9.27a* shows a practical leading-edge detector circuit. Here, the Schmitt's input is tied to ground via *R*, and *C*–*R* have a time constant that is short relative to the period of the input waveform. The leading edge of the input signal is thus converted into the 'spike' waveform shown, and this spike is then converted into a good clean pulse waveform via the Schmitt. The circuit generates a positive-going output pulse with a period (*P*) of roughly 0.7 *CR*.

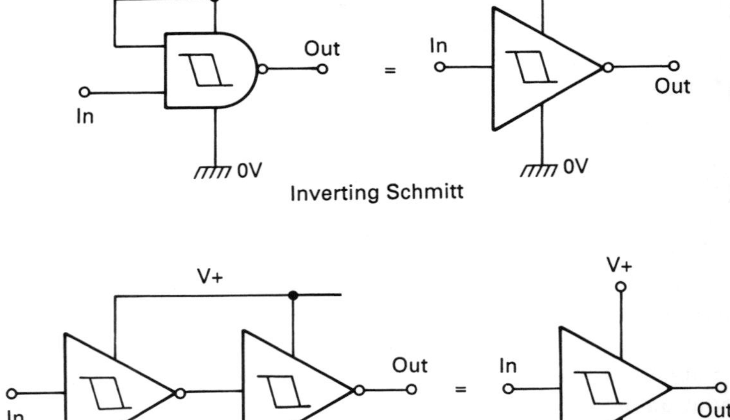


Figure 9.26. *Ways of using a 4093B CMOS two-input NOR gate to make an inverting or non-inverting Schmitt trigger stage.*

Note: P ≃ 0.7 CR

(a)

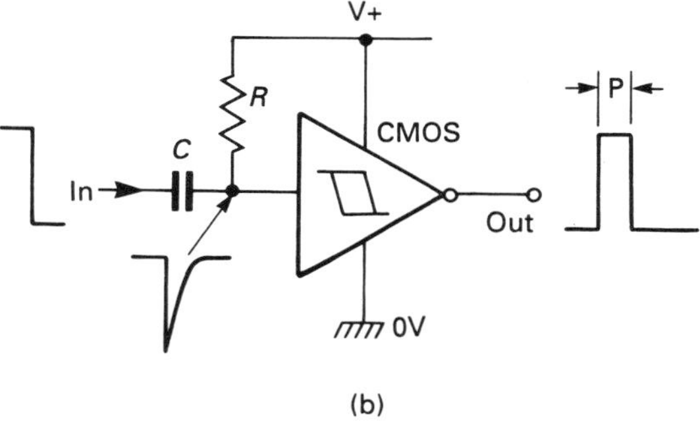


(b)

Figure 9.27. *CMOS leading-edge (a) or trailing-edge (b) detector circuits.*

*Figure 9.27b* shows how to make a trailing-edge detecting half-mono. In this case the CMOS Schmitt input is tied to the positive supply rail via *R*, and *C–R* again has a short time constant. The circuit also generates a positive-going output pulse with a period of roughly 0.7 *CR*.

## Circuit variants

Two useful variants of the edge-detecting half-mono circuit are the 'noiseless' push-botton switch of *Figure 9.28*, which effectively eliminates the adverse effects of switch contact bounce and noise,

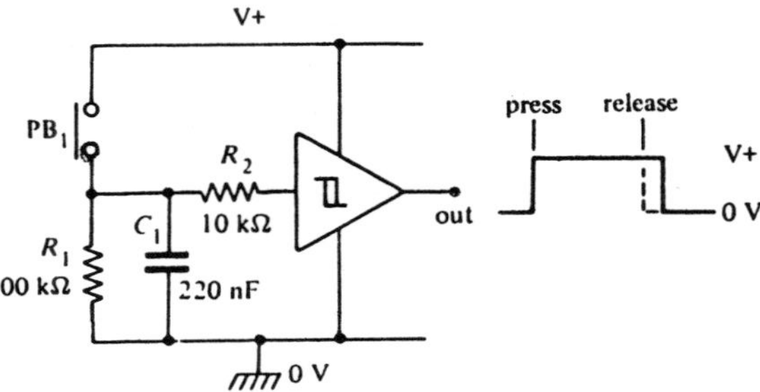


Figure 9.28. *CMOS 'noiseless' push-button switch.*

and the power-on reset-pulse generator circuit of *Figure 9.29*, which generates a reset pulse when power is first applied to the circuit.

In *Figure 9.28*, the Schmitt's input is grounded via $R_1$ and $R_2$, so the circuit's output is normally low. When push-button switch $PB_1$ is closed, $C_1$ charges rapidly to the full positive supply value, driving the Schmitt output high, but when $PB_1$ is released again $C_1$ discharges relatively slowly via $R_1$, and the Schmitt output does not return low until roughly 20ms later. The circuit thus ignores the transient switching effects of $PB_1$ noise and contact bounce, etc., and generates a clean output pulse with a period roughly 20ms longer than the mean duration of the $PB_1$ closure.

The *Figure 9.29* 'power-on reset-pulse generator' circuit produces a 700ms pulse (suitable for resetting external circuitry,

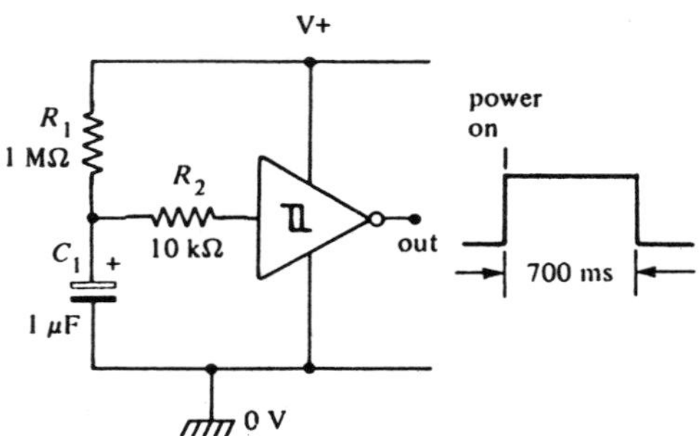


Figure 9.29. *CMOS power-on reset-pulse generator.*

etc.) when power is first applied. When power is initially connected $C_1$ is fully discharged, so the Schmitt input is pulled low and its output is switched high; $C_1$ then charges via $R_1$ until, after about 700ms, the $C_1$ voltage rises to such a level that the Schmitt output switches low, completing the switch-on output pulse.

## 4001B/4011B CMOS monostable circuits

The cheapest and easiest way of making a standard monostable is to use a CMOS 4001B quad two-input NOR gate or a 4011B quad two-input NAND gate IC in one of the configurations shown in *Figures 9.30* or *9.31*. Note, however, that the output pulse widths of these circuits are subject to fairly large variations between individual ICs and with variations in supply-rail voltage, and these circuits are thus not suitable for use in high-precision applications.

*Figures 9.30* and *9.31* show alternative versions of the standard monostable circuit, each using only two of the four available gates in the specified CMOS package. In these circuits the output pulse duration is set by the $C_1-R_1$ values, and approximates $0.7 \times C_1 \times R_1$. Thus, when $R_1$ has a value of 1M5 the pulse period is roughly one second per μF of $C_1$ value. In practice, $C_1$ can have any value from about 100pF to a few thousand microfarads, and $R_1$ can vary from 4k7 to 10M.

Note that in these circuits the input trigger pulse or signal can be direct coupled and its duration has little effect on the length of

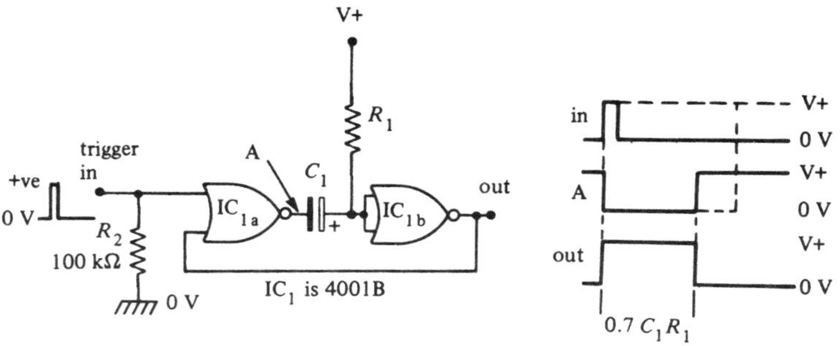


Figure 9.30. *CMOS two-gate NOR monostable.*

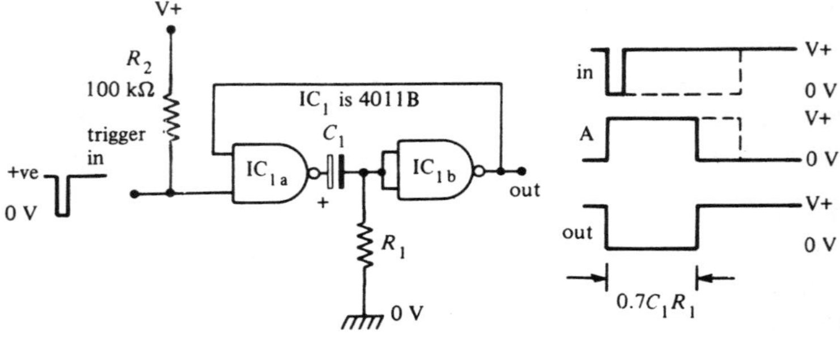


Figure 9.31. *CMOS two-gate NAND monostable.*

the generated output pulse. The NOR version of the circuit (*Figure 9.30*) has a normally low output and is triggered by the edge of a positive-going input signal, and the NAND version (*Figure 9.31*) has a normally high output and is triggered by the edge of a negative-going input signal.

Also note that the pulse signal appearing at *A* has a period equal to that of either the output pulse or the input trigger pulse, whichever is the greater of the two. This feature is of value when making pulse-length comparators and over-speed alarms, etc.

The operating principle of these monostable circuits is fairly simple. Look first at the case of the *Figure 9.30* circuit, in which $CI_{1a}$ is wired as a NOR gate and $IC_{1b}$ is wired as an inverter. When this circuit is in the quiescent state the trigger input terminal is held low by $R_2$, and the output of $IC_{1b}$ is also low. Thus, both inputs of $IC_{1a}$ are low, so $IC_{1a}$ output is forced high and $C_1$ is discharged.

When a positive trigger signal is applied to the circuit the output of $IC_{1a}$ is immediately forced low and (since $C_1$ is discharged at this moment) pulls the $IC_{1b}$ input low and thus drives the $IC_{1b}$ output high; $IC_{1b}$ output is coupled back to the $IC_{1a}$ input, however, and thus forces the $IC_{1a}$ output to remain low irrespective of the prevailing state of the trigger signal. As soon as the $IC_{1a}$ output switches low, $C_1$ starts to charge up via $R_1$ and, after a delay determined by the $C_1-R_1$ values, the $C_1$ voltage rises to such a level that the output of $IC_{1b}$ starts to swing low, terminating the output pulse. If the trigger signal is still high at this moment, the pulse terminates non-regeneratively, but if the trigger signal is low (absent) at this moment the pulse terminates regeneratively.

The *Figure 9.31* circuit operates in a similar way, except that $IC_{1a}$ is wired as a NAND gate, with its trigger input terminal tied to the positive supply rail via $R_2$, and the $R_1$ timing resistor is taken to ground.

## 4047B and 4098B CMOS monostables

A number of dedicated CMOS and TTL monostable pulse-generator ICs are available; the best known of the CMOS devices are the 4047B monostable/astable IC and the 4098B dual monostable (a greatly improved version of the 4528B). These ICs have rather poor pulse-width accuracy and stability, but are quite versatile and can be triggered by either the positive or the negative edge of an input signal, and can be used in either the standard or the re-triggerable mode. *Figure 9.32* shows the outlines and pin notations of the two ICs.

The 4047B actually houses an astable multi and a frequency-divider stage, plus logic networks. When used in the monostable mode the trigger signal starts the astable and resets the counter, driving its $Q$ output high. After a number of $C-R$ controlled astable cycles the counter flips over and simultaneously kills the astable and switches the $Q$ output low, completing the operating sequence. Consequently, the $C-R$ timing components produce relatively long output pulse periods, this period approximating $2.5 \times C \times R$.

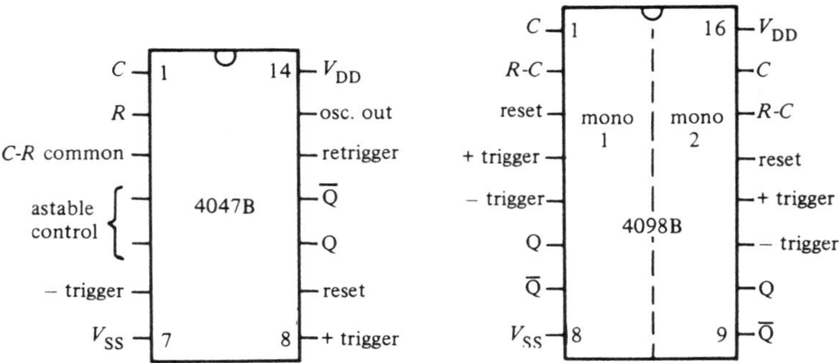


Figure 9.32. *Outlines and pin notations of the 4047B monostable/astable and 4098B dual monostable CMOS ICs.*

In practice, *R* can have any value from 10k to 10M. *C* must be a non-polarized capacitor with a value greater than 1nF. *Figures 9.33a* and *9.33b* show how to connect the IC as a standard monostable triggered by either positive (a) or negative (b) input edges, and *Figure 9.33c* shows how to connect the monostable in the retriggerable mode. Note that these circuits can be reset at any time by pulling RESET pin-9 high.

The 4098B is a fairly simple dual monostable, in which the two mono sections share common supply connections but can otherwise be used independently. Mono-1 is housed on the left side (pins 1 to 7) of the IC, and mono-2 on the right side (pins 9 to 15) of the IC. The timing period of each mono is controlled by a single resistor (*R*) and capacitor (*C*), and approximates $0.5 \times C \times R$. The value of *R* can be anywhere in the range from 5k0 to 10M, and that of *C* in the range from 20pF to 100μF. *Figure 9.34* shows a variety of ways of using the 4098B. Note that in these diagrams the bracketed numbers relate to the pin connections of mono-2, and the plain numbers to mono-1, and that the RESET terminal (pins 3 or 13) is shown disabled.

*Figures 9.34a* and *9.34b* show how to use the IC to make retriggerable monostables that are triggered by positive or negative input edges respectively. In *Figure 9.34a* the trigger signal is fed to the '+TRIG' pin and the '−TRIG' pin is tied low. In *Figure 9.34b* the trigger signal is applied to the '−TRIG' pin and the '+TRIG' pin is tied high.

*Figures 9.34c* and *9.34d* show how to use the IC to make standard (non-retriggerable) monostables that are triggered by positive or negative edges respectively. These circuits are similar to those mentioned above except that the unused trigger pin is coupled to either the *Q* or the not-*Q* output, so that trigger pulses are blocked once a timing cycle has been initiated.

Finally, *Figure 9.34e* shows how the unused half of the IC must be connected when only a single monostable is wanted from the package. The '−TRIG' pin is tied low, and the '+TRIG' and RESET pins are tied high.

## The 74121 TTL monostable

The 74121 is a dedicated TTL monostable pulse generator IC that can usefully generate output pulse widths from a few tens of

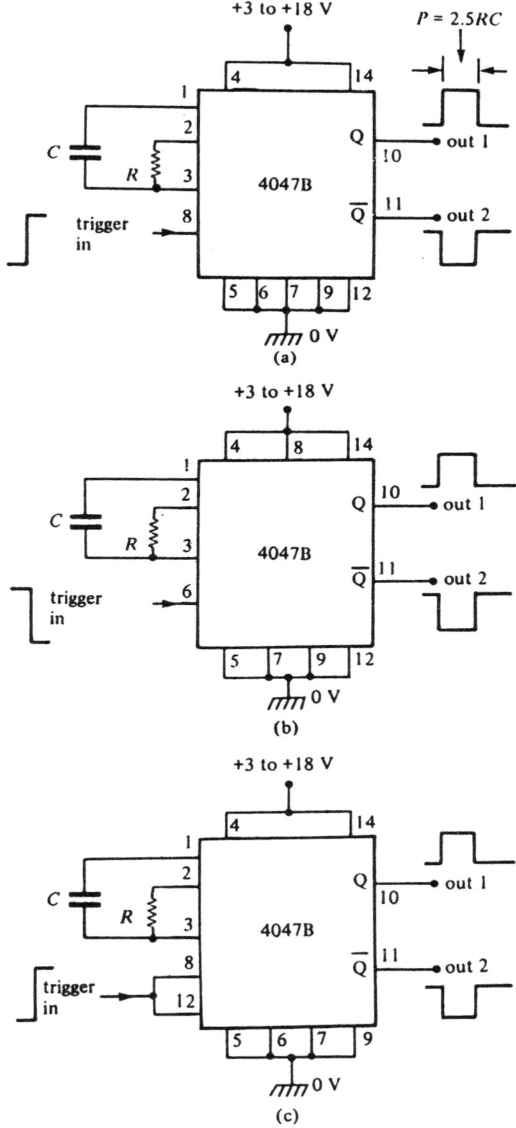


Figure 9.33. *Various ways of using the 4047B as a monostable: (a) positive-edge-triggered monostable; (b) negative-edge-triggered monostable; (c) retriggerable monostable, positive-edge triggered.*

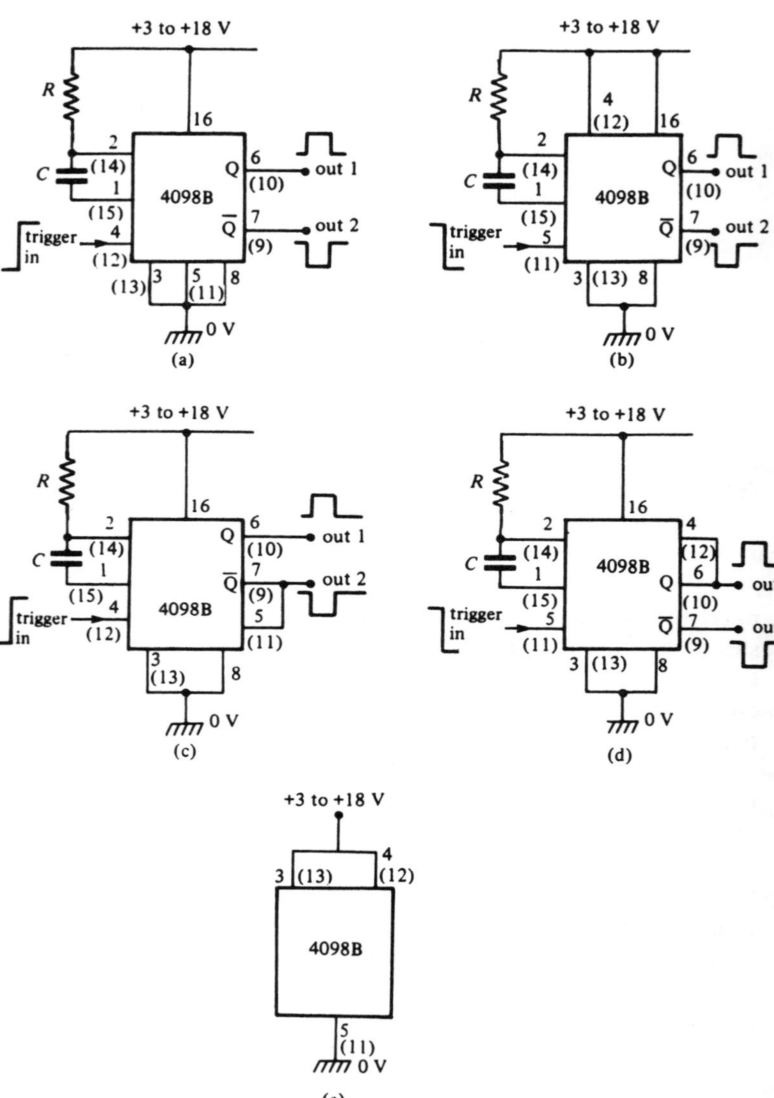


Figure 9.34. *Various ways of using the 4098B monostable: (a) positive-edge-triggering, retriggerable mono; (b) negative-edge-triggering, retriggerable mono; (c) positive-edge-triggering (non-retriggerable mono); (d) negative-edge-triggering (non-retriggerable mono); (e) connections for each unused section of the I.C.*

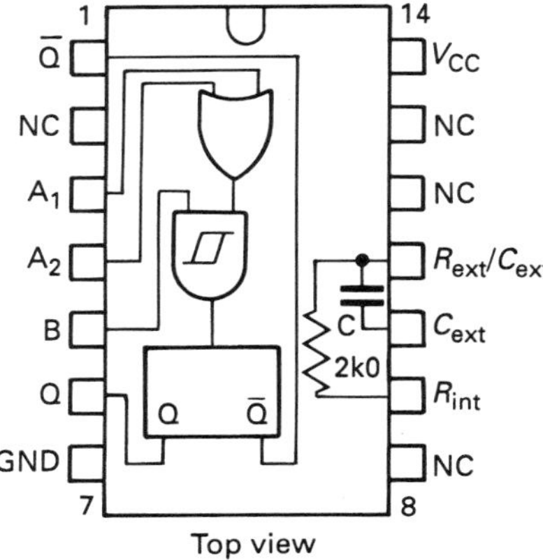


Figure 9.35. *Outline, pin notations, and simplified internal circuit of the 74121 TTL monostable multivibrator IC.*

nanoseconds up to a several hundred milliseconds. *Figure 9.35* shows the outline, pin notations, and simplified internal circuit of the device, which can be triggered on either the leading or trailing edges of an input waveform, and has three alternative input trigger terminals.

The normal way to trigger this IC is to tie pins 3 ($A_1$) and 4 ($A_2$) low (at logic-0) and apply the trigger signal to its pin-5 *B* input terminal; *Figure 9.36* show the IC used in this way and connected as a simple 30ns pulse generator (using its built-in timing components), with the trigger signal applied to pin-5 via a transistor buffer stage. Pin-5 is connected to an internal Schmitt gate, which in this mode triggers the monostable on the leading edge of the input waveform; these inputs can have slow-rising edges.

An alternative way to trigger the 74121 is to disconnect input *B* or tie it to logic-0, and apply the trigger signal (which must have sharp leading and trailing edges) to pins 3 ($A_1$) and/or 4 ($A_2$) of the IC. $A_1$ and $A_2$ are negative-edge-triggered logic inputs, and trigger the monostable when the input switches low.

Dealing next with the IC's timing circuitry, note that the IC has three timing-component terminals. A low-value timing capacitor is built into the IC, and can be augmented by external capacitors

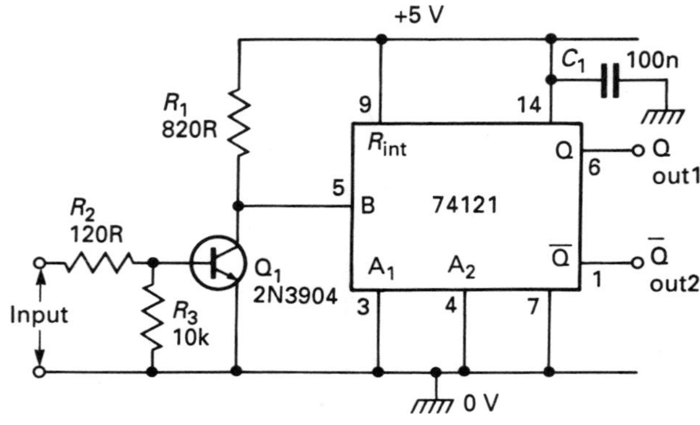


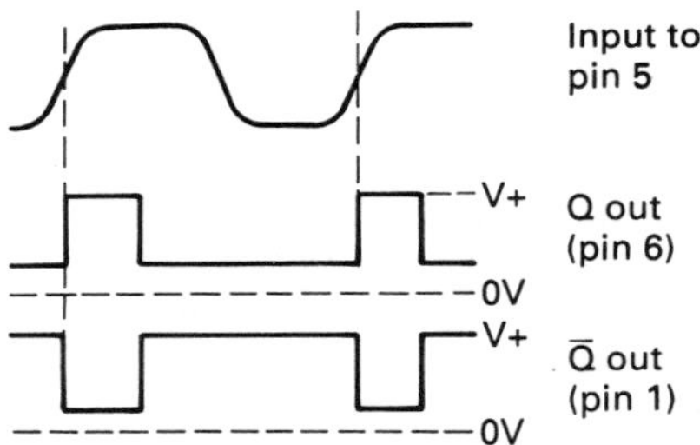


Figure 9.36. *30ns TTL pulse generator using 'B' input leading-edge triggering.*

wired between pin-10 and pin-11 (positive terminals of polarized capacitors should go to pin-11). The IC also houses a 2k0 resistor, which can be used as a timing component by wiring pin-9 to pin-14, either directly or via an external series resistor (maximum value 40k); alternatively, the internal resistor can be ignored and an external timing resistor (1k4 to 40k) can be wired between pin-11 and pin-14. Whichever connection is used, the output pulse width $= 0.7R_TC_T$, where width is in milliseconds, $R_T$ is the total timing resistance in kilohms, and $C_T$ is the timing capacitance in microfarads. Note, incidentally, that the *Figure 9.36* circuit uses the IC's internal timing components only.

*Figure 9.37* shows how the basic *Figure 9.36* circuit can be used as an add-on pulse generator that spans the range 100ns to

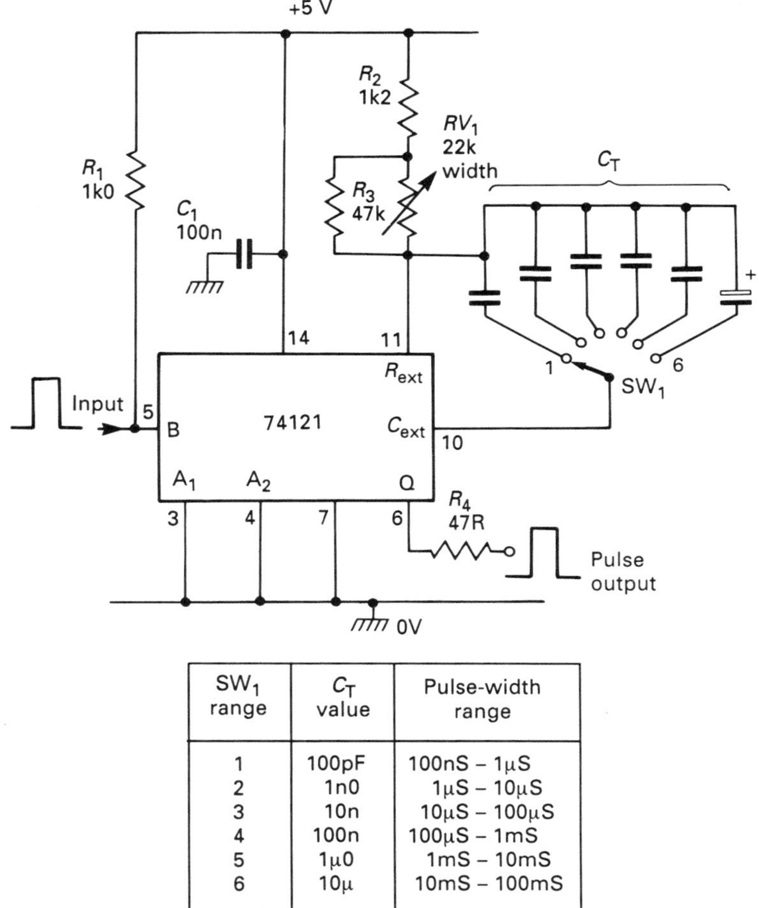


| SW1 range | CT value | Pulse-width range |
|---|---|---|
| 1 | 100pF | 100nS – 1μS |
| 2 | 1n0 | 1μS – 10μS |
| 3 | 10n | 10μS – 100μS |
| 4 | 100n | 100μS – 1mS |
| 5 | 1μ0 | 1mS – 10mS |
| 6 | 10μ | 10mS – 100mS |

Figure 9.37. *High-performance add-on TTL pulse generator spans 100ns to 100ms.*

100ms in six decade ranges, using both internal and external timing resistors and decade-switched external capacitors.

*Figure 9.38* shows how two of the above circuits can be coupled together to make an add-on wide-range delayed pulse generator, which does not generate its final output pulse until some pre-set time after the arrival of the initial trigger pulse. Note that this circuit gives both inverted and non-inverted outputs, which are

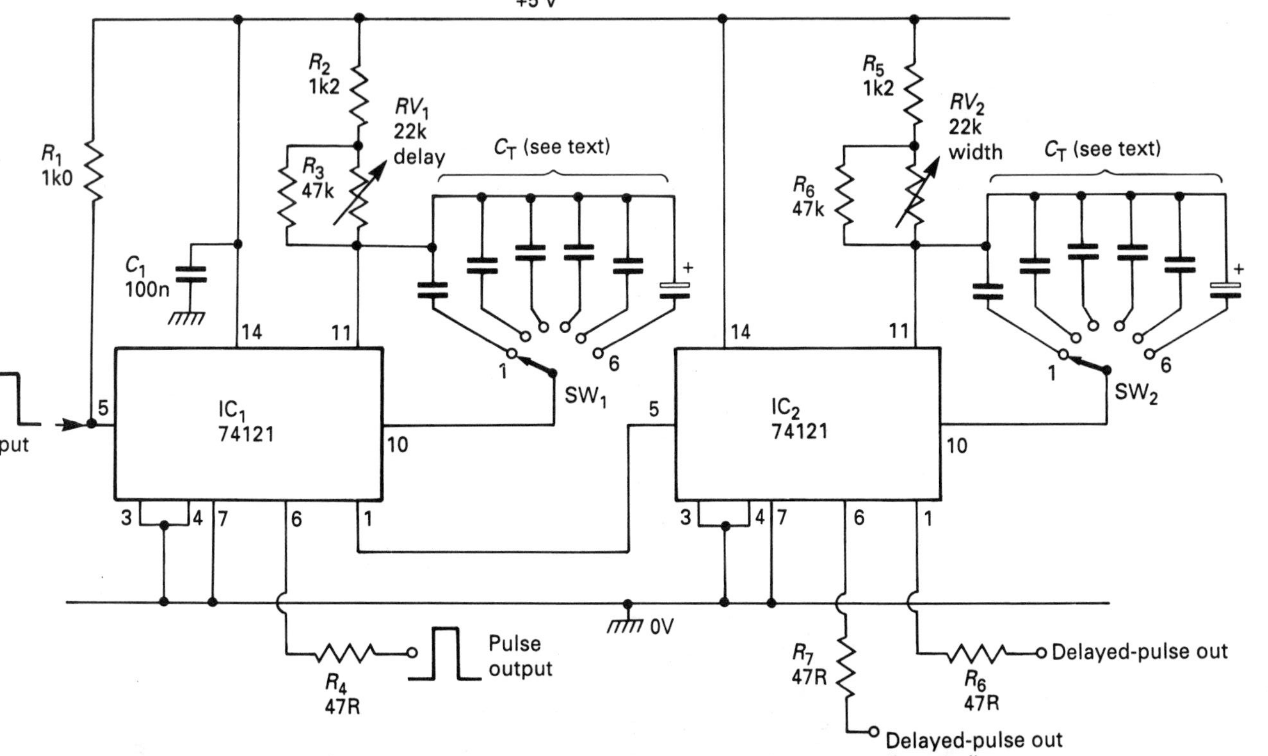


Figure 9.38. *High-performance add-on TTL delayed pulse generator spans 100ns to 100ms.*

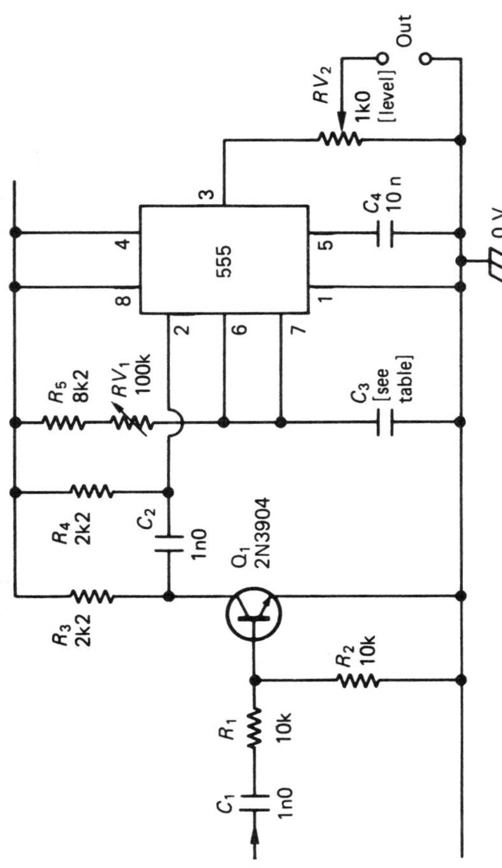


| $C_3$ *value* | *Pulse width range* |
|---|---|
| 10 μF | 90 ms–1.2 s |
| 1 μF | 9 ms–120 ms |
| 100 nF | 900 μs–12 ms |
| 10 nF | 90 μs–1.2 ms |
| 1 nF | 9 μs–120 μs |

Figure 9.39. *Simple add-on pulse generator is triggered by rectangular input signals.*

each of fixed amplitude and are short-circuit protected via 47Ω series resistors. Its timing periods and $C_T$ values are identical to those listed in the table of *Figure 9.37*.

## 555-based pulse generators

The 555 'timer' IC makes an excellent triggered pulse generator. It is triggered by signals fed to pin-2, and the output pulses are taken from pin-3. It has excellent pulse-width stability, and can be used to generate pulse periods from 5μs to hundreds of seconds. Its maximum useful pulse repetition frequency is about 100kHz.

Any trigger signal reaching pin-2 must be a carefully shaped negative-going pulse; its amplitude must switch from an OFF value above $\frac{2}{3}V_{CC}$ to an ON value below $\frac{1}{3}V_{CC}$ (triggering actually occurs as pin-2 drops through the $\frac{1}{3}V_{CC}$ value), and its width must be greater than 100ns but less than that of the desired output pulse, so that the trigger signal is removed by the time the monostable pulse ends.

One way of generating suitable 555 trigger signals is to first convert external input signals into good square waves that swing fully between the supply-rail values, and to then couple these to pin-2 of the 555 via a short time-constant $C-R$ differentiating network, which converts the leading or trailing edges into suitable trigger pulses. *Figure 9.39* shows a circuit that uses this principle,

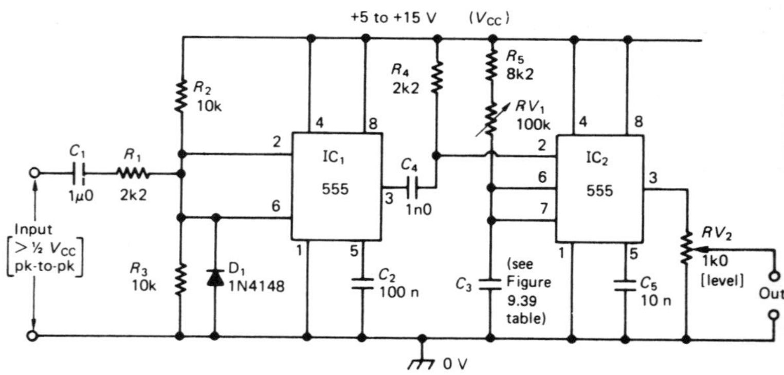


Figure 9.40. *Improved add-on pulse generator is triggered by any input waveform.*

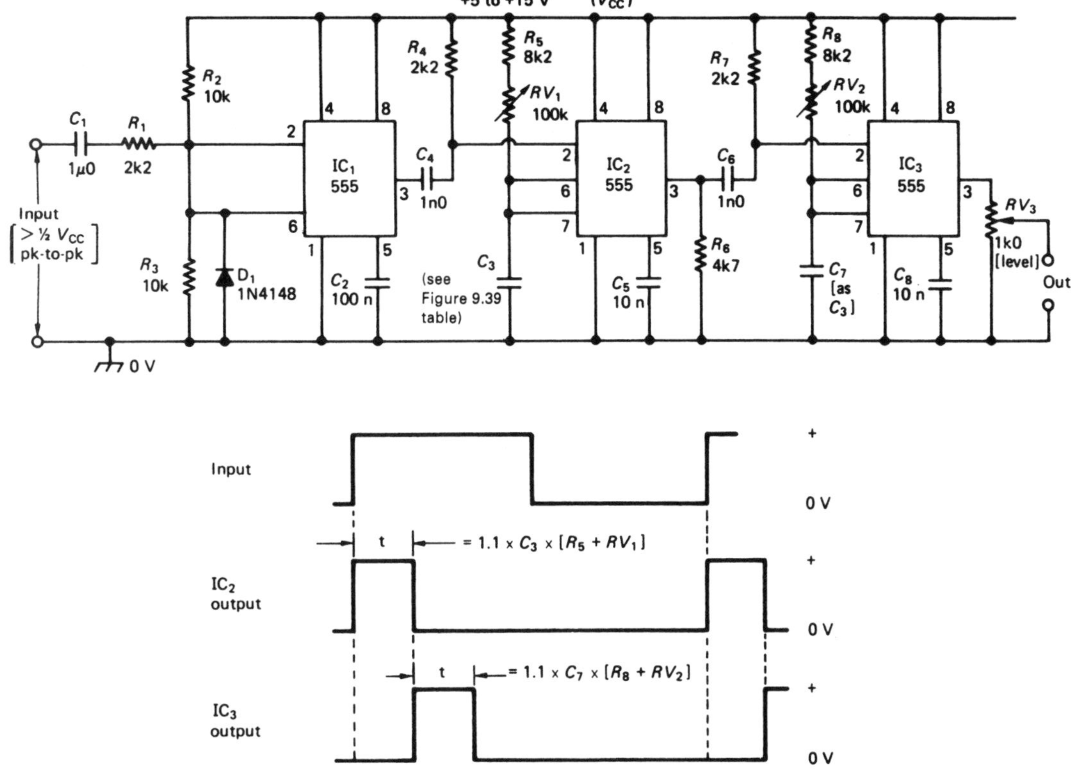


Figure 9.41. *Add-on delayed-pulse generator is triggered by any input waveform.*

but is meant for use with input signals that are already in square form.

Here, $Q_1$ converts the input signal into one that switches fully between the supply-rail values, and these are fed to pin-2 via the $C_2-R_4$ differentiating network. This circuit can be used as an add-on pulse generator in conjunction with an existing square-wave generator. Variable-amplitude output pulses are available via $RV_2$, and their widths are variable over a decade range via $RV_1$ and can be switched in decade ranges by using the $C_3$ values shown in the table; the total pulse width range spans 9μs to 1.2s. $C_4$ decouples pin-5 and improves circuit stability.

*Figure 9.40* shows how the above circuit can be modified so that it can be directly driven by any type of input, including a sine wave. Here, $IC_1$ is wired as a Schmitt trigger and converts all inputs signals into a rectangular form that is used to drive the $IC_2$ monostable in the same way as described above. This circuit can be used as an add-on pulse generator in conjunction with any free-running generator that gives peak-to-peak outputs greater than $\frac{1}{2}V_{CC}$.

Finally, *Figure 9.41* shows how three 555 ICs can be used to make an add-on delayed-pulse generator, in which $IC_1$ is used as a Schmitt trigger, $IC_2$ is a monostable that is used to control the pulse's delay width, and $IC_3$ is used as the final pulse generator. The final output pulse appears some delayed time (set via $IC_2$) after the application of the initial input trigger signal. Note that the $C_3$ values of the *Figures 9.40* and *9.41* circuits are identical to those listed in the table of *Figure 9.39*.

# 10 Special waveform generator circuits

The last two chapters have concentrated on circuits that generate sine waves, square waves, and triggered-pulse waveforms. Many other types of waveform generator are used in modern instrumentation and test gear, however; amongst the best known of these are triangle and sawtooth generators, white-noise and pink-noise generators, and crystal-controlled oscillators. Practical waveform generator circuits of all these types are described in this chapter.

## Linear triangle-wave generators

Linear triangle waveforms are particularly useful for checking cross-over distortion in low-frequency (audio) amplifiers and op-amps, etc. The best way to generate such a waveform is via the basic op-amp 'function generator' circuit of *Figure 10.1*, which also generates a useful square-wave output waveform. Here, $IC_1$ is wired as an integrator, driven from the output of $IC_2$, and $IC_2$

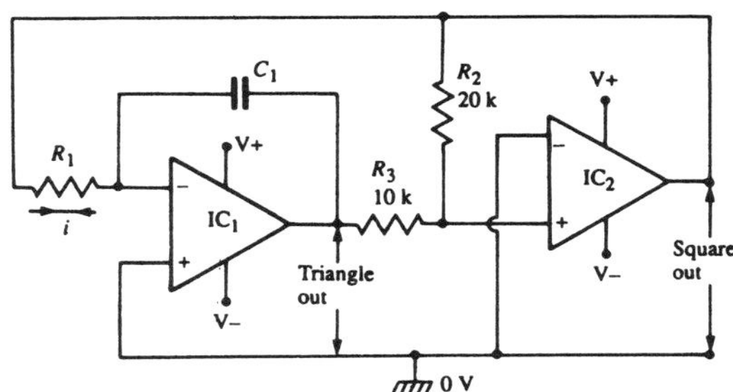


Figure 10.1. *Basic linear triangle-wave generator.*

is wired as a differential voltage comparator, driven from the output of $IC_1$ via potential divider $R_2-R_3$, which is connected between the outputs of $IC_1$ and $IC_2$. The square-wave output of $IC_2$ switches alternately between positive and negative saturation. The circuit functions as follows.

Suppose initially that the $IC_1$ output is positive and $IC_2$'s output has just switched to positive saturation. The inverting input of $IC_1$ is a virtual earth point, so a current ($i$) of $+V_{sat}/R_1$ flows into $R_1$, causing $IC_1$'s output to start swinging down linearly at a rate of $i/C_1$ volts per second. This output is fed, via the $R_2-R_3$ divider, to $IC_2$'s non-inverting input, which has its inverting terminal referenced directly to ground.

Consequently, the output of $IC_1$ swings linearly to a negative value until the $R_2-R_3$ junction voltage falls to zero, at which point $IC_2$ enters a regenerative switching phase in which its output abruptly switches to negative saturation. This reverses the inputs of $IC_1$ and $IC_2$, so the $IC_1$ output starts to rise linearly, until it reaches a positive value at which the $R_2-R_3$ junction voltage reaches the zero volts reference value, initiating another switching action. The whole process then repeats *ad infinitum*.

Important points to note about this circuit are that the peak-to-peak amplitude of the linear triangle waveform is controlled by the $R_2-R_3$ ratio, and that the operating frequency can be altered by changing either the ratios of $R_2-R_3$, the values of $R_1$ or $C_1$, or by feeding $R_1$ from a potential divider connected to the output of $IC_2$ (rather than directly from the $IC_2$ output). *Figure 10.2* shows a practical variable-frequency triangle/square generator using the latter technique.

In *Figure 10.2*, the input current to $C_1$ (obtained from $RV_2-R_2$) can be varied over a 10:1 range via $RV_1$, enabling the frequency to be varied from 100Hz to 1kHz; $RV_2$ enables the full-scale frequency to be set to precisely 1kHz. The amplitude of the linear triangle output waveform is fully variable via $RV_3$, and that of the square-wave output via $RV_4$. The square-wave output gives typical rise and fall times of less than 1μs.

The *Figure 10.2* circuit generates symmetrical output waveforms, since $C_1$ alternately charges and discharges at equal current values (set by $RV_2-R_2$, etc). *Figure 10.3* shows the circuit modified to make a variable-symmetry ramp and square-wave generator, in which the slope of the ramp and the M–S ratio of the square-wave is variable via $RV_2$. $C_1$ alternately charges via $R_2-D_1$ and

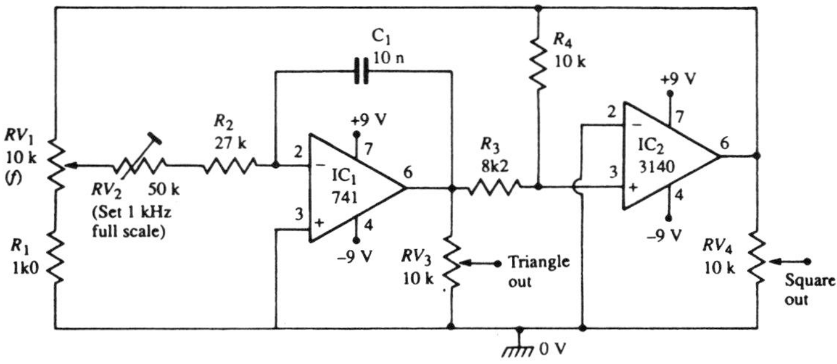


Figure 10.2. *100Hz to 1kHz triangle/square generator.*

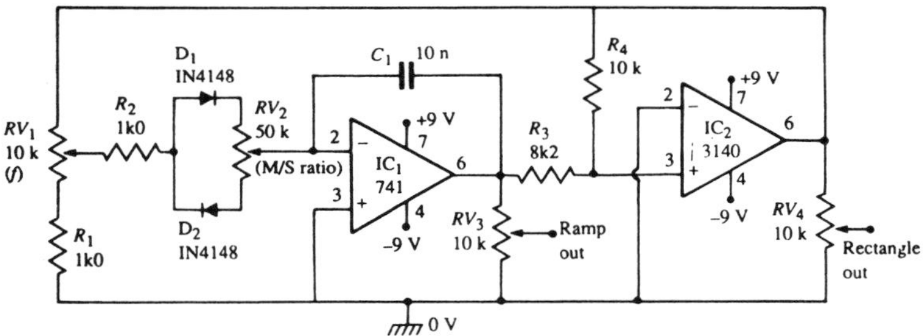


Figure 10.3. *100Hz to 1kHz ramp/rectangle generator with variable slope and M–S ratio.*

the upper half of $RV_2$, and discharges via $R_2 - D_2$ and the lower half of $RV_2$.

## A UJT linear sawtooth generator

Linear sawtooth waveforms are widely used as time bases for oscilloscopes and wobbulators, etc. One of the easiest ways to make a linear sawtooth generator is to use a unijunction transistor (UJT) in the configuration shown in *Figure 10.4*. Here, $Q_1$ (plus $R_1 - D_1 - R_2 - RV_1 - R_3$) are wired as a constant-current generator, with current variable from 35μA to 390μA via $RV_1$, and in each operating cycle charges $C_1$ linearly until its charge voltage reaches the 'peak point' or firing voltage of the UJT, at which point the

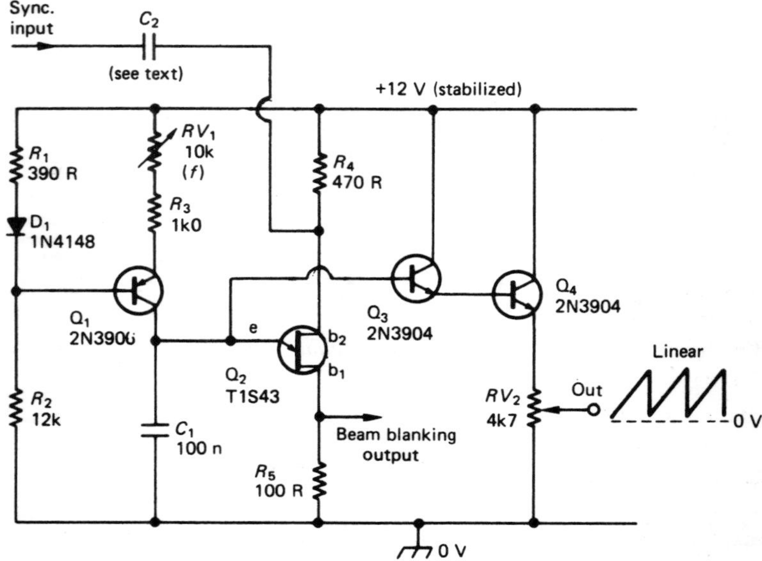


Figure 10.4. *UJT-based oscilloscope time-base generator.*

UJT turns on and rapidly discharges $C_1$ until its discharge current falls to the UJT's 'valley point' or unlatching value, at which point the UJT turns off and $C_1$ starts to recharge again, and the sequence repeats *ad infinitum*.

Thus, a free-running linear sawtooth is generated across $C_1$ and can be fed to external circuits via buffer transistors $Q_2$–$Q_3$ and $RV_2$. With the $C_1$ value shown the frequency is variable from 60Hz to 700Hz via $RV_1$; it can be varied from below 0.1Hz to above 100kHz by using alternative $C_1$ values.

The *Figure 10.4* circuit can be used as a simple free-running time-base generator for an oscilloscope. In this application the sawtooth output should be fed to the oscilloscope's **external time-base** socket, and the positive 'flyback' pulses from $R_5$ can be taken via a high-voltage blocking capacitor and used for beam blanking. The sawtooth can be synchronized to an external signal that is fed to $Q_2$ via $C_2$; this signal (which must have a peak amplitude between 200mV and 1V0) modulates the triggering points of $Q_2$ and thus synchronizes the oscillator and input signals. Note that $C_2$ must have an impedance less than 470Ω at the sync signal frequency; if the sync signal is rectangular, with short rise and fall times, $C_2$ can simply be given a value of 470pF.

## 555 linear sawtooth generators

A 555 timer IC can be used as a triggered linear sawtooth generator by wiring it as a modified monostable multivibrator or pulse generator (see Chapter 9), with its timing capacitor charged via a constant-current generator, as shown in *Figure 10.5*. Here, $Q_1$ is used as the constant-current generator, and the output waveform is taken from across timing capacitor $C_4$ via $Q_2$ and $RV_2$.

When a capacitor is charged via a constant-current generator its voltage rises linearly at a rate of $I/C$ volts per second, where $I$ is the charge current in amperes and $C$ is the capacitance in farads. Using more practical quantities, the rate of voltage rise can also be expressed as mA/μF volts per ms. Note that rise rate can be increased by either increasing the charge current of decreasing the capacitance value.

In *Figure 10.5* the charging current can be varied from about 100μA to 1.1mA via $RV_1$, giving rates of rise variable from 10V/ms to 110V/ms on the 10nF timing capacitor. Now, each monostable cycle of the 555 ends at the point where the $C_4$ voltage

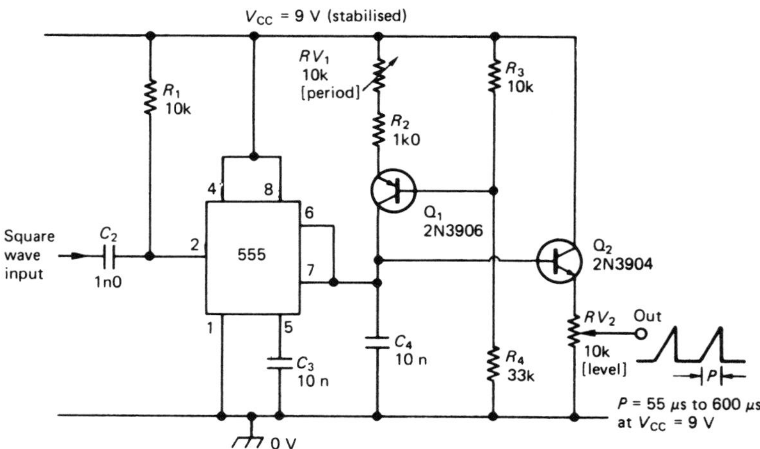


Figure 10.5. *Triggered linear sawtooth generator.*

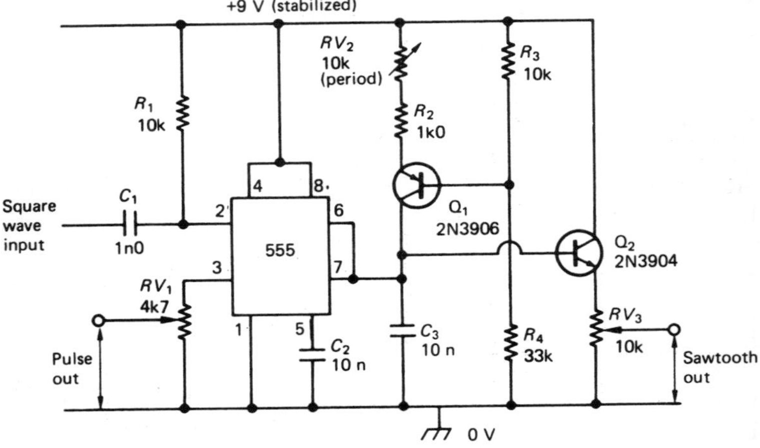


Figure 10.6. *Triggered 55µs to 600µs pulse and sawtooth generator.*

reaches $\frac{2}{3}V_{CC}$, so, assuming that a 9V supply is used (giving an 'end' value of 6V), it can be seen that the circuit's sawtooth cycles have periods variable from 600µs (= $\frac{6}{10}$ms) to 55µs (= $\frac{6}{110}$ms) respectively. Periods can be increased beyond these values by increasing the $C_4$ value, or vice versa. The circuit's supply rail voltage must be stabilized to give stable timing.

*Figure 10.6* shows how the above circuit can be modified for use as a triggered pulse and linear-sawtooth generator, with the pulse output taken from pin-3 of the IC via $RV_1$.

*Figure 10.7* shows the basic *Figure 10.5* circuit modified for use as an oscilloscope time base generator. The 555 is triggered by square waves derived from external waveforms via a suitable 'trigger' selector circuit, and the ramp output waveform is fed to the 'scope's $X$ plates via a suitable amplifier stage; the pin-3 output of the 555 provides bright-up pulses to the $Z$ axis of the 'scope tube during the ramp period, ensuring that the tube is blanked when the time base is inactive.

The minimum useful ramp period obtainable from *Figure 10.7* (using a 1n0 capacitor in the $C_3$ position) is about 5µs which, when expanded to give full deflection on a ten-division 'scope screen, gives a maximum time-base speed of 0.5µs per division. The circuit gives excellent signal synchronization at trigger frequencies up to about 150kHz; at higher frequencies the input

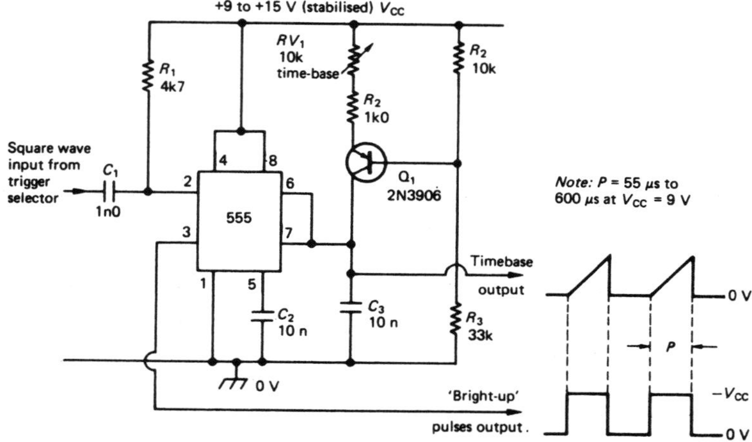


Figure 10.7. *Oscilloscope triggered time-base generator circuit.*

trigger signals should be reduced via a single- or multi-decade frequency divider; using this technique, the time base can be used to view input signals up to many megahertz.

*Figure 10.8* shows, in basic form, a simple but effective trigger signal generator that can be used with the above circuit. $SW_1$ enables the trigger signal to be derived *int*ernally via the 'scope's

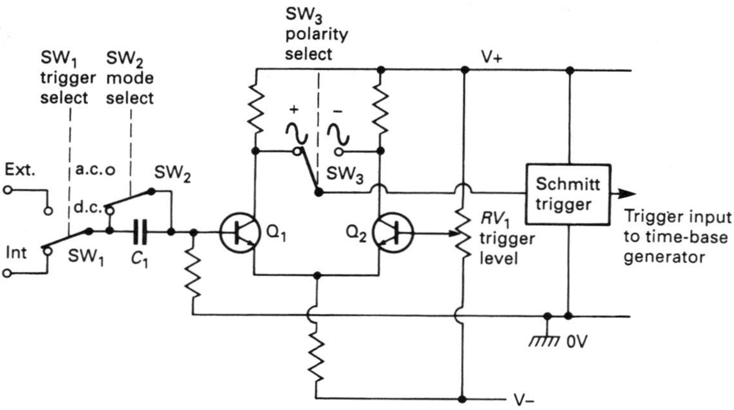


Figure 10.8. *Basic dual-polarity time-base signal generator.*

*Y* amplifier, or *ext*ernally via a suitable terminal; $SW_2$ enables the selected signal to be a.c. or d.c. coupled to the input of the $Q_1$–$Q_2$ phase-splitting differential amplifier. $SW_3$ enables either in-phase or anti-phase ('+' or '−') outputs to be taken from the phase-splitter and fed to the Schmitt trigger, and $RV_1$ lets the Schmitt 'switch' at any desired point on the selected waveform; the Schmitt's output couples directly to the $C_1$ input of the *Figure 10.7* time-base generator.

## White-noise generators

White noise can be described as a signal containing a full spectrum of randomly generated frequencies, all with randomly determined amplitudes, but which have equal power *per bandwidth unit* when averaged over a reasonable unit of time. White noise is of value in testing AF and RF amplifiers, etc.

White noise can be generated using either analogue or digital techniques. Zener diodes act as excellent sources of analogue white noise, and *Figure 10.9* shows a simple but useful circuit that uses one of these as its basic noise source. Here, $R_1$ and the zener diode form a d.c. negative feedback loop between the collector and base of common-emitter amplifier $Q_1$ and thus stabilize its

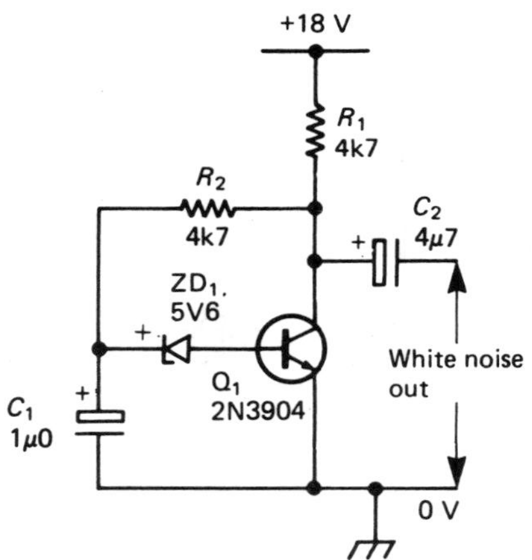


Figure 10.9. *White-noise generator.*

d.c. working levels, but the loop is a.c. decoupled via $C_1$, so that the zener acts as a noise source and is in series with $Q_1$ base. The zener can be any 5.6V type, and $Q_1$ simply amplifies its noise and provides a useful (typically about 1V peak-to-peak) white-noise output at its collector.

The base–emitter junction of an ordinary npn transistor acts as a zener diode when reverse biased and can thus be used as an inexpensive white-noise source; that of the 2N3904 typically zeners at about 5.6V, and *Figure 10.10* shows how it can be used as a noise-generating zener in the *Figure 10.9* circuit.

Simulated white noise can be generated digitally via a maximum length pseudo-random sequence generator; *Figure 10.11* illustrates the basic principle. Here, an 18-stage shift register is clocked at 30kHz and wired so that its **data** terminal logic is fed forward one step on the arrival of each clock pulse, but this **data** is derived by EX–ORing the outputs of stages 5, 9 and 18 so that a pseudo-random or jumbled output sequence is generated; this apparently random sequence in fact repeats every few seconds, but (because its digital output is very rich in harmonics) otherwise acts like perfect white noise.

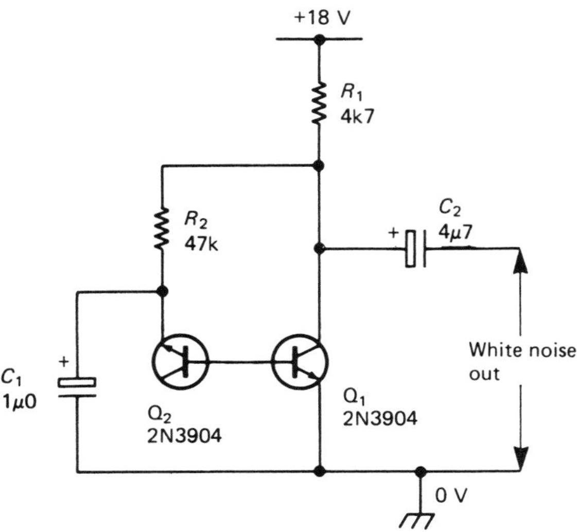


Figure 10.10. *Alternative white-noise generator.*

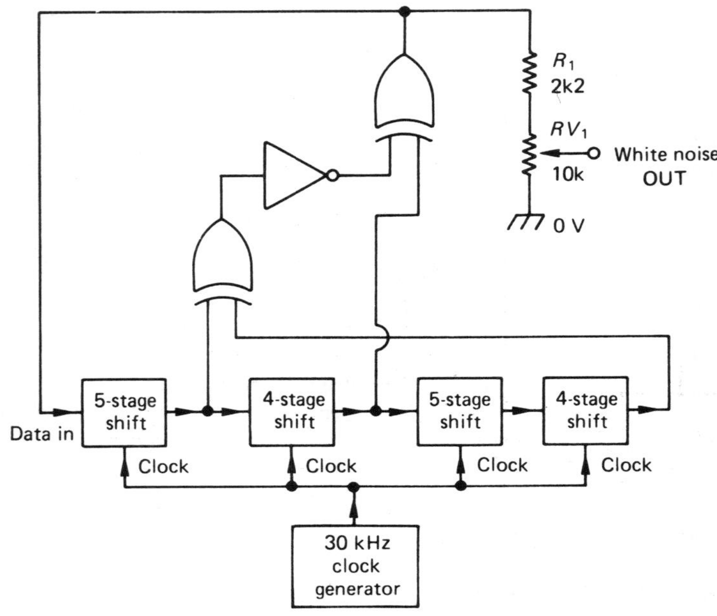


Figure 10.11. *Block diagram of digital white-noise generator.*

*Figure 10.12* shows a practical CMOS version of the digital white noise generator. Here, the 18 stages of shift register are obtained from $IC_2$, and the 30kHz clock generator is formed via $IC_{1a}$–$IC_{1b}$, which are wired as an astable multivibrator, and EX–ORing is obtained via $IC_{1c}$–$IC_{1d}$ and $Q_1$. The white-noise output signal amplitude is variable via $RV_1$.

## Pink noise

White noise is a signal with a power (energy) content that is constant at all units of bandwidth. Thus, the energy of a 100Hz bandwidth white-noise signal is the same at 1kHz as it is at 10kHz: but 100Hz bandwidths are 10 times more common at 10kHz than they are at 1kHz, and it can thus be seen that (by definition) the output level of a white-noise generator rises at rate of 3dB per octave. Thus, if one listens to (or measures) white-

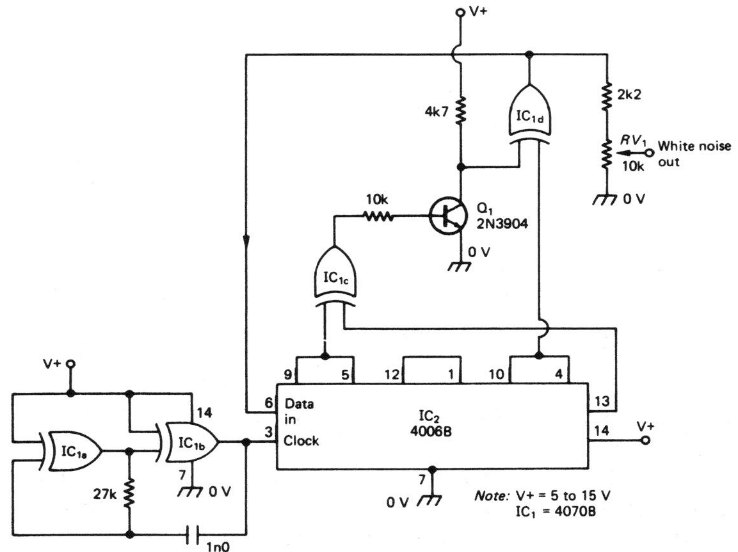


Figure 10.12. *Practical digital white-noise generator.*

noise signals, they are naturally dominated by high-frequency 'hiss'.

A far more useful noise signal is one in which the output level is flat over the whole frequency band, so that (for example) the frequency responses of an amplifier, filter, or graphic equalizer can be quickly checked by feeding this 'noise' signal to its input and measuring the frequency levels at its output. Noise with this specific characteristic is known as 'pink' noise, and is normally generated by feeding ordinary white noise through an $R-C$ filter that is configured to give a first-order slope of $-3$dB/octave. *Figure 10.13* shows an 'add-on' filter that is designed for this purpose and gives (when used with any of the above white noise generators) a pink-noise characteristic that is within $\frac{1}{4}$dB of this value over the entire 10Hz to 40kHz frequency range.

## Crystal oscillators

Crystal oscillators generate waveforms with great frequency precision. They use piezo-electric quartz crystals as electromechanical

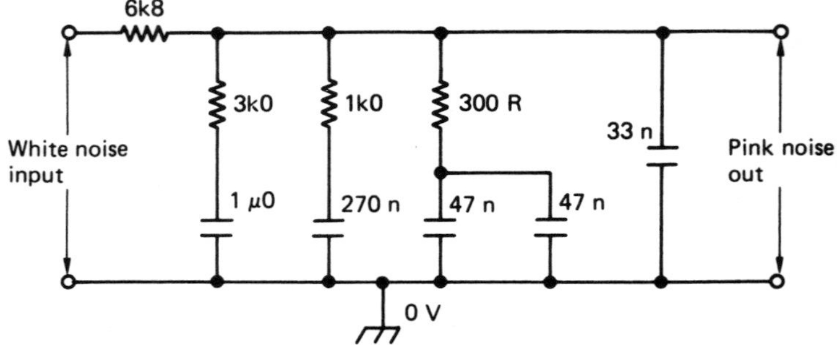


Figure 10.13. *'Add-on' white-noise to pink-noise converter.*

resonators or tuned circuits with typical effective *Q*'s of about 100 000; these crystals provide roughly 1000 times greater frequency stability than a conventional *LC* tank circuit. The crystal's resonant frequency (which may vary from a few kilohertz to 100 megahertz) is determined by its mechanical dimensions. All quartz crystals have both series and parallel natural-resonance modes, and are cut to provide *calibrated* resonance in only one of these modes; series-mode devices present a low impedance at resonance, while parallel-mode devices present a high impedance at resonance.

*Figure 10.14* shows the symbol and typical equivalent electrical circuit of a quartz crystal; it also shows the typical frequency–

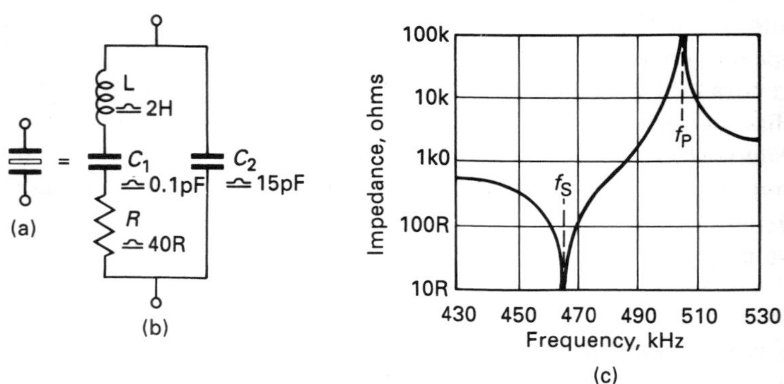


Figure 10.14. *Quartz crystal symbol, typical equivalent circuit, and typical response curve of a 465kHz series-resonant crystal.*

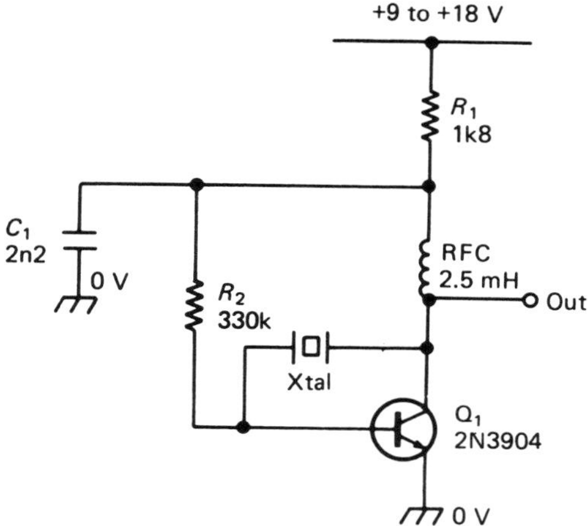


Figure 10.15. *Wide-range Pierce oscillator with parallel-mode crystal.*

impedance response curve of a crystal that is cut to give series resonance at 465kHz; note that this particular crystal also has an uncalibrated parallel resonant mode at 505kHz.

*Figures 10.15* to *10.18* show some practical transistor-based crystal oscillator circuits. The *Figure 10.15* design is based on the Pierce oscillator, and can be directly used with virtually any good 100kHz to 5MHz parallel-mode crystal.

*Figure 10.16* shows a 100kHz oscillator that is designed for use with a series-mode crystal. In this case the circuit is wired as a Colpitts oscillator, and the $L_1$–$C_1$–$C_2$ tank circuit is designed to resonate at the same frequency as the crystal.

*Figure 10.17* shows an outstandingly useful two-transistor oscillator that can be used with virtually any 50kHz to 10MHz series-resonant crystal. In this design $Q_1$ is wired as a common-base amplifier and $Q_2$ is an emitter follower, and the output signal (from the $Q_2$ emitter) is fed back to the input ($Q_1$-emitter) via $C_2$ and the series-resonant crystal. This really is an excellent circuit, and will oscillate with almost any crystal that shows the slightest sign of life.

Finally, *Figure 10.18* shows a popular variation of the Colpitts oscillator, in which $Q_1$ is wired as a voltage follower and the crystal provides the voltage gain needed for oscillation. Note that in this circuit (and that of *Figure 10.17*) a small 'trimmer' capacitor

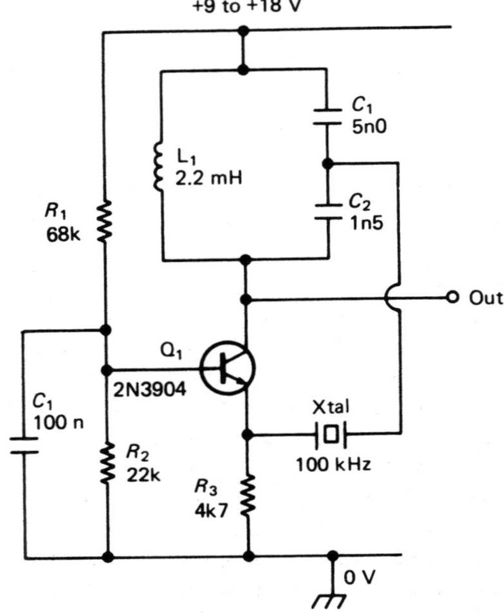


Figure 10.16. *100kHz Colpitts oscillator using series-mode crystal.*

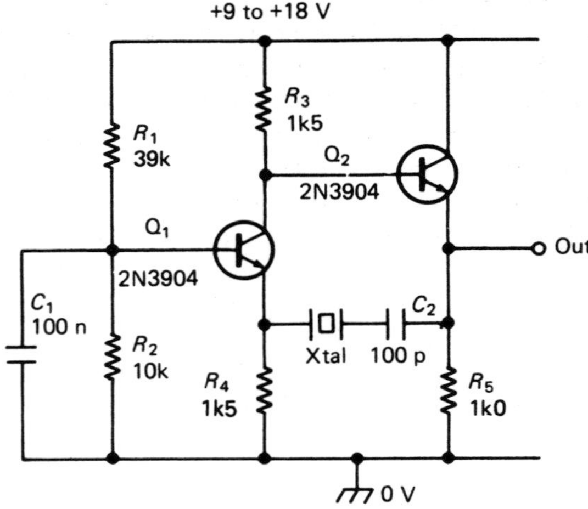


Figure 10.17. *Wide-range (50kHz to 10kHz) oscillator can be used with almost any series-mode crystal.*

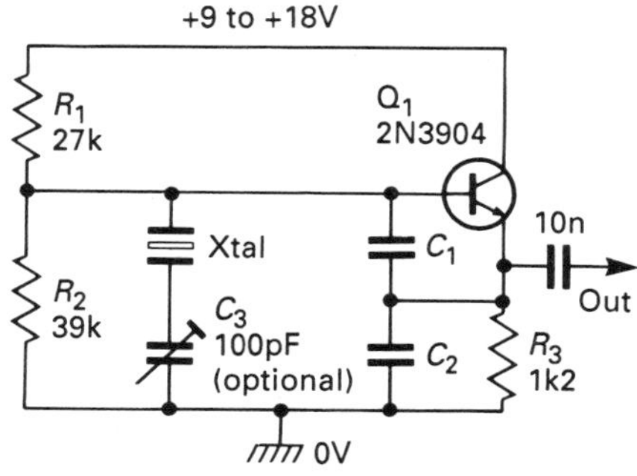


| $f_{range}$ | $C_1$ | $C_2$ |
|---|---|---|
| 100kHz – 2MHz<br>2MHz – 10MHz<br>10MHz – 20MHz | 2n7<br>220p<br>110p | 1n0<br>220p<br>100p |

Typical $C_1$ – $C_2$ values

Figure 10.18. *Untuned Colpitts oscillator using series-resonant crystal.*

($C_3$) is wired in series with the crystal and enables its frequency to be varied over a narrow range.

Some simple TTL or CMOS digital gates and buffers can be made to act as crystal oscillators by first biasing them into the linear amplifier mode and then connecting the crystal into a positive feedback path between the amplifier's output and input. *Figures 10.19* and *10.20* show examples of such circuits. The

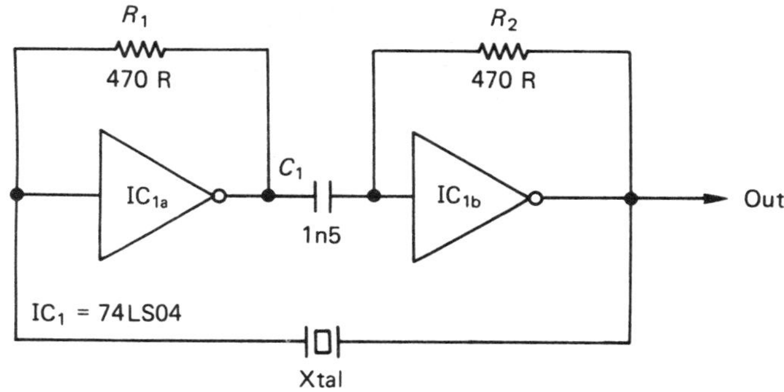


Figure 10.19. *TTL-based crystal oscillator.*

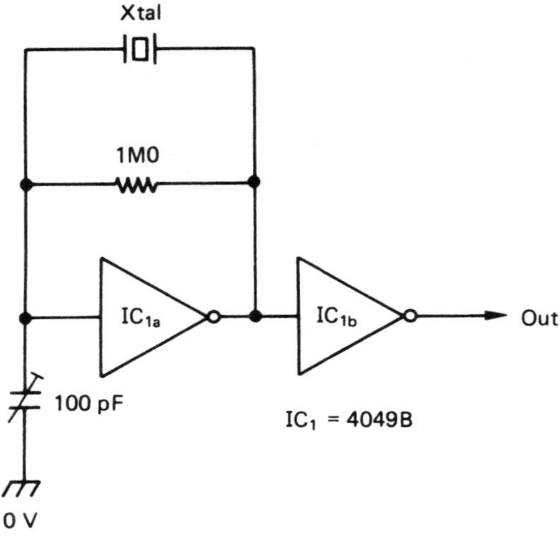


Figure 10.20. *CMOS-based crystal oscillator.*

*Figure 10.19* TTL design uses two 74LS04 hex-inverter stages which are each biased into the linear mode via 470Ω output-to-input feedback resistors and then a.c. coupled in series via $C_1$, to give zero overall phase shift; the circuit is then made to oscillate by wiring the crystal (which must be a series-resonant type) between the output and input. This circuit can operate from a few hundred kilohertz to above 10MHz.

The *Figure 10.20* CMOS circuit is based on a pair of 4049B hex-inverter stages; the first stage is used as a crystal oscillator by wiring it into the linear ampifier mode via $R_1$ and feeding the output back to the input via the parallel-resonant crystal; the second stage is used as a simple output buffer.

## Multi-decade crystal calibrators

A crystal oscillator can be used to provide precision submultiples of the crystal frequency by feeding its output through a suitable number of digital divider stages. One popular application of this technique is in the multi-decade 'crystal calibrator', which is used to generate a basic 1MHz precision signal, which is then divided down via a set of cascaded decade dividers to generate standard frequency–period outputs of (usually) 100kHz/10μs, 10kHz/100μs, 1kHz/1ms, etc. *Figures 10.21* and *10.22* show examples of practical TTL-based and CMOS-based six-decade calibrators of this type; each circuit is configured to provide symmetrical square-wave outputs on all ranges, which extend down to 1Hz/1s. The TTL-based design typically consumes 60mA from its 5V supply; the CMOS-based design consumes less than 2mA from 9V.

## A linear staircase generator

A linear staircase generator has both input and output terminals, and its basic action is such that its output starts at a low level but then rises by a discrete step each time an input pulse is applied, until eventually, after a predetermined number of input cycles, the output switches abruptly back to the low level and the whole sequence starts to repeat. The output thus takes the form of a 'staircase' with a predetermined number of steps; staircase generators can thus be used as pulse counters, frequency dividers, or step-voltage generators for use in transistor curve tracers, etc.

*Figure 10.23* shows a practical linear staircase generator circuit. $Q_1$ is a simple common emitter amplifier and controls constant-current generator $Q_2$, which controls the charging current of capacitor $C_1$, which is coupled to the input of UJT $Q_3$. Normally the circuit's input is low, so $Q_1$ and $Q_2$ are cut off and no charge is fed to $C_1$. Each time that a constant-width positive input pulse arrives $Q_1$ and $Q_2$ are driven on and a charge current is fed into $C_1$, which charges linearly for the duration of the pulse; the $C_1$ voltage thus rises by a fixed amount each time an input pulse is applied, until eventually, after a predetermined number of pulses, the $C_1$ voltage reaches the trigger value of $Q_3$, at which point the UJT fires and discharges $C_1$, thus restarting the operating cycle.

If the input pulses of this circuit are applied at a constant frequency a linear staircase waveform is developed across $C_1$, and a brief output pulse appears across $R_7$ each time the UJT fires. If the input frequency is not constant a non-linear staircase is developed across $C_1$, but a brief output pulse again appears across $R_7$ after a predetermined number of input pulses have been applied; stable count/division ratios or staircase steps from two to about twenty can be obtained.

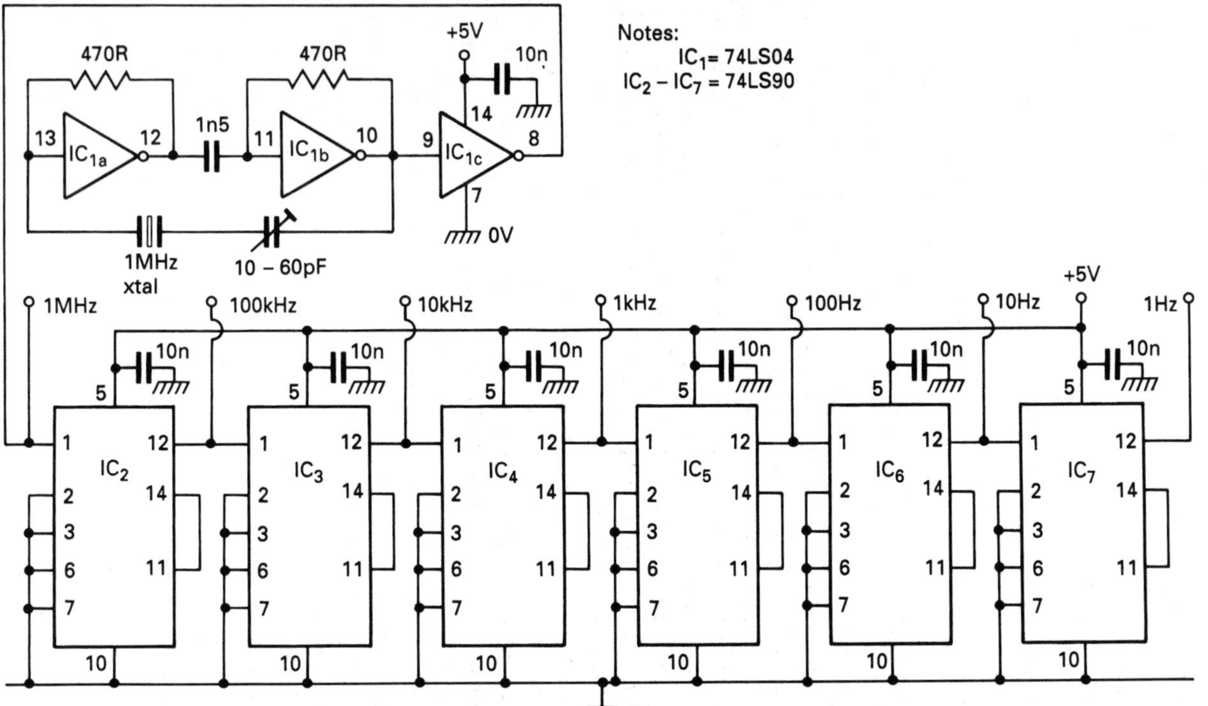


*Figure 10.21. TTL-based six-decade crystal calibrator.*

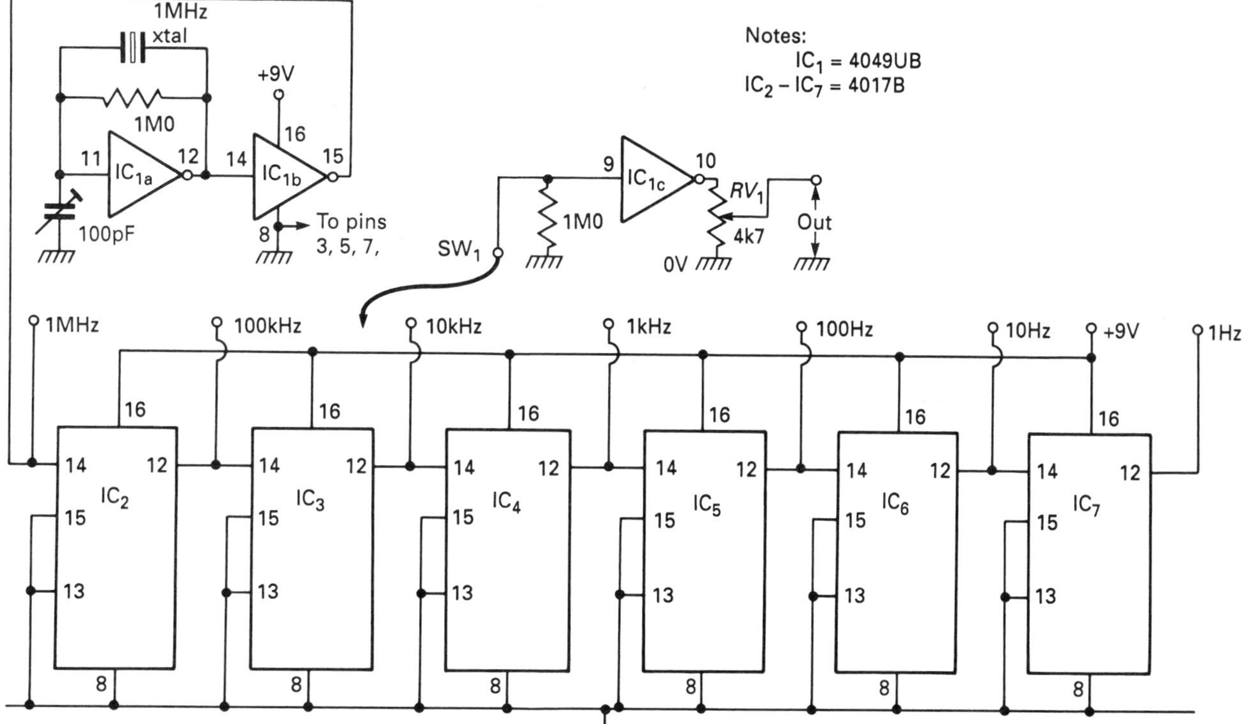


Figure 10.22. *CMOS-based six-decade crystal calibrator.*

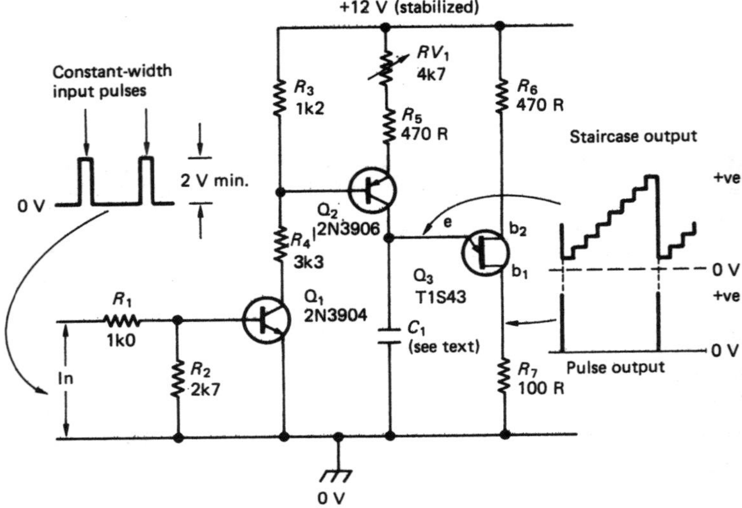


Figure 10.23. *Linear staircase generator circuit.*

This circuit must be fed with constant-width input pulses with a width that is small relative to the pulse repetition period. The $C_1$ value is determined by these considerations, and is best found by trial and error; the division ratio is variable over a 10:1 range via $RV_1$. Note that the staircase output waveform is available across $C_1$ at a high impedance level; it can be made available at a low impedance level by interposing a Darlington emitter follower buffer stage between $C_1$ and the final output terminal of the circuit.

# 11 D.C. power-supply circuits

This chapter looks at power supply systems and circuits. It deals first with ways of deriving D.C. power from A.C. power lines, then goes on to look at practical D.C. voltage-regulator circuits, and ends by examining low-power voltage-converter circuits which can, for example, be used to generate a higher-value or reversed-polarity voltage supply from an existing D.C. power source.

## A.C./D.C. converter basics

There are three basic ways of deriving a stable D.C. supply from an A.C. power line, and these are shown in basic form in *Figures 11.1* to *11.3*. The conventional way (*Figure 11.1*) is to use a step-down transformer and a rectifier and storage capacitor to generate (with an overall efficiency of about 85 per cent) an unregulated D.C. supply that is electrically insulated from the A.C. supply, and to then stabilize the D.C. output voltage via a linear regulator circuit, which typically has an efficiency slightly better than 50 per cent, thus giving an overall power conversion efficiency of about 45 per cent.

These conventional systems are simple and reliable, generate zero RFI, and give excellent ripple reduction and voltage regu-

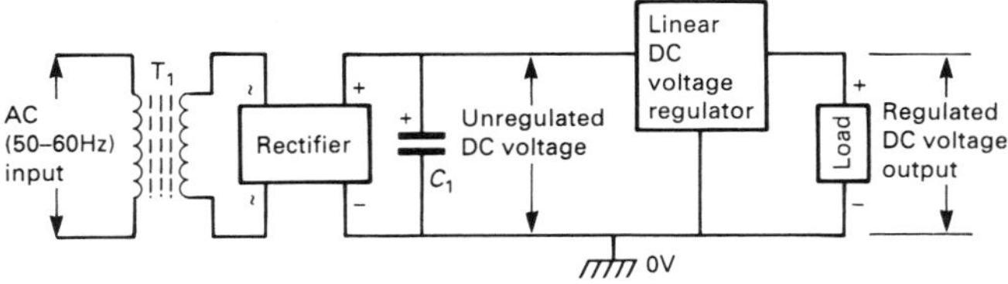


Figure 11.1. *Conventional regulated D.C. power supply.*

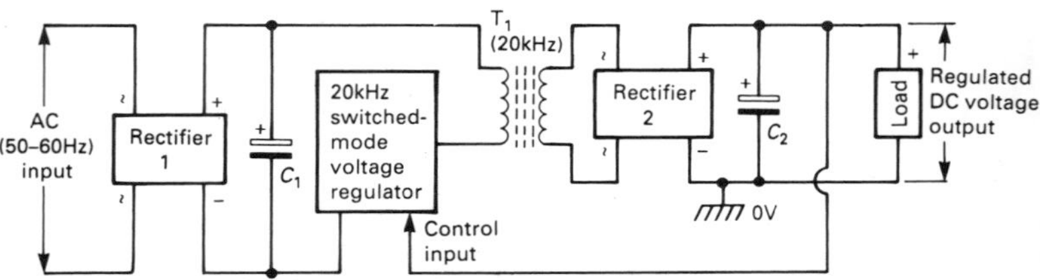


Figure 11.2. *Switched-mode regulated D.C. power supply.*

lation, but are rather bulky and heavy, because (a) the transformer operates at the 50–60Hz supply line frequency, and (b) a heat sink is needed to dissipate the power wasted by the low conversion efficiency. They are the most widely used type of regulator system.

An alternative but rarely used A.C./D.C. conversion system uses the switched-mode technique shown in *Figure 11.2*. Here, the A.C. power line voltage is directly converted to D.C. via a rectifier and storage capacitor, and this D.C. is used to power a series-connected 20kHz switched-mode (variable M–S ratio) voltage regulator and isolating transformer, which has its output converted back to D.C. via another rectifier and storage capacitor; part of the D.C. output is fed back to the switched-mode voltage regulator, to complete a control loop.

Switched-mode systems are very efficient (typically about 85 per cent) and compact (because heat-sink requirements are minimal and the isolating transformer works at 20kHz), but generate massive RFI and give poorer ripple rejection and voltage regulation than the conventional system. Such systems briefly came into vogue in the late 1970s, but are now rarely used, because of their severe RFI problems.

The third A.C./D.C. conversion system, shown in *Figure 11.3*, is a compromise between the other two. It uses a conventional step-down transformer and a rectifier and storage capacitor to generate an unregulated D.C. supply that is electrically isolated from the A.C. power line, but then uses a highly efficient switched-mode voltage regulator and an $L-C$ filter system and a feedback loop to convert it into a well-regulated D.C. output voltage.

Systems using switched-mode regulators are very efficient (about 80 per cent) and quite compact (because heat-sink requirements are minimal), but are fairly complex and expensive and generate a lot of RFI. They are often used in desktop computers and in other very compact equipment that is not RFI-sensitive.

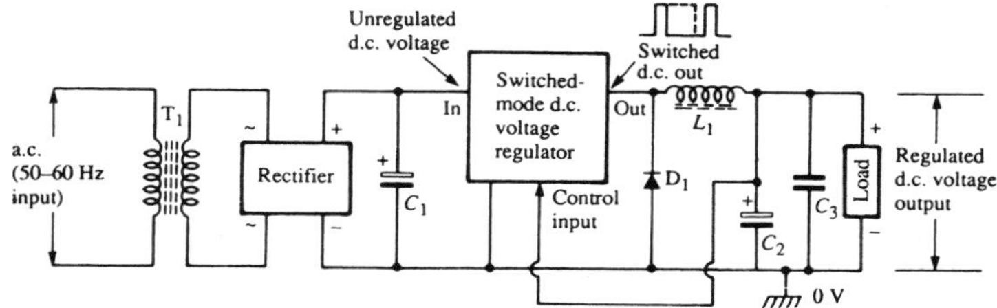


Figure 11.3. *Basic switched-mode voltage regulator circuit.*

## Basic power-supply circuits

Most modern electronic equipment uses either the *Figure 11.1* or *11.3* type of power supply, each of which uses a step-down transformer and a rectifier and storage capacitor to act as a *basic power supply* or A.C./D.C. converter that generates (with an overall efficiency of about 85 per cent) a smooth but unregulated D.C. supply that is electrically insulated from the A.C. supply.

*Figures 11.4* to *11.7* show the four most widely used basic power supply circuits. The *Figure 11.4* design provides a single-ended D.C. supply from a single-ended transformer and bridge rectifier combination, and gives a performance virtually identical to that of the *Figure 11.5* centre-tapped transformer circuit. Each of the *Figure 11.6* and *11.7* circuits provides split or dual D.C. supplies with nearly identical performances. The rules for designing these four circuits are quite simple, as follows.

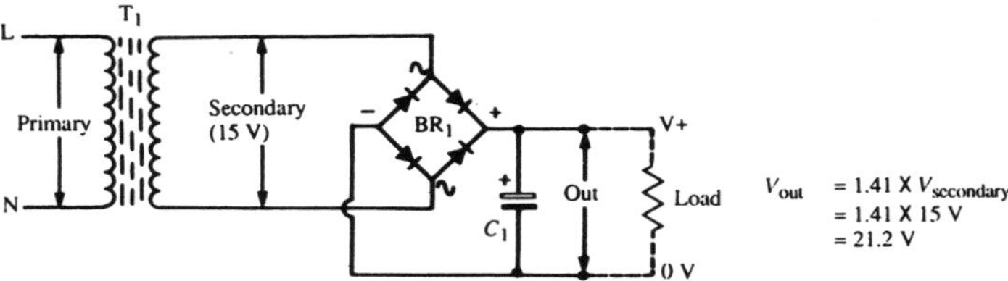


Figure 11.4. *Basic single-ended power supply using a single-ended transformer and bridge rectifier.*

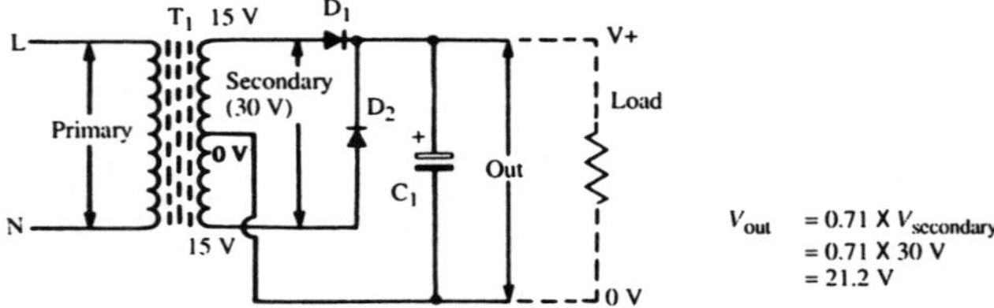


Figure 11.5. *Basic single-ended power supply using a centre-tapped transformer and two rectifiers.*

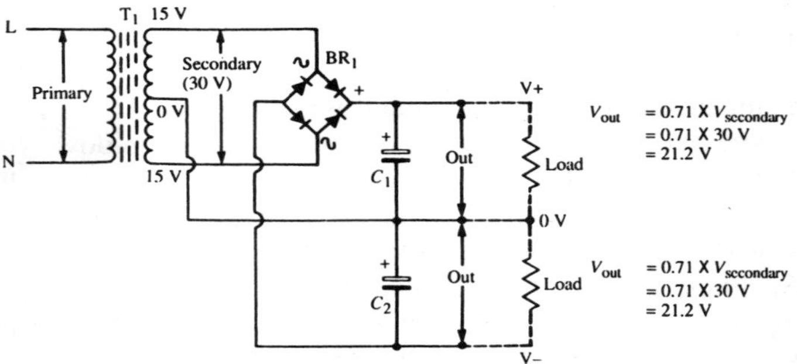


Figure 11.6. *Basic split or dual power supply using a centre-tapped transformer and bridge rectifier.*

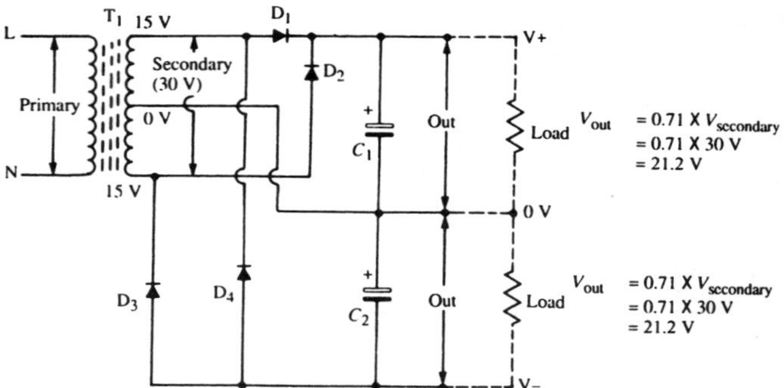


Figure 11.7. *Basic split or dual power supply using a centre-tapped transformer and individual rectifiers.*

## Transformer–rectifier selection

The three most important parameters of a transformer are its secondary voltage, its power rating, and its regulation factor. The secondary voltage is always quoted in r.m.s. terms at full rated power load, and the power load is quoted in terms of volt-amperes or watts. Thus, a 15V 20VA transformer gives a secondary voltage of 15V r.m.s. when its output is loaded by 20W. When the load is removed (reduced to zero) the secondary voltage rises by an amount implied by the **regulation factor**. Thus, the output of a 15V transformer with a 10 per cent regulation factor (a typical value) rises to 16.5V when the output is unloaded.

Note that the transformer's r.m.s. output voltage is *not* the same as the D.C. output voltage of the complete full-wave rectified power supply which, as shown in *Figure 11.8*, is in fact 1.41 times greater than that of a single-ended transformer, or 0.71 times that of a centre-tapped transformer (ignoring rectifier losses). Thus, a single-ended 15V r.m.s. transformer with 10 per cent regulation gives an output of about 21V at full rated load (just under 1A at 20VA rating) and 23.1V at zero load. When rectifier losses are taken into account the output voltages are slightly lower than shown in the graph. In the two-rectifier circuits of *Figures 11.5* and *11.7* the losses are about 600mV, and in the bridge circuits of

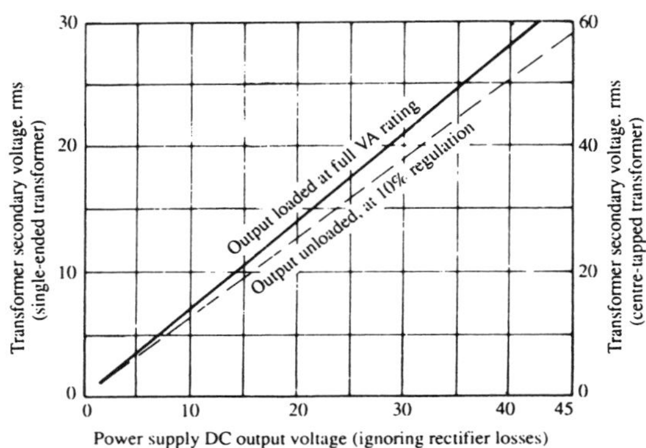


Figure 11.8. *Transformer selection chart. To use, decide on the required loaded D.C. output voltage (say 21V), then read across to find the corresponding transformer secondary voltage (15V single-ended or 30V centre-tapped).*

*Figures 11.4* and *11.6* they are about 1.2V. For maximum safety, the rectifiers should have current ratings at least equal to the D.C. output currents.

Thus, to select a transformer for a particular task, first decide the D.C. output voltage and current that is needed, to establish the transformer's minimum VA rating, then consult the graph of *Figure 11.8* to find the transformer secondary r.m.s. voltage that corresponds to the required D.C. voltage.

## The filter capacitor

The filter capacitor converts the rectifier's output into a smooth D.C. voltage; its two most important parameters are its working voltage, which must be greater than the off-load output value of the power supply, and its capacitance value, which determines the amount of ripple that will appear on the D.C. output when current is drawn from the circuit.

As a rule of thumb, in a full-wave rectified power supply operating from a 50–60Hz power line, an output load of 100mA causes a ripple waveform of about 700mV peak-to-peak to be developed on a 1000μF filter capacitor; the ripple magnitude is directly proportional to load current and inversely proportional to the capacitance value, as shown in the design guide of *Figure 11.9*. In most practical applications the ripple should be kept

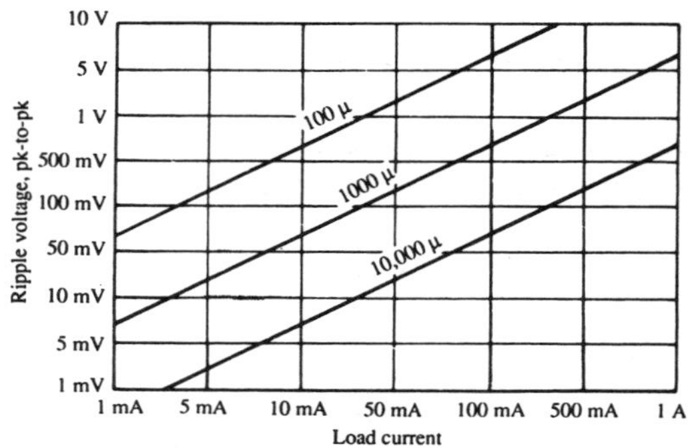


Figure 11.9. *Filter capacitor selection chart, relating capacitor size to ripple voltage and load current in a full-wave rectified 50–60Hz powered circuit.*

below 1.5V peak-to-peak under full-load conditions. If very low ripple is needed, the basic power supply can be used to feed a simple voltage regulator, which can easily reduce the ripple by a factor of 60dB or so.

## Zener-based voltage regulator

Practical voltage regulators vary from simple zener diode circuits, designed to provide load currents up to only a few milliamperes to fixed- or variable-voltage high-current circuits designed around dedicated three-terminal voltage regulator ICs. Circuits of all these types are shown in the next few sections of this chapter.

*Figure 11.10* shows a zener diode used to generate a fixed reference voltage by passing a current of about 5mA through it via current-limiting resistor *R*; the output voltage is not greatly influenced by sensible variations in the diode current value, and these may be caused by variations in the values of *R* or the supply voltage, or by drawing current from the output of the circuit. This basic circuit can thus be made to act as a simple voltage regulator, generating output load currents up to a few tens of milliamperes, by merely selecting the *R* value as shown in *Figure 11.11*.

Here, the value of *R* is selected so that it passes the maximum desired output current plus 5mA; consequently, when the specified maximum output load current is being drawn the zener passes only 5mA, but when zero load current is being drawn it passes all of the *R* current, and the zener dissipates maximum power; the zener's power rating must not be exceeded under this 'no load' condition.

The available output current of a zener regulator can be greatly increased by wiring a current-boosting voltage follower into its

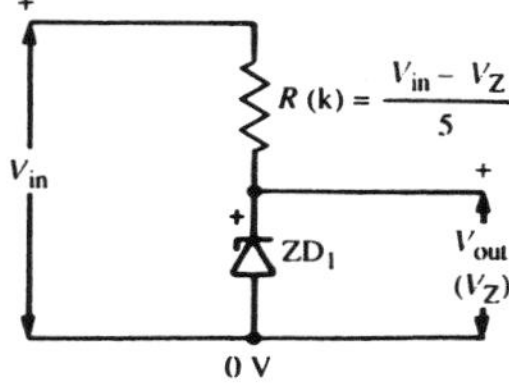


Figure 11.10. *This basic zener 'reference' circuit is biased at about 5mA.*

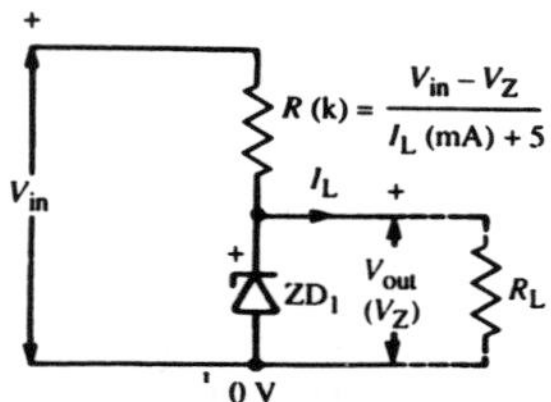


Figure 11.11. *This basic zener 'regulator' circuit can supply load currents of a few tens of milliamperes.*

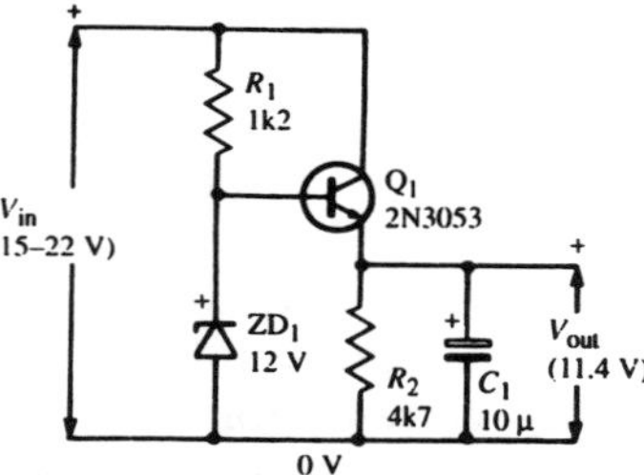


Figure 11.12. *This series-pass zener-based regulator circuit gives an output of 11.4V and can supply load currents up to about 100mA.*

output, as shown in the series-pass voltage regulator circuits of *Figures 11.12* and *11.13*. In *Figure 11.12*, $Q_1$ acts as the voltage-following current booster, and gives an output that is about 600mV below the zener value; this circuit gives reasonably good regulation. In *Figure 11.13*, $Q_1$ and the CA3140 op-amp form a precision current-boosting voltage follower that gives an output equal to the zener value under all load conditions; this circuit gives excellent voltage regulation. Note that the output load current of each of these circuits is limited to about 100mA by the power rating of $Q_1$; higher currents can be obtained by replacing $Q_1$ with a power Darlington transistor.

## Fixed three-terminal regulator circuits

Fixed-voltage regulator design is greatly simplified by using three-terminal regulator ICs such as the '78xxx' series of positive

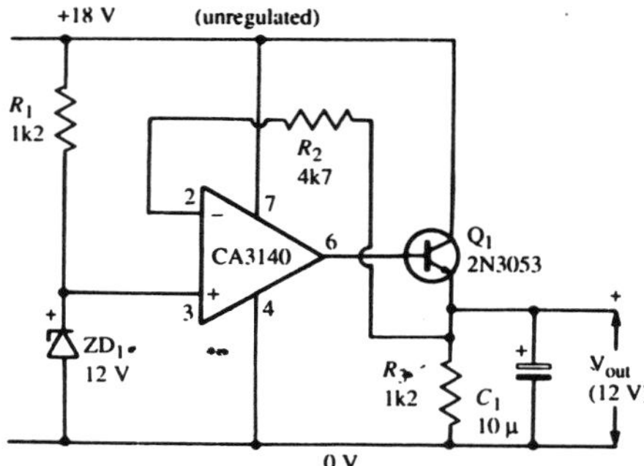


Figure 11.13. *This op-amp-based regulator gives an output of 12V at load currents up to 100mA and gives excellent regulation.*

regulators and the '79xxx' series of negative regulators, which incorporate features such as built-in fold-back current limiting and thermal protection, etc. These ICs are available with a variety of current and output voltage ratings, as indicated by the 'xxx' suffix; current ratings are indicated by the first part of the suffix ($L$ = 100mA, blank = 1A, $S$ = 2A), and the voltage ratings by the last two parts of the suffix (standard values are 5V, 12V, 15V and 24V). Thus, a 7805 device gives a 5V positive output at a 1A rating, and a 79L15 device gives a 15V negative output at a 100mA rating.

Three-terminal regulators are very easy to use, as shown in *Figures 11.14* to *11.16*, which show positive, negative and dual regulator circuits respectively. The ICs shown are 12V types with

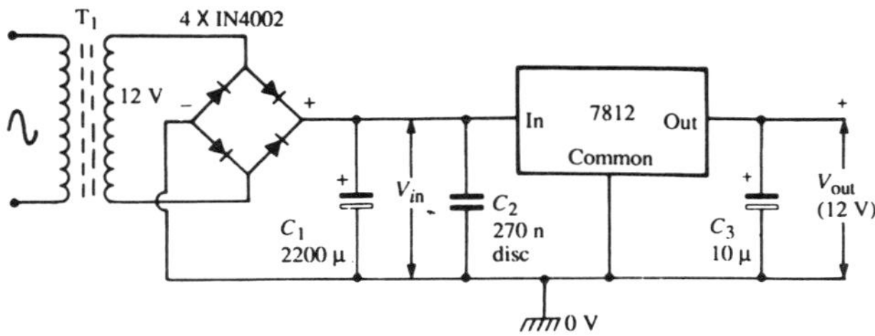


Figure 11.14. *Connections for using a three-terminal positive regulator, in this case a 12V, 1A '78' type.*

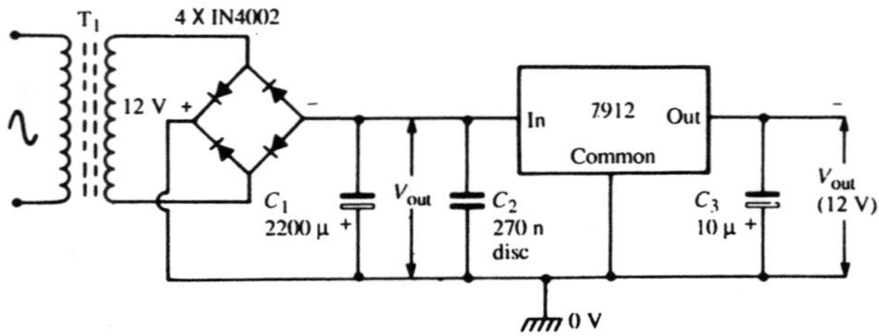


Figure 11.15. *Connections for using a three-terminal negative regulator, in this case a 12V, 1A '79' type.*

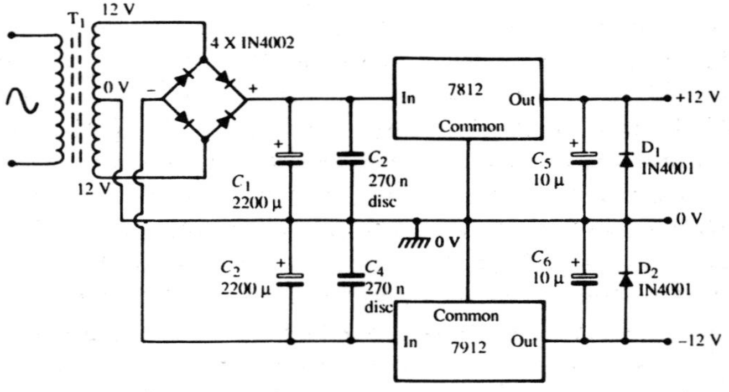


Figure 11.16. *Complete circuit of a 12V, 1A dual power supply using three-terminal regulator ICs.*

1A ratings, but the basic circuits are valid for all other voltage values, provided that the unregulated input is at least 3V more than the desired output voltage; a 270nF or greater disc (ceramic) capacitor must be wired close to the IC's input terminal, and a 10μF electrolytic wired across the output. The regulator ICs give about 60dB of ripple rejection, so 1V of input ripple appears as a mere 1mV of ripple on the regulated output.

## Voltage variation

The output voltage of a three-terminal regulator IC is actually referenced to the IC's 'common' terminal, which is normally (but

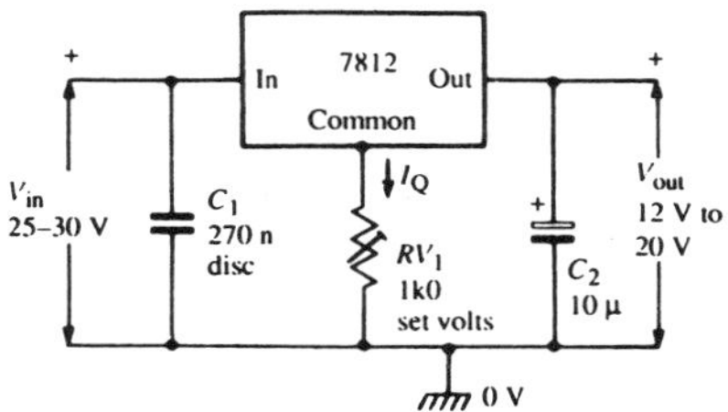


Figure 11.17. *Very simple method of varying the output voltage of a three-terminal regulator.*

not necessarily) grounded. Most regulator ICs draw quiescent currents of only a few milliamperes, which flow to ground via this common terminal, and the IC's regulated output voltage can thus be raised above the designed value by biasing this terminal with a suitable voltage, making it easy to get odd-ball output voltage values from these 'fixed voltage' regulators. *Figures 11.17* to *11.19* show ways of achieving this.

In *Figure 11.17* the bias voltage is obtained by passing the IC's quiescent current (about 8mA) to ground via $RV_1$. This design is adequate for many applications, but the output voltage shifts slightly with changes in quiescent current. The effects of such changes can be minimized by using the *Figure 11.18* design, in which the $RV_1$ bias voltage equals the sum of the quiescent current and the bias current set by $R_1$ (12mA in this example). If a fixed output with a value other than the designed voltage is needed, wire a zener diode in series with the common terminal as shown in *Figure 11.19*, the output voltage then being equal to the sum of the zener and regulator voltages.

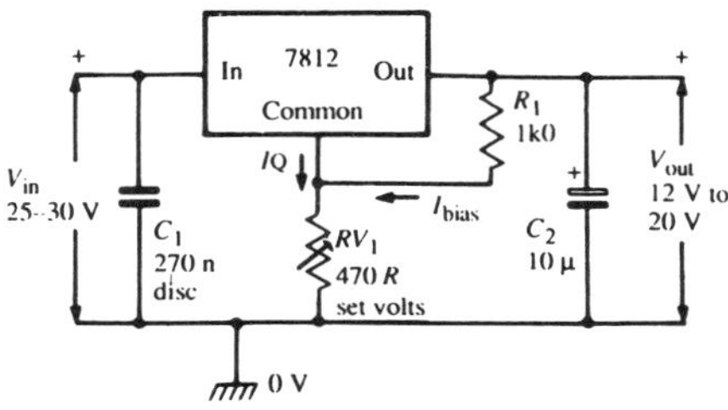


Figure 11.18. *An improved method of varying the output of a three-terminal regulator.*

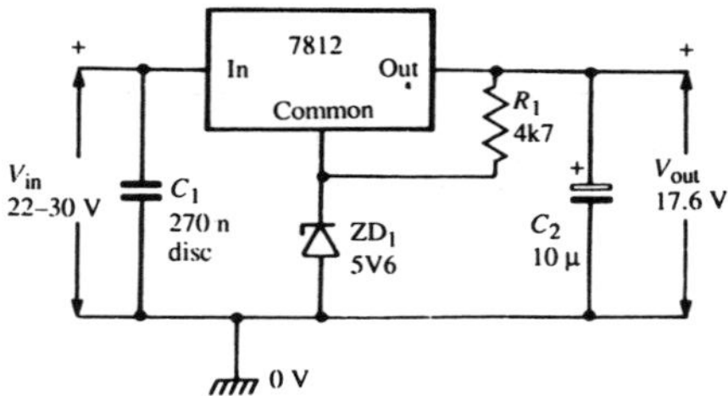


Figure 11.19. *The output voltage of a three-terminal regulator can be increased by wiring a suitable zener diode in series with the common terminal.*

## Current boosting

The output current capacity of a three-terminal regulator can be raised by using the *Figure 11.20* circuit, in which current boosting is available via $Q_1$. Note that $R_1$ is wired in series with the IC; at low currents insufficient voltage is developed across $R_1$ to turn $Q_1$ on, so all the load current is provided by the IC, but at 600mA or greater enough voltage (500mV) is developed to turn $Q_1$ on, so $Q_1$ supplies all current above 600mA. *Figure 11.21* shows the circuit modified to provide by-pass transistor $Q_1$ with overload current limiting via 0.12Ω current-sensing resistor $R_2$ and turn-off transistor $Q_2$, which automatically limit the output current to about 5A.

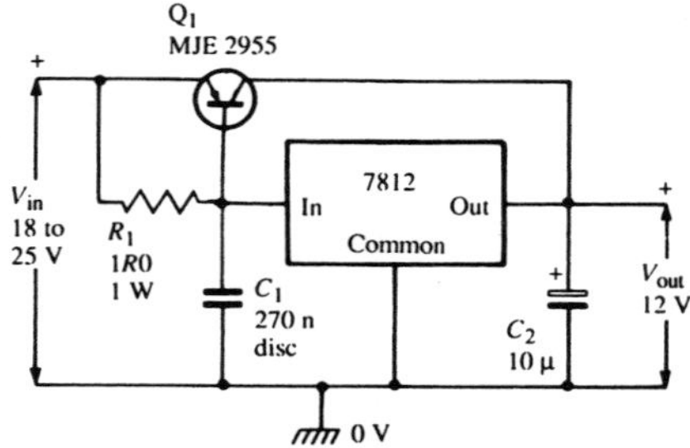


Figure 11.20. *The output current capacity of a three-terminal regulator can be boosted via an external transistor. This circuit can supply 5A at a regulated 12V.*

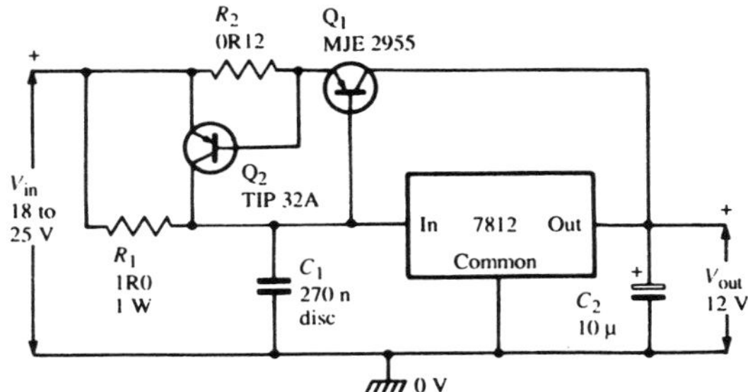


Figure 11.21. *This version of the 5A regulator has overload protection provided via* $Q_2$.

## Variable three-terminal regulator circuits

The 78xxx and 79xxx range of three-terminal regulator ICs are designed for fixed-voltage applications, although their outputs can in fact be varied over limited ranges. Variable regulated output voltages can best be obtain by using 317K or 338K three-terminal 'variable' regulator ICs. *Figure 11.22* shows the outline,

| Parameter | 317 K | 338 K |
|---|---|---|
| Input voltage range | 4–40 V | 4–40 V |
| Output voltage range | 1.25–37 V | 1.25–32 V |
| Output current rating | 1.5 A | 5 A |
| Line regulation | 0.02% | 0.02% |
| Load regulation | 0.1% | 0.1% |
| Ripple rejection | 65 dB | 60 dB |

$$V_{out} = 1.25\left(1 + \frac{RV_1}{R_1}\right)$$

$\simeq$ 1.25–30 V

Figure 11.22. *Outline, basic data and application circuit of the 317K and 338K variable-voltage three-terminal regulators.*

basic data and the basic variable regulator circuit applicable to these two devices, each of which has built-in fold-back current limiting and thermal protection and is housed in a T03 steel package. The major difference between the devices is that the 317K has a 1.5A current rating compared to the 5A rating of the 338K. Major features of both devices are that their output terminals are 1.25V above their 'adjust' terminals, which pass quiescent currents of a mere 50μA or so.

Thus, in the *Figure 11.22* circuit, the 1.25V difference between the 'adjust' and output terminals makes several milliamperes flow to ground via $RV_1$ and generates a variable voltage on the 'adjust' terminal. In practice the output of this circuit can be varied from 1.25 to 33V via $RV_1$, provided that the unregulated input voltage is at least 3V greater than the output. Alternative voltage ranges can be obtained by using other values of $R_1$ and/or $RV_1$, but for best stability the $R_1$ current should be at least 3.5mA.

The basic *Figure 11.22* circuit can be modified in several ways; its ripple rejection factor can be increased from 65dB to 80dB by wiring a 10μF bypass capacitor across $RV_1$, as shown in *Figure 11.23*; $D_1$ stops the capacitor discharging into the IC if its output is short-circuited. *Figure 11.24* shows it further modified by increasing $C_2$ to 100μF (to reduce the transient output impedance) and using $D_2$ to protect the IC against damage from $C_2$'s stored energy if an input short occurs. Finally, *Figure 11.25* shows it modified so that its output is variable down to 0V, rather than to only 1.25V. This is achieved by using a 35V negative rail and a pair of series-connected diodes that clamp the low end of $RV_1$ to −1.25V.

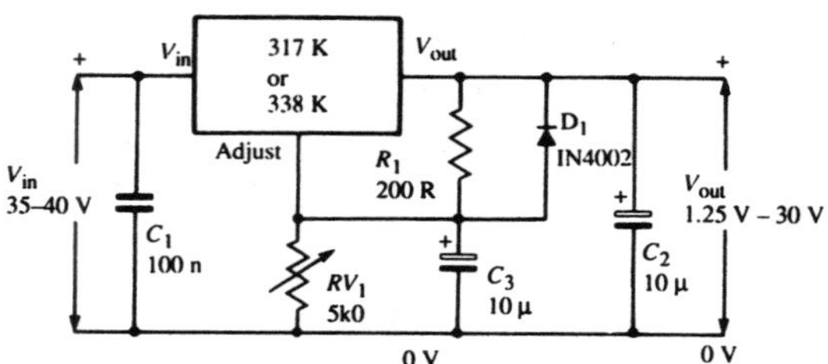


Figure 11.23. *This version of the variable-voltage regulator has 80dB of ripple rejection.*

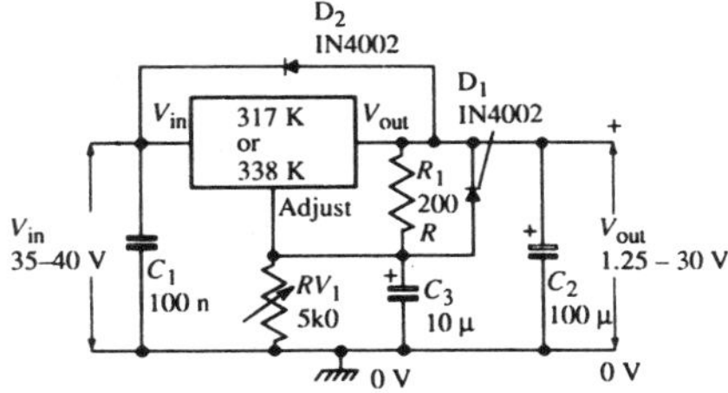


Figure 11.24. *This version of the regulator has 80dB ripple rejection, a low-impedance transient response, and full input and output short-circuit protection.*

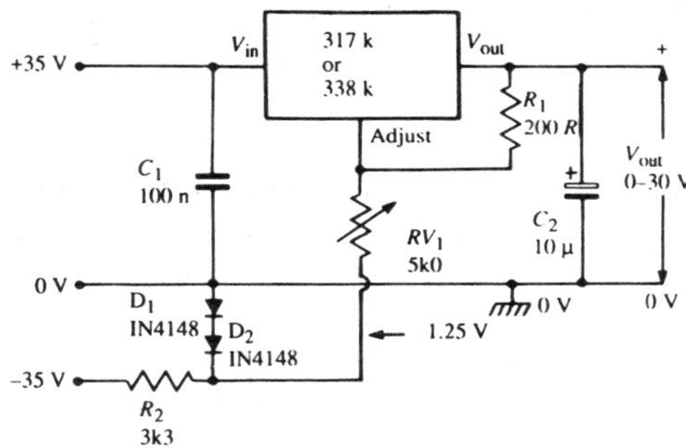


Figure 11.25. *The output of this version of the regulator is fully variable from zero to 30V.*

## Switched-mode regulator basics

*Figure 11.26* shows the basic operating principle of the switched-mode voltage regulator. The unregulated D.C. voltage is fed to the variable M–S ratio (often called 'pulse-width modulated', or PWM) generator (which typically operates at about 20kHz) and to series-pass transistor $Q_1$, so that a powerful variable M–S ratio waveform (with a peak amplitude of $V_{pk}$) is generated at the $D_1-L_1$ junction. $D_1$ forms part of the $L_1-C_1$ filter network, which integrates this M–S waveform and gives a smooth D.C. output of $V_{pk} \times M/(M + S)$. Self-regulation is achieved by feeding part of the D.C. output back to the generator's **Control input**.

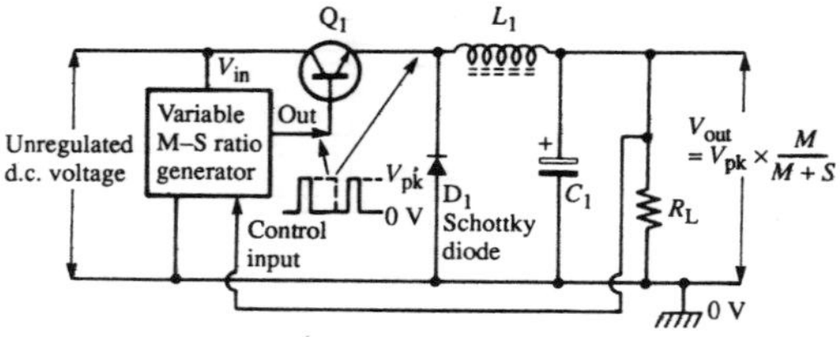

Figure 11.26. *Switched-mode voltage regulator basic circuit.*

The *Figure 11.26* circuit is very efficient, since $Q_1$ operates as a power switch and wastes little energy and generates little heat, and the $L_1-C_1$ filter values can be quite small, since the generator operates at a high frequency. Practical switched-mode regulators are best built using dedicated ICs such as the L296.

## L296 circuits

The L296 is a sophisticated switched-mode voltage regulator capable of supplying 5.1V to 40V at 4A maximum. *Figure 11.27* shows its outline and pin notations; its 15-lead plastic power package has an integral ground-connected metal mounting tab.

The L296 houses a sawtooth oscillator, a 5.1V reference and comparator, and various logic and sensing circuits. *Figure 11.28*

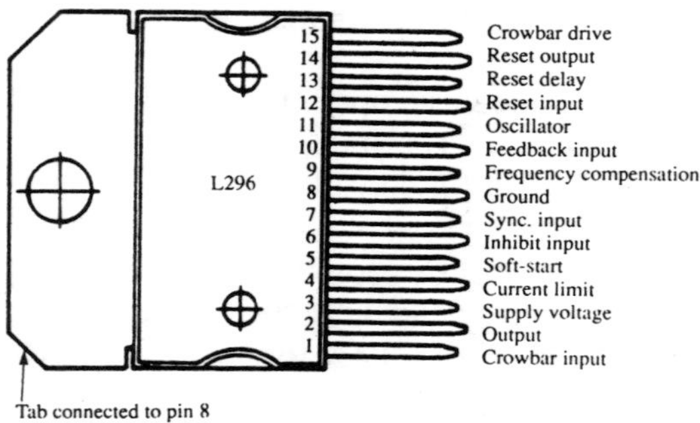


Figure 11.27. *Outline and pin notations of the L296 switched-mode voltage regulator.*

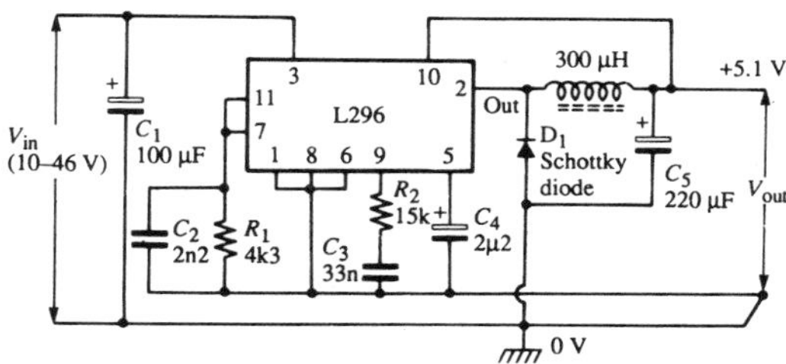


Figure 11.28. *Minimum-count 5V1/4A switched-mode voltage regulator; note the signal and power ground paths.*

shows the simplest (minimum component count) way of using the L296, as a 5.1V regulator with a 4A current rating; $C_2-R_1$ set the sawtooth oscillator frequency to 100kHz, $C_3-R_2$ set the feedback time constants, $C_4$ gives a slow-start action (at initial power-up), and the regulated output is set at 5.1V (the internal reference value) by shorting pin 10 to the output. Note that $D_1$ is a Schottky type, that $C_1$ and $C_5$ need high ripple current ratings, and that signal and power grounds must be made as shown.

*Figure 11.29* shows the circuit modified to give a variable (5.1V to 15V) output by making the feedback connection via the $RV_1-R_3$ divider ($V_{out} = 5.1\text{V} \times [RV_1 + R_3]/R_3$) and by adding $C_6$; pin 10 is shorted to pin 12, to give the circuit automatic start-up reset.

Note that several L296s can use the same oscillator (thus avoiding intermodulation problems) by using the system of *Figure 11.30*, where the oscillator of one L296 is used to drive the pin-7 SYNC pins of the others, which have their OSC terminals left open.

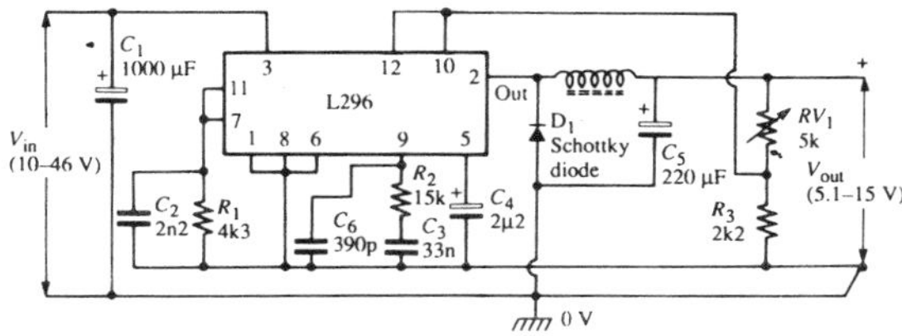


Figure 11.29. *Variable (5V1 to 15V) 4A switched-mode regulated supply.*

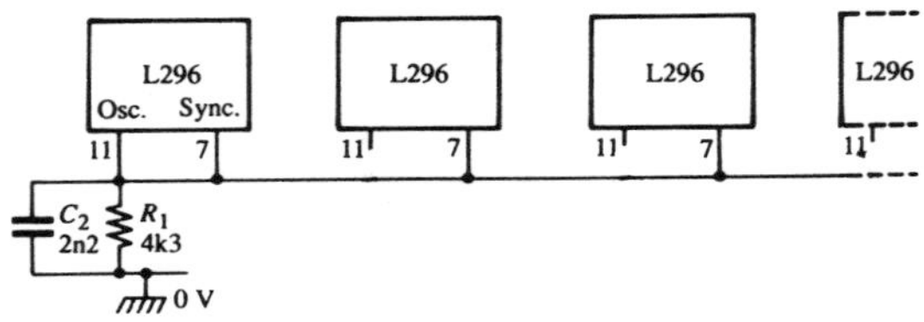


Figure 11.30. *Multiple L296 operation via a single oscillator.*

## Voltage-converter basics

Electronic voltage converters are circuits used to generate a higher-value supply from an existing low-voltage D.C. source, or to generate a negative D.C. supply from an existing positive D.C. voltage source, etc. Such circuits are fairly easy to design and build, using either readily available components or special-purpose ICs such as the ICL7660 voltage converter. A variety of low-power versions of such circuits are shown in the remainder of this chapter.

A D.C. voltage can easily be converted into one of greater value or reversed polarity by using the D.C. supply to power a free-running square-wave generator which has its output fed to a multi-section capacitor–diode voltage multiplier network, which thus provides the desired 'converted' output voltage. If a positive output voltage is needed, the multiplier must give a non-inverting action, as in *Figure 11.31a*, and if a negative output is required it must give an inverting action, as in *Figure 11.31b*.

Practical converters of this type can use a variety of types of multivibrator circuit (bipolar or FET transistor, CMOS or TTL IC, etc) as their basic free-running square-wave generators; in all cases, however, the generator should operate at a frequency in the range 1kHz to 10kHz, so that the multiplier section can operate with good efficiency while using fairly low values of 'multiplying' capacitor.

One of the easiest ways of making practical voltage converters of this type is to use type-555 'timer' ICs (which can supply fairly high output currents) as the free-running square-wave generators, and *Figures 11.32* to *11.35* show a selection of practical circuits of this type; in each case the 555 is wired as a free-running astable multivibrator and operates at about 3kHz (determined by the $R_1$–$R_2$–$C_2$ values); $C_1$ and $C_3$ both help enhance circuit stability.

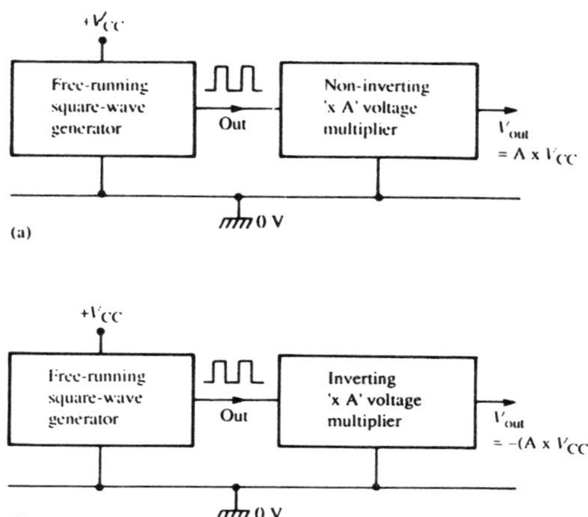


Figure 11.31. *(a) Voltage converter with positive output, and (b) voltage converter with negative output.*

The *Figure 11.32* circuit acts as a D.C. voltage-doubler, and generates a D.C. output voltage roughly double that of the 555's supply line via the $C_4$−$D_1$−$C_5$−$C_2$ capacitor−diode voltage-doubler network, which produces the '2 × $V_{CC}$' output voltage. This '2 × $V_{CC}$' is the approximate value of the unloaded output voltage; the precise value equals 2 × $V_{peak}$, minus ($V_{df1}$ + $V_{df2}$), where $V_{peak}$ is the peak output voltage of the square-wave generator and '$V_{df}$' is the forward volt drop (about 600mV) of each

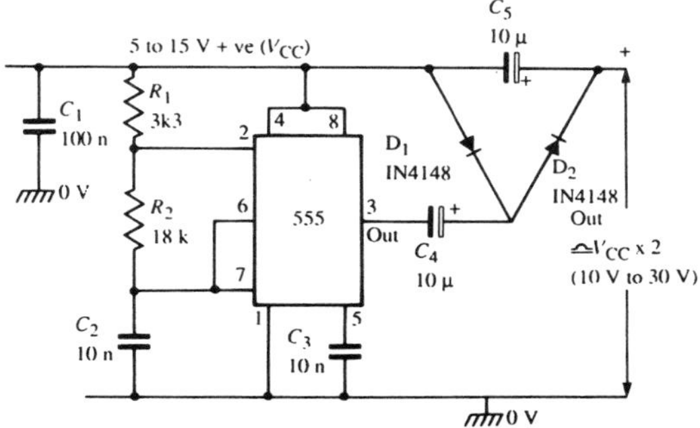


Figure 11.32. *D.C. voltage-doubler circuit.*

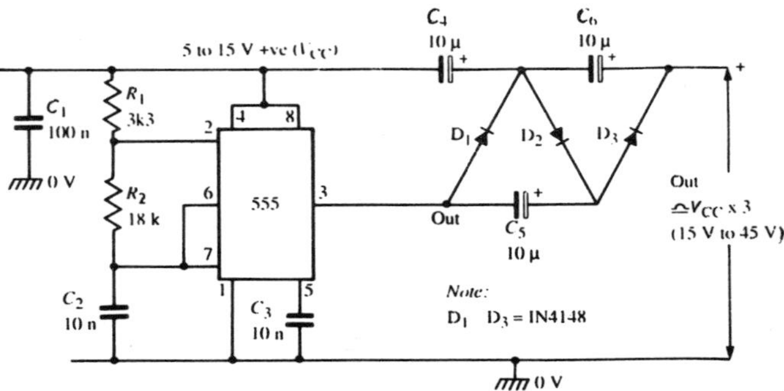


Figure 11.33. *D.C. voltage-tripler circuit.*

'multiplier' diode. The output voltage decreases when the output is loaded.

The *Figure 11.32* circuit can be used with any D.C. supply in the range 5 to 15V and can thus provide a 'voltage-doubled' output of 10 to 30V. Greater outputs can be obtained by adding more multiplier stages to the circuit. *Figure 11.33*, for example, shows how to make a D.C. voltage tripler, which can provide outputs in the range 15 to 45V, and *Figure 11.34* shows a D.C. voltage quadrupler, which gives outputs in the 20 to 60V range.

A particularly useful type of 555 converter is the D.C. negative-voltage generator, which produces an output voltage almost equal in amplitude but opposite in polarity to that of the IC supply line. This type of circuit can be used to provide a split-supply output

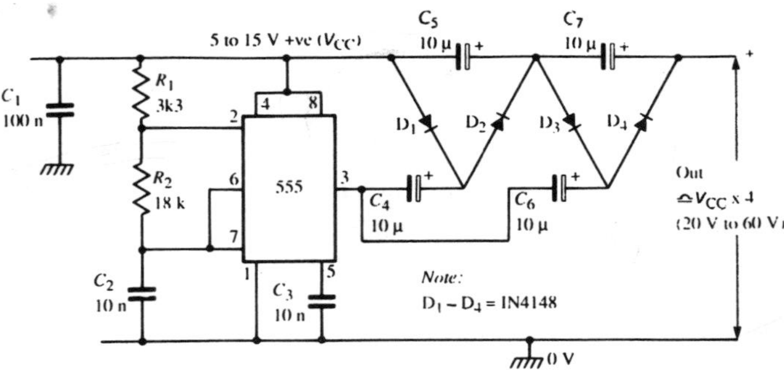


Figure 11.34. *D.C. voltage quadrupler circuit.*

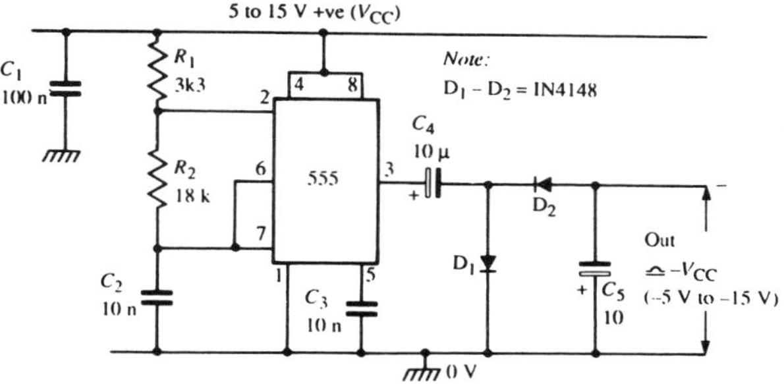


Figure 11.35. *D.C. negative-voltage generator.*

for powering op-amps, etc., from a single-ended power supply. *Figure 11.35* shows an example of such a circuit, which operates at 3kHz and drives a voltage-doubler ($C_4-D_1-C_5-D_2$) output stage.

## High-voltage generation

The 'voltage multiplier' method of generating increased output voltages is usually cost-effective only when multiplier ratios of less than six are needed. When very large step-up ratios are needed (as, for example, when hundreds of volts must be generated via a 12V supply), it is often better to use the output of a low-voltage oscillator or square-wave generator to drive a step-up voltage transformer that provides a high-value A.C. voltage on its secondary (output) winding, which can (if desired) be converted back to D.C. via a rectifier-filter network. *Figures 11.36* to *11.38* show practical low-power high-voltage generators of these types.

The *Figure 11.36* circuit acts as a D.C.-to-D.C. converter which generates a 300V D.C. output from a 9V D.C. power supply. $Q_1$ and its associated circuitry form a Hartley $L-C$ oscillator, with the low-voltage primary winding of 9V–0–9V to 250V transformer $T_1$ forming the $L$ part of the oscillator, which is tuned via $C_2$. The supply voltage is stepped up to about 350V peak at the $T_1$ secondary, and is rectified and smoothed via $D_1-C_3$. With no permanent load on $C_3$ the capacitor can deliver a powerful but non-lethal 'belt'; with a permanent load applied the output falls to about 300V at a load current of a few milliamperes.

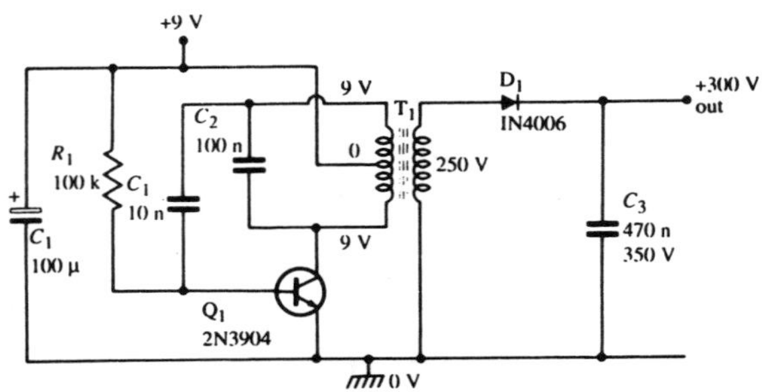


Figure 11.36. *9V-to-300V D.C.-to-D.C. converter.*

The *Figure 11.37* circuit can be used to drive a neon lamp or generate a low-current high-value (up to a few hundred volts) D.C. voltage from a low-value (5 to 15V) D.C. supply. The 555 is wired as a 3kHz astable multivibrator that drives $T_1$ via $R_3$. $T_1$ is a small audio transformer with a turns ratio sufficient to give the desired output voltage, e.g. with a 10V supply and a 1:20 $T_1$ turns ratio, the transformer gives an unloaded D.C. output of 200V peak; this A.C. voltage can easily be converted to D.C. via a half-wave rectifier and filter capacitor, as shown.

Finally, the *Figure 11.38* D.C.-to-A.C. inverter circuit produces an A.C. output at the A.C. power-line frequency and voltage. The 555 is wired as a low-frequency (variable from 50 to 60Hz via $RV_1$) astable that feeds its power-boosted (via $Q_1-Q_2$) output into the low-voltage 'input' of reverse-connected filament trans-

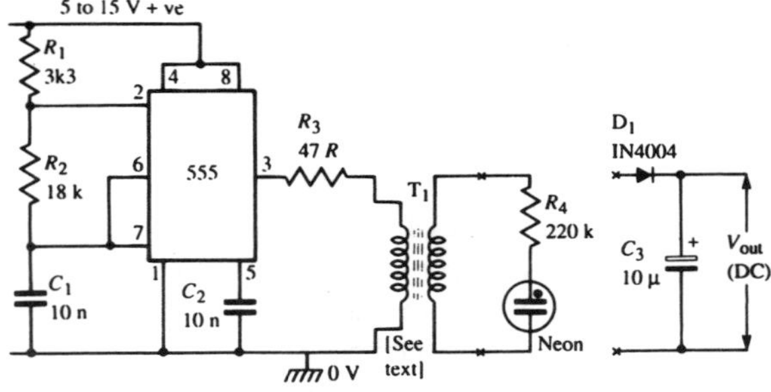


Figure 11.37. *Neon-lamp driver or 'high-voltage' generator.*

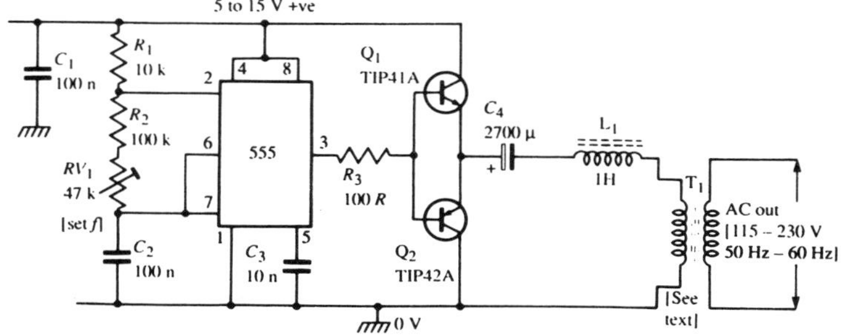


Figure 11.38. *D.C.-to-A.C. inverter.*

former $T_1$, which has the desired 'step-up' turns ratio. $C_4$ and $L_1$ act as a filter that ensures that the power signal feeding into the transformer is essentially a sine wave.

## The ICL7660

The ICL7660 is a dedicated voltage converter IC that generates an equal-value negative supply from a positive source, i.e. if powered from a +5V supply it generates a −5V output. It can be used with a +1.5 to 10V D.C. supply, and has a typical voltage conversion efficiency of 99.9 per cent (!) when its output is unloaded; when the output is loaded it acts like a voltage source with a 70Ω output impedance, and can supply maximum currents of about 40mA.

*Figure 11.39* shows the ICL7660's outline and pin designations. The IC operates in a way similar to that of the *Figure 11.32* 'oscillator and voltage-multiplier' circuit, but with far greater efficiency. The ICL7660 chip houses a very efficient square-wave

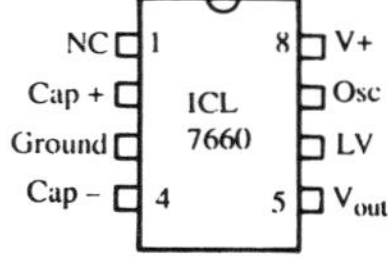


Figure 11.39 *Outline and pin notations of the ICL7660 voltage converter IC.*

generator that operates (without the use of external components) at about 10kHz and has an output that switches fully between the supply-rail values; it also houses an ultra-efficient set of logic-driven multiplier 'diodes' that, when used with two external capacitors, enables voltage-doubling to be achieved with near-perfect efficiency. These 'diodes' are actually MOS power switches, driven in such a way that each 'diode' switch automatically closes when forward biased and opens when reverse biased, thus giving 99.9 per cent operating efficiency.

The ICL7660 is an easy device to use, but note that none of its terminals must ever be connected to a voltage above *V*+ or below GROUND. If the IC is to be used with supplies in the range 1.5 to 3.5V, the pin-6 LV terminal must be grounded; at supply values above 3.5V, pin-6 must be left open circuit, and at values greater than 6.5V a protection diode must be wired in series with OUTPUT pin-5. *Figures 11.40* to *11.48* show a selection of practical application circuits in which these design rules are applied.

## ICL7660 circuits

The most popular application of the ICL7660 is as a simple negative voltage converter, and *Figures 11.40* to *11.42* show basic circuits of this type; in each case, $C_1$ and $C_2$ are 'multiplier' capacitors and each has a value of 10μF. The *Figure 11.40* circuit uses 1.5−3.5V supplies, and needs only two external components. *Figure 11.41* is similar, but uses supplies in the 3.5 to 6.5V range

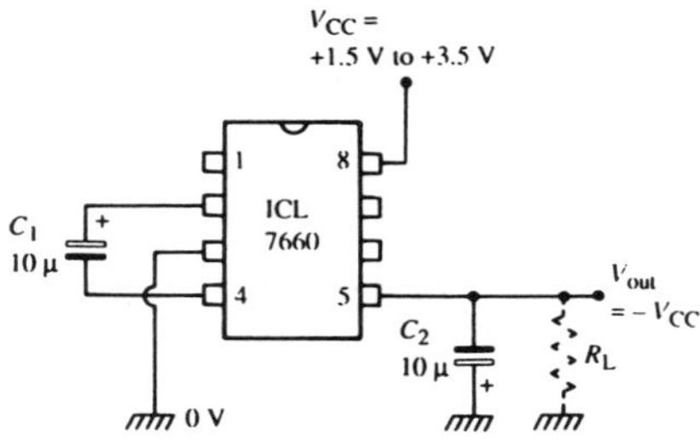


Figure 11.40. *Negative voltage converter using 1.5V to 3.5V supply.*

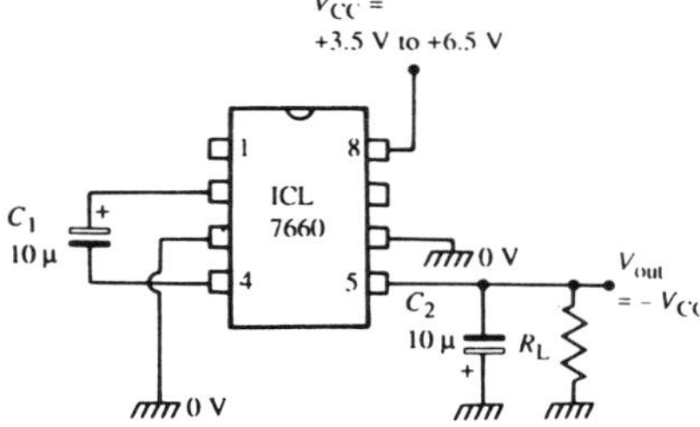


Figure 11.41. *Negative voltage converter using 3.5V to 6.5V supply.*

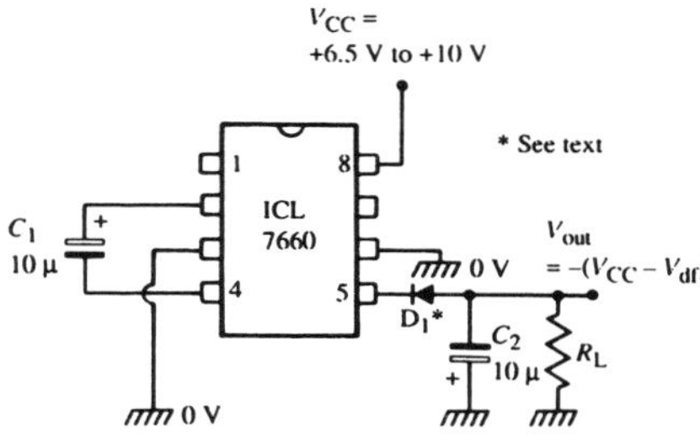


Figure 11.42. *Negative voltage converter using 6.5V to 10V supply.*

and thus has pin-6 grounded; finally, *Figure 11.42* uses supplies in the range 6.5 to 10V, and has $D_1$ wired in series with output pin-5, to protect it against excessive reverse biasing from $C_2$ when the power supplies are removed; this diode reduces the available output voltage by $V_{df}$, the forward volt drop of the diode; to keep this volt drop to minimum values, $D_1$ should be a Schottky or germanium type.

A useful feature of the ICL7660 is that numbers of these ICs (up to a maximum of ten) can be cascaded to give voltage-conversion factors greater than unity. Thus, if three stages are cascaded, they give a final output voltage of $-3V_{CC}$, etc. *Figure 11.43* shows the connections for cascading two of these stages; any additional stages should be connected in the same way as the right-hand IC of this diagram.

In some applications the user may want to reduce the ICL7660's oscillator frequency; one way of doing this is to wire capacitor $C_x$

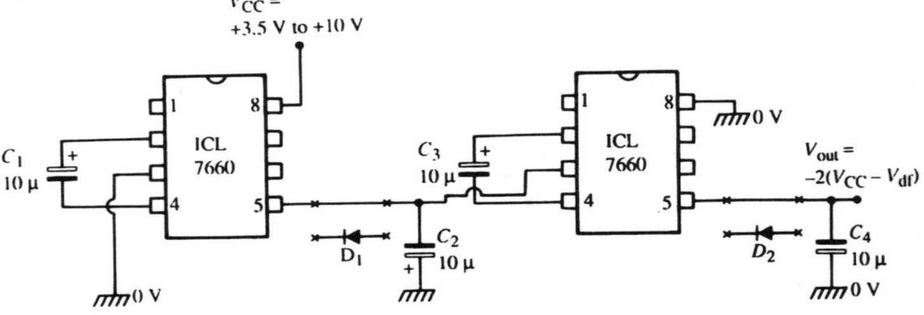


Figure 11.43. *Cascading devices for increased output voltage.*

between pins 7 and 8, as in *Figure 11.44*; *Figure 11.45* shows the relationship between the $C_x$ and frequency values; thus, a $C_x$ value of 100pF reduces the frequency by a factor of ten, from 10kHz to 1kHz. Note that, to compensate for this 10:1 frequency reduction and maintain the circuit efficiency, the $C_1$ and $C_2$ values should be increased by a similar factor (to about 100μF each).

Another way of reducing the oscillator frequency is to use pin-7 to over-drive the oscillator via an external clock, as shown in *Figure 11.46*. The clock signal must be fed to pin-7 via a 1k0 series resistor ($R_1$), and should switch fully between the two supply-rail values; in the diagram, a CMOS gate is wired as an inverting buffer stage, to ensure such switching.

Another use of the ICL7660 IC is as a positive voltage multiplier, to give a positive output of almost double the original supply-voltage value. *Figure 11.47* shows the circuit connections. The pin-2 oscillator output drives a conventional capacitor–diode

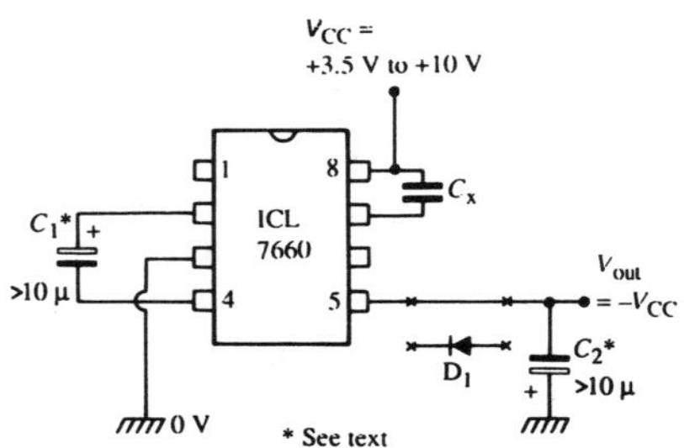


Figure 11.44. *Reducing oscillator frequency.*

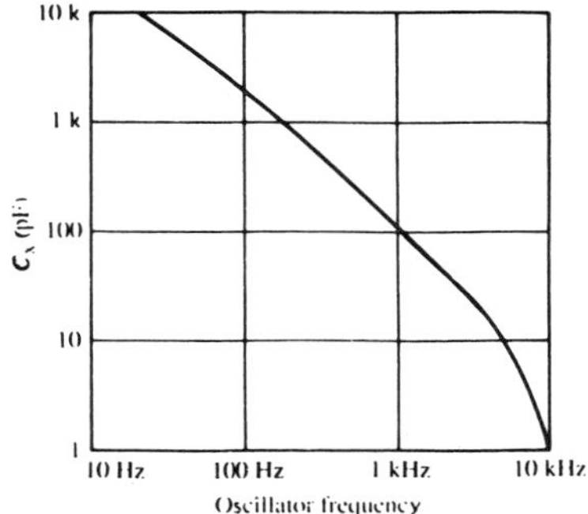


**Figure 11.45.** *$C_x$/oscillator-frequency graph.*

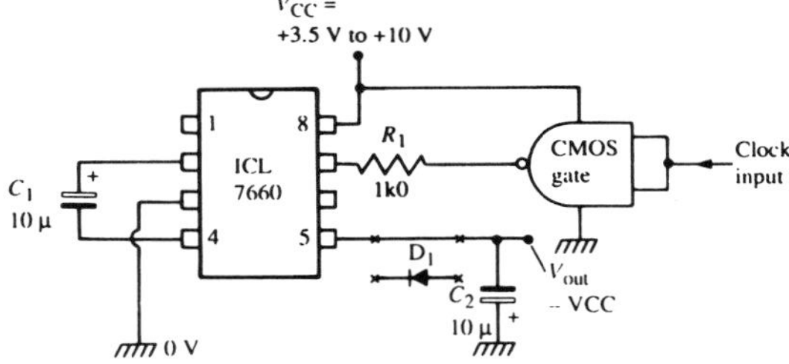


**Figure 11.46.** *External clocking of the ICL7660.*

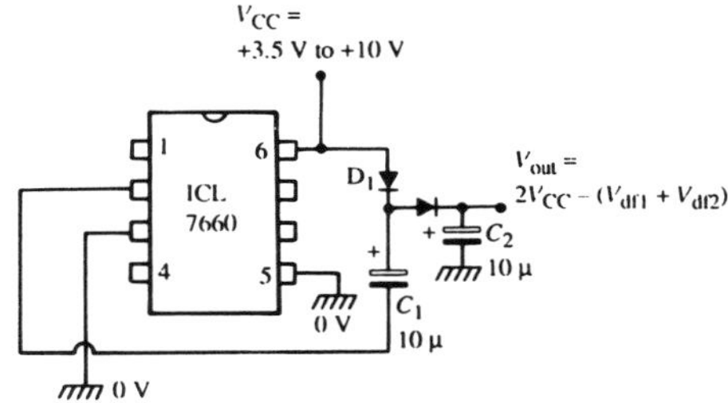


**Figure 11.47.** *Positive voltage multiplier.*

voltage-doubler network; note that these two diodes reduce the available output voltage by an amount equal to their combined forward volt drops, so should ideally be low-loss Schottky or germanium types.

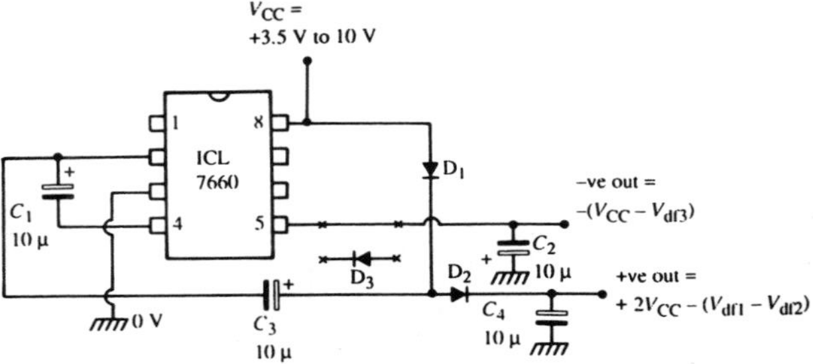


Figure 11.48. *Combined positive voltage multiplier and negative voltage converter.*

Finally, to complete this look at ICL7660 applications, *Figure 11.48* shows how the circuits of *Figures 11.41/11.42* and *11.46* can be used to make a combined positive-voltage multiplier and negative-voltage converter with dual output voltage rails; each rail has an output impedance of about 100Ω.

# 12 Miscellaneous test gear circuits

This final chapter looks at a miscellaneous collection of useful instrumentation and test-gear circuits, of types that cannot conveniently be fitted under any of the earlier chapter headings. They range from simple **go/no-go** testers to oscilloscope trace doublers and triggered time bases. The chapter starts off by looking at practical dot- and bar-graph meters.

## LED bar-graph basics

LED bar-graph displays are solid-state 'moving-light' devices that make excellent low-definition analogue-indicating meters. They use a line of ordinary LEDs to represent scale length, and in use several adjacent LEDs may be illuminated simultaneously to form a light 'bar' that gives an analogue indication of a parameter's value. Alternatively, only a single LED may be illuminated, to give a 'dot' indication of parameter value. They were mentioned briefly in Chapter 1, and their typical displays are illustrated in *Figure 1.16*.

Analogue-indicating bar-graph meters are fast acting and unaffected by vibration or attitude. They have a typical linear accuracy of 0.5 per cent, and their scales can easily be given any desired shape (a vertical or horizontal line, an arc or circle, etc.); individual LED colours can be mixed to emphasize particular sections of the display. Scale definition depends on the number of LEDs used; a 10-LED display gives adequate resolution for many purposes. Electronic 'over-range' detectors can easily be activated from the driver ICs and used to sound an alarm and/or flash the entire display under the over-range condition.

A number of special bar-graph driver ICs are available for

activating LED bar-graph displays, and the best known of these are the LM3914 family of devices, which can be cascaded to drive up to 100 LEDs, in either 'bar' or 'dot' mode.

## LM3914 basic principles

The LM3914 family of dot/bar-graph driver ICs are fairly complex and highly versatile devices, housed in 18-pin DIL packages and each capable of directly driving up to ten LEDs in either 'dot' or 'bar' mode. The family comprises three devices, the LM3914 being a linear-scaled unit and the LM3915 and LM3916 being log and semi-log devices respectively.

All three members of the family use similar internal circuitry, and *Figure 12.1* shows that of the linear-scaled LM3914, together with the connections for making it act as a 10-LED 0–1.2V meter. Each of the IC's ten LED-driving voltage comparators has its inverting terminal taken to the IC's input pin via the unity-gain buffer, and its non-inverting or 'reference' terminal taken to a specific tap on the floating-precision 10-stage potential divider, which is shown driven via an integral 1.2V floating reference. Each LED-driving comparator can sink up to 30mA; the sink currents are internally limited, and can be externally pre-set via $R_1$.

The IC also contains a logic network that can be set (via pin-9) to give either a dot or bar display from the outputs of the ten comparators. Thus, if the *Figure 12.1* circuit is set for bar-mode operation, the output of the first (lowest) comparator conducts and turn $LED_1$ on when the input voltage reaches its 0.12V reference value, and $LED_2$ turns on at the 0.24V reference value of the second comparator, so that both $LED_1$ and $LED_2$ are on; as the input voltage is further increased, more and more comparators and LEDs are turned on until eventually, when the input rises to 1.2V, the last comparator and $LED_{10}$ turn on, at which point all ten LEDs are illuminated. A similar kind of action is obtained when the LM3914 logic is set for dot mode operation, except that only one LED turns on at any given time; at zero volts, no LEDs are on, and at above 1.2V only $LED_{10}$ is on.

The **on** current of each LED is roughly ten times the output current of the 1.2V source, which can supply up to 3mA and

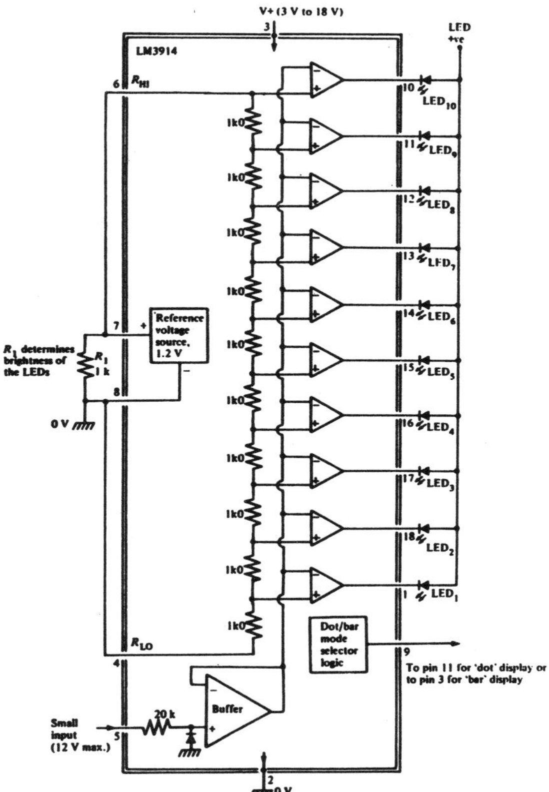


Figure 12.1. *Internal circuit of the LM3914, with connections for making a 10-LED 0–1.2V linear meter with dot or bar display.*

thus enables LED currents of up to 30mA to be set via $R_1$. If, for example, a total resistance of 1k2 is placed across pin-7 and pin-8, the 1.2V source will pass 1mA and each LED can pass 10mA maximum. Note that the IC can pass total currents up to 300mA when used in the bar mode with all ten LEDs on, but the IC has a maximum power rating of only 660mW, so there is a danger of exceeding this rating in bar-mode operation. In practice, the IC can use D.C. supplies in the range 3 to 25V, and the LEDs can use the same supply as the IC or can be independently powered; this latter option can be used to keep the IC's power dissipation at minimal level.

The IC's internal ten-stage divider is fully floating, and can be powered from either internal or external sources. If, for example, the top of the chain is connected to a 10V source, the IC will function as a 0–10V meter if the low end of the chain is grounded, or as a 'restricted-range' 5V-to-10V meter if the low end of the chain is connected to a 5V. The divider voltage must not exceed the pin-3 value minus 2V. The IC's internal voltage reference gives a nominal output of 1.28V (limits are 1.2V to 1.32V), but can be externally 'programmed' to produce effective reference values up to 12V.

The major difference between the three members of the LM3914 family lays in the resistance values used in the internal ten-stage potential divider. In the LM3914 these resistors have equal values, and thus produce a linear display of ten equal steps. In the LM3915 the resistors are logarithmically weighted, and thus produce a log display that spans 30dB in ten 3dB steps. In the LM3916 the resistors are weighted in a semi-log fashion and produce a display that is specifically suited to VU-meter applications.

## Dot-mode LM3914 circuits

*Figures 12.2* to *12.5* show various ways of using the LM3914 IC to make ten-LED dot-mode voltmeters. Note that in all cases pin-9 is wired to pin-11 to give dot-mode operation, and that a 10μF capacitor is wired between pins 2 and 3 to enhance circuit stability.

*Figure 12.2* shows a variable-range (1.2V to 1000V F.S.D.) voltmeter. The low ends of the internal reference and divider are grounded and their top ends are joined together, so the meter has a basic F.S.D. sensitivity of 1.2V, but variable ranging is provided by the $R_x$–$R_1$ potential divider at the input of the circuit. Thus, when $R_x$ is zero, F.S.D. is 1.2V, but when $R_x$ is 90k the F.S.D. is 12V. $R_2$ sets the **LED on** current at about 10mA.

*Figure 12.3* shows a fixed-range 0-to-10V meter, using an external 10V zener diode (connected to the top of the internal divider) as a reference voltage. The circuit's supply voltage must be at least 2V greater than the zener value.

*Figure 12.4* shows the IC's internal reference used to generate a variable voltage, enabling the meter F.S.D. value to be set

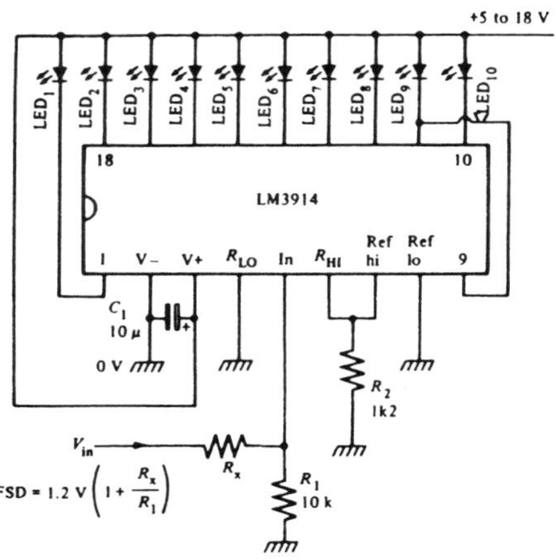


Figure 12.2. *1.2–1000V F.S.D. dot-mode voltmeter.*

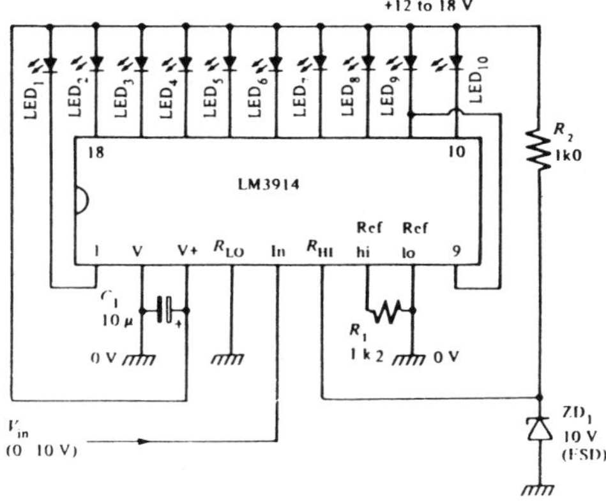


Figure 12.3. *10V F.S.D. meter using an external reference.*

anywhere in the range 1.2V to 10V. Here, the 1mA current (set by $R_1$) of the floating 1.2V internal reference flows to ground via $RV_1$, and the resulting $RV_1$ voltage raises the reference pins (7 and 8) above zero. If, for example, $RV_1$ is set to 2k4, pin-8 will be at 2.4V and pin-7 at 3.6V. $RV_1$ thus enables the pin-7 voltage (connected to the top of the internal divider) to be varied from 1.2V to about 10V, and sets the meter's F.S.D. value within these limits.

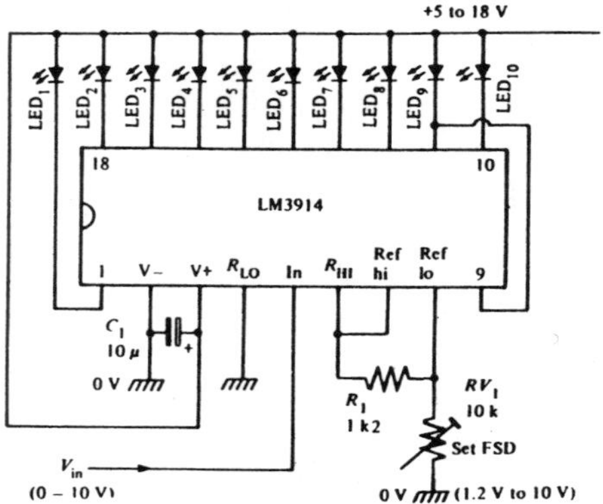


Figure 12.4. *An alternative variable-range (1.2–10V) dot-mode voltmeter.*

*Figure 12.5* shows an expanded-scale meter that spans 10 to 15V. $RV_2$ sets the LED current to 12mA but also applies a 0 to 1.2V reference to the low end of the internal divider; thus, if $RV_2$ sets 0.8V on pin-4 the basic meter will read voltages in the range 0.8 to 1.2V only. By fitting potential divider $R_x$–$RV_1$ to the circuit's input, this range can be increased to, say, 10 to 15V, or whatever range is desired.

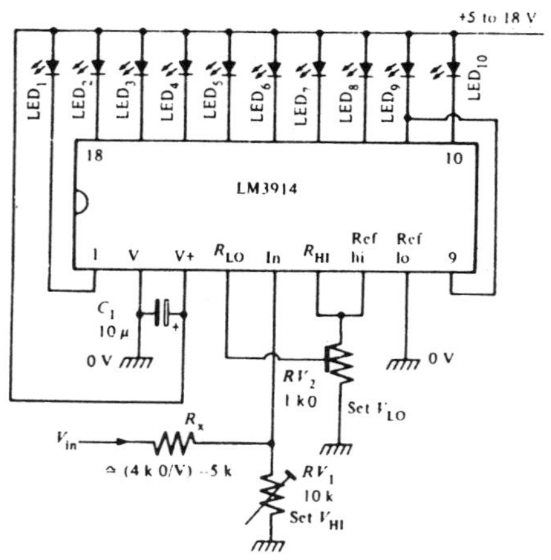


Figure 12.5. *Expanded-scale (10–15V) dot-mode voltmeter.*

## LM3914 bar-mode voltmeters

The dot-mode circuits of *Figures 12.2* to *12.5* can be made to give bar-mode operation by shorting pin-9 to pin-3, rather than to pin-11. When using bar mode, however, the IC's power rating must not be exceeded by allowing excessive output-terminal voltages to be developed when all ten LEDs are on. LEDs 'drop' about 2V when conducting, so one way around this problem is to power the LEDs from their own low-voltage (3 to 5V) supply, as shown in *Figure 12.6*. Another solution is to power the IC and the LEDs from the same supply, but to wire a current-limiting resistor in series with each LED, as in *Figure 12.7*, so that the IC's outputs saturate when the LEDs are on.

*Figure 12.8* shows yet another way of getting a bar display without excessive power dissipation. Here the LEDs are all wired in series, but with each one connected to an individual output of the IC, which is wired for dot-mode operation. Thus, when $LED_5$ is driven on it draws its current via LEDs 1 to 4, so all five LEDs are on but the total LED current is equal to that of a single LED. The LED supply to this curcuit must be greater than the sum of all LED volt drops, but within the voltage limits of the IC; a regulated 24V supply is thus needed.

*Figure 12.9* shows a modification of the above circuit, which enables it to be powered from an unregulated 12 to 18V supply. In this case the LEDs are split into two chains, and the transistors are used to switch the lower (LEDs 1 to 5) chain on when the

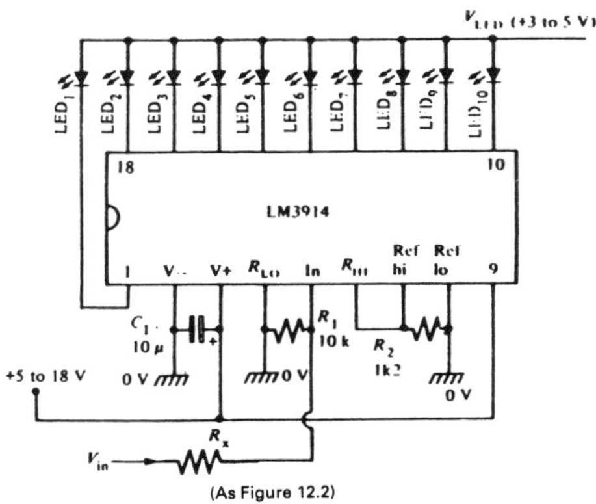


Figure 12.6. *Bar-display voltmeter with separate LED supply.*

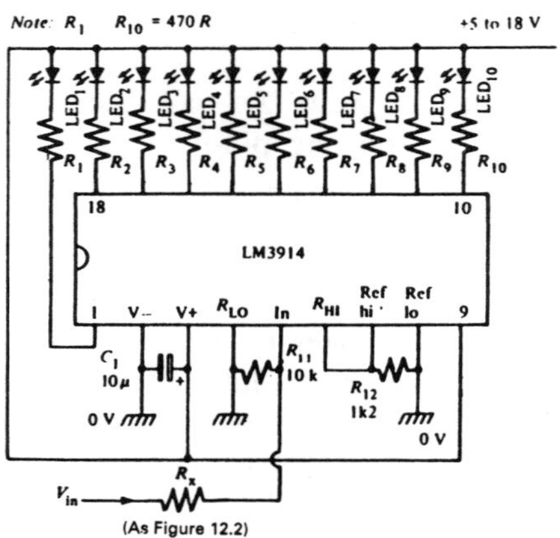


Figure 12.7. *Bar-display voltmeter with common LED supply.*

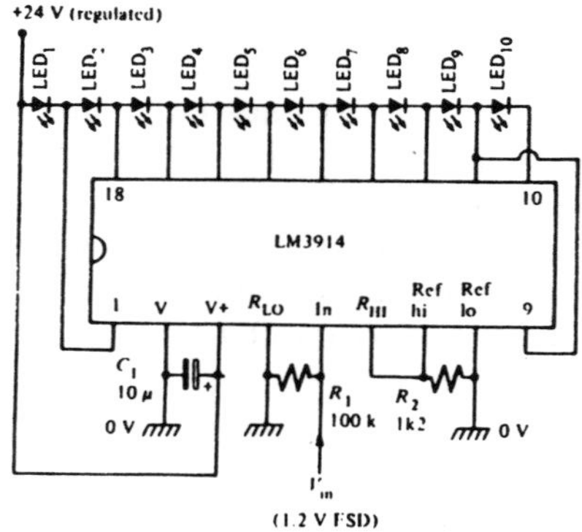


Figure 12.8. *Method of obtaining a bar display with dot-mode operation and minimal current consumption.*

upper chain is active; the maximum total LED current is equal to twice the current of a single LED.

## 20-LED voltmeters

To complete this look at bar-graph circuits, *Figures 12.10* and *12.11* show how pairs of LM3914s can be inter-connected to

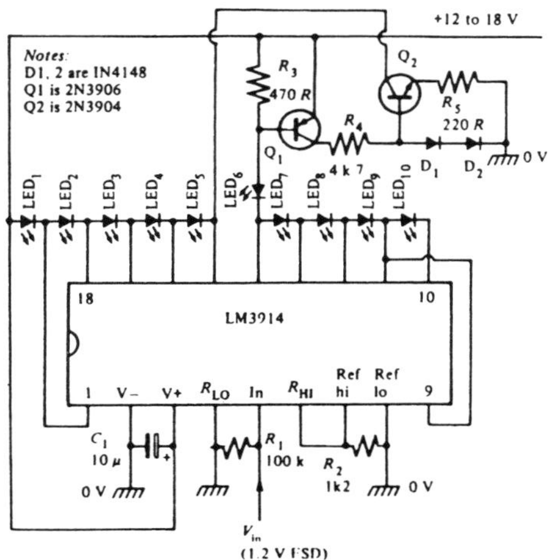


Figure 12.9. *Modification of the* Figure 12.8 *circuit, for operation from unregulated 12 to 18V supplies.*

make 20-LED 0 to 2.4V meters. Here, the input terminals of both ICs are wired in parallel, but $IC_1$ is configured to read 0 to 1.2V and $IC_2$ is configured to read 1.2 to 2.4V. In the latter case, the low end of $IC_2$'s potential divider is coupled to the 1.2V reference of $IC_1$ and the top end of the divider is taken to the top of the $IC_2$'s 1.2V reference, which is raised 1.2V above that of $IC_1$.

The *Figure 12.10* circuit is wired for dot-mode operation; note that pin-9 of $IC_1$ is wired to pin-1 of $IC_2$, pin-9 of $IC_2$ is wired to pin-11 of $IC_2$, and that a 22k resistor is wired in parallel with $LED_9$ of $IC_1$.

The *Figure 12.11* circuit is wired for bar-mode operation. The connections are similar to those above, except that pin-9 is taken to pin-3 of each IC, and a 470Ω current-limiting resistor is wired in series with each LED to reduce power dissipation of the ICs.

The voltage-ranging of these 20-LED meters can easily be altered by using techniques that have already been described. Note that although all of the designs shown are devoted to the LM3914 IC, the LM3915 and LM3916 ICs can in fact be directly substituted in most of these circuits, to give log and semi-log displays respectively. Also note that an over-range alarm can be fitted to an LM3914-type IC by wiring a transistor in series with the 'top'

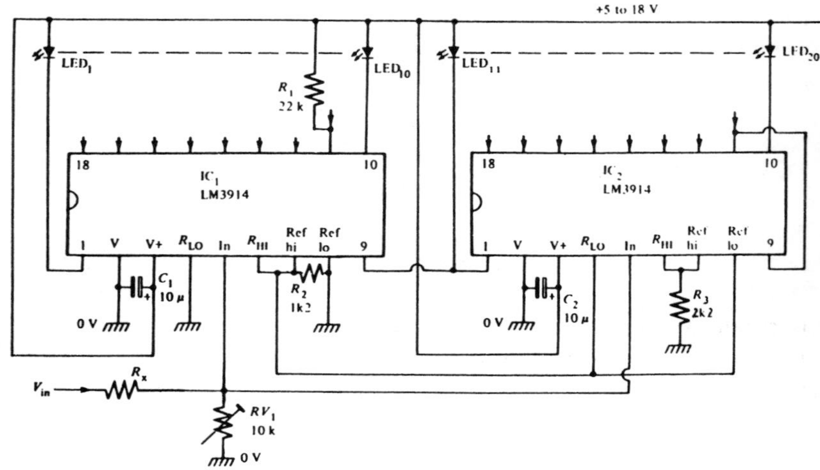


Figure 12.10. *Dot-mode 20-LED voltmeter (F.S.D. = 2.4V when* $R_x$ = 0).

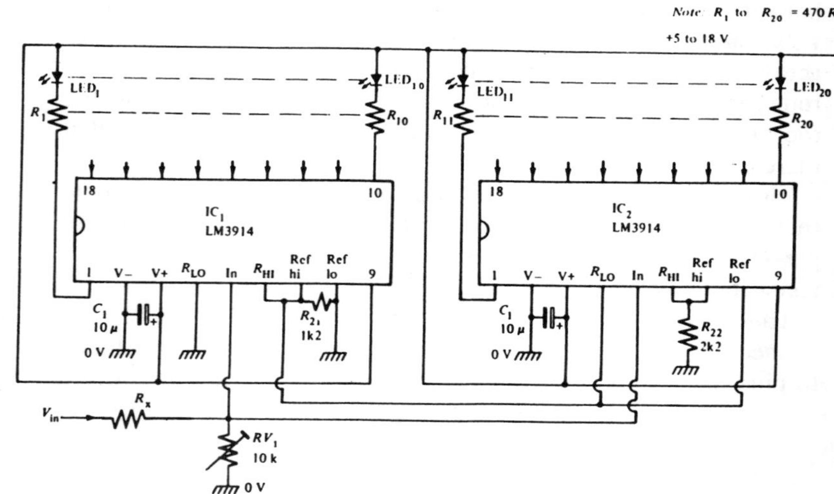


Figure 12.11. *Bar-mode 20-LED voltmeter (F.S.D. = 2.4V when* $R_x$ *= 0).*

LED to detect the full-scale state, and by wiring a transistor switch in series with the LED-brightness resistor to pulse the display on and off under the 'over-range' condition.

## Diode and transistor testers

The simplest instrument that can be used to check out any diode or LED is a basic 'function' tester; *Figure 12.12* shows a device of this type. Here, with $SW_1$ closed, the LED glows if a good diode is connected across the $D$ terminals in the polarity shown, and remains fully off if the diode is connected in reverse; the LED remains off under both conditions if the diode is open-circuit, or turns partially or fully on under both conditions if the diode is excessively leaky or forms a short-circuit. Similar results occur if an LED is substituted for a diode, except that it glows when connected in the 'diode' polarity. This circuit thus gives an easy check of diode/LED polarity and functioning, and (since the LED glows if a low resistance is placed across its $D$ terminals) can also be used as a 'continuity' tester.

*Figure 12.13* shows the basic circuit modified to give an audio-visual output, thus improving its value as a continuity tester. The action is such that $Q_1$ turns on and activates a low-power alarm-tone generator if a resistance of less than 8k0 is connected across the $D$ terminals; this tone generator can be a ready-built commercial unit or a home-built circuit.

*Figure 12.14* shows how the circuit can be further modified so that it also acts as a transistor function checker. Here, with a good transistor (one with a β or 'gain' value greater than 10) connected in place, and with $SW_3$ turned to the 'β' position, the

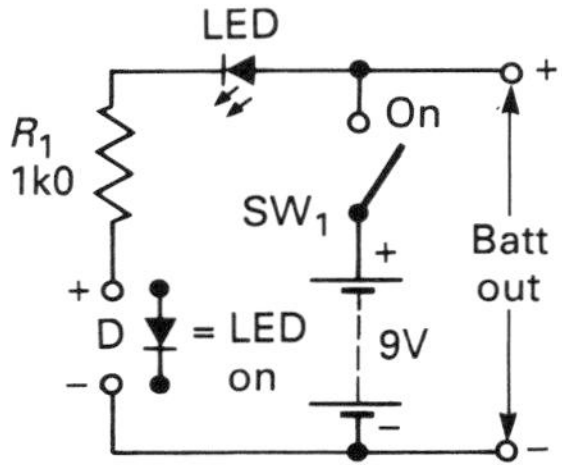


Figure 12.12. *Simple diode/LED function checker.*

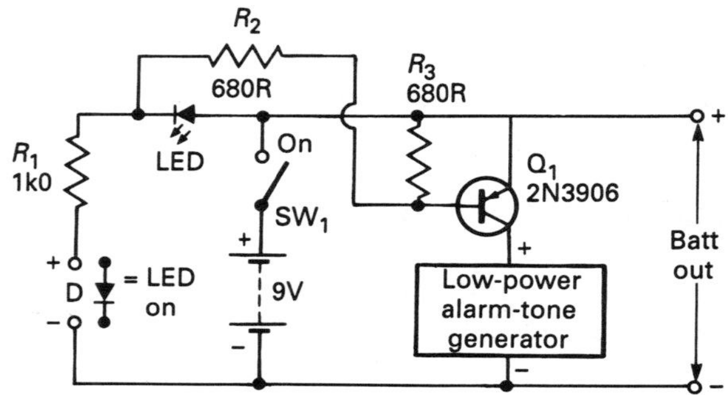


Figure 12.13. *Combined diode/LED function checker and continuity tester.*

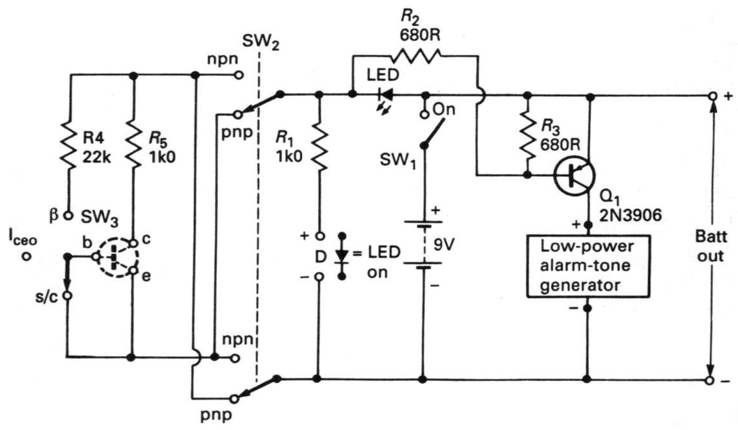


Figure 12.14. *Combined diode/LED/transistor function checker and continuity tester.*

LED and alarm activate when $SW_2$ is set to the appropriate 'npn' or 'pnp' position; the LED should turn fully off when $SW_3$ is set to the S/C and Iceo positions.

Finally, *Figure 12.15* shows how the *Figure 12.13* circuit can be combined with a proper transistor tester to form a truly useful and versatile instrument. The transistor tester can be used in conjunction with either an external or built-in 1mA moving-coil meter, and gives full-scale β ranges of 100, 250, and 1000, with a typical measurement accuracy (using a 9V battery supply) of ±10

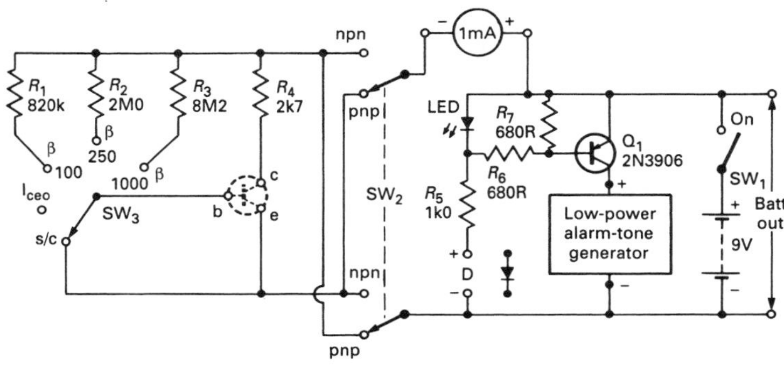


Figure 12.15. *Combined transistor tester, diode/LED checker, and continuity tester.*

per cent. This tester does not activate the LED or alarm-generator circuitry.

Note that the *Figures 12.12* to *12.15* circuits are each shown fitted with a battery ON/OFF switch and a pair of BATT OUT terminals; these enable each unit to function as a spare battery supply when $SW_1$ is closed, or to be powered from an external source (connected to the BATT OUT terminals) when $SW_1$ is open.

*Figures 12.16* and *12.17* show inexpensive but excellent low-power alarm-tone generator circuits that can be used with the

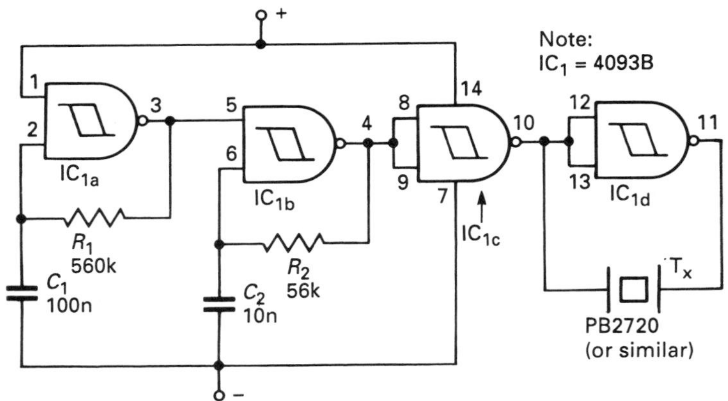


Figure 12.16. *Low-power pulsed-tone generator.*

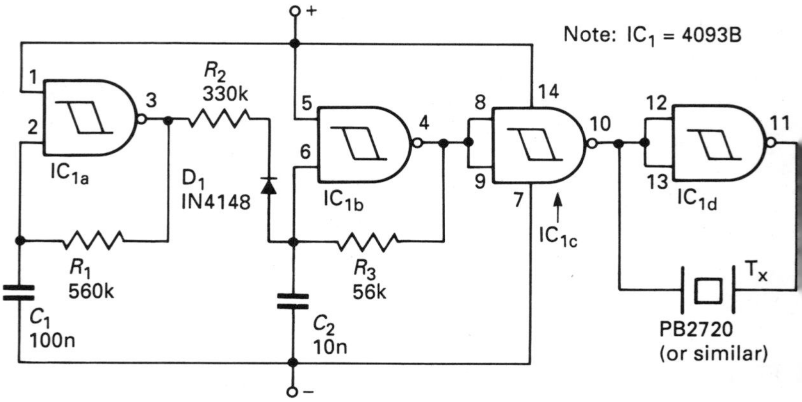

Figure 12.17. *Low-power warble-tone generator.*

*Figures 12.13* to *12.15* designs. Each of these uses a single 4093B CMOS IC and a Toko PB2720 or similar piezo-electric transducer to form a super-efficient sound generator that consumes a mere 1mA from a 9V supply. In each circuit, $IC_{1a}$ is a 20Hz square-wave generator, and $IC_{1b}$ is a 1.7kHz square-wave generator that drives the PB2720 in the super-efficient 'bridge' mode via $IC_{1c}$ and $IC_{1d}$. In the *Figure 12.16* design $IC_{1a}$ is used to gate $IC_{1b}$ on and off at a 20Hz rate, so this circuit generates a pulsed-tone output. In the *Figure 12.17* design $IC_{1a}$ is used to frequency-shift $IC_{1b}$ at a 20Hz rate, so this circuit generates a warble-tone output.

## TTL logic checkers

Another simple but useful 'LED' type of instrument is the TTL logic-state checker, and *Figures 12.19* and *12.20* show circuits of this type, which are powered from the TTL circuit's own 5V supply. By convention, a TTL logic-0 voltage state is defined as being less than 0.8V, and a logic-1 state is greater than 2.8V but less than 5.0V; voltages in the range 0.8 to 2.8V are regarded as 'ambiguous'. Relating these definitions to the *Figures 12.19* and *12.20* circuits, note the following points.

The simple but widely used *Figure 12.19* circuit relies on the fact that a red LED does not 'glow' significantly until at least 2V

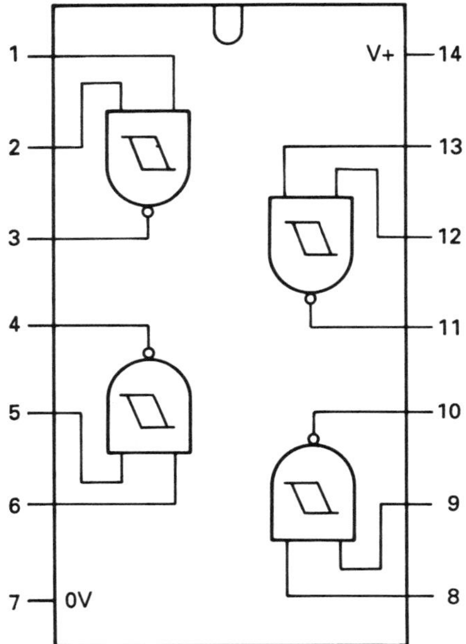


Figure 12.18. *4093B outline.*

are applied to it. Thus, when the circuit is in use, the LED is off if the probe is applied to a voltage greater than 3.0V, thus giving a reasonable indication of a logic-1 state, and turns on when the probe is connected to a value less than 3V, thus giving a highly probable (but possibly ambiguous) indication of a logic-0 state. This simple instrument has a TTL fan-in of about five.

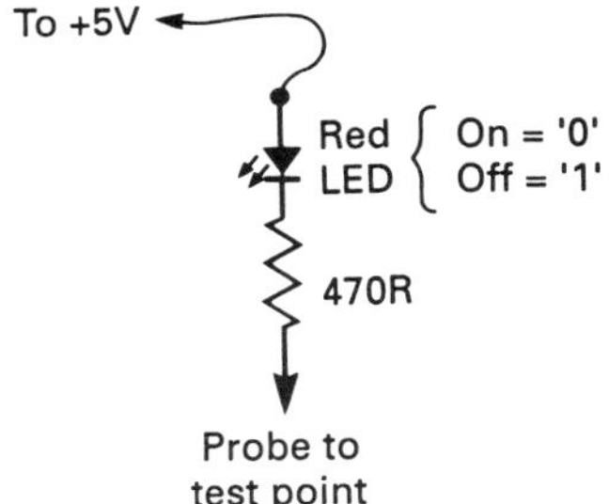


Figure 12.19. *Ultra-simple TTL logic checker.*

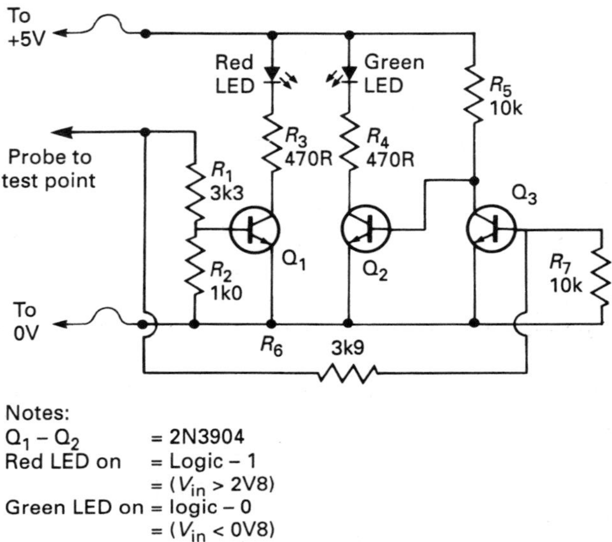


Figure 12.20. *Good-quality TTL logic checker.*

The *Figure 12.20* circuit uses two LED indicators and gives an unambiguous indication of TTL logic state. If the probe input voltage is less than 0V8, $Q_3$ (which is driven via the $R_6-R_7$ divider) is cut off, enabling $Q_2$ to turn on via $R_5$; the green LED turns on under this condition, indicating a logic-0 state. If the probe input is greater than 0V8 but less than 2V8, $Q_3$ is driven on and disables $Q_2$, and $Q_1$ is also off; both LEDs are off under this condition, indicating an 'ambiguous' state. Finally, if the input is greater than 2V8, $Q_1$ (which is driven via the $R_1-R_2$ divider) is driven on, but $Q_2$ remains disabled via $Q_3$; the red LED turns on under this condition, indicating a logic-1 state. This excellent logic checker has a very low TTL fan-in value.

## Go/no-go testers

Designers of production-line test equipment often have to devise circuits that help an unskilled operator decide whether or not an item is within design limits; such a circuit is known as a **go/no-go** tester. If the parameters being tested take (or can be converted into) the form of a d.c. voltage or current, or a simple resistance, the go/no-go tester may be based on one or other of the designs shown in *Figures 12.21* to *12.32*.

*Figures 12.21* and *12.22* show, in basic form, two simple types of voltage-testing go/no-go circuits. These use op-amps as voltage comparators, and their outputs switch from one saturated state to the other when one input voltage goes above or below the level of the other input voltage. They use 3140 CMOS op-amps, which can accept input voltages down to the negative rail value, and have an output that can swing to within 2V of the positive rail and to within a few millivolts of the negative supply rail value.

In *Figure 12.21* a fixed reference voltage ($V_{ref}$) is generated via $R_2$–$ZD_1$ and fed to the op-amp's non-inverting input terminal, and 'test' voltage $V_{in}$ is fed to its inverting input via current-limiter $R_1$. When $V_{in}$ is below $V_{ref}$ the op-amp output goes high (to positive saturation), and when $V_{in}$ is above $V_{ref}$ the output goes low (to negative saturation), as shown. The 3140 has an open-loop d.c. voltage gain of about 100dB, so the circuit's output can be shifted from the high to the low state (or vice versa) by shifting the input voltage a mere 100μV or so above or below the fixed reference voltage value. This circuit thus acts as a precision 'under-voltage' switch, in which the op-amp output goes high when $V_{in}$ falls below $V_{ref}$. Its action can be reversed, so that it acts as a precision 'over-voltage' switch, in which the output goes high when $V_{in}$ exceeds $V_{ref}$, by simply transposing the op-amp's input connections, as shown in *Figure 12.22*.

In practice, the $V_{ref}$ and the direct $V_{in}$ values of these two circuits can have have any value from 0V up to within 2V of the

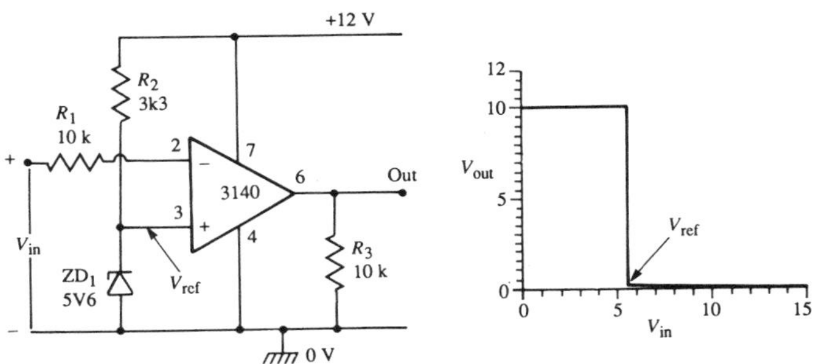


Figure 12.21. *Basic comparator-type go/no-go under-voltage switch.*

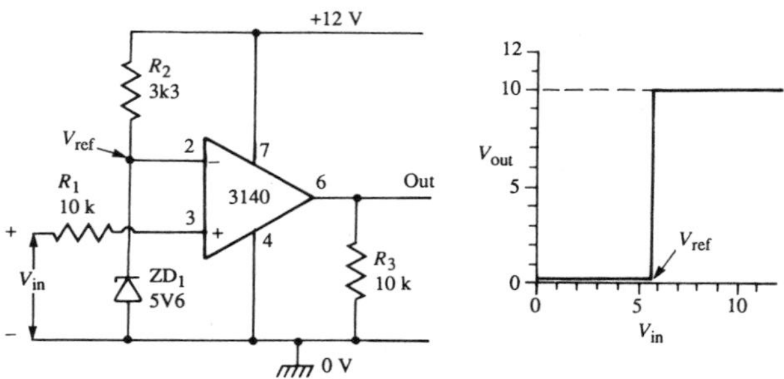


Figure 12.22. *Basic comparator-type* ***go/no-go*** *over-voltage switch.*

positive supply-rail value. Either circuit can thus be made to 'switch' at any desired value between these limits by interposing a pre-set potentiometer between a fixed voltage reference source and the input pin of the op-amp; the circuits can be made to 'switch' at $V_{in}$ values above the basic limit by feeding $V_{in}$ to the op-amp's input via a simple potential divider.

These basic voltage comparator circuits give a simple 'switching' action in which the op-amp is driven into the linear (non-saturated) mode when the input voltage is within a few tens of microvolts of $V_{ref}$; the op-amp output generates lots of spurious noise under this condition. In some applications this noise may be unacceptable, in which case the problem can be overcome by modifying the circuits so that a fraction of the op-amp's output voltage is fed back to the non-inverting input terminal, to give a regenerative switching action in which a degree of hysteresis or 'backlash' is imposed on the voltage switching levels.

*Figures 12.23* to *12.26* show how the above-mentioned points can be put to practical use to make various types of 'special' voltage comparator circuits; many other variations are possible.

*Figures 12.23* and *12.24* show the basic comparator circuits modified to give variable voltage switching, using $RV_1$ to set the $V_{ref}$ 'switching' voltage at a value in the range 0 to 5V6, and to give regenerative ('noiseless') switching by feeding part of the op-amp output back to the non-inverting terminal via $R_3$; note in the *Figure 12.24* design that the input is shunted via $R_5$, to ensure controlled hysteresis.

*Figures 12.25* and *12.26* show examples of circuits modified to give high-value variable-voltage (0 to 130V) switching, using a

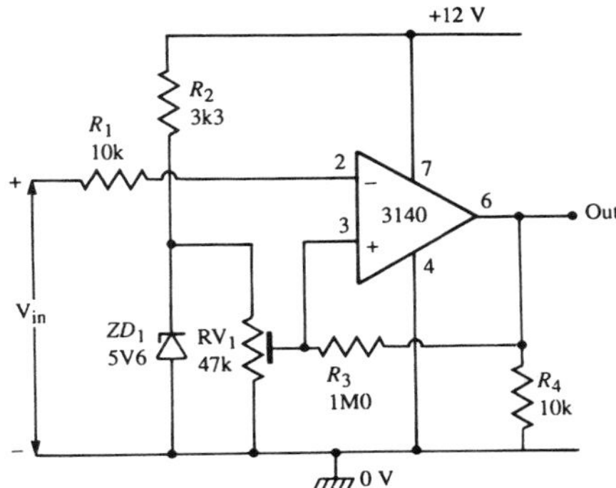


Figure 12.23. *Variable under-voltage switch with regenerative feedback.*

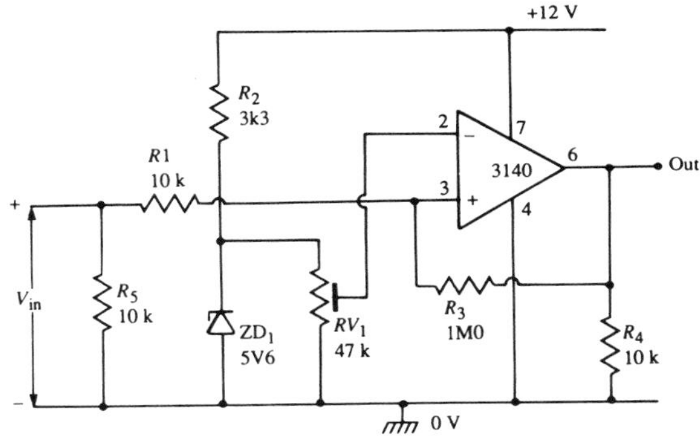


Figure 12.24. *Varible over-voltage switch with regenerative feedback.*

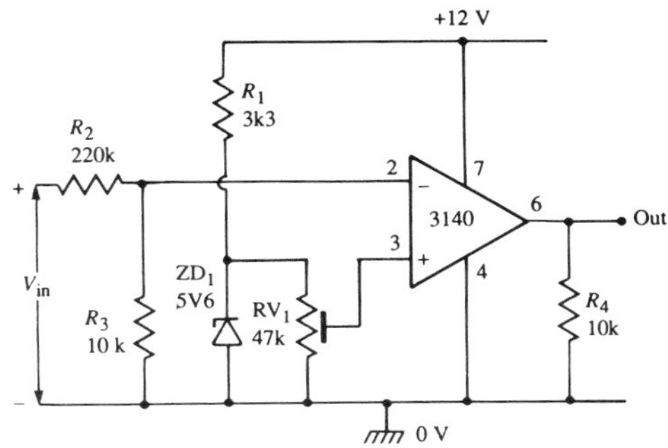


Figure 12.25. *High-value (0–130V) under-voltage switch.*

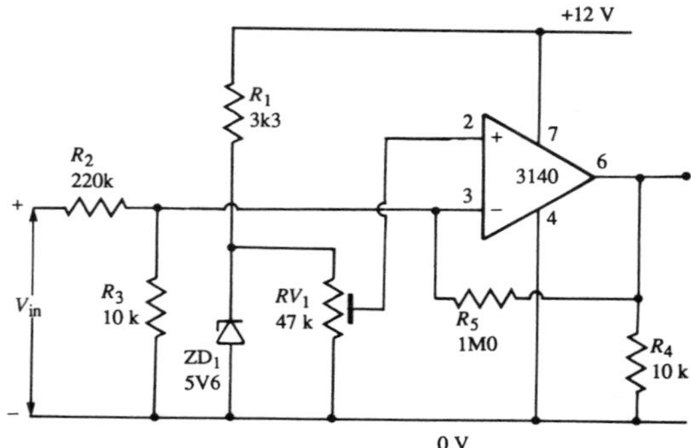


Figure 12.26. *High-value (0–130V) regenerative over-voltage switch.*

potential divider ($R_2$–$R_3$) interposed between $V_{in}$ and the input of the op-amp; the *Figure 12.25* circuit gives non-regenerative switching; the *Figure 12.26* design gives regenerative switching.

## Window comparators

The go/no-go voltage comparator circuits described so far give an output transition when their inputs go above or below a single reference voltage value. It is a fairly simple matter to interconnect a pair of voltage comparators so that an output transition occurs when the inputs fall between, or go outside of, a *pair* of reference voltage levels. *Figure 12.27* shows the basic circuit configuration, which is generally known as a window comparator or discriminator.

The action of the *Figure 12.27* circuit is such that the output of the upper op-amp goes high when $V_{in}$ exceeds the 6V $V_U$ 'upper limit' reference value, and the output of the lower op-amp goes high when $V_{in}$ falls below the 4V $V_L$ 'lower limit' reference value. The outputs of the two op-amps are fed to $R_4$ via diode OR gate $D_1$–$D_2$, so the final output is low when $V_{in}$ is within the limits set by $V_U$ and $V_L$, but goes high whenever the input goes beyond these limits.

The action of the *Figure 12.27* circuit can be reversed, so that its output goes high only when the input voltage is within the 'window' limits, by taking the output signal via a simple inverter stage. Alternatively, the required action can be obtained by trans-

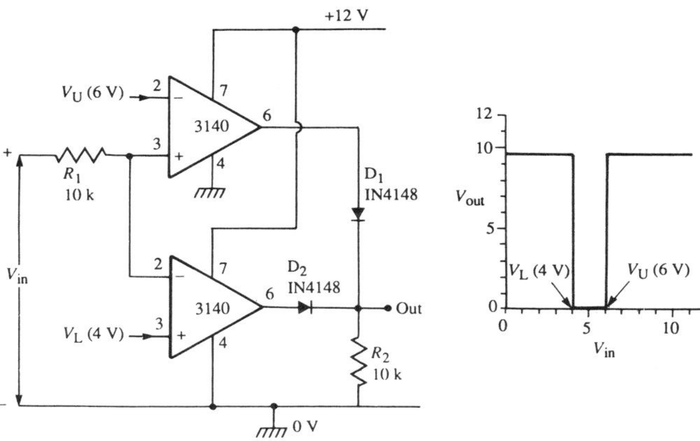


Figure 12.27. *The output of this* **go/no-go** *tester goes high if* $V_{in}$ *goes above* $V_U$ *or below* $V_L$.

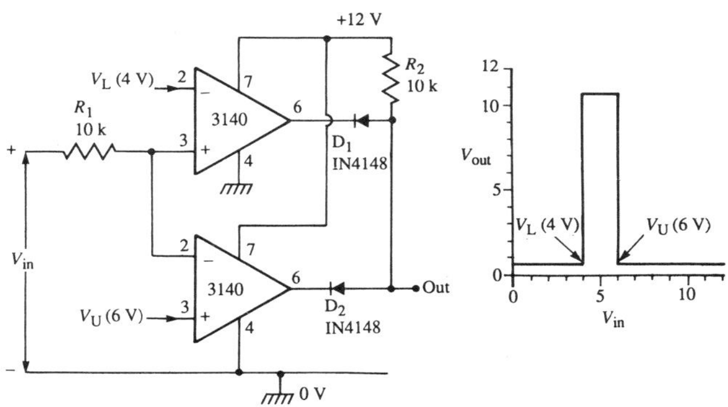


Figure 12.28. *The output of this* **go/no-go** *tester goes high if* $V_{in}$ *falls within the* $V_U$ *and* $V_L$ *limits.*

posing the two reference voltages and taking the output via a diode AND gate, as shown in *Figure 12.28*.

## Current- and resistance-activated circuits

Voltage and window comparators can be activated via any parameter that can be turned into an analogue voltage, and thus can easily be adapted to be activated via variations in current levels or resistance values. *Figures 12.29* to *12.32* show some examples of practical circuits of these types.

*Figure 12.29* shows a comparator used as an over-current switch that gives a high output when the load current exceeds a value pre-set via $RV_1$; the value of $R_x$ is chosen so that it develops about 100mV at the required trip current level. Thus, a fixed half-supply reference voltage is fed to pin-3 of the op-amp via $R_3-R_4$ and a similar but current-dependent voltage is fed to pin-2 via $R_x-R_1-RV_1-R_2$; in effect, these two sets of components are configured as a Wheatstone bridge, with one side feeding pin-3 and the other side feeding pin-2, and the op-amp is used as a bridge-balance detector. Consequently, the trip points of the circuit are not significantly influenced by supply-voltage variations but are highly sensitive to load current variations. The circuit's action can be reversed, so that it acts as an under-current switch by simply transposing the op-amp's input connections.

*Figures 12.30* to *12.32* show various ways of using comparator circuits as resistance-activated switches. All of these circuits use $R_x$ and $R_{ref}$ as two of the arms of a Wheatstone bridge and use the op-amp as a simple bridge-balance detector, so that the switching point of each circuit is independent of supply-line variations. In all cases, $R_{ref}$ should equal the designed 'nominal' value or $R_x$, which ideally should be within the range 500R to 5M0. In the *Figure 12.30* circuit the effective value of $R_{ref}$ is variable by ±5 per cent via $RV_1$, and the op-amp output goes high and energizes the output load when $R_x$ exceeds $R_{ref}$; the

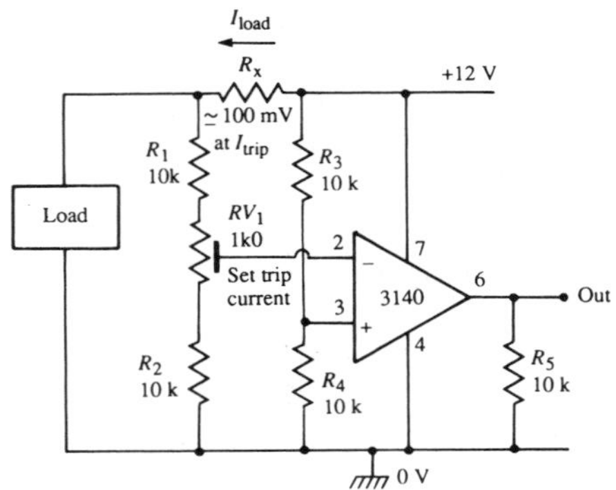


Figure 12.29. *The output of this* ***go/no-go*** *tester goes high if* $I_{LOAD}$ *exceeds a pre-set value.*

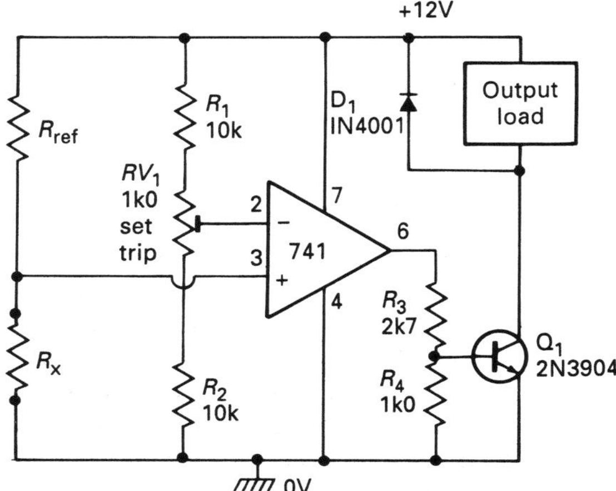


Figure 12.30. *The output of this tester turn on if* $R_x$ *exceeds* $R_{ref}$.

circuit action can be reversed, so that the output goes high when $R_x$ is below $R_{ref}$ by simply transposing the $R_x$ and $R_{ref}$ positions. The output load can take the form of a LED or an audible alarm or a relay, etc.; $D_1$ is used to protect $Q_1$ against back-e.m.f. damage if a highly inductive load (such as a relay) is used.

*Figure 12.31* shows two of the above types of circuit interconnected so that the output of $IC_1$ goes high and activates load

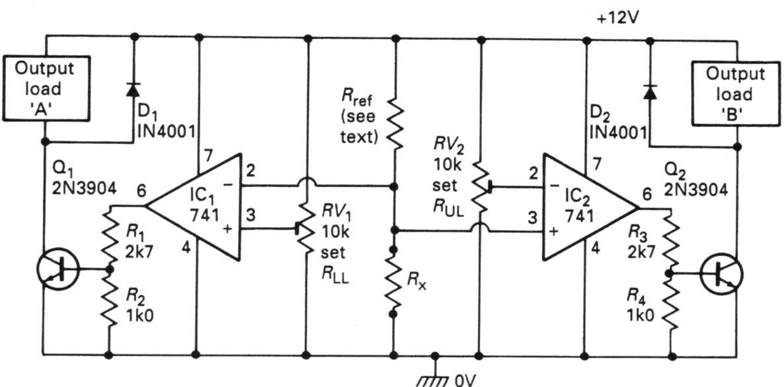


Figure 12.31. *Out-of-limits resistance tester with independent 'high' and 'low' outputs.*

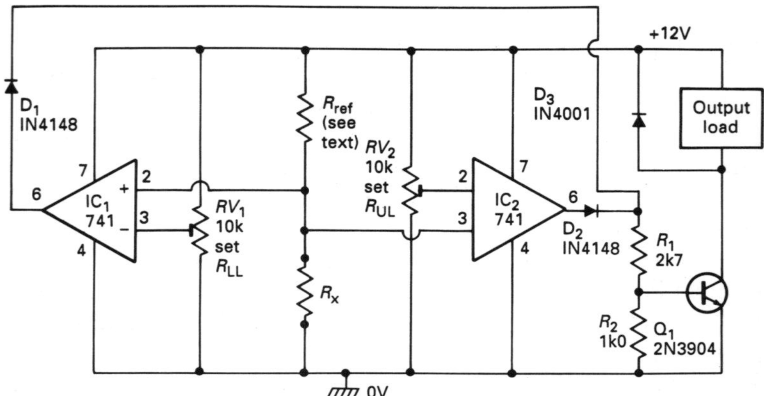


Figure 12.32. *Out-of-limits resistance tester with single output.*

*A* if $R_x$ is less than a lower-limit ($R_U$) value set by $RV_1$, and the output of $IC_2$ goes high and activates load *B* if $R_x$ is greater than an upper-limit ($R_{UL}$) value set by $RV_2$. Finally, *Figure 12.32* shows this circuit modified so that a single output load is activated (via diode OR-gate $D_1$–$D_2$) if the $R_x$ value goes beyond the $R_{LL}$ and $R_{UL}$ limits set via $RV_1$ and $RV_2$.

## Instrument probes

A 'probe' can be loosely defined as a device that enables a piece of test gear to make electrical contact with a desired point in a circuit that is being tested, for the purpose of either injecting a signal into that point or inspecting the signals that exist at that point. *Figures 12.33* to *12.40* show examples of the most widely used types of probe.

The simplest way of connecting an instrument such as a multimeter to a test point is via a pair of flexible leads or *test prods*, as shown in *Figure 12.33*. These are useful mainly in d.c. and low-frequency, low-impedance applications; in high-impedance applications they tend to pick up lots of stray low-frequency (power-line) radiation, and in all applications they are prone (because they form linear inductors) to pick up lots of RF radiation, even if their ends are shorted together.

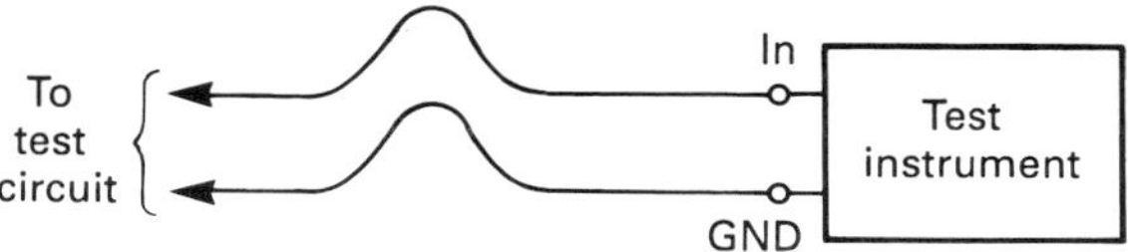


Figure 12.33. *An instrument using test* prods.

An obvious way to overcome the above problems is to replace the two individual leads with a suitable length of shielded cable, as shown in *Figure 12.34*, with the inner cable acting as the input probe and the shield acting as the common or ground connection. This type of probe is widely used, and serves (for example) as a unity-gain (×1) 'scope probe, and usually has a length of about 1.5m. A big drawback with this type of probe is that it has a fairly high input capacitance; a typical value is 55pF, and this presents a reactance of only 2k9 at 1MHz.

One way around *this* particular snag is to wire a buffer resistor in series with the probe's input line, as in the '×10' 'scope probe circuit of *Figure 12.35*. Here, $R_1$ and the 'scope's input resistance ($R_2$) form a ×10 resistive attenuator; the lower leg ($R_2$) of this is shunted by $C_2$ (the 'scope's input capacitance) and $C_c$ (the shielded cable's capacitance); these total 80pF, so $R_1$ must be shunted by a capacitance of one-ninth of this value (8.9pF) to give wide-band frequency compensation; $C_1$ is used for this purpose. In use, $C_1$'s value is set on test by feeding a good 1kHz square wave to the 'scope via the probe and then trimming $C_1$ to give the correct 'square' waveform as shown in the diagram. Typically, a probe of this type has an actual input impedance of about 11pF, and this presents a reactance of about 14k5 at 1MHz.

*Figure 12.36* shows a high-voltage probe for use with a 100µA moving-coil meter, which has a basic sensitivity of 10k/V. The

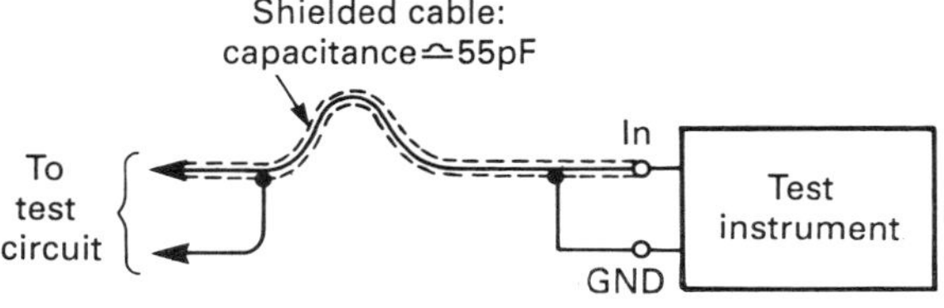


Figure 12.34. *An instrument using a direct (unity-gain) shielded* probe.

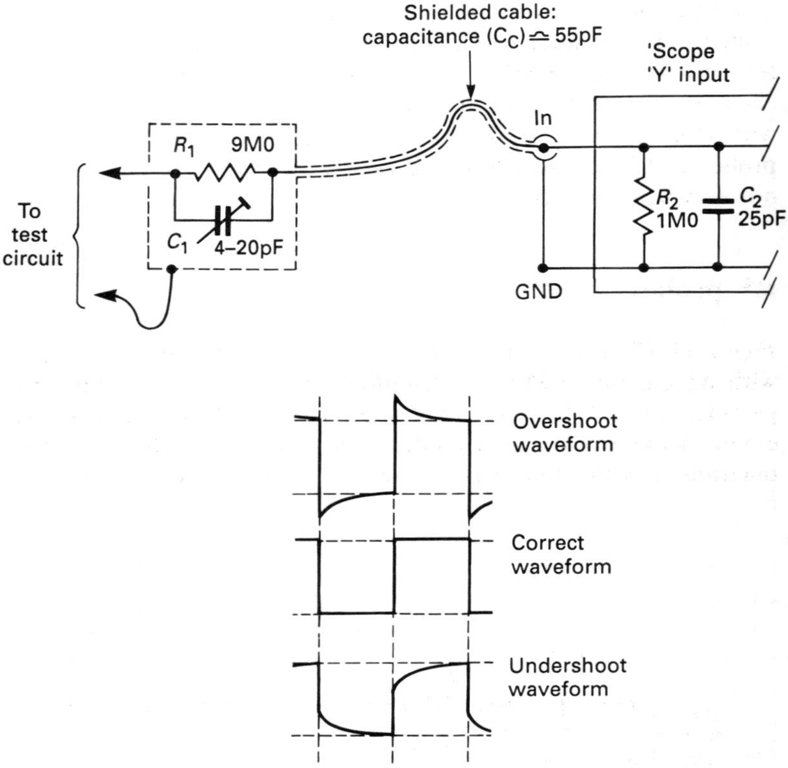

Shielded cable:
capacitance ($C_C$) ≏ 55pF
'Scope
'Y' input
In
$R_1$ 9M0
To
test
circuit
$C_1$ 4–20pF
$R_2$
1M0
$C_2$
25pF
GND
Overshoot
waveform
Correct
waveform
Undershoot
waveform


Figure 12.35. *Typical ×10 'scope probe, plus setting-up 'square' waveforms.*

10 × 10 MΩ, 1/2-watt high-voltage
resistors, series wired
To
test
circuit
In
100μA
moving-coil
meter
100 megohms
GND


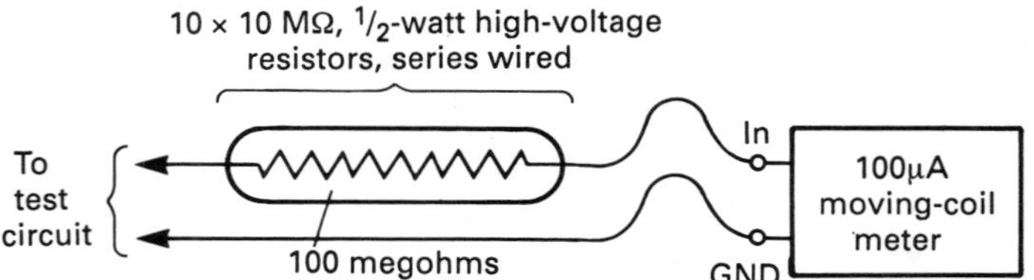

Figure 12.36. *High-voltage probe giving a 10kV F.S.D. reading on a 100μA D.C. meter.*

meter thus needs a total series probe resistance of 100MΩ to give it an F.S.D. sensitivity of 10kV. If this resistance is made up of ten series-wired 10MΩ resistors, 1kV will be generated across each resistor at F.S.D.; they must thus be high-voltage types, with (for safety reasons) voltage ratings of at least 2kV. The probe must be constructed with great care, to ensure that it does not endanger the operator when in use.

## RF probes

*Figure 12.37* shows an RF-to-d.c. converter probe suitable for use with an electronic D.C. volt/millivolt meter with an input impedance of 10MΩ. $C_1$ and $D_1$ of this widely misunderstood circuit actually work as a diode 'clamp' which, as shown in the diagram, ties the low part of the $C_1$–$D_1$ junction waveform to

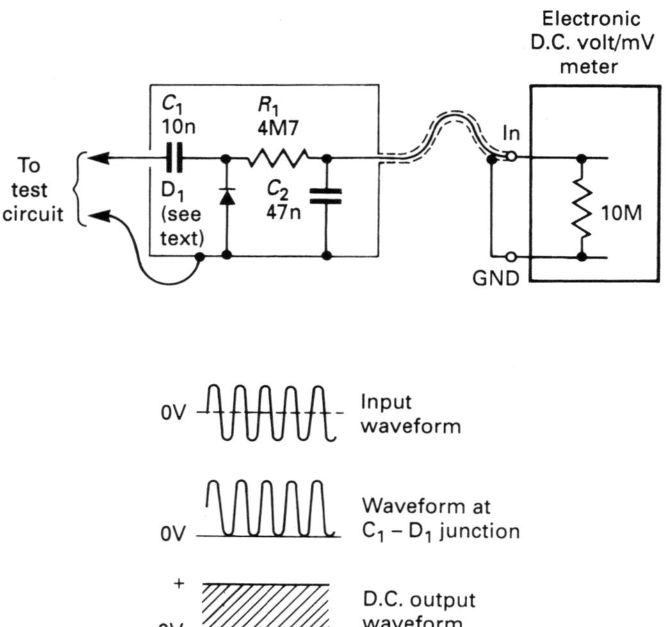


Figure 12.37. *RF probe: gives a signal strength reading on a high-impedance (10MΩ) d.c. voltmeter.*

near-zero volts; the resulting waveform thus has a positive mean d.c. value directly proportional to the RF signal's a.c. value. $R_1$–$C_2$ convert the resulting signal to smooth d.c., and $R_1$ and the 10MΩ input impedance of the electronic voltmeter form a potential divider that gives form-factor correction and (ideally) makes this voltage equal to the r.m.s. value of a sine-wave input signal, assuming that the signal amplitude is greater than a couple of volts. $D_1$ must be a sensitive germanium signal diode, such as an IN34A or OA91, etc., in which case the probe may have a useful bandwidth that extends well above 100MHz, and gives a useful performance as a 'relative value' indicator at signal levels down to about 200mV. The circuit can be made to give a negative (rather than positive) d.c. output by simply reversing the polarity of $D_1$.

The *Figure 12.38* circuit is a simple modification of the above type of probe, with $R_1$ replaced with a sensitive (IN34A or OA91, etc.) germanium diode, so that $C_2$ charges to the peak value of the $C_1$–$D_1$ junction signal; this probe thus gives a positive d.c. output voltage proportional to the peak-to-peak value of the RF input signal. Note that the electronic voltmeter's input resistance acts as a discharge path for $C_2$, and influences the probe's ability to follow rapid variation in input signal levels.

*Figure 12.39* shows a simple AM 'demodulator' type of RF probe, which has an input impedance of about 10k. The probe's output consists of the demodulated AM signal superimposed on a d.c. component proportional to the amplitude of the RF input carrier wave. If desired, this d.c. component can be removed by taking the output via a blocking capacitor. This type of probe is useful in 'signal tracer' applications.

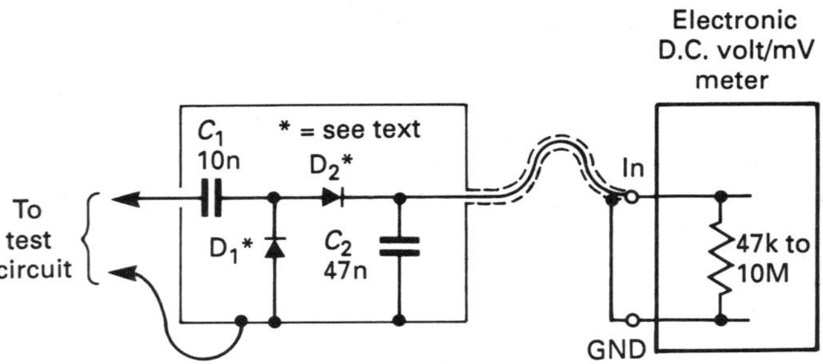


Figure 12.38. *RF peak-to-peak voltage-detecting probe.*

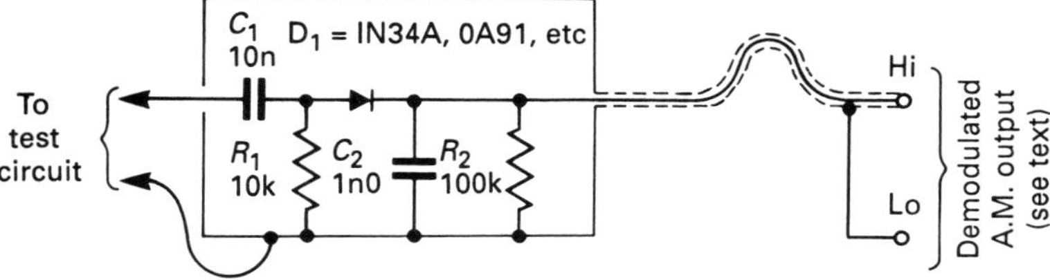


Figure 12.39. *AM demodulator probe.*

Finally, *Figure 12.40* shows a useful type of 'trouble-shooting' probe, a combined signal injector and AF/RF signal tracer. When $SW_1$ is set to *inject* position '1', $Q_1$ and $Q_2$ form an astable multivibrator that feeds a 1kHz square wave to the probe tip via $C_1-R_1$; this waveform is rich in harmonics, so if injected into any AF or RF stage of an AM radio will produce an audible tone on the radio's loadspeaker, unless one of the radio's stages is faulty; by choosing a suitable injection point, the position of a faulty stage can be found. When $SW_1$ is switched to *trace* position 2, the circuit is configured as a pair of cascaded common-emitter amplifiers, with the probe input coupled to the $Q_1$ base, and the $Q_2$ output feeding into a magnetic earpiece or headset; any weak AF signals fed to the probe are amplified and thus made audible, and any amplitude-modulated RF signals fed to the probe are demodulated by the non-linear action of $Q_1$ and the resulting AF

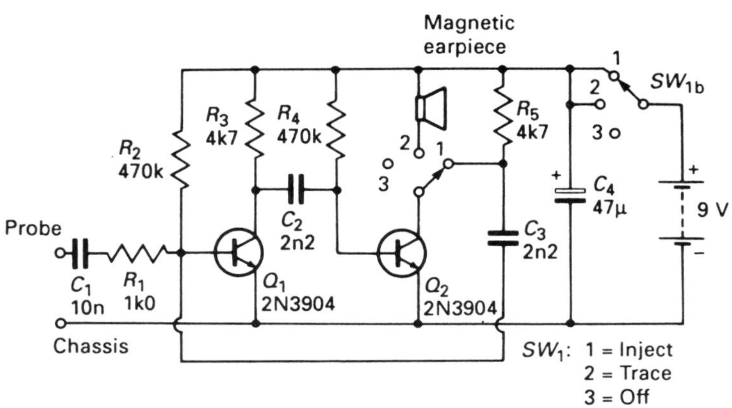


Figure 12.40. *Trouble-shooters 'signal injector-tracer' probe.*

signals made audible; by connecting the probe to suitable points in a circuit, the 'tracer' can thus be used to trouble-shoot a faulty radio, etc.

## RF sniffers and tell-tales

RF sniffers and tell-tales are close relatives of the ordinary probe, but enable the user to inspect an RF signal by probing into its radiated field, rather than by making direct contact with the signal source.

An RF sniffer is an untuned gadget that simply detects and indicates the presence of any reasonably powerful RF field, but conveys no special information as to its strength or frequency. *Figure 12.41* shows a simple RF sniffer with a metered output; it is not a very sensitive design and needs an input (across $L_1$) of a few hundred millivolts to give a reasonable reading, but operates to above 100MHz.

*Figure 12.42* shows a more sensitive sniffer circuit that gives an audio-visual output and can detect RF inputs as low as 40mV. In this design $D_2$ ensures that $Q_1$'s base–emitter junction is slightly forward biased when zero input is applied; $Q_1$ conducts and the LED glows dimly under this condition. Any RF signals picked up by $L_1$ are detected–demodulated via $D_1$ and RF-filtered by $C_1$–$R_1$, and further increase both $Q_1$'s forward bias and the LED's brightness level; if the RF input signal is amplitude modulated an

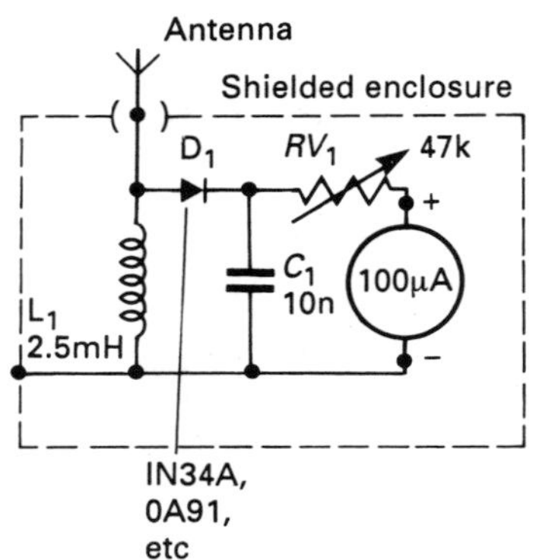


Figure 12.41. *RF sniffer, with metered output.*

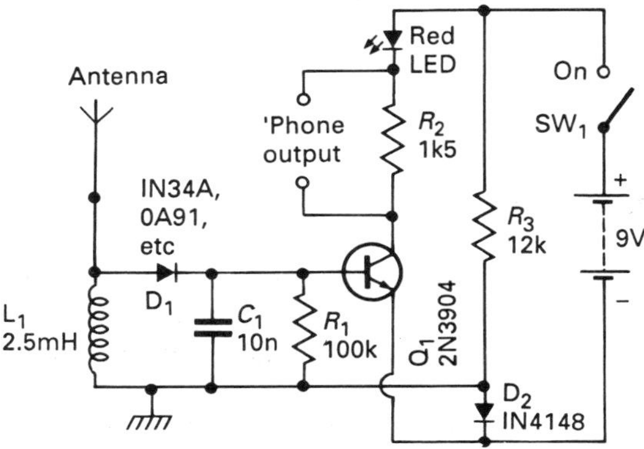


Figure 12.42. *RF sniffer with audio-visual output.*

amplified version of its modulation signal appears across $R_2$ and can be heard on a pair of 'phones connected across the circuit's output terminals. This circuit gives a useful performance to above 100MHz.

*Figure 12.43* shows a modified version of the above design. It uses the slightly forward-biased base–emitter junction of $Q_1$ to carry out the detector–demodulator action, and $R_1$–$C_1$ to give

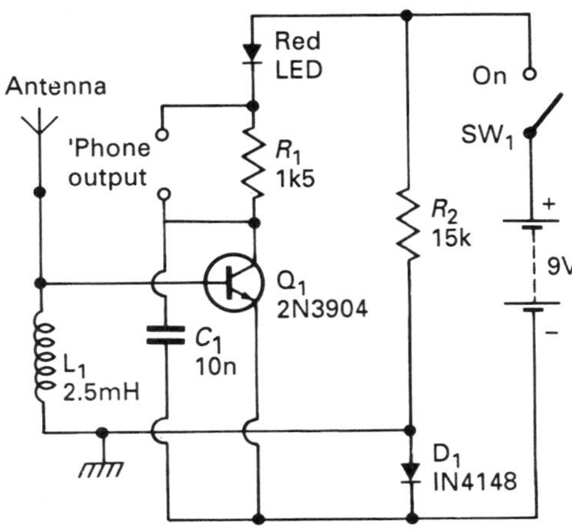


Figure 12.43. *RF sniffer with improved sensitivity.*

the RF-filtering action. This circuit can detect input signal levels down to about 20mV, but its useful bandwidth is limited to about 50MHz; because of its relatively high sensitivity, it will usually pick up a wide-band splatter of broadcast radio signals if fitted with a metre or so of antenna.

An RF 'tell-tale' is an instrument that detects the presence of an RF field and presents the user with useful information about it. The two best-known versions of such an instrument are the *field strength meter*, which gives the user a reading of the *relative* strength of the signal (for tuning purposes, etc.), and the *wave-meter*, which tells the user the frequency of the detected RF signal. These are, in effect, tuned versions of the basic sniffer circuit of *Figure 12.41*, and *Figure 12.44* shows a couple of circuits that are typical of the genre.

The $L_1$ (or $T_1$) and $C_1$ values of the *Figure 12.44* circuits must be chosen to suit the frequency-band of interest; often, the tuning coil is externally mounted and used as an antenna. A field-strength meter is usually designed to operate over only a narrow spread of frequencies, and $C_1$ may be a trimmer capacitor. A wavemeter is usually designed to operate over a very wide frequency band; it may use a set of plug-in coils, and its tuning coil is invariably fitted with a calibrated tuning scale that gives a direct reading of the tuned frequency. An ordinary pocket radio with a suitably calibrated scale can be directly used as a sensitive wavemeter.

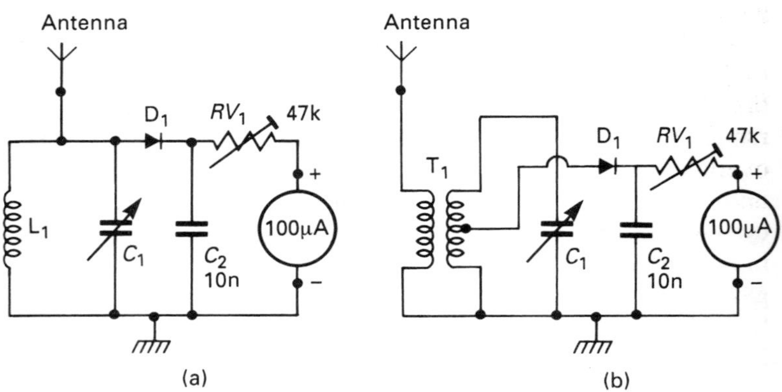


Figure 12.44. *Typical wavemeter/field-strength-meter circuits.*

## Special analogue meter circuits

Moving-coil 'analogue' meters have certain advantages over digital types, particularly in indicating varying parameter values, and have far better definition than even the very best 'bar-graph' types of meter. These factors make them attractive for use in a number of 'special' applications, such as linear-scaled analogue frequency or capacitance meters, etc. *Figures 12.45* and *12.46* show practical circuits of these two particular types; these may be built as either self-contained instruments or as add-on units for use with an external 100μA meter or multi-meter.

The 8-range frequency meter circuit of *Figure 12.45* spans 10Hz to 250kHz, has an input impedance of 1M0, needs an input signal amplitude of 100mV r.m.s. or greater, and consumes a quiescent current of less than 1mA (note that $IC_3$ is a 7555, which is a CMOS version of the popular 555 'timer' IC). The circuit's input signals are buffered and amplified by $Q_1-Q_2$, converted into square waves via $IC_{1a}$, and then fed (either directly or via decade-divider stages $IC_{2a}$ and $IC_{2b}$) to $C_3-R_7-IC_{1b}$, which convert each input cycle into a negative-going 5μs pulse that triggers monostable pulse generator $IC_3$. The width of each $IC_3$ output pulse is regulated by the $R_8-R_9-C_4-C_5$ set of components, and the pulse amplitude is precision-regulated (at about 1.8V peak) by the red LED; these precision pulses are fed to the meter via $RV_1$ or $RV_2$; the meter's natural action is such that it integrates the output pulses and gives a deflection that is directly proportional to the pulse repitition frequency; the meter thus gives a direct reading of input frequency.

The *Figure 12.45* circuit is carefully designed so that, on each range, the $IC_3$ output pulse width is approximately one-third of the F.S.D. 'frequency' period (i.e. 330μs on the 1kHz [1ms] range, etc.). This technique protects the meter against excessive overloading and protects the instrument against false reading under over-range conditions (in which $IC_3$ is driven into a skip-cycling mode). To initially set up this circuit, connect a suitable input signal, set $SW_1$ to range 2 and $SW_2$ to '×1', and trim $RV_1$ to gave an F.S.D. reading of 1kHz; now switch $SW_2$ to '×2.5' (or '×3' if preferred) and trim $RV_2$ to give an F.S.D. reading of 2.5kHz (or 3kHz). The setting-up is then complete.

The linear-scaled capacitance meter circuit of *Figure 12.46* has ten ranges, spanning 100pF to 2.5μF F.S.D., and on its most

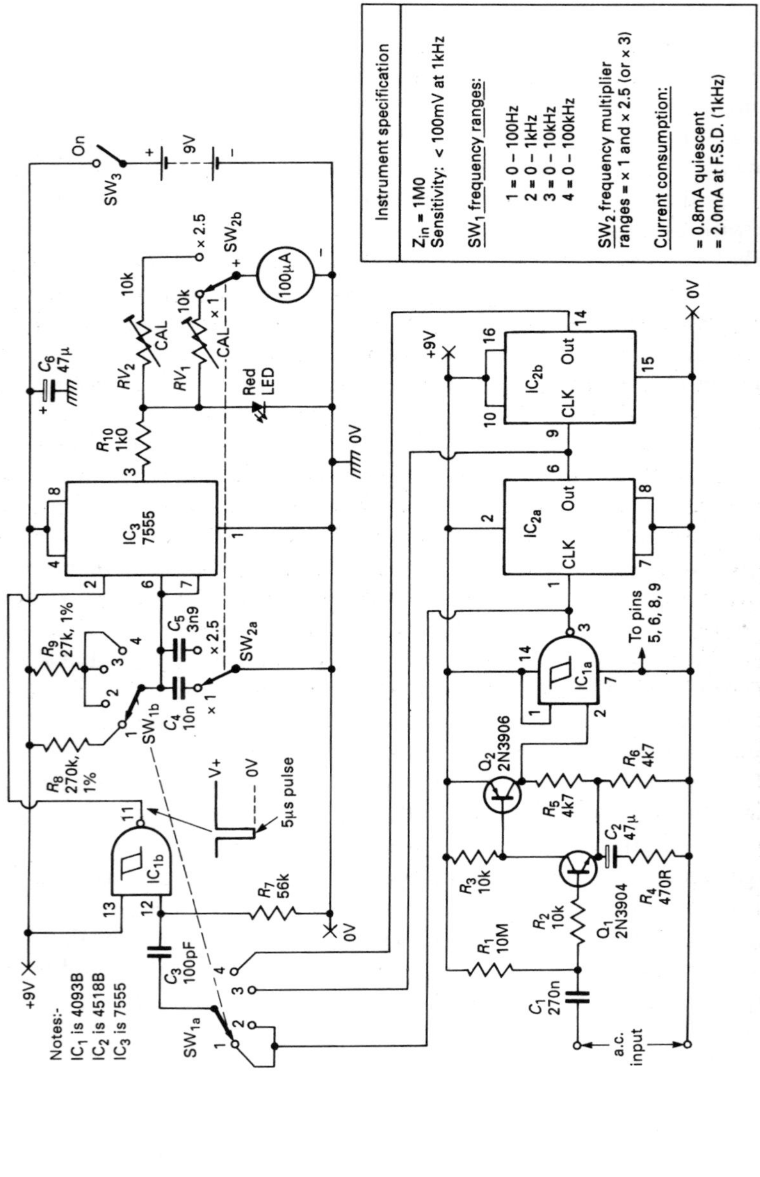
Instrument specification
$Z_{in}$ = 1M0
Sensitivity: < 100mV at 1kHz
$SW_1$ frequency ranges:
1 = 0 – 100Hz
2 = 0 – 1kHz
3 = 0 – 10kHz
4 = 0 – 100kHz
$SW_2$ frequency multiplier ranges = × 1 and × 2.5 (or × 3)
Current consumption:
= 0.8mA quiescent
= 2.0mA at F.S.D. (1kHz)
Notes:-
$IC_1$ is 4093B
$IC_2$ is 4518B
$IC_3$ is 7555
+9V
0V
On
$SW_3$
9V
$C_6$ 47µ
$R_{10}$ 1k0
$RV_2$ 10k CAL
$RV_1$ 10k CAL
Red LED
100µA
$SW_{2b}$
× 2.5
× 1
$IC_3$ 7555
$R_9$ 27k, 1%
$R_8$ 270k, 1%
$SW_{1b}$
$C_4$ 10n
$C_5$ 3n9
$SW_{2a}$
V+
5µs pulse
$IC_{1b}$
$R_7$ 56k
$C_3$ 100pF
$SW_{1a}$
$IC_{2a}$
$IC_{2b}$
CLK
Out
To pins 5, 6, 8, 9
$IC_{1a}$
$Q_2$ 2N3906
$R_6$ 4k7
$R_5$ 4k7
$C_2$ 47µ
$R_3$ 10k
$R_4$ 470R
$R_1$ 10M
$R_2$ 10k
$Q_1$ 2N3904
$C_1$ 270n
a.c. input

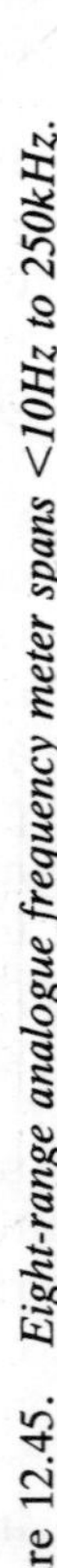

Figure 12.45. *Eight-range analogue frequency meter spans <10Hz to 250kHz.*

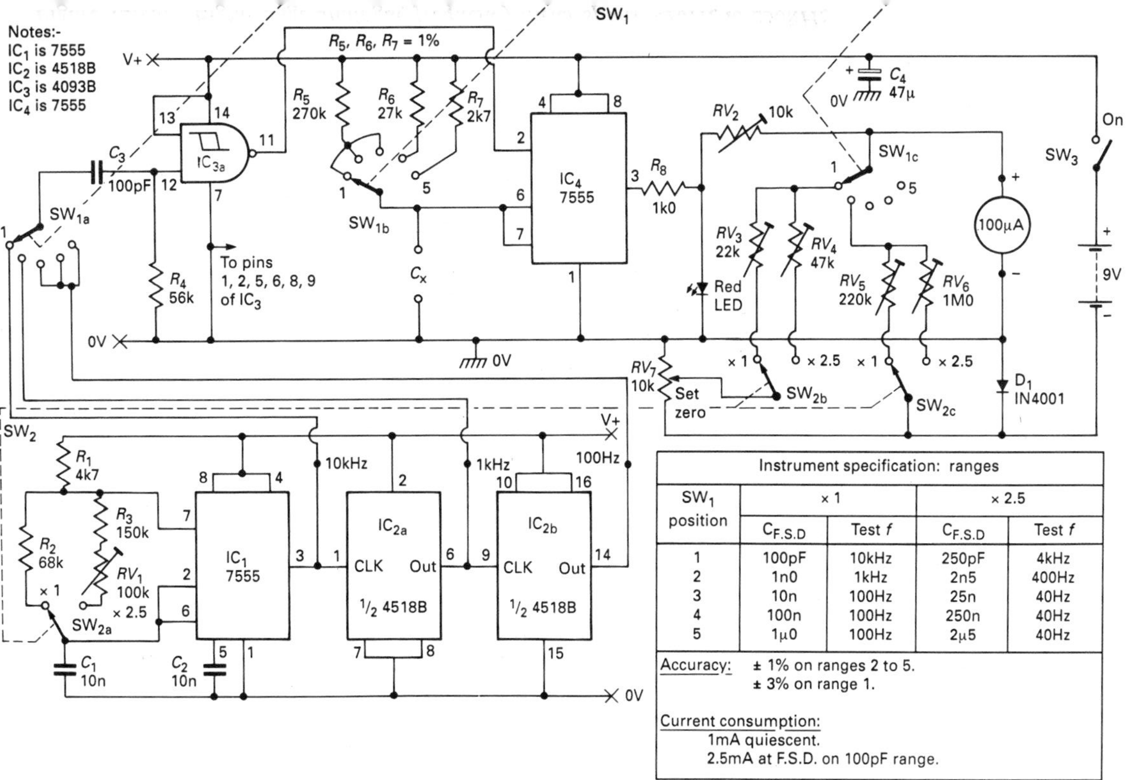


Instrument specification: ranges

| SW1 position | × 1 $C_{F.S.D}$ | × 1 Test *f* | × 2.5 $C_{F.S.D}$ | × 2.5 Test *f* |
|---|---|---|---|---|
| 1 | 100pF | 10kHz | 250pF | 4kHz |
| 2 | 1n0 | 1kHz | 2n5 | 400Hz |
| 3 | 10n | 100Hz | 25n | 40Hz |
| 4 | 100n | 100Hz | 250n | 40Hz |
| 5 | 1μ0 | 100Hz | 2μ5 | 40Hz |

Accuracy: ± 1% on ranges 2 to 5.
± 3% on range 1.

Current consumption:
1mA quiescent.
2.5mA at F.S.D. on 100pF range.

Figure 12.46. *Ten-range linear-scale analogue 'C' meter spans 0pF to 2.5μF.*

sensitive ranges has facilities for perfectly nulling out 'stray' capacitance on its test terminals, thus enabling the instrument to give direct and accurate readings of capacitance values as low as 2 or 3pF. In this design $IC_1$ acts as a stable 10kHz or 4kHz squarewave generator, and has its output fed (either directly or via decade-divider stages $IC_{2a}$ and $IC_{2b}$) to $C_3$–$R_4$–$IC_{3a}$, which convert each cycle into a negative-going 5μs pulse that triggers monostable pulse generator $IC_4$. The width of each $IC_4$ output pulse is determined by $C_x$ and the $R_5$–$R_6$–$R_7$ set of components, and the pulse amplitude is precision-regulated (at about 1.8V peak) by the red LED; these pulses are fed to the meter via $RV_2$; the meter integrates the output pulses and gives a deflection that, since the pulse repetition frequency is fixed on each range, is directly proportional to the pulse width and thus the $C_x$ value.

Each time $IC_4$ is triggered it generates an output pulse, even if no external $C_x$ value is connected; in this case the pulse may be attributed to 'stray' capacitance. On ranges 3 to 5 the practical effects of 'stray' are minute, and the meter reading is directly proportional to the external $C_x$ value. On the more sensitive ranges, however, the effect of 'stray' is such that the meter tends to give a positive 'offset' reading with no $C_x$ value connected. In the *Figure 12.46* design this offset action is countered with the help of $D_1$, which effectively generates a −600mV supply rail; on range 2 the offset is quite small, and $RV_5$ or $RV_6$ and this rail are used to apply a pre-set negative current to the meter that counters the positive offset and thus gives a zero reading with zero input. On range 1 the offset is fairly large and may be variable, so a variable negative rail is created via $RV_7$ and, with $RV_7$ set to mid-value, $RV_3$ or $RV_4$ are used to apply a pre-set negative current to the meter and thus produce a zero reading with zero input. On these 'compensated' ranges the meter actually gives a reading of $IC_4$'s incremental capacitance, and this equals the external $C_x$ value applied to the '$C_x$' terminals.

To initially set up the *Figure 12.46* circuit, set it to the 10n range, connect a precision 10n capacitor in the $C_x$ position, and trim $RV_2$ for F.S.D. on the meter. Now switch to the 25n range, connect a precision 22n or 25n capacitor in the $C_x$ position, and trim $RV_1$ for the appropriate reading. Next, remove $C_x$, switch to the 2n5 range, and trim $RV_6$ for zero meter reading; now switch to the 1n0 range and trim $RV_5$ for zero reading. Finally, set $RV_7$ to mid-value, and trim $RV_3$ on the 100pF range and $RV_4$ on the 250pF range for zero reading. The setting-up is then complete.

## Non-linear (semi-log) amplifier

A non-linear amplifier is a handy little add-on gadget that enables a linear a.c. meter to respond to a wide spread of signal amplitudes without the need for range changing; it is particularly useful in nulling and bridge-balancing applications. *Figure 12.47* shows an inverting amplifier of this type; it gives non-linear amplification via a pair of silicon feedback diodes; when small inputs are applied these diodes act as high resistances and the circuit gives high gain, but when large signals are applied they act like low resistances and the gain is low. The gain varies in a semi-logarithmic manner; sensitivity can be varied via $R_1$; the table shows actual performance details; note that a 1000:1 change in input amplitude can cause as little as a 2:1 change in output level.

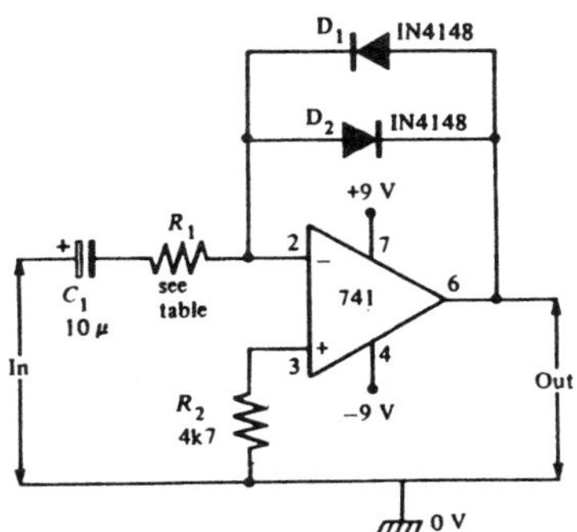


| $V_{in}$ (rms) | $R_1$ = 1k0 | | $R_1$ = 10 k | |
|---|---|---|---|---|
| | $V_{out}$ (mV rms) | $V_{gain}$ | $V_{out}$ (mV rms) | $V_{gain}$ |
| 1 mV | 110 | × 110 | 21 | × 21 |
| 10 mV | 330 | × 33 | 170 | × 17 |
| 100 mV | 450 | × 4.5 | 360 | × 3.6 |
| 1 V | 560 | × 0.56 | 470 | × 0.47 |
| 10 V | 600 | × 0.07 | 560 | × 0.056 |

Figure 12.47. *Circuit and performance details of a semi-log amplifier.*

## Extra-useful test rigs

Many unusual or sophisticated tests or measurements can be carried out without the use of special test gear, by simply making proper use of 'standard' test gear items such as 'scopes and signal generators and a few simple test rigs. *Figures 12.48* to *12.52* show examples of such systems.

*Figure 12.48* shows an ultra-simple rig for checking the functioning of any crystal. When the RF generator is tuned away from the crystal frequency a low-amplitude trace is seen on the 'scope. When the frequency equals the crystal's low-impedance series-resonant value the trace amplitude rises sharply; if the frequency is further increased the trace amplitude drops sharply (to near-zero) when the frequency coincides with the crystal's high-impedance parallel-resonant mode value.

*Figure 12.49* shows a rig that gives an accurate readout of capacitance values from a few picafarads to 5μF on a 'scope screen. The basic principle used here is that, if capacitor $C_x$ and resistor $R_s$ are wired in series (as a potential divider) and driven from an a.c. source as shown, the output voltage generated across $R_s$ will, *if the impedance of* $C_x$ *is very large relative to* $R_s$, be directly proportional to the $C_x$ value. The *Figure 12.49* circuit can be used to carry out measurements within an accuracy of 5 per cent by using it as follows.

To initially set up the circuit for use on any desired range, select the $f_{IN}$ and $R_s$ values shown in the table, set the 'scope's input sensitivity to 0.5V/div (or 0.5V/cm), set $SW_1$ to IN, and adjust the $f_{IN}$ peak-to-peak amplitude to equal five divisions (or 5cm, or roughly 1V r.m.s.) on the 'scope screen. Now set $SW_1$ to OUT, connect a resistor equal to the listed '$X_{c_x}$ at F.S.D.' value

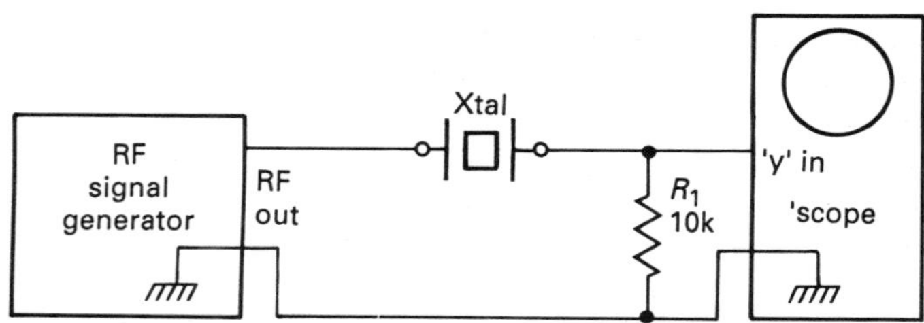


Figure 12.48. *Crystal-checking test rig.*

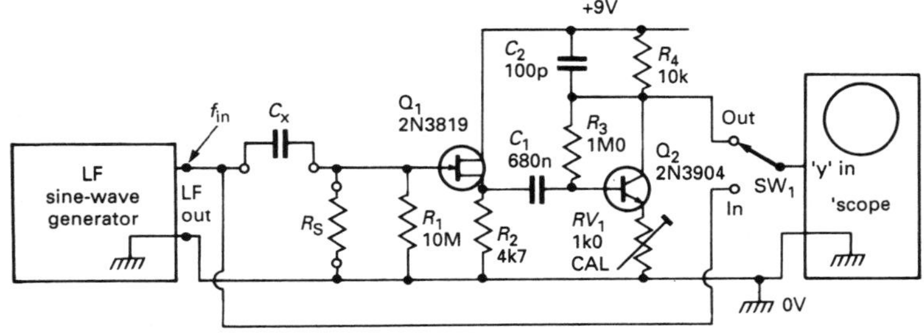


| '$C_x$' range | 'Scope sensitivity | $f_{in}$ | $R_S$ | $X_{Cx}$ at F.S.D. |
|---|---|---|---|---|
| 0 – 50pF | 10pF/div | 15.9kHz | 10k | 200k |
| 0 – 500pF | 100pF/div | 1.59kHz | 10k | 200k |
| 0 – 5nF | 1nF/div | 159Hz | 10k | 200k |
| 0 – 50nF | 10nF/div | 159Hz | 1k0 | 20k |
| 0 – 500nF | 100nF/div | 159Hz | 100R | 2k0 |
| 0 – 5μF | 1μF/div | 159Hz | 10R | 200R |

Figure 12.49. *Accurate capacitance-measuring test rig.*

(= 20 × $R_s$ in the $C_x$ position, and trim $RV_1$ to give a signal amplitude of five divisions on the 'scope (the $Q_1$–$Q_2$ amplifier has a gain of ×21 under this condition). That completes the initial calibration procedure. Now simply connect a test capacitor in the $C_x$ position and read its amplitude on the 'scope; the table shows its range sensitivity in terms of capacitance-per-division. Once the circuit has been initially calibrated as described, it can be used on any other ranges by simply selecting the appropriate $f_{IN}$ and $R_s$ values and checking (via $SW_1$) that the $f_{IN}$ amplitude equals five 'scope divisions.

*Figure 12.50* shows the above circuit modified for use as an inductance-indicating test rig that can be used to measure $L$ values from a few hundred microhenries up to 50H. It is used in a manner similar to that already described, except that in the initial calibration stage $L_x$ is replaced with a resistor equal to the listed '$X_{L_x}$ at F.S.D.' value (= $R_s$/20).

Note that, since these two rigs are calibrated to give zero error at F.S.D., under which condition there is only a 20:1 ratio between the $R_s$ and $X_c$ (or $X_L$) 'divider' impedances, the rigs produce rising errors at component values below the F.S.D. value, as

| 'Lx' range | 'Scope sensitivity | $f_{in}$ | $R_S$ | $X_{Lx}$ at F.S.D. |
|---|---|---|---|---|
| 0 – 5mH | 1mH/div | 15.9kHz | 10k | 500R |
| 0 – 50mH | 10mH/div | 1.59kHz | 10k | 500R |
| 0 – 500mH | 100mH/div | 159Hz | 10k | 500R |
| 0 – 5H | 1H/div | 159Hz | 100k | 5k0 |
| 0 – 50H | 10H/div | 159Hz | 1M0 | 50k |

Figure 12.50. *Accurate inductance-measuring test rig.*

shown in the graph of *Figure 12.51*. Thus, if the test component's value is 50 per cent of the F.S.D. value, the 'scope gives a reading that is 2.5 per cent high, and at 10 per cent of the F.S.D. value it gives a reading that is 4.5 per cent high, etc.; in these

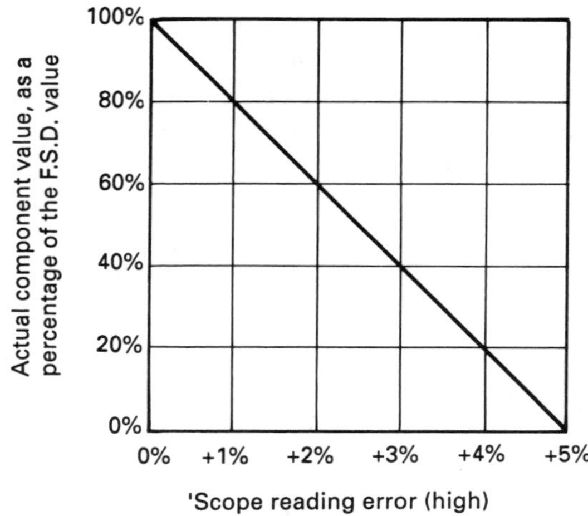


Figure 12.51. *Error-correction graph for use with the capacitance- and inductance-measuring test rigs.*

examples the true value of the test components can be deduced by reducing their indicated values by 2.5 per cent and 4.5 per cent respectively. The *Figure 12.51* graph thus enables measured component value errors to be reduced to near-zero.

## A pseudo *Q*-meter

The delightfully simple test rig of *Figure 12.52* can be used to make simple *Q* measurements, or to measure inductance values from a fraction of a microhenry to tens of microhenries with excellent precision. $R_1$ and $R_2$ act as a 100:1 attenuator that injects a low-impedance (1R0) signal into the $L-C$ tuned circuit. This impedance is low enough not to have too severe an effect on the tuned circuit's *Q*, and the approximate *Q*-value can be found as follows.

To measure *Q*, first bring the $L-C$ tuned circuit to resonance via the RF generator, and then use the 'scope probe to monitor the output level of the signal generator and adjust the amplitude to fill five divisions on the 'scope trace. Now transfer the 'scope probe to the rig's output (across *C*), recheck the tuning, and note the signal amplitude in trace divisions; the *Q* value equals this number multiplied by 20, i.e. $Q = 100$ if five divisions are filled.

The rig can be used to measure *L* values as follows. Fit the test inductor in place on the rig, and fit a precision (1 per cent) 100pF capacitor in the *C* position. Connect the 'scope probe to the circuit's output. The probe has a typical input capacitance of 11pF, and this, combined with about 2pF of strays, brings the

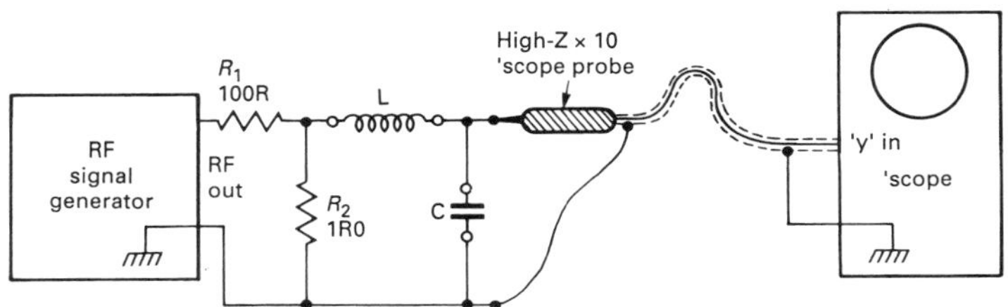


Figure 12.52. *Pseudo Q-meter test rig; can be used to measure low values of inductance, etc.*

$X_L = 2\pi fL = 6.28\Omega$ per µH per MHz, i.e., 10MHz × 50µH = 3k14

$X_C = \dfrac{1}{2\pi fC} = \dfrac{159k}{\text{per pF per MHz}}$, i.e., 10MHz × 50pF = 320R

At resonance:

$L = \dfrac{1000{,}000}{(2\pi f)^2 \times C}$ $\qquad f = \dfrac{1000}{2\pi\sqrt{LC}}$

$C = \dfrac{1000{,}000}{(2\pi f)^2 \times L}$ $\qquad Q = \dfrac{X_L}{R}$

where L = µH, *C* = pF, *f* = MHz

Figure 12.53. *Useful formulae for use with the pseudo* Q*-meter.*

effective $C$ value of the tuned circuit up to within ±2 per cent of 113pF. Now adjust the RF generator frequency and bring the tuned circuit to resonance ($= f$). Now calculate the $L$ value on the basis of

$$L = 1\,000\,000/[(2\pi f)^2 \times 113],$$

where $L$ is in microhenries and $f$ is in megahertz. *Figure 12.53* lists some formulae of value when using the pseudo $Q$-meter test rig.

## 'Scope accessories

The usefulness of many simple oscilloscopes can be increased with the aid of various accessories and add-on units. One very simple accessory is a 'scope calibrator, and *Figure 12.54* shows such a unit. Here, $IC_1$ generates a 1kHz (1ms period) square-wave output, and $IC_2$ divides this by ten and gives a 100Hz (10ms period) square-wave output. These outputs are selected via $SW_2$, precision amplitude-limited via $R_3$ and the red LED, and attenuated to precisely 1V peak-to-peak via $RV_2$, thus enabling the 'scope to be calibrated on both its $X$ and $Y$ axis.

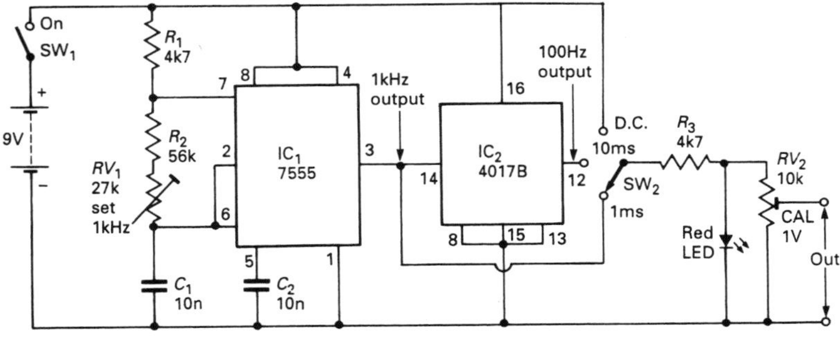


Figure 12.54. *'Scope calibrator gives 1ms and 10ms, 1V peak-to-peak outputs.*

To calibrate this unit's output amplitude, simply set $SW_2$ to the DC position, monitor the output via a digital voltmeter (or DMM) and trim $RV_2$ to give a reading of precisely 1V. To calibrate its timing, set $SW_2$ to '1ms', monitor the output via a digital frequency meter (DFM), and set $RV_1$ for a 1kHz reading. If a DFM is not available, the unit can be calibrated by using the 'miser's' technique of *Figure 12.55*, in which the 'scope is set to use an external *X* input signal derived from the A.C. power line via a step-down isolating transformer, and the calibrator's 100Hz output is fed to the *Y* input, thus generating a Lissajous figure; if a 50Hz power line is used, trim $RV_1$ (in the calibrator) to give a stationary 'sideways 8' figure (with 2 *X* lobes and 1 *Y* lobe) as shown. If a 60Hz power line is used a more complex 'balance' figure is generated, and has 5 *X* lobes and 3 *Y* lobes.

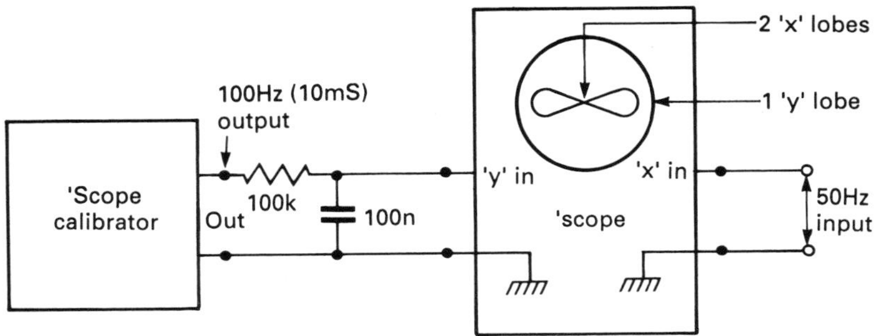


Figure 12.55. *Miser's method of setting the calibrator's frequency.*

One very popular oscilloscope accessory is the trace doubler. These come in two basic types, and operate in either the 'chopped trace' or the 'alternate trace' mode. *Figure 12.56* shows the basic circuit and waveforms of a 'chopper' type of doubler. $SW_1$ is a fast electronic change-over switch that is activated by the square-wave 'chopper' generator and has its output fed to the 'scope's D.C. *Y*-channel input, and the 'scope's timebase can be synchronized to either the CHANNEL 1 or CHANNEL 2 input via $SW_2$. Thus, on one half of each chopper (square-wave) cycle the 'scope's input is connected to the CHANNEL 1 input, and the trace can be shifted via $RV_1$, and on the next half-cycle it is connected to the CHANNEL 2 input and can be trace-shifted via $RV_2$.

If the chopper frequency is high relative to the input signal frequency a *single* 'scope trace might take the form shown in *Figure 12.56*; in reality, however, the 'scope's time base is locked to the unchopped input signal, so the vertical hatch lines will (unless the input and chopper signals are harmonically locked) appear in a different position on each successive trace, and thus disappear and leave a visual illusion of two clean and independent traces. If the chopper frequency is very low relative to the input

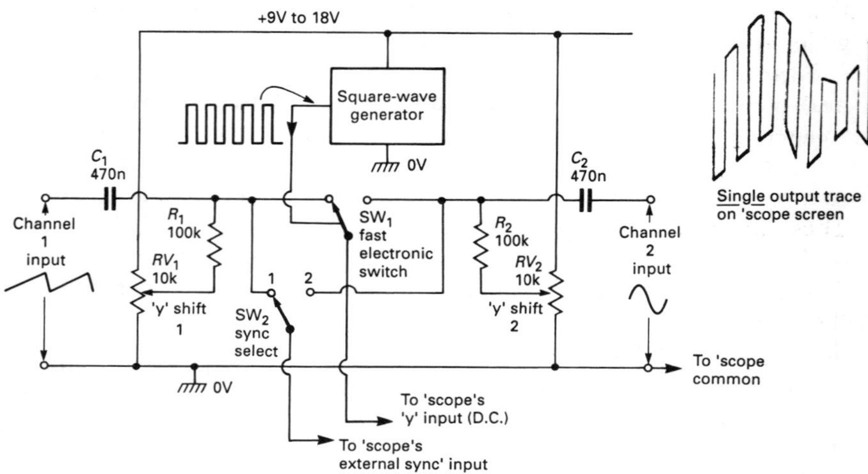


Figure 12.56. *Basic chopper-type 'scope trace-doubler circuit and waveforms.*

frequency the 'scope's *Y* input is alternately connected to CHANNEL 1 for several timebase sweeps and then to CHANNEL 2 for several timebase sweeps, and (provided that the channel switching occurs more than 50 times per second) a clean 'dual trace' picture again appears. Note that this second type of action is similar to that of an 'alternate trace' type of doubler, except that in a true 'alternate trace' system the trace switching rate is synchronized to the 'scope's timebase rate.

## Practical trace multipliers

*Figure 12.57* shows a super-simple but very practical and efficient version of a chopper-type trace doubler. It is designed round a CMOS 4016 quad bilateral switch IC, and uses $IC_{1b}$ and $IC_{1c}$ as a cross-coupled astable multivibrator or square-wave generator that drives an electronic change-over switch made up by $IC_{1a}$ and $IC_{1d}$. The chopper frequency can be switched between 700Hz and 7.5kHz via $SW_2$, and the 'scope's time base can be synchronized to either the CHANNEL 1 or CHANNEL 2 input via $SW_1$. Each channel has an input impedance of about 100k, has its own *Y*-shift control, can handle peak-to-peak input signals within the limits of the unit's battery voltage, and has a useful bandwidth that (on the prototype) extends well beyond 10MHz, with negligible crosstalk between channels.

*Figure 12.58* shows a four-channel version of the simple trace multiplier circuit. In this case $IC_1$ operates as a 500Hz or 10kHz square-wave 'clock' generator and has its output divided down by four-stage ripple counter $IC_2$, which activates the $IC_{3a}$ to $IC_{3d}$ channel switches in an $A-B-C-D$ auto-repeating sequence. Thus, in each four-step sequence, Channel *A* is switched on during the first clock cycle, Channel *B* during the second, Channel *C* during the third, and Channel *D* during the fourth; the sequence then repeats *ad infinitum*, and four seemingly-independent traces are displayed on the 'scope screen.

The basic *Figures 12.57* and *12.58* circuits can be usefully modified in a variety of ways. They can, for example, easily be fitted with high-impedance input buffers and attenuators, or be provided with a variety of switching options. *Figure 12.59* shows a moderately sophisticated version of such a circuit. Each of its two channels has a 1M0 input impedance to a FET buffer stage and a

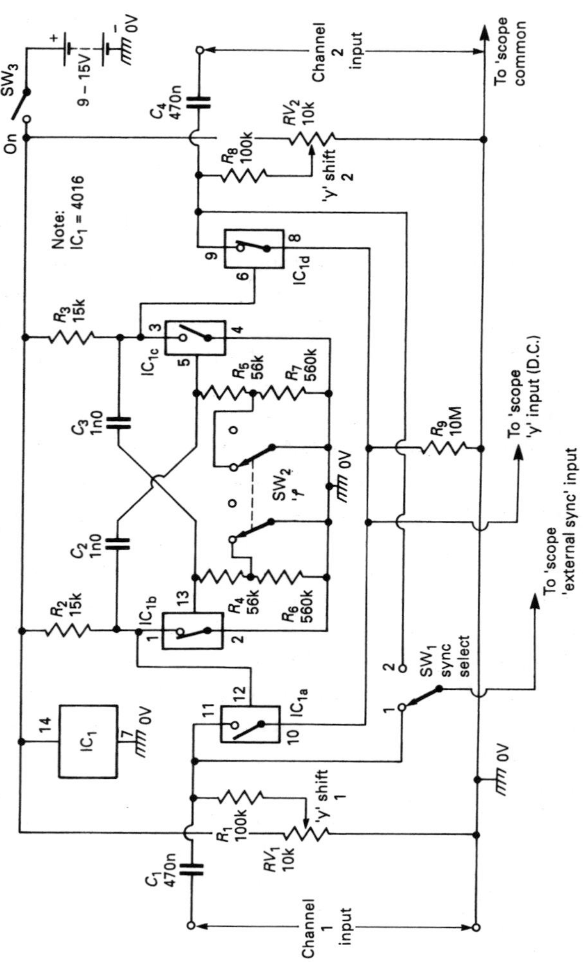


Figure 12.57. *This super-simple trace-doubler gives a good performance up to several MHz.*

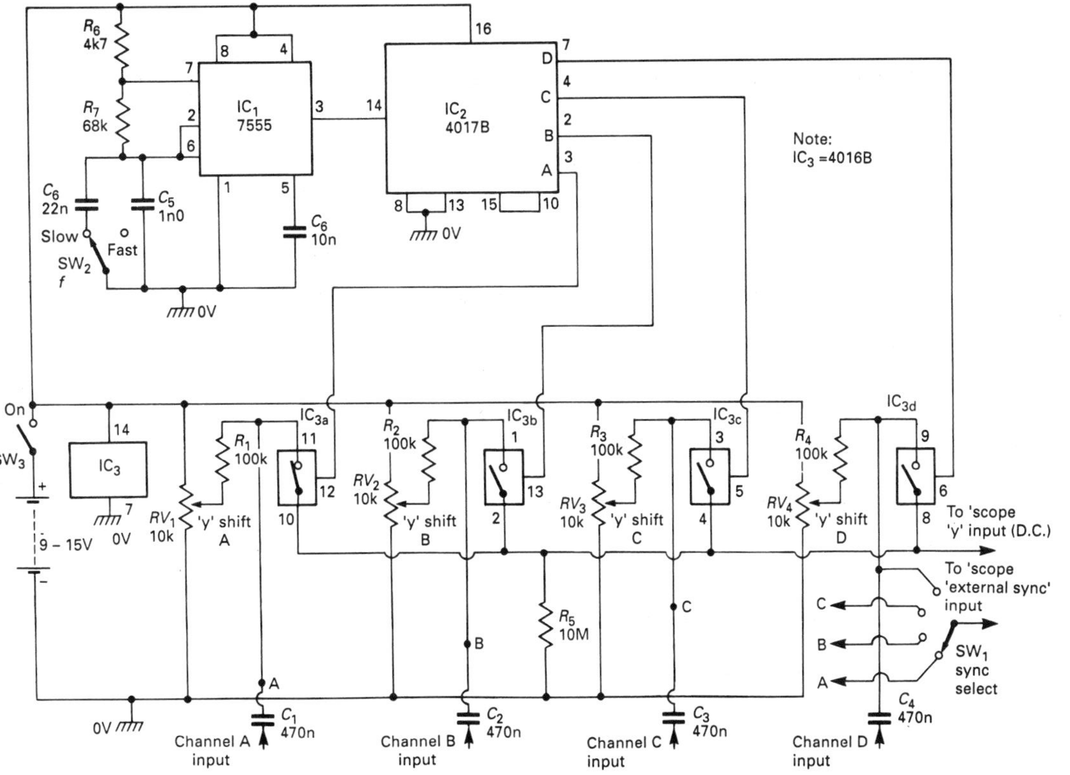


Figure 12.58. *Simple four-channel trace multiplier.*

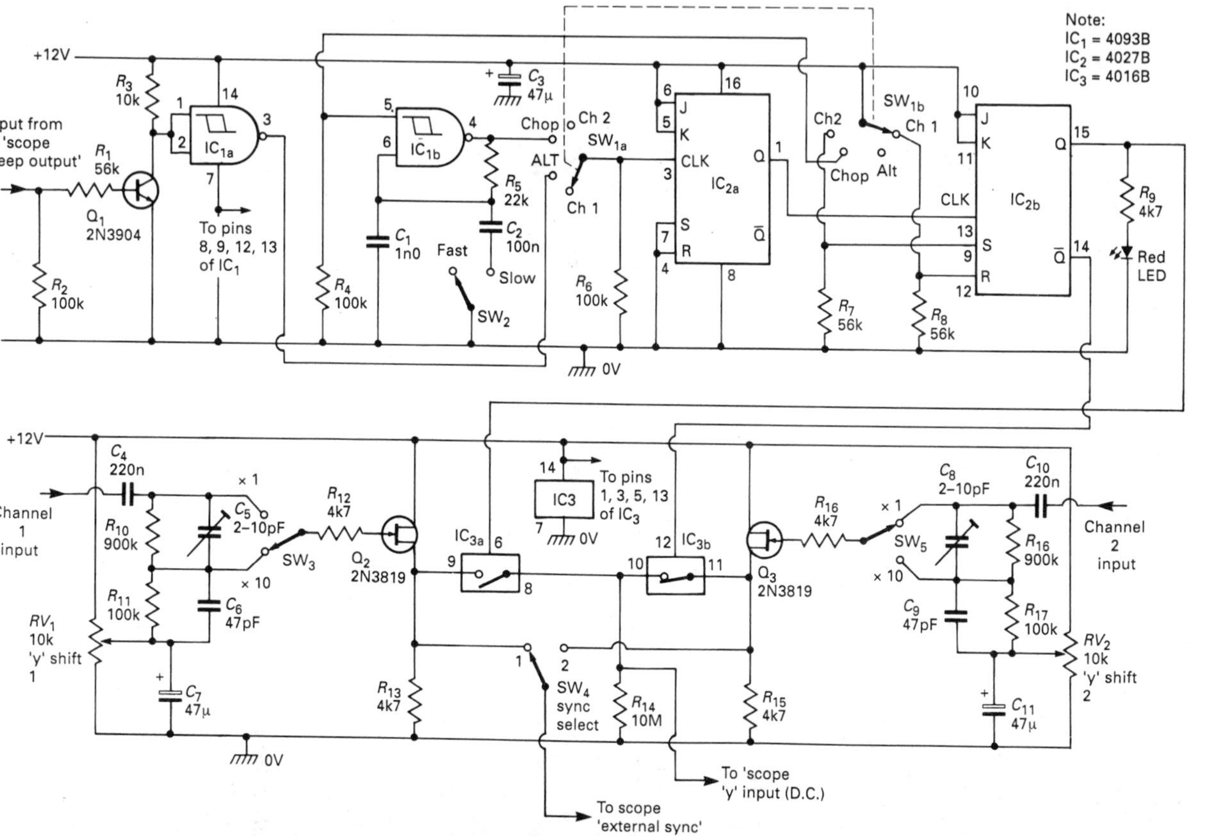


Figure 12.59. *FET-input trace doubler with* ***chopped*** *and* ***alternate*** *mode options.*

two-step ($\times 1$ or $\times 10$) compensated attenuator, and can be operated in any of four alternative modes (selected via $SW_1$). In the CHI mode only Channel 1 is displayed; the red LED turns fully on in this mode. In the ALT (alternate) mode the trace-doubling action is synchronized to the 'scope's time base via the $Q_1-IC_{1a}$ network, and alternately displays Channel 1 for two time-base sweeps, then Channel 2 for two sweeps, and so on; the red LED glows or flickers under this condition. In the CHOP mode the doubler gives normal 'chopped' switching action via oscillator $IC_{1b}$, which is activated in this mode only; two different speeds can be selected via $SW_2$. Finally, in the CH2 mode only Channel 2 is displayed; the red LED is fully off in this mode.

## A triggered time base

Most modern oscilloscopes have excellent time bases, but some older instruments based on valve (tube) technology have rather poor ones; the usefulness of such instruments may be enhanced with the aid of a modern 'add-on' triggered timebase unit, but such a unit can only be of real value if the 'scope itself has some facility for enabling an external time-base signal to be *direct coupled* to the 'scope's $X$-amplifier, and for giving *direct coupling* to the 'scope's brilliance control circuitry. Unfortunately, very few 'old' 'scopes have such facilities.

Most old 'scopes offer only the poor a.c.-coupled facilities shown in *Figure 12.60*, with brilliance control (with a 0.1ms time constant) via the $Z_{IN}$ terminal, and with sweep control (with a 33ms time constant) via the $X_{IN}$ terminal. Because of this a.c.-coupling the $X$ trace's screen position varies with the time base's on/off ratio and is thus unstable. Also, if the time-base period is longer than 20ms (equal to a sweep speed of about 2ms/div) the waveform reaching the 'scope's $X$ plates may be severely distorted, as shown in *Figure 12.60*(c).

Thus, a reader who wishes to use a modern triggered time-base unit with an old 'scope must be prepared to carry out drastic surgery on the 'scope itself, so that it provides the direct-coupled facilities described. With all of these limitations and qualifications in mind, *Figures 12.61* and *12.62* show the block diagram and full circuit diagram of such a unit, for the benefit of the brave and the stout hearted.

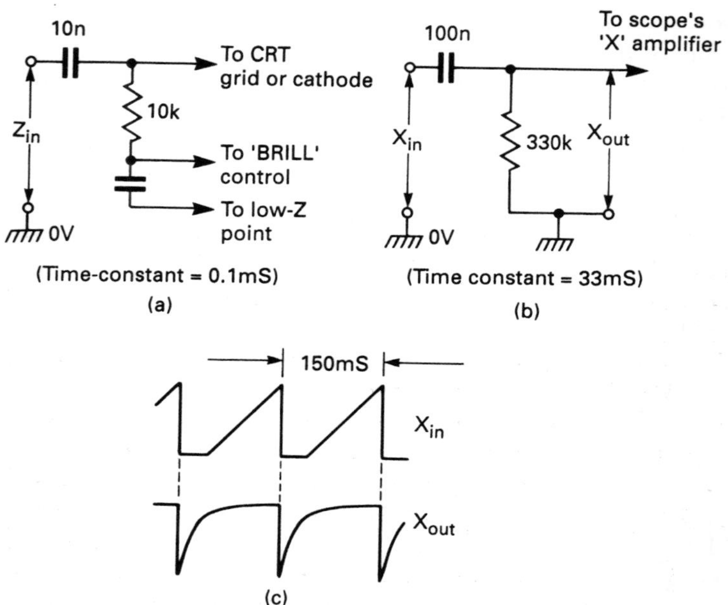


Figure 12.60. *Typical $Z_{IN}$ (a) and $X_{IN}$ (b) equivalent inputs of old-style 'scopes: (c) shows distortion imposed on a sawtooth waveform by the $X_{IN}$ network.*

The input signal to the *Figure 12.61/62* circuit is derived from the 'scope's $Y$ amplifier and is buffered via FET source-follower $Q_1$ and then fed, via $RV_1$, to the $Q_2-Q_3$ phase-splitting amplifier, which gives a nominal ×10 voltage gain. The signal is then fed, via $SW_1$, to Schmitt trigger $IC_{1a}$, which converts it into a good square (or pulse) waveform; $RV_2$ can be adjusted on test to set the converter's sensitivity to maximum (typically about 300mV peak-to-peak).

$IC_{1a}$'s square-wave output is fed, via $C_5-R_{12}-D_1$, to $IC_{1b}$, which converts its leading edge into a negative-going 2μs pulse. This pulse is fed, via $D_3$, to pin-2 of $IC_2$ and flips $IC_2$ into a monostable timing period in which $C_T$ charges linearly via constant-current generator $Q_4$ until the timing period is complete, at which point the $C_T$ voltage switches abruptly to zero; $IC_2$ thus generates a triggered and linear sawtooth waveform, which is fed to the outside world via source follower $Q_5$.

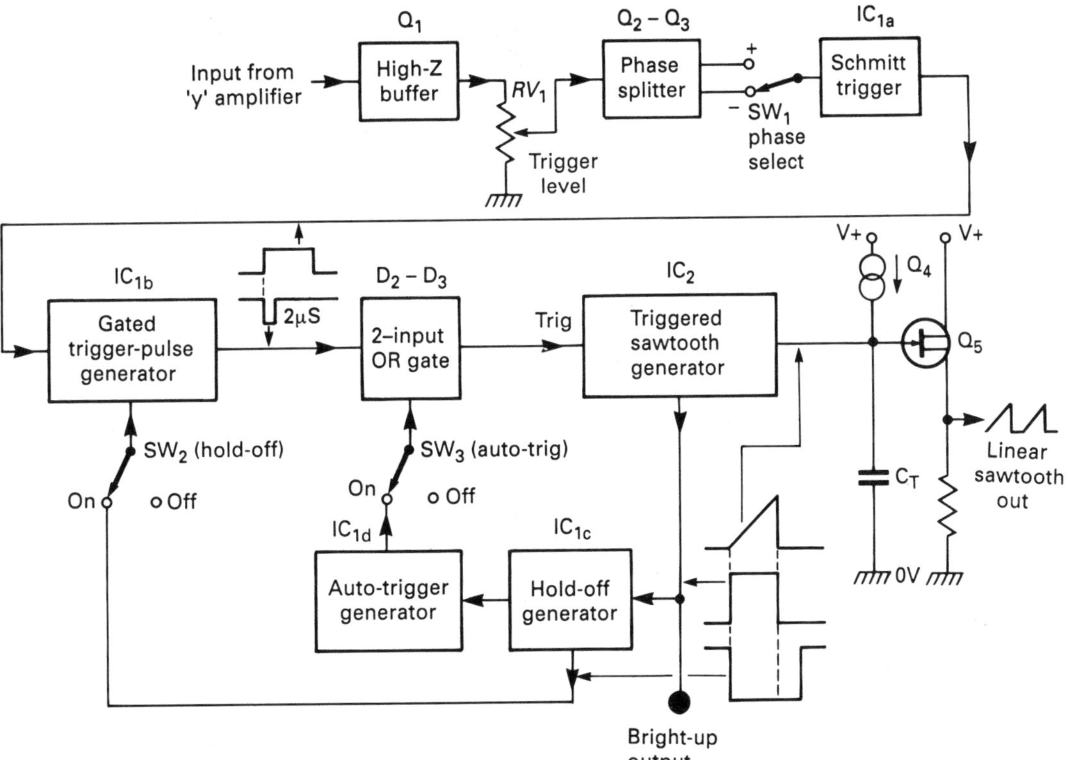


Figure 12.61. *Block diagram of the triggered time-base generator.*

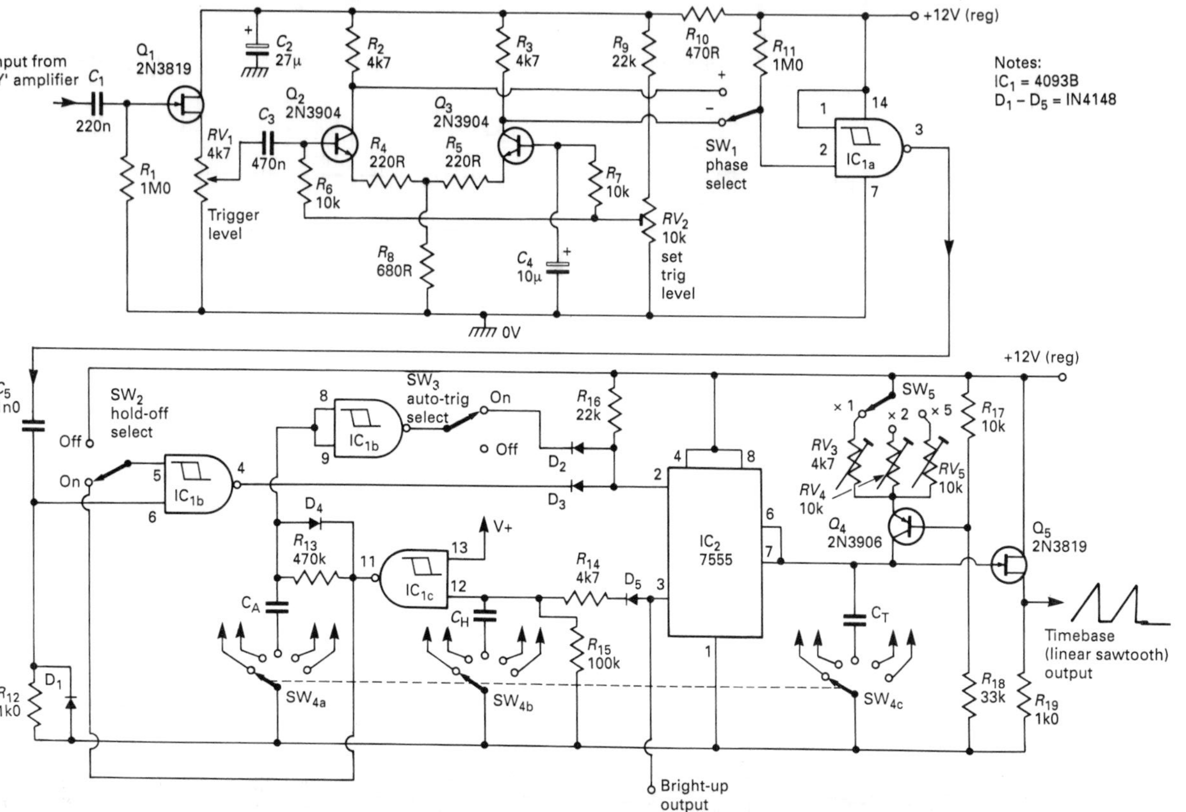


Figure 12.62. *Triggered timebase generator ($SW_4$–$SW_5$ range switching is shown simplified).*

| Timebase speed | Capacitor values | | |
|---|---|---|---|
| | $C_T$ | $C_H$ | $C_A$ |
| 1μS/div | 1n0 | 100pF | 1n0 |
| 10μS/div | 10n | 1n0 | 10n |
| 100μS/div | 100n | 10n | 100n |
| 1mS/div | 1μ0 | 100n | 1μ0 |
| 10mS/div | 10μ | 470n | 10μ |

Figure 12.63. *Timing capacitor values for the time-base generator circuit.*

Note that pin-3 of $IC_2$ flips high for the duration of each timing cycle, and thus provides a useful 'bright-up' control signal; it can also be used, via $D_5-R_{14}-C_{11}-R_{15}-IC_{1c}$, to feed a 'hold-off' control signal to $IC_{1b}$, to prevent immediate re-triggering of $IC_2$. $IC_{1d}$ is used, via $D_4-R_{13}-C_A$ and $IC_{1c}$, to generate an auto-trig pulse (fed to $IC_2$ via $D_2$) that fires $IC_2$ periodically (to provide the user with a reassuring 'scope trace, rather than a blank screen) if normal trigger signals are absent for abnormal periods of time. The time-base circuit must be powered via a well-regulated 12V supply.

The time-base speeds of the circuit are variable over five decade ranges (from 1μs/div to 10ms/div) via $SW_4$; these speeds can be multiplied by factors of ×1, ×2, or ×5 via $SW_5$, which can be precisely adjusted on test via presets $RV_3$ to $RV_5$. *Figure 12.63* lists the appropriate $C_A$ (*A*uto-control delay), $C_H$ (*H*old-off control), and $C_T$ (main *T*iming control) capacitor values for use on the decade ranges.

## A digital frequency meter

Digital frequency meters are relatively simple instruments that give an accurate and direct numeric readout of a test signal's operating frequency. *Figure 12.64* shows the typical block diagram of a digital frequency meter with an eight-digit display. External input signals are buffered and converted into square waves via a pre-amplifier network and then fed to the input of the eight-decade resettable counter, which is controlled via a **start/stop** gate and a precision time-base generator; various decade-related time-base periods can be selected via $SW_1$.

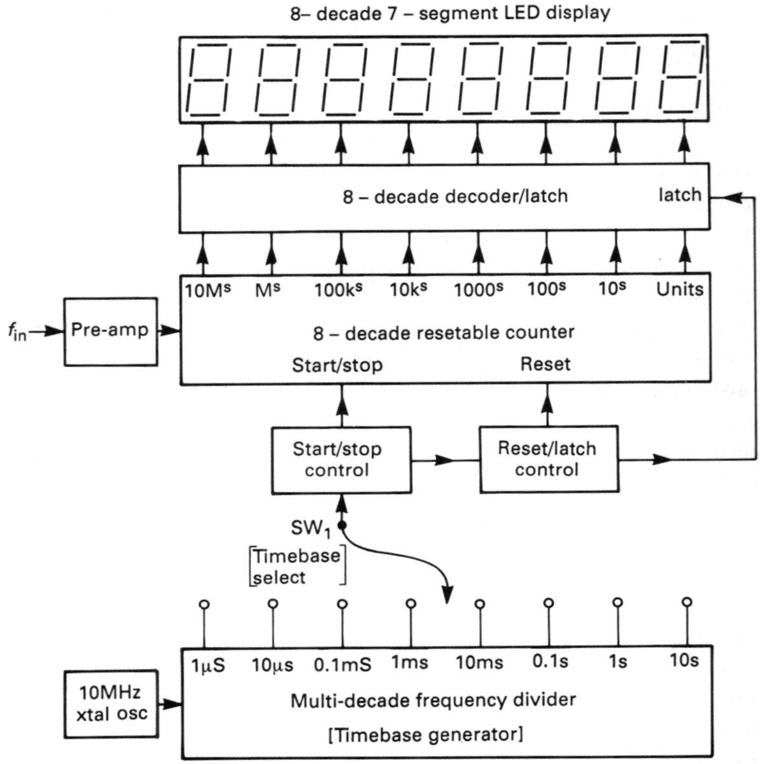

8– decade 7 – segment LED display

8 – decade decoder/latch
latch

10M^s M^s 100k^s 10k^s 1000^s 100^s 10^s Units
$f_{in}$
Pre-amp
8 – decade resetable counter
Start/stop
Reset

Start/stop control
Reset/latch control

$SW_1$
[Timebase select]

1µS 10µs 0.1mS 1ms 10ms 0.1s 1s 10s
10MHz xtal osc
Multi-decade frequency divider
[Timebase generator]

Figure 12.64. *Typical block diagram of an eight-decade digital frequency meter.*

Suppose a time-base period of 1s is selected; prior to the start of each timing cycle the eight-decade counter is reset to zero; as soon as the time-base period begins a **start** pulse initiates the square-wave-counting action, and at the end of the period a **stop** pulse terminates the counting action. At this point the counter holds a precise binary-coded count of the number of square waves counted in the 1s period. This data is now latched into the decoder circuitry and presented on the eight-digit seven-segment LED display. The counter then auto-resets to zero, and the circuit is then ready to carry out another **count – latch-and-display – reset** operation.

Note that if a 1s time-base period is selected the meter will display frequency to within ±1Hz but will give a very slow display action, and if a 10ms time base is used it will display frequency to within ±100Hz and give rapid count/display action. Also note that the circuit can be re-configured to act as a precision timer (rather than frequency meter) by feeding the time-base output (say 1μs) to the input of the counter and using the external (to be timed) signal to control the counter's start/stop action; a circuit with this operating mode option is known as a counter/timer or universal counter unit.

The easiest and cheapest way to build a digital frequency meter or universal counter is with the aid of a dedicated LSI IC. GE/Intersil produce some excellent ICs of these types. The best known of these are the ICM7216 series of 28-pin devices, which are designed to drive eight-digit seven-segment LED displays and can operate up to 10MHz in the 'frequency count' mode; there are four devices in this series, and each has its own unique

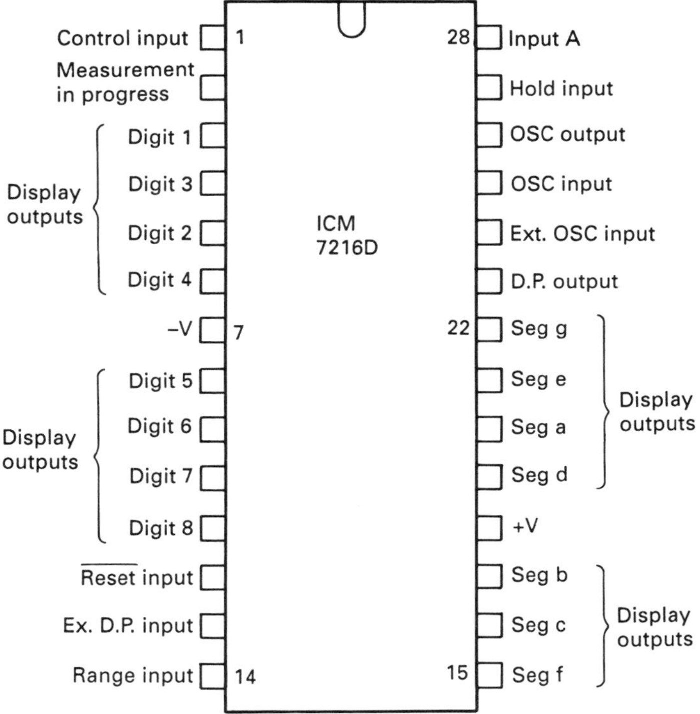


Figure 12.65. *Outline and pin notations of the ICM7216D 10Mhz frequency counter IC.*

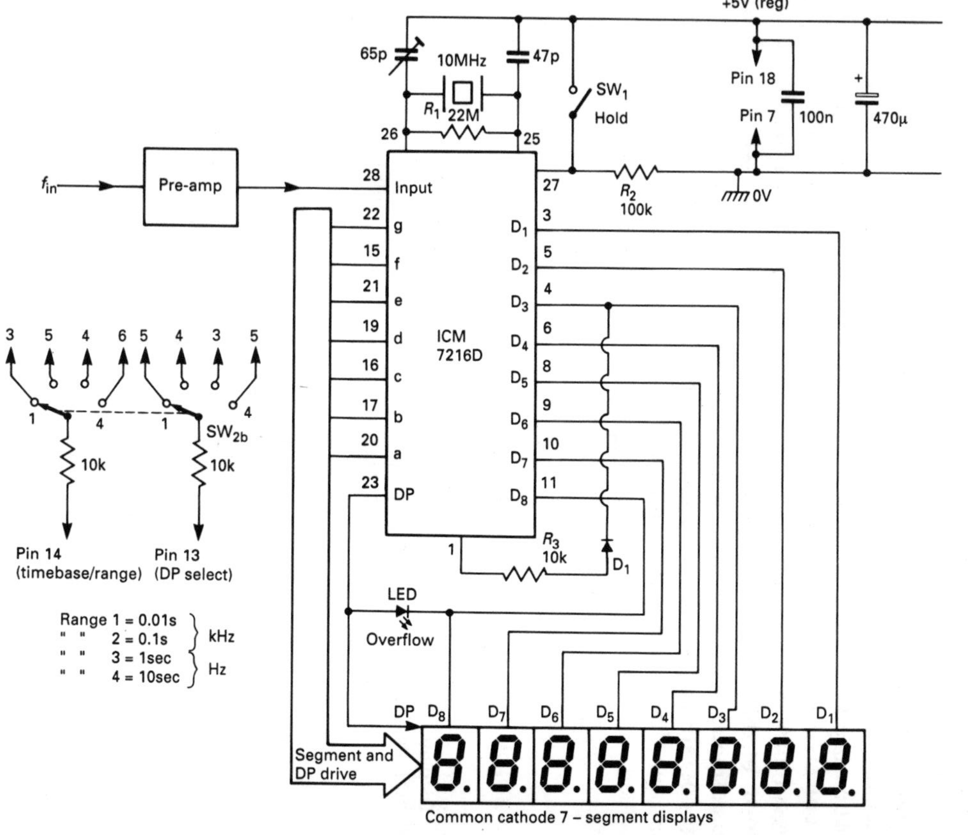


Figure 12.66. *Basic ICM7216D digital frequency meter circuit.*

function and set of pin connection. The ICM7216A and ICM7216B are universal counters, driving common anode and common cathode displays respectively, and the ICM7216C and ICM7216D are frequency counters, driving common anode and common cathode displays respectively.

*Figures 12.65* and *12.66* show the outline and practical usage diagram of the ICM7216D 10MHz frequency counter IC. The IC is clocked via a 10MHz crystal oscillator on pins 25 and 26, and the display is multiplex-driven and provided with automatic leading-zero suppression and other refinements. The LED (connected between pins 11 and 23) gives display overflow indication, $R_3-D_1$ 'enable' the decimal point display, and $SW_{2b}$ controls the decimal-point selection; $SW_{2a}$ selects the time-base period. The entire circuit is powered via a regulated 5V supply. The signal input (pin 28) to the IC must be of TTL form and can be provided via a suitable pre-amplifier to give counting up to 10MHz, or via a prescaler to give counts beyond this limit.

## Pre-amplifiers and prescalers

*Figure 12.67* shows an efficient but simple and inexpensive pre-amplifier that converts input signals into a square or pulse form

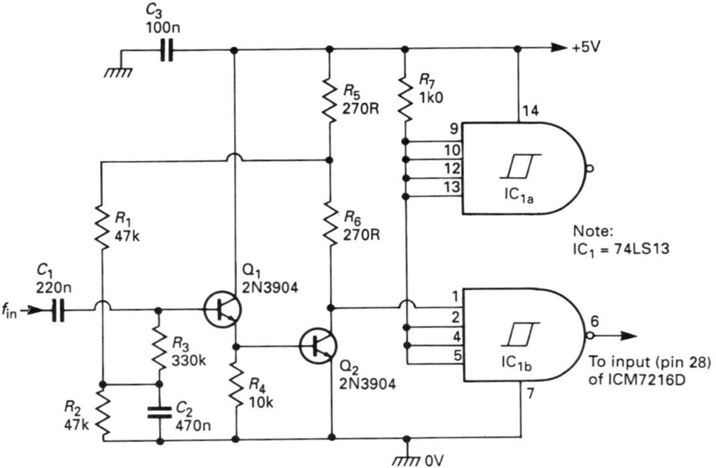


Figure 12.67. *General-purpose 10Hz to 10MHz pre-amp.*

suitable for driving the *Figure 12.66* digital frequency meter. It has an input impedance of 150k, operates at frequencies ranging from 10Hz to about 10MHz, and has a sine-wave 'trigger' sensitivity of about 10mV r.m.s. at low (below 100kHz) frequencies and about 100mV at 10MHz.

The operating range of the digital frequency meter can be extended by feeding the test signals to its input via a suitable prescaler, i.e. its range can be extended to a theoretical maximum of 100MHz via a divide-by-10 prescaler, or to 1GHz via a divide-by-100 prescaler. *Figures 12.68* to *12.71* show some examples of basic circuits of these types; when using these, note that it is necessary to alter the decimal-point selection (via $SW_{2b}$) in the *Figure 12.66* circuit.

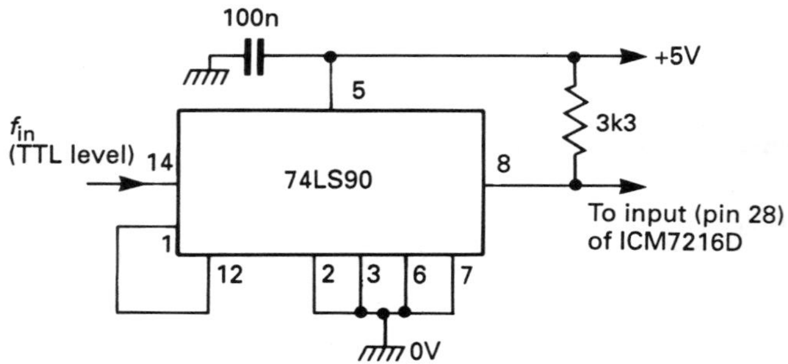


Figure 12.68. *Divide-by-10 prescaler works up to 50MHz.*

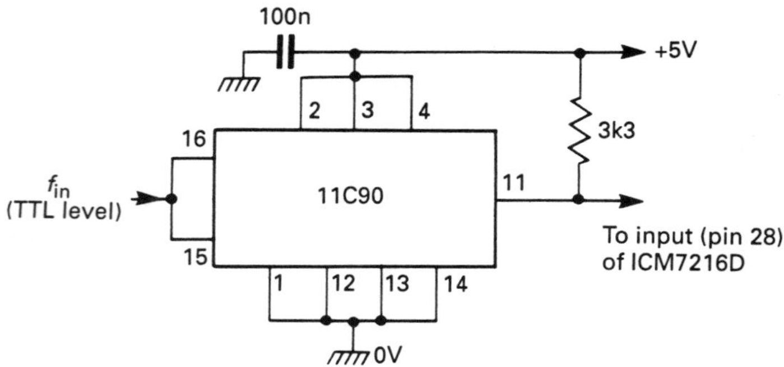


Figure 12.69. *TTL-driven divide-by-10 prescaler works up to 600MHz.*

The simple divide-by-10 prescaler of *Figure 12.68* works up to 50MHz and uses a readily available 74LS90 IC. The similar circuit of *Figure 12.69* uses a National Semiconductor 11C90 ECL (emitter-coupled logic) decade divider IC that can operate to above 600MHz and easily extends the counter's upper frequency limit to 100MHz. Note that both of these ICs need a TTL-level input.

The divide-by-100 prescaler of *Figure 12.70* uses a Plessey/Siemens SP8629 device that houses a wide-band pre-amplifier and a set of ECL dividers and can operate to above 150MHz. As shown, the IC is used with a low-impedance (usually 50 to 100Ω)

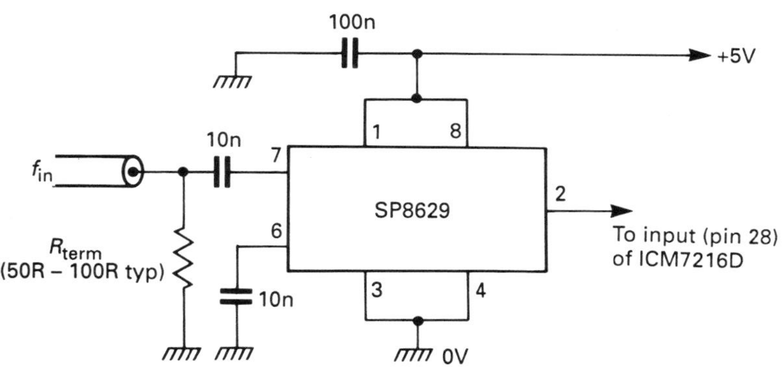


Figure 12.70. *Divide-by-100 prescaler works up to 150MHz.*

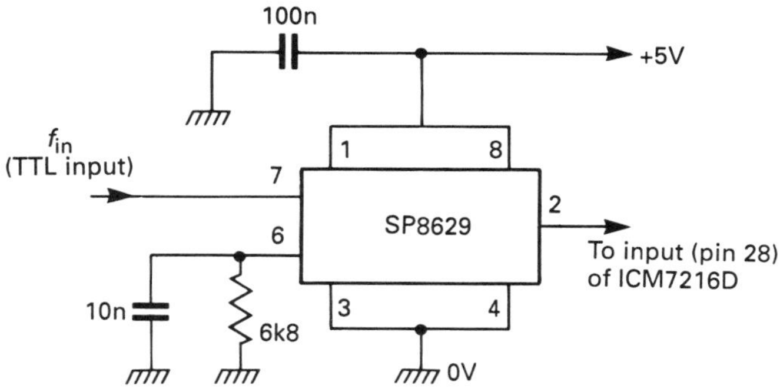


Figure 12.71. *150MHz divide-by-10 prescaler driven by TTL input.*

terminated input; its *minimum* operating frequency with a sine-wave input is 10MHz in this mode, but it can be used down to near-zero frequency if the input signal is of square or pulse form or has a slew rate better than 50V/μs. Finally, *Figure 12.71* shows this circuit reconfigured for use with a direct TTL input.

# Appendix: Design charts

To conclude this volume, five useful filter and waveform-generator design charts are presented. The methods of using these charts are as follows.

## Frequency-period-wavelength conversion chart

The chart in *Figure A.1* enables frequency, period and wavelength to be rapidly and accurately correlated. The chart is used by simply locating the known parameter value in the appropriate column, and then reading the adjacent equivalent values of the alternative parameters.

**Example**. Find the period and wavelength equal to 20MHz.

**Solution**. Locate 20MHz in the centre (frequency) column, and read the equivalent period (50ns) and wavelength (15m) values directly. The key of *Figure A.1* shows how the chart can be used to cover the frequency range 0.001Hz (1mHz) to 1000GHz, with appropriate changes in the period and wavelength designations.

## Symmetrical twin-T or Wien-bridge component selection charts

The charts in *Figures A.2* and *A.3* enable the *R* and *C* values of a symmetrical twin-T or Wien bridge oscillator or filter network of known frequency (or the frequency for known *R* and *C* values) to be rapidly and accurately determined: *Figure A.2* enables the approximate parameter values to be determined, and *Figure A.3*

| *p* | *f* | λ |
|---|---|---|
| SECONDS | mHz | METRES x $10^9$ |
| ms | Hz | METRES x $10^6$ |
| μs | kHz | METRES x $10^3$ |
| ns | MHz | METRES |
| ps | GHz | mm |

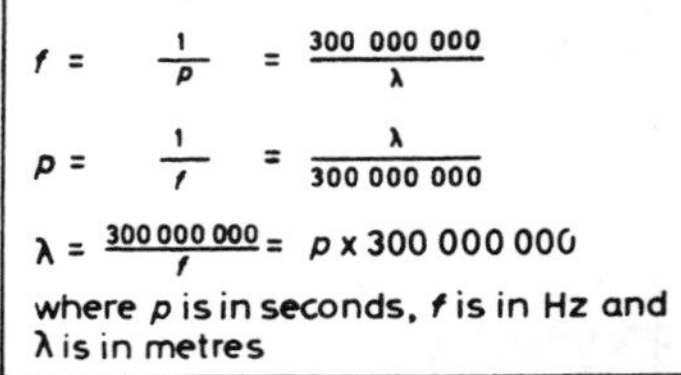

$$f = \frac{1}{p} = \frac{300\ 000\ 000}{\lambda}$$

$$p = \frac{1}{f} = \frac{\lambda}{300\ 000\ 000}$$

$$\lambda = \frac{300\ 000\ 000}{f} = p \times 300\ 000\ 000$$

where *p* is in seconds, *f* is in Hz and λ is in metres

p f λ
1000 900 800 700 600 500 400 300 200 100
1 2 3 4 5 6 7 8 9 10
300 200 100 90 80 70 60 50 40 30
p f λ
100 90 80 70 60 50 40 30 20 10
10 20 30 40 50 60 70 80 90 100
30 20 10 9 8 7 6 5 4 3
p f λ
10 9 8 7 6 5 4 3 2 1
100 200 300 400 500 600 700 800 900 1000
3 2 1 0·9 0·8 0·7 0·6 0·5 0·4 0·3

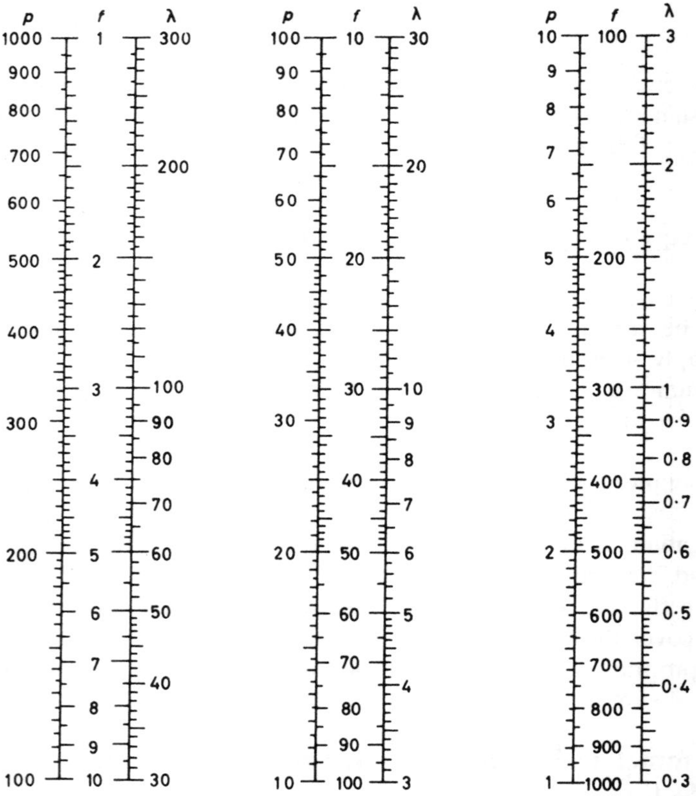

Figure A.1. *Frequency-period-wavelength conversion chart.*

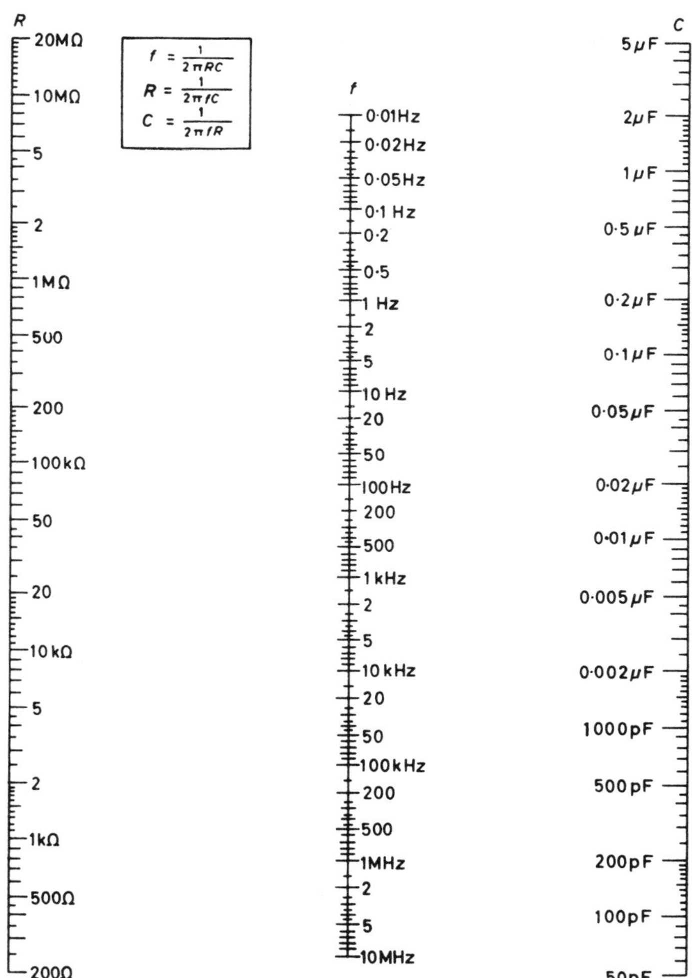


Figure A.2. *Symmetrical twin-T or Wien-bridge component-selector chart; can be used in conjunction with* Figure A.3 *to obtain greater definition.*

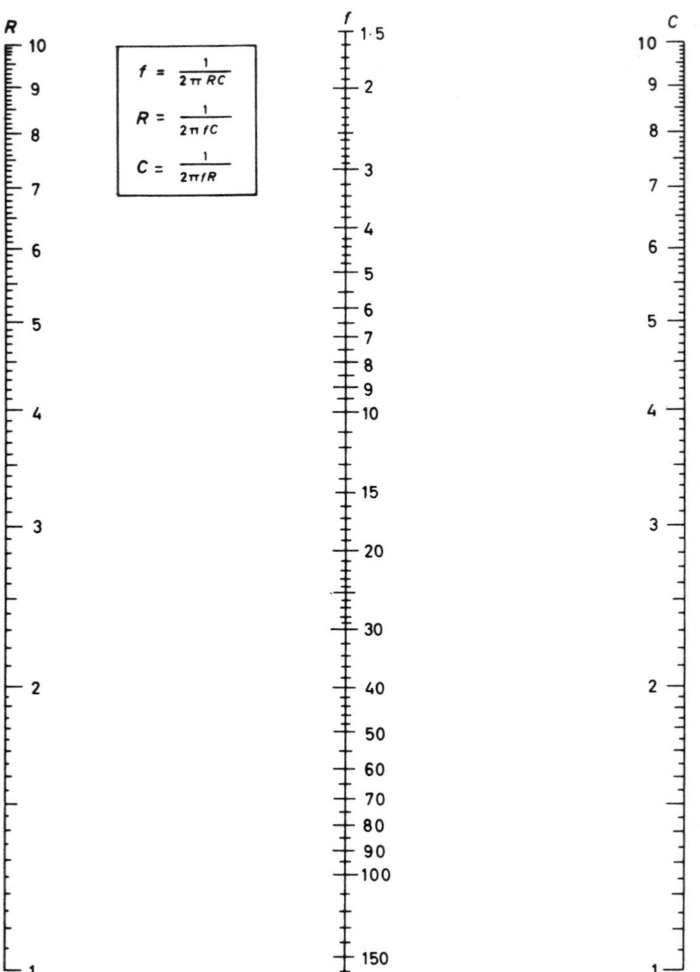


Figure A.3. *Symmetrical twin-T or Wien-bridge component-selection chart with expanded scale, to be used in conjunction with* Figure A.2; *all numerical values can be increased or decreased in decade multiples.*

enables these approximate values to be translated into precise ones. The charts are used by simply laying a ruler or perspex straight edge so that it cuts two known parameter values, and then reading the value of the third parameter at the point where its scales are cut.

**Example**. A 1kHz Wien-bridge oscillator is to be made using *C* values that are decade multiples or submultiples of 1, and with *R* values that are greater than 2k0 but less than 100k. Find the required *R* and *C* values.

**Solution**. Use *Figure A.2* to find the approximate *R* and *C* values. Pivot the straight edge on the 1kHz point of the centre scale, and rotate the straight edge so that it sweeps between the designated *R* limits until a qualifying *C* value is located. Read off the *C* (0.01μF) and *R* (about 15k) values.

Use *Figure A.3* to find the precise *R* values required. Lay the straight edge so that it cuts the 10 value (equal to 1kHz) of the frequency column and the 10 value (equal to 0.01μF) of the *C* column, and read off the *R* value of 1.59 (equal to 15.9kΩ) at which the straight edge cuts the *R* column. Note that all numeric values of the *Figure A.3* chart can be increased or decreased in decade multiples. Hence the values needed to make the 1kHz Wien-bridge oscillator are 0.01μF and 15.9kΩ.

## L–C tuned circuit component selection chart

Two charts are presented in *Figures A.4* and *A.5*; between them they enable the *C* and *L* values of a tuned circuit of a known frequency (or the frequency resulting from known values of *C* and *L*) to be rapidly and accurately determined. The two charts are intended to be used in conjunction. *Figure A.4* enables the approximate parameter values to be determined, and *Figure A.5* enables these approximate values to be translated into precise ones. The charts are used by simply laying a ruler or perspex straight edge so that it cuts two known parameter values, and then reading the value of the third parameter at the point where its scales are cut.

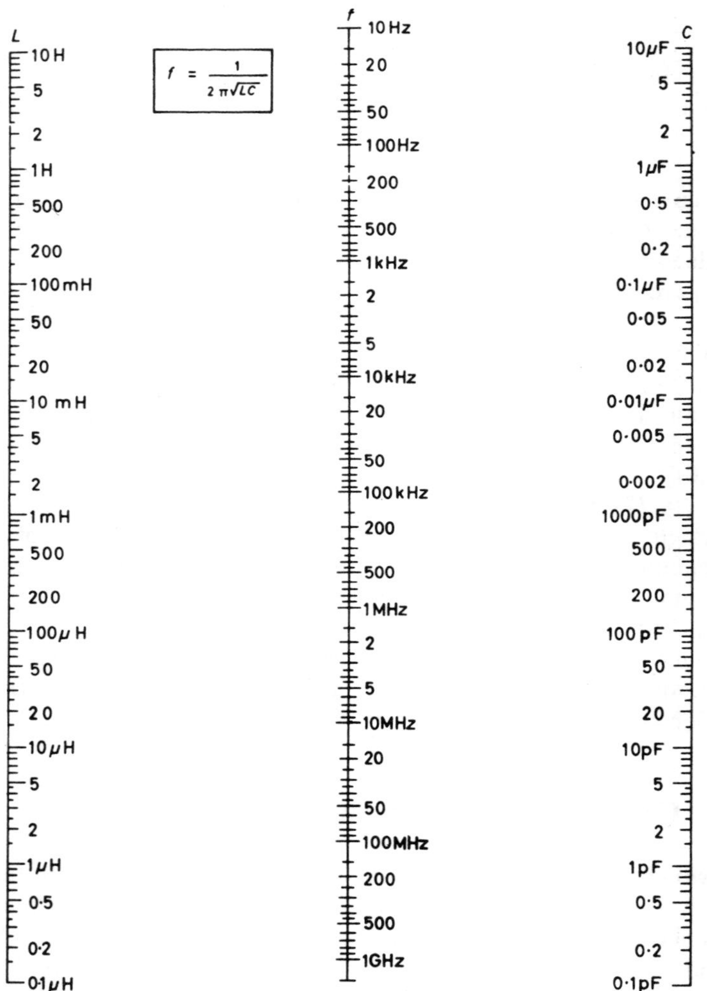


Figure A.4. L–C *tuned circuit component-selection chart; can be used in conjunction with* Figure A.5 *to obtain greater definition.*

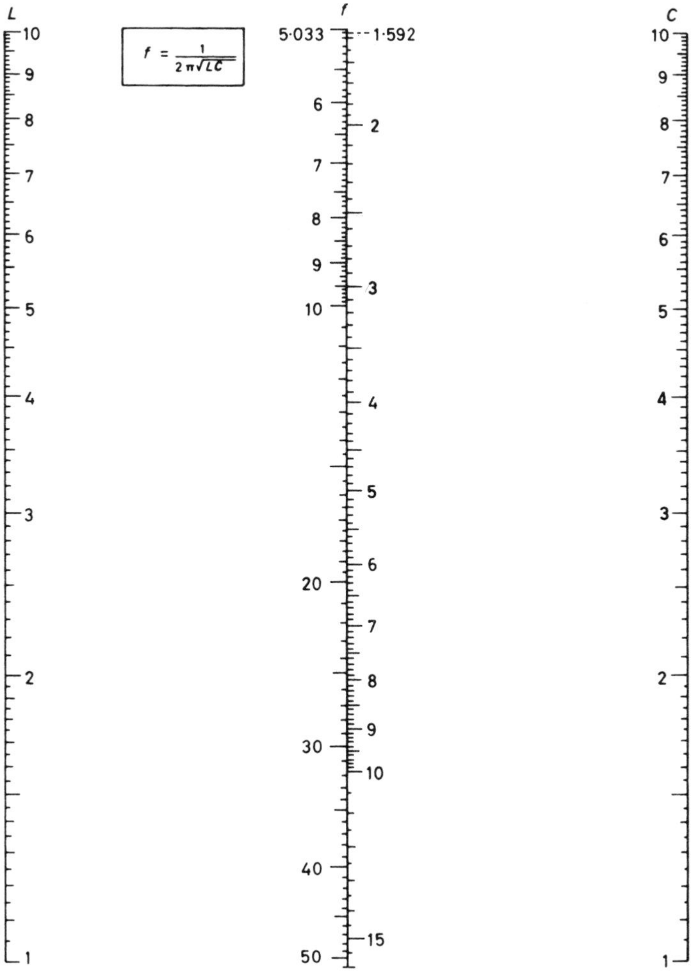

$$f = \frac{1}{2\pi\sqrt{LC}}$$

Figure A.5. L–C *tuned circuit component-selection chart with expanded scale, to be used in conjunction with* Figure A.4; *all numerical values can be increased or decreased in decade multiples.*

**Example**. Find the resonant frequency of a 200μH coil and a 100pF capacitance.

**Solution**. Use *Figure A.4* to find the approximate frequency value. Lay the straight edge so that it cuts the 200μH and 100pF values, and read the frequency value as approximately 1.1MHz.

Use *Figure A.5* to find the precise frequency value. Lay the straight edge so that it cuts the 2 value (equal to 200μH) of the *L* column and the 1 or 10 value (equal to 100pF) of the *C* column, and read off the values of 11.25/3.57 or 35.7/11.25 on the frequency column. Clearly, the 11.25 value (equal to 1.125MHz) is the correct one that approximates 1.1MHz. Note that all numeric values of the *Figure A.5* chart can be increased or decreased in decade multiples in conjunction with the results of the *Figure A.4* chart.

# Index

## Circuits by type number